# READINGS IN
# Ecology and Ecological Genetics

# READINGS IN

# Ecology and Ecological Genetics

EDITED BY

Joseph H. Connell, David B. Mertz,
and
William W. Murdoch

HARPER & ROW, PUBLISHERS

NEW YORK, EVANSTON, AND LONDON

# CONTENTS

# CONTENTS

# PREFACE

This book has been designed to introduce undergraduate students to the original literature of ecology. We feel that the lecturer and the textbook will present the ideas and principles of ecology, but that the student must also read examples of actual studies, written by the ecologist who did the work, for an understanding of the practice of the science. The book developed from the way we teach the undergraduate ecology course at the University of California at Santa Barbara. In this 10-week course, about a hundred students write several essays on original ecological papers. These range from critical essays of single papers to essays synthesizing a number of original papers. This puts a tremendous strain on the library system; consequently, this book is an attempt to make many of the papers easily available to the student. It seemed worthwhile to expand the list so that it would serve more than our own restricted needs, an exercise which proved highly educational. We hope that the student will also benefit from the exercise and will be stimulated to inquire further into some of the interesting literature we were not able to include.

The criteria we used in choosing papers are not easily defined. The major criterion was that the paper should describe original work; within this framework we have emphasized experimental papers. We feel it is rather easy to cover theory in lectures, while a detailed presentation of data is hard to give. Also, the best way to get a feeling for the type of work ecologists do

is to read their research papers. Within this limitation we have not tried to choose "model," "classical," or "important" papers, though we have not resisted the impulse to try to choose good papers. We have covered a wide and representative range of topics. Many of the good and interesting research papers in ecology, however, are long, hence we have excluded them so that we could present a larger variety of papers.

This book is divided into three sections, and each section has an introduction which attempts to present the recent literature to the student. Section I has a special introduction to demography, a subject which students often find difficult and which is discussed in some of the papers. The divisions are to some extent artificial, and some papers could be in more than one section. This illustrates the point that the ecologist works, at least in nature, in a community of evolving species, and though he may select one population to study at one point in time, he must always be aware of the larger matrix in which his population exists.

The literature of ecology is scattered widely in many journals. The following is a list of the principal ecological journals: *Ecology, Ecological Monographs, Evolution, Journal of Animal Ecology, Journal of Applied Ecology, Journal of Ecology, Journal of Theoretical Biology, Limnology and Oceanography, Oecologia, Oikos, Researches on Population Ecology, and The American Naturalist.*

We would like to thank the authors who gave us permission to include their papers

in this book. We would also like to ac-
knowledge the help of the following people
who gave us advice in selecting papers:
M. Bergen, M. Cody, J. Cubit, F. Evans,
E. Fager, M. Fawcett, L. Fox, P. Frank,
A. Ghent, R. Gill, G. Hardin, L. Hendrick-
son, H. Horn, C. Istock, D. Janzen, A.
Johnson, C. Krebs, E. Leigh, R. Lewontin,
R. MacArthur, R. Merrill, H. Mooney, C.
Onuf, G. Orians, T. Park, C. Peterson, D.
Potts, R. Reed, R. Root, J. St. Amant, G.
Salt, R. Smith, R. Sokal, A. Sokoloff, F. Son-
leitner, A. Stiven, R. Taylor, K. Watt, C.
Weidert, R. Whittaker, and E. Wilson.

J. H. C.
D. B. M.
W. W. M.

# READINGS IN
# Ecology and Ecological Genetics

# Life Histories and Ecological Genetics

For many purposes the life history of a plant or animal may be summarized using three items of information: the total number of times it gives birth, its age each time it gives birth, and its age at death. In this connection the term births means fertile eggs or seeds or live births, whichever may be appropriate. When ecologists assemble these measurements for various members of a population and compare the results obtained for different individuals, they invariably find that no two population members—not even ones which live under essentially identical conditions—possess identical life histories. Typically there is tremendous variation. Some individuals live to an advanced age and leave many descendants, others die early in life before they are old enough to reproduce, and still others may live a long time but never produce a single offspring. Even individuals who have the same number of births will differ among themselves in the ages at which they become parents. In Darwinian terms, the population members who contribute the most descendants to future generations are called the fittest, and both the numbers of births and their spacing over the life span are components of fitness. Variation in life-history patterns, and the concomitant variation in individual fitness, is one of the requisites for evolution by natural selection. But it is not the only requisite. In addition there must be at least a partial dependence of the variation in life histories on the genetic variation which also resides in populations. In other words the genetic differ-ences between individuals must contribute to the observed variation in fitness. Since each parent passes some of its genes on to each of its progeny (exactly half of them are passed on in sexual forms), those alleles which are associated with high fitness tend to be preserved in the population. The alleles which confer relatively lowered fitness tend to be lost. This is the essence of the theory of evolution by natural selection.

Traditionally, the description of plant and animal life histories has been the province of natural historians and ecologists. The lot of describing genetic variation and its evolutionary causes and implications has fallen to population geneticists. In this way one biological discipline has been concerned in part with the components of fitness, i.e., the life-history features of organisms, and a distinctly different discipline has concerned itself with the genetic aspects of fitness. This regrettable separation of ecology and population genetics has proved a barrier to the development of evolutionary theory. For example, the mathematical foundation of the theory of population genetics, which largely ignores life-history considerations, was conceived in the 1920s mainly by Fisher, Wright, and Haldane, and was summarized in essentially its present-day form by Fisher in 1930 (see second edition, 1958), Wright (1931), and Haldane (1932). However, the population consequences of life-history phenomena as they relate to fitness and natural selection were first discussed more than 20 years later by Cole (1954.) Since then only a few workers have contributed to this field, and only recently does there seem to be a strong interest developing in it (Selections 1–4 in this book; also see Holgate, 1967; Cohen, 1966 and 1967; MacArthur and Wilson, 1967; Frank, 1968; and Mertz, 1970). The only book to date devoted solely to the mathematics of population growth (Keyfitz, 1968) makes no mention of evolutionary theory, and one of the most modern books on mathematical population genetics (Ewens, 1969) does not cite either Cole's work or that of Lotka (1956) and Leslie (1945, 1948a, and 1948b) who have been the principal architects of theories of population growth based on life-history attributes.

In all fairness to population theoreticians, the mathematical difficulties posed in attempting to incorporate life-history considerations into evolutionary theory seem almost insurmountable, given present-day techniques. At a theoretical level, at least, the two fields seem destined to continue their separate ways for some time. However, there has long been an interest in evolutionary ecology (Allee et al., 1949, Section 5), and many population geneticists are thinking and conducting their research along more or less ecological lines. Sheppard (1960) and Ford (1964) review some of the British work in ecological genetics. Sokal and Sonleitner (1968) and Turner (1968) have made recent research contributions in this field. Andrewartha and Birch (1954), Birch (1960), and Ehrlich and Holm (1962) are authors who have argued for new approaches toward the unification of population ecology and population genetics. Recent symposium volumes edited by Baker and Stebbins (1965) and Lewontin (1968) illustrate other new developments in this field, and several papers in the three volumes, *Evolutionary Biology*, (Dobzhansky, Hecht, and Steere, 1967, 1968, and 1969) are pertinent.

This section of our book includes life-history studies and various kinds of genetical and evolutionary studies which are more or less ecological in their orientation.

From what these papers do and do not have in common, it is possible to gather an impression of the state of this field and the diversity of approaches to the evolutionary study of population. Inasmuch as the movement in the direction of a unified population biology takes different forms in the hands of different workers, it is impossible to predict what its future course will be. One thing is certain, however: increasingly more effort will be put into this kind of research.

Students wanting to learn more about the basic ideas of population genetics should consult Dobzhansky (1951), Lerner (1958), Spiess (1962), Williams (1966), and Wallace (1968). Of the books which treat mathematical population genetics, the ones by Li (1955) and Falconer (1961) are especially suitable for introductory purposes. Li (1967) reviews the theory of evolution by natural selection. Students with adequate mathematical training might do best to go on to the more advanced books by Kempthorne (1957), Moran (1962), and Ewens (1969). Levins (1968) has developed some interesting approaches to the theory of evolution in changing environments.

So far as the mathematics of population growth is concerned, the most modern and comprehensive account is given by Keyfitz (1968). Lotka (1956) treats the theory of continuously breeding populations and is still a rich source of ideas for ecologists. For introductory purposes Birch (1948) and Andrewartha and Birch (1954) are recommended. Cole's (1954) paper is advanced, but readers will benefit from it regardless of the state of their mathematical training. Unfortunately all of these sources will prove difficult for beginning students, and, partly to obviate these difficulties and partly as an introduction to the life-history papers included here, we offer an elementary account of the theory of population growth based on the life-history attributes of the population members. This follows the literature cited.

D.B.M.

# I. LIFE HISTORIES AND ECOLOGICAL GENETICS

## LITERATURE CITED

ALLEE, W. C., A. E. EMERSON, O. PARK, T. PARK, AND K. P. SCHMIDT. 1949. *Principles of Animal Ecology*. Saunders, Philadelphia.

ANDREWARTHA, H. G., AND L. C. BIRCH. 1954. *The Distribution and Abundance of Animals*. Univ. of Chicago Press, Chicago.

BAKER, H. G., AND G. L. STEBBINS (Eds.). 1965. *The Genetics of Colonizing Species*. Academic Press, New York.

BIRCH, L. C. 1948. The intrinsic rate of natural increase of an insect population. Journal of Animal Ecology 17: 15-26.

BIRCH, L. C. 1960. The genetic factor in population ecology. American Naturalist 94: 5-24.

COHEN, D. 1966. Optimizing reproduction in a randomly varying environment. Journal of Theoretical Biology 12: 119-129.

COHEN, D. 1967. Optimizing reproduction in a randomly varying environment when a correlation may exist between the conditions at a time a choice has to be made and the subsequent outcome. Journal of Theoretical Biology 16: 1-14.

COLE, L. C. 1954. The population consequences of life history phenomena. Quarterly Review of Biology 29: 103-137.

DOBZHANSKY, TH. 1951. *Genetics and the Origin of Species*. Columbia Univ. Press, New York.

DOBZHANSKY, TH., M. K. HECHT, AND W. C. STEERE (Eds.). 1967. (Vol. I), 1968 (Vol. II), and 1969 (Vol. III). *Evolutionary Biology*. Appleton-Century-Crofts, New York.

EHRLICH, P. R., AND R. W. HOLM. 1962. Patterns and populations. Science 137: 652-657.

EWENS, W. J. 1969. *Population Genetics*. Methuen, London.

FALCONER, D. S. 1961. *Introduction to Quantitative Genetics*. Oliver and Boyd, Edinburgh.

FISHER, R. A. 1958. *The Genetical Theory of Natural Selection*. 2nd ed. Dover, New York.

FORD, E. B. 1964. *Ecological Genetics*. Wiley, New York.

FRANK, P. 1968. Life histories and community stability. Ecology 49: 355-357.

HALDANE, J. B. S. 1932. *The Causes of Evolution*. Harper & Row, New York.

HOLGATE, P. 1967. Population survival and life history phenomena. Journal of Theoretical Biology 14: 1-10.

KEMPTHORNE, O. 1957. *An Introduction to Genetic Statistics*. Wiley, New York.

KEYFITZ, N. 1968. *Introduction to the Mathematics of Populations*. Addison-Wesley, Reading, Mass.

LERNER, I. M. 1958. *The Genetic Basis of Selection*. Wiley, New York.

LESLIE, P. H. 1945. On the use of matrices in certain population mathematics. Biometrika 33: 183-212.

LESLIE, P. H. 1948a. Some further notes on the use of matrices in population mathematics. Biometrika 35: 213-245.

LESLIE, P. H. 1948b. On the distribution in time of the births in successive generations. Journal of the Royal Statistical Society, Series A, 111: 44-53.

LEVINS, R. 1968. *Evolution in Changing Environments*. Princeton Univ. Press, Princeton, N.J.

LEWONTIN, R. C. (Ed.). 1968. *Population Biology and Evolution*. Syracuse Univ. Press, Syracuse, N.Y.

LI, C. C. 1955. *Population Genetics*. Univ. of Chicago Press, Chicago.

LI, C. C. 1967. Genetic equilibrium under selection. Biometrics 23: 397-484.

LOTKA, A. J. 1956. *Elements of Mathematical Biology*. Dover, New York.

MACARTHUR, R. H., AND E. O. WILSON. 1967. *The Theory of Island Biogeography*. Princeton Univ. Press, Princeton, N.J.

MERTZ, D. B. 1970. Life history phenomena in increasing and decreasing populations. International Symposium on Statistical Ecology; in press.

MORAN, P. A. P. 1962. *The Statistical Processes of Evolutionary Theory*. Clarendon Press, Oxford.

SHEPPARD, P. M. 1960. *Natural Selection and Heredity*. Harper & Row, New York.

SOKAL, R. R., AND F. J. SONLEITNER. 1968. The ecology of selection in hybrid populations of *Tribolium castaneum*. Ecological Monographs 38: 345-379.

SPIESS, E. B. (Ed.). 1962. *Papers on Animal Population Genetics*. Little, Brown and Co., Boston.

TURNER, J. R. G. 1968. The ecological genetics of *Acleris comariana* (Zeller) (Lepidoptera: Tortricidae), a pest of strawberry. Journal of Animal Ecology 37: 489-520.

WALLACE, B. 1968. *Topics in Population Genetics*. Norton, New York.

WILLIAMS, G. C. 1966. *Adaptation and Natural Selection*. Princeton Univ. Press, Princeton, N.J.

WRIGHT, S. 1931. Evolution in Mendelian populations. Genetics 16: 97-159.

# NOTES ON METHODS
## USED IN LIFE-HISTORY STUDIES

This is an attempt to explain in a nontechnical way some of the ideas and methods used in life-history studies. Equations do appear in this discussion, but much of the approach is tabular, and I have tried to explain the procedures as fully as possible in words. The theory developed here is part of *demography*, i.e., the science of vital statistics of populations.

The outcomes developed here take the form of mathematical models of population growth and provide procedures for calculating the seasonal changes in numbers for populations of organisms possessing certain known life-history attributes. Model A describes seasonally breeding populations with nonoverlapping generations; Model B describes seasonal breeders with overlapping generations. Each model involves a structure—a specific set of hypotheses which in turn leads to explicit equations and procedures for describing changes in the system. Each model also involves numerical constants, called *parameters*, which must be specified before the state of the system can be calculated. Usually, biologists have to estimate these parameters, either from experiments or descriptive material; the estimates are called *statistics*. However, when the models are to be used for conceptual or heuristic purposes, it is often convenient to assign the parameter values arbitrarily.

The hypotheses incorporated into a mathematical model are usually simplifications; this helps to make the model more tractable and understandable, but it may lead to outcomes which are unrealistic to a lesser or greater degree. For example, the models presented here permit the variable, population size, to take noninteger values, something that could never happen for real populations. In addition real populations can do things that the artificial (calculated) populations cannot do—the calculated populations cannot undergo random outbreaks, crashes, or extinction. These difficulties arise because the models are deterministic, i.e., from the starting conditions and other parameters, they permit the calculation of the exact state of the system in any season without making allowance for chance events. Mathematical models which describe the system in terms of probabilities, and which incorporate chance mechanisms into their structure, are called *stochastic* or *probabilistic* models. They have the advantage of being more realistic than deterministic models, but they often involve serious mathematical difficulties of the sort we are trying to avoid here. However, the description accompanying Model B will involve probabilistic language. For example, the terms "expectation," and "expected," "random," and "probability" will be used. This mixing of probabilistic language with deterministic reasoning is common in population models and amounts to a tacit admission that a stochastic representation would be preferable to a deterministic one. The language at least is a step in the direction of realism and should be encouraged for this reason. However, in many fields and for more elementary discussions, fully stochastic development of a theory must be abandoned for the sake of mathematical simplicity. Fortunately, the words "expectation," "random," and "probability," which have very technical meanings to students of probability theory, are also common in ordinary English usage, and their intuitive meanings are not especially misleading.

Up to this point I have discussed mathematical attributes of the models but not the biological assumptions involved. These assumptions have been chosen in order to obtain descriptions of population growth which are as general as possible. Paradoxically, in order to obtain generality from a mathematical model, it is often necessary to invoke very unrealistic assumptions. Here for example, I make unrealistic assumptions about the sexual composition of the population (Model B), about the constancy of the environment in which population members live, and about the absence of evolutionary change over time. I also assume that rates of reproduction and mortality are the same regardless of population size. This is partly in the interest of mathematical simplicity and tractability, but also because I have no particular kind of organism in mind and therefore no basis for choosing which set of assumptions would be realistic ones. This will be an advantage rather than a disadvantage when the models are used to clarify certain ecological concepts, the concept of generation time for example, or as an aid in developing ecological intuition. Indeed, one of the chief benefits to be gained from models of this sort is an intuition for population growth processes and their consequences. However, the generality will be a disadvantage for those who want to use the models to describe the behavior of particular kinds of populations living in changing environments. Models for this kind of situation will have to be more complicated than the ones used here, but they can be built by combining the structural elements of the present models with new elements which apply to the specified situation. This is another reason for building unrealistically simple models: from them we learn something about the craft of model-building and we are prepared to go on to more complicated and specialized formulations.

## MODEL A. SEASONAL BREEDERS WITH NONOVERLAPPING GENERATIONS

This type of life history is typical of annual plants and animals, but the pattern need not necessarily be annual. (For the 17-year cicada the duration of a season is 17 years.)

Starting at some arbitrary point in season zero, call the initial population size $N_0$. Suppose that exactly one season later each individual has died and been replaced on the average by $\lambda$ offspring. Then, calling $N_1$ the population size after one season,

$$N_1 = \lambda N_0 \ .$$

If this life history is repeated again for a second season,

$$N_2 = \lambda N_1 = \lambda(\lambda N_0) = \lambda^2 N_0 \ .$$

A third season gives:

$$N_3 = \lambda N_2 = \lambda(\lambda^2 N_0) = \lambda^3 N_0 \ ,$$

and, in general, for $t$ such seasons,

$$N_t = \lambda^t N_0 \ , \tag{1}$$

where $N_t$ is population size in the $t$th season. $\lambda$ is the factor of population multiplication per head per season and may be called the *finite rate of natural increase*. Note that, since $\lambda^0 = 1$, equation (1) holds even in the 0th season.

Since $1, \lambda, \lambda^2, \lambda^3, \ldots, \lambda^t$ are terms in a geometric series, this form of population multiplication is called geometric population growth. Inasmuch as generations do not overlap, successive seasons correspond to successive generations, and ecologists have no hesitation in defining *generation time* as the duration of a season. In Model B, I shall show that the concept of generation time is not so clear-cut when generations are permitted to overlap.

Model A is particularly useful for calculating the consequences of unlimited population growth for a given number of generations. For example, starting with 5 individuals of an annual plant population that doubled every year, in 10 years the population size would be 5120. In 20 years population size would reach 5,242,880.

Model A is the simplest of the population growth models for seasonal breeders. Only two parameters are required, $N_0$ and $\lambda$. Model B, which is taken up next, is more complex and involves more assumptions and parameters. The parameters required express the initial population size, the initial age distribution, and the survival and reproductive characteristics of population members of various ages.

## MODEL B. SEASONAL BREEDERS
### WITH OVERLAPPING GENERATIONS

Keyfitz (1968) describes a variety of approaches to a mathematical description for this type of population growth. The one used here is related to the difference equation method.

It is traditional in discussing more complex types of population growth to keep track of the females only, i.e., to assume the population consists only of females. This is not a serious limitation, for it is easy to imagine the consequences of adding a male population which grows in a similar way. But it is necessary to keep in mind that, by population members, I mean females, and, by births, I mean daughter births.

Some of the other assumptions of the model are similar to the ones used for Model A. From season to season there is assumed to be no change in the population's life-history attributes, and this implies no significant evolutionary or environmental changes. It also means that population birth and death rates do not vary in response to the crowding which results from population growth. The resulting kind of population growth is then an idealization: It could not be sustained indefinitely, or even for a very long period of time, by most real populations.

The important difference between Models A and B is that B takes account of the consequences of aging in terms of changing birth and death rates. This is shown in Tables 1–3 which record in different ways the parameters describing birth and death attributes of a hypothetical female population.

TABLE 1. An expected age schedule of deaths for a hypothetical population. The life span of population members is divided into six intervals of one year each, and the value of $x$ denotes age at the beginning of an interval. $D(x)$ gives the number of deaths expected during the interval. $S(x)$ gives the expected number of survivors at the beginning of the interval. The table is based on 1000 live births.

| $x$ | $D(x)$ | $S(x)$ |
|---|---|---|
| 0 | 200 | 1000 |
| 1 | 300 | 800 |
| 2 | 200 | 500 |
| 3 | 200 | 300 |
| 4 | 100 | 100 |
| 5 |  | 0 |

An *expected* age schedule of deaths for the hypothetical population, based on 1000 of its members, is presented in Table 1. I use the term "expected" here, because, if several samples of 1000 females were followed through life, there would be variability among samples in the ages at death. The expectation, a word used in probability theory, may be thought of in this example as the true average behavior of samples of 1000. Actual samples would only approximate the expectation. At birth the 1000 organisms are aged zero, the first value of $x$ in the table. The intervals are equal to the time elapsed between breeding seasons, and I shall call them years. Thus the population reproduces annually. In the table, $x$ represents the age at the beginning of the interval, $D(x)$ is the number of females dying during the interval, and $S(x)$ is the number of females who live to enter the interval. No female lives past 5 years; $D(4)$ shows that the last 100 of them die during the fifth year of life. $S(x) = 1000$ at birth (age zero), and thereafter it can be calculated by subtracting the numbers of deaths in the preceding years, i.e., for every age but zero, $S(x) = S(x-1) - D(x-1)$.[1]

[1] In expressions like $S(x)$, $S(x-1)$, $D(x-1)$, etc., the terms in parentheses are *arguments* of the functions. For example, $S(x)$ is read "S of x" and means: the value of $S$ associated with a particular value of $x$. In some life-history papers, as in the ones included in this book, the argument appears as a subscript as in $S_x$. Here, however, I have used subscripts to identify the seasons.

TABLE 2. A different way of representing the age schedule of deaths shown in Table 1. The meaning of the $x$ column is unchanged. However, $D(x)$ and $S(x)$ have been converted to proportions and are now called, respectively, $q(x)$ the *age-specific death rate*, and $l(x)$, the *life-table factor* or *age-specific survivorship*. The new column, $p(x) = 1 - q(x)$, is the proportion of those alive at the beginning of the interval which will survive the interval.

| $x$ | $q(x)$ | $p(x)$ | $l(x)$ |
|---|---|---|---|
| 0 | 0.2 | 0.8 | 1.0 |
| 1 | 0.375 | 0.625 | 0.8 |
| 2 | 0.4 | 0.6 | 0.5 |
| 3 | 0.667 | 0.333 | 0.3 |
| 4 | 1.0 | 0 | 0.1 |
| 5 | | | 0 |

The $S(x)$ column in Table 1 may be converted to proportions by dividing each entry by 1000. Similarly, dividing $D(x)$ by $S(x)$ gives the proportion of females alive at the beginning of the interval which are dead at the beginning of the next interval. In Table 2 $S(x)/1000$ is called $l(x)$, $D(x)/S(x)$ is called $q(x)$, and a third column, $p(x)$ is added. $p(x)$ is formed by subtracting $q(x)$ from unity; it is the proportionate survival of females alive at the beginning of the interval. Recapitulating: $l(x)$ is the proportion of females who live from birth to age $x$, $q(x)$ is the death rate of females aged $x$, and $p(x)$ is their survival rate. Both $q(x)$ and $p(x)$ are expressed for the interval $x$ to $x + 1$. Since $l(x)$, $q(x)$, and $p(x)$ are computed from the *expectations* which appear in Table 1, they are themselves *expected* proportions. For our purposes these expected proportions may be called *probabilities*. $q(x)$, the probability that a female alive at the beginning of the interval will die during the interval, is called the *age-specific death rate* for age $x$, and $l(x)$, the probability of living from birth to age $x$, is called *age-specific survivorship* or the *life-table factor*. Tables 1 and 2 are types of *life tables*, or, perhaps, they had better be called expected life tables, since they contain expectations rather than the observed numbers dying in each interval. The life tables in Selection 1 of this book contain the numbers dying in a real population, i.e., real data rather than theoretical expectations.

In Table 2, since 0.5 is the proportion of population members which are still alive at age 2, and, since 0.6 is the proportion of those alive at age 2 which will still be alive at 3, it stands to reason that the proportion living from birth to age 3 will be the product, $(0.5)(0.6) = 0.3$, which is the entry for $l(3)$. In general $l(x + 1) = l(x)p(x)$. Also, $l(4) = p(0)p(1)p(2)p(3)$ as may be confirmed by calculating the product from Table 2. By definition $l(0) = 1$, and for other values of $x$, $l(x) = p(0)p(1) \ldots p(x - 1)$.

The $l(x)$ column, calculated in Table 2 from the age schedule of deaths, is one of the two *life-history functions*. The other life-history function is $m(x)$, the expected number of daughter births which a female will produce at age $x$ if she is alive at age $x$. This is in fact the age schedule of births expressed as the true average for females alive at age $x$. $m(x)$ is called the *age-specific birth rate*. Suppose the average female produced no births until age 2, at which time, if she were still alive, she would produce 3 daughters. And suppose that females alive at age 3 produced on the average 2 daughters, and that thereafter, reproduction ceased. This information, together with $l(x)$, appears in Table 3.

TABLE 3. An $l(x)m(x)$ table. The $x$ and $l(x)$ columns are taken from Table 2. Besides giving the age schedule of deaths in the form of the $l(x)$ values, the table gives *age-specific birth rates*, i.e., $m(x)$ values. $m(x)$ is the expected number of daughters which will be produced at age $x$ by a female who is still alive at age $x$. The $l(x)m(x)$ entries give the expected number of births at age $x$ expressed for newborn females rather than just for females who live to age $x$. The *gross reproductive rate*, G.R.R., the sum of the $m(x)$ column, is the expected total number of births produced by a female who lives through all of the age groups. The sum of the $l(x)m(x)$ column is called the *net reproductive rate*, $R_0$, and is the expected number of daughters produced by each female who enters the population.

| $x$ | $l(x)$ | $m(x)$ | $l(x)m(x)$ |
|---|---|---|---|
| 0 | 1.0 | 0 | 0 |
| 1 | 0.8 | 0 | 0 |
| 2 | 0.5 | 3 | 1.5 |
| 3 | 0.3 | 2 | 0.6 |
| 4 | 0.1 | 0 | 0 |
| 5 | 0 | | 0 |
| | | G.R.R. = 5 | $R_0$ = 2.1 |

Table 3, which I call an $l(x)m(x)$ product table, is then a summary of the life-history functions, $l(x)$ and $m(x)$, and, in this sense, it is a summary of the expected life history for each population member. In this form it is often called an *age schedule of births and deaths*. It is the collection of parameters needed to calculate population growth given the starting conditions. The initial assumption that the life-history characteristics of the population do not change from season to season is incorporated into the model by assigning constant values over time to $l(x)$ and $m(x)$.

The $l(x)m(x)$ column in Table 3 gives the reproductive expectations at age $x$ for a female entering the population. For example, $m(2) = 3$ tells us that a female alive at age 2 is expected to produce 3 births at that age. However, at birth her probability of living to age 2 is given by $l(2) = 0.5$. Reckoning from birth the average female would be expected to produce $(0.5)(3)$ or 1.5 daughters at age 2, and this is the entry given for age 2 in the $l(x)m(x)$ column. Summing the $l(x)m(x)$ values for all ages gives the expected lifetime production of daughters for a newborn female, and this quantity is called $R_0$, the *net reproductive rate*. Since we are concerned with daughters only, if $R_0$ were equal to unity, the average female would exactly replace herself. In Table 3, $R_0$ is 2.1, meaning that the average female produces 2.1 times the number of daughter progeny needed to replace herself. Such a population would tend to grow, but, if $R_0$ were less than unity, it would decline because the average female would fall short of replacing herself. If a female lived through all of the age groups in the table, her expected reproduction would be given by the sum of the $m(x)$ column, G.R.R. in Table 3. This is the *gross reproductive rate*, a parameter which is estimated in many life-history studies.

Table 4 is another $l(x)m(x)$ table to which I have added a $p(x)$ column which will be useful for later calculations. $p(x)$ is usually not shown in $l(x)m(x)$ tables. A comparison of Tables 3 and 4 shows that the populations represented by the two tables differ in their life histories, since both the $l(x)$

TABLE 4. An $l(x)m(x)$ table. A $p(x)$ column, expressing the proportionate survivorship of living females from age $x$ to $x + 1$, has been added because these values will be useful in calculating Tables 5 and 6.

| $x$ | $p(x)$ | $l(x)$ | $m(x)$ | $l(x)m(x)$ |
|---|---|---|---|---|
| 0 | 0.5 | 1.0 | 0 | 0 |
| 1 | 1.0 | 0.5 | 0 | 0 |
| 2 | 0.5 | 0.5 | 2 | 1 |
| 3 | 0.5 | 0.25 | 3 | 0.75 |
| 4 | 0 | 0.125 | 1 | 0.125 |
| 5 | | 0 | | 0 |
| | | | G.R.R. $= 6$ | $R_0 = 1.875$ |

and $m(x)$ columns are different and so are the gross and net reproductive rates. However, in many respects the two life histories are similar. Both types of organisms can live no longer than 5 seasons and both have a prereproductive life of 2 seasons. A major difference is that the population described in Table 3 is capable of living for one season of postreproductive life, whereas some reproduction occurs in the final season of life in Table 4. This illustrates the way in which life histories can be compared by inspecting $l(x)m(x)$ tables.

Table 5 shows how a hypothetical population history can be computed from the information contained in Table 4. For convenience the reproductive seasons are called years. Besides the entries in the $l(x)m(x)$ table (Table 4), the only additional parameters which must be specified are the initial numbers of females in each of the age groups, i.e., the initial state of the system. The population illustrated in Table 5 begins in year zero with one 2-year-old and two 4-year-olds. The population history is followed for 6 years, and parts (a), (b), and (c) of the table represent successive stages of its completion. In 5(a) the initial population is shown for year 0, and the survival of the original population members is followed through the remaining years. The survivors were computed year by year by multiplying the number in each age group by its survival factor, $p(x)$, and transferring the resulting product to the next age group in the next year.

I have designated arbitrarily that Table

TABLE 5. Stages in the computation of an artificial census history based on the population life history shown in Table 4. The population is followed in time through six years, and, for each year, the age distribution is given. The text describes the computation method in detail. 5(a): the initial population consisting of one 2-year-old and two 4-year-olds (in year 0) and their survival through successive years. 5(b): the initial population plus the 4 births in year 0 and their survival through successive years. 5(c): the completed table showing the initial population, the births for years 0 through 6, and the survival of all population members through year 6; total population sizes are also shown for each year.

5(a)

| Age Group | | | | Year | | | |
|---|---|---|---|---|---|---|---|
| | 0 | 1 | 2 | 3 | 4 | 5 | 6 |
| 0 | | | | | | | |
| 1 | 0 | | | | | | |
| 2 | 1 | 0 | | | | | |
| 3 | 0 | 0.5 | 0 | | | | |
| 4 | 2 | 0 | 0.25 | 0 | | | |
| 5 | 0 | 0 | 0 | 0 | 0 | | |

5(b)

| Age Group | | | | Year | | | |
|---|---|---|---|---|---|---|---|
| | 0 | 1 | 2 | 3 | 4 | 5 | 6 |
| 0 | 4 | | | | | | |
| 1 | 0 | 2 | | | | | |
| 2 | 1 | 0 | 2 | | | | |
| 3 | 0 | 0.5 | 0 | 1 | | | |
| 4 | 2 | 0 | 0.25 | 0 | 0.5 | | |
| 5 | 0 | 0 | 0 | 0 | 0 | 0 | |

5(c)

| Age Group | | | | Year | | | |
|---|---|---|---|---|---|---|---|
| | 0 | 1 | 2 | 3 | 4 | 5 | 6 |
| 0 | 4 | 1.5 | 4.25 | 4.5 | 5.88 | 7.88 | 9.78 |
| 1 | 0 | 2 | 0.75 | 2.12 | 2.25 | 2.94 | 3.94 |
| 2 | 1 | 0 | 2 | 0.75 | 2.12 | 2.25 | 2.94 |
| 3 | 0 | 0.5 | 0 | 1 | 0.38 | 1.06 | 1.12 |
| 4 | 2 | 0 | 0.25 | 0 | 0.50 | 0.19 | 0.53 |
| 5 | 0 | 0 | 0 | 0 | 0 | 0 | 0 |
| Total | 7 | 4 | 7.25 | 8.38 | 11.12 | 14.31 | 18.31 |

In 5(c) the table is completed by computing the births for the remaining years and calculating their survival through time. Total population sizes are also indicated for each year. For each year the number of newborn was computed by multiplying the number in each age group by the $m(x)$ value for that age and then summing over all of the ages. For example the entry for age 0 in year 3 is: $(2.125)(0) + (0.75)(2) + (1)(3) + (0)(1) = 4.5$. This procedure is expressed more generally as follows. Calling the number of births in the $t$th year $N_t(0)$ and the number aged $x$ in the $t$th year $N_t(x)$,

$$N_t(0) = N_t(1)m(1) + N_t(2)m(2) + N_t(3)m(3) + N_t(4)m(4) \quad . \quad (2)$$

This may also be written:

$$N_t(0) = \sum_{x=1}^{4} N_t(x)m(x) \quad . \quad (3)$$

The $\Sigma$ notation indicates that this is to be a sum, and the index variables, $x = 1$ and 4, indicate that the terms in the sum may be found by replacing $x$ first by 1, then by 2, then by 3, and finally by 4, in this way obtaining the 4 terms on the right side of equation (2). This sum may also be written:

$$N_t(0) = \sum_{x=1}^{\infty} N_t(x)m(x) \quad , \quad (4)$$

which indicates an infinite number of terms. This is the same as equation (3) for this particular life history because $N_t(x)$ is always zero for $x \geqq 5$. Therefore, writing an infinite sum involves only the addition of an infinite number of zeros to the original sum.

In order to make sure he understands these computations, the student should repeat the calculations in Table 5 and later tables. The entire table should be computed without rounding; then the individual entries should be rounded to two decimal places. Otherwise discrepancies will arise from cumulative rounding errors.

The procedures used in constructing Table 5 may be applied to any seasonally breeding population, but, of course, the tabular method becomes more cumbersome

5 begins in year 0 at the very moment that the population members are giving birth. At this very instant the 2-year-old gives rise to two births and each 4-year-old gives rise to one birth, a total of 4 births. In 5(b) these births are shown and their survival is recorded year by year through the remaining age groups, diagonally down the table to the right.

for more complex life cycles or if the population is followed for many more seasons. Leslie (1945, 1948a and 1948b) gives an alternative approach which employs matrices; this method is the most satisfactory one for following population growth of this kind. Using a computer to perform the matrix operations, it is possible to allow the life history of the population to vary from season to season in response either to changing environments or to changing population density (see e.g., Darwin and Williams, 1964). In this way quite realistic population projections can be constructed, if the ecologist can provide reasonable parameter values for the calculations.

Table 6 will be helpful for examining the consequences of initial age distribution

TABLE 6. Artificial census histories generated from the life history shown in Table 4. 6(a): population started with one 0-year-old; 6(b): population started with one 1-year-old; 6(c): population started with one 2-year-old; 6(d): population started with one 3-year-old; 6(e): population started with one 4-year-old.

| 6(a) Age Group | Year | | | | | | | | |
|---|---|---|---|---|---|---|---|---|---|
| | 0 | 1 | 2 | 3 | 4 | 5 | 6 | 7 | 8 |
| 0 | 1 | 0 | 1 | 0.75 | 1.12 | 1.5 | 1.81 | 2.44 | 3.08 |
| 1 | 0 | 0.5 | 0 | 0.5 | 0.38 | 0.56 | 0.75 | 0.91 | 1.22 |
| 2 | 0 | 0 | 0.5 | 0 | 0.5 | 0.38 | 0.56 | 0.75 | 0.91 |
| 3 | 0 | 0 | 0 | 0.25 | 0 | 0.25 | 0.19 | 0.28 | 0.38 |
| 4 | 0 | 0 | 0 | 0 | 0.12 | 0 | 0.12 | 0.09 | 0.14 |
| 5 | 0 | 0 | 0 | 0 | 0 | 0 | 0 | 0 | 0 |
| Total | 1 | 0.5 | 1.5 | 1.5 | 2.12 | 2.69 | 3.44 | 4.47 | 5.72 |
| 6(b) | | | | | | | | | |
| 0 | 0 | 2 | 1.5 | 2.25 | 3 | 3.62 | 4.88 | 6.16 | 7.97 |
| 1 | 1 | 0 | 1 | 0.75 | 1.12 | 1.5 | 1.81 | 2.44 | 3.08 |
| 2 | 0 | 1 | 0 | 1 | 0.75 | 1.12 | 1.5 | 1.81 | 2.44 |
| 3 | 0 | 0 | 0.5 | 0 | 0.5 | 0.38 | 0.56 | 0.75 | 0.91 |
| 4 | 0 | 0 | 0 | 0.25 | 0 | 0.25 | 0.19 | 0.28 | 0.38 |
| 5 | 0 | 0 | 0 | 0 | 0 | 0 | 0 | 0 | 0 |
| Total | 1 | 3 | 3 | 4.25 | 5.38 | 6.88 | 8.94 | 11.44 | 14.77 |
| 6(c) | | | | | | | | | |
| 0 | 2 | 1.5 | 2.25 | 3 | 3.62 | 4.88 | 6.16 | 7.97 | 10.27 |
| 1 | 0 | 1 | 0.75 | 1.12 | 1.5 | 1.81 | 2.44 | 3.08 | 3.98 |
| 2 | 1 | 0 | 1 | 0.75 | 1.12 | 1.5 | 1.81 | 2.44 | 3.08 |
| 3 | 0 | 0.5 | 0 | 0.5 | 0.38 | 0.56 | 0.75 | 0.91 | 1.22 |
| 4 | 0 | 0 | 0.25 | 0 | 0.25 | 0.19 | 0.28 | 0.38 | 0.45 |
| 5 | 0 | 0 | 0 | 0 | 0 | 0 | 0 | 0 | 0 |
| Total | 3 | 3 | 4.25 | 5.38 | 6.88 | 8.94 | 11.44 | 14.77 | 19.00 |
| 6(d) | | | | | | | | | |
| 0 | 3 | 0.5 | 3 | 2.75 | 3.75 | 5.06 | 6.19 | 8.22 | 10.45 |
| 1 | 0 | 1.5 | 0.25 | 1.5 | 1.38 | 1.88 | 2.53 | 3.09 | 4.11 |
| 2 | 0 | 0 | 1.5 | 0.25 | 1.5 | 1.38 | 1.88 | 2.53 | 3.09 |
| 3 | 1 | 0 | 0 | 0.75 | 0.12 | 0.75 | 0.69 | 0.94 | 1.27 |
| 4 | 0 | 0.5 | 0 | 0 | 0.38 | 0.06 | 0.38 | 0.34 | 0.47 |
| 5 | 0 | 0 | 0 | 0 | 0 | 0 | 0 | 0 | 0 |
| Total | 4 | 2.5 | 4.75 | 5.25 | 7.12 | 9.12 | 11.66 | 15.12 | 19.39 |
| 6(e) | | | | | | | | | |
| 0 | 1 | 0 | 1 | 0.75 | 1.12 | 1.5 | 1.81 | 2.44 | 3.08 |
| 1 | 0 | 0.5 | 0 | 0.5 | 0.38 | 0.56 | 0.75 | 0.91 | 1.22 |
| 2 | 0 | 0 | 0.5 | 0 | 0.5 | 0.38 | 0.56 | 0.75 | 0.91 |
| 3 | 0 | 0 | 0 | 0.25 | 0 | 0.25 | 0.19 | 0.28 | 0.38 |
| 4 | 1 | 0 | 0 | 0 | 0.12 | 0 | 0.12 | 0.09 | 0.14 |
| 5 | 0 | 0 | 0 | 0 | 0 | 0 | 0 | 0 | 0 |
| Total | 2 | 0.5 | 1.5 | 1.5 | 2.12 | 2.69 | 3.44 | 4.47 | 5.72 |

upon subsequent population growth. Each part of Table 6 is like the completed Table 5(c) except that, for each population in Table 6, there is only a single founding member in year 0. The 5 populations differ only in the age of the single founder. If there were, for example, 5 founders rather than one, then every entry in the appropriate table would have to be multiplied by 5. (In addition to the founder, the births in year zero are also shown as in Table 5(b) and 5(c).) To reconstruct the growth of a population founded with members from several age groups, it is only necessary to add the tables together. For example, Table 5(c) is given by the sum of 6(c) plus twice 6(e).

Eight years of census history are given for each of the populations depicted in Table 6. For any year it is easy to calculate the *age distribution*, i.e., the proportion of the total population formed by the members of each of the age groups. This is done by dividing the numbers in each of the age groups by the total population size. For example, in 6(a) for year 5, the age distribution is:

| | |
|---|---|
| 0-year-olds: | $1.5/2.69 = 0.56$ |
| 1-year-olds: | $0.56/2.69 = 0.21$ |
| 2-year-olds: | $0.38/2.69 = 0.14$ |
| 3-year-olds: | $0.25/2.69 = 0.09$ |
| 4-year-olds: | $0/2.69 = 0$ |
| $\geq$ 5 years: | $0/2.69 = 0$ |

Calling $c_t(x)$ the proportionate abundance of the $x$th age group in the $t$th year, the general equation is:

$$c_t(x) = \frac{N_t(x)}{\sum\limits_{y=0}^{\infty} N_t(y)} . \tag{5}$$

Values of $c_t(x)$ for years 4 and 8 are shown in Table 7. The values of $c_8(x)$ show that, although the different populations were founded with individuals belonging to different age groups, they all rather quickly attain about the same age distribution. Although the approach to this final *stable age distribution* is gradual, the earliest age groups conform to it rather nicely by year 4. This tabular example illustrates a law of

TABLE 7. Age distributions generated at the end of the fourth and eighth years by the populations in Table 6. The age distribution is the proportionate frequencies of the age groups comprising the population.

*Age distribution at the end of year 4:*

| Age Group | 6(a) | 6(b) | Population 6(c) | 6(d) | 6(e) |
|---|---|---|---|---|---|
| 0 | 0.53 | 0.56 | 0.53 | 0.53 | 0.53 |
| 1 | 0.18 | 0.21 | 0.22 | 0.19 | 0.18 |
| 2 | 0.24 | 0.14 | 0.16 | 0.21 | 0.24 |
| 3 | 0 | 0.09 | 0.05 | 0.02 | 0 |
| 4 | 0.06 | 0 | 0.04 | 0.05 | 0.06 |

*Age distribution at the end of year 8:*

| Age Group | 6(a) | 6(b) | Population 6(c) | 6(d) | 6(e) |
|---|---|---|---|---|---|
| 0 | 0.54 | 0.54 | 0.54 | 0.54 | 0.54 |
| 1 | 0.21 | 0.21 | 0.21 | 0.21 | 0.21 |
| 2 | 0.16 | 0.17 | 0.16 | 0.16 | 0.16 |
| 3 | 0.07 | 0.06 | 0.06 | 0.07 | 0.07 |
| 4 | 0.02 | 0.03 | 0.02 | 0.02 | 0.02 |

population growth which was proved by Sharpe and Lotka (1911) and which always holds for populations of continuous breeders: regardless of the starting conditions, *continuously breeding* populations tend asymptotically to the same stable age distribution providing they all possess the same (unchanging) life-history functions, $l(x)$ and $m(x)$. Once the stable age distribution is attained there is no further change. However, for *seasonally breeding* populations, it does not always follow that a stable age distribution will be attained. Repeating cycles of age distribution are possible, depending on the initial conditions and the values taken by $l(x)$ and $m(x)$. As an example it is instructive to follow the growth of a population with the following life-history functions:

| $x$ | $l(x)$ | $m(x)$ |
|---|---|---|
| 0 | 1 | 0 |
| 1 | 1/2 | 0 |
| 2 | 1/6 | 6 |
| 3 | 0 | |

If a population with this life history is founded with equal numbers in the 0, 1, and 2 age groups, the resulting census history will show a cycle with a 3-year period.

However, using procedures described later in this discussion, it is possible to compute a stable age distribution for this kind of population. If the population is set up initially with this stable age distribution, the equilibrium condition will persist. For other initial conditions, i.e., ones which lead to cycles, the population cannot achieve the stable condition. Life histories which will lead to cycles are most easily identified using Leslie's matrix theory of population growth. For the purposes of this discussion I have intentionally chosen a population which will not produce cycles.

Table 8 shows the factor of population increase for each of the populations in Table 6 for each of the 8 years of growth. It is calculated by dividing the yearly total, before rounding, by the total of the previous year. It is evident from the table that a stability comes about such that, by the eighth year, the annual rate of increase is about 1.28 or 1.29 per head per year. This illustrates another law of population growth proved by Sharpe and Lotka (1911): Once a population has attained its stable age distribution, the rate of increase per head per season becomes constant. This was proved originally for continuous breeders, but it holds for any population which attains a stable age distribution. The eventual rate of increase is called the *finite rate of increase*, λ, the same term used earlier to describe geometric population growth for seasonal breeders which do not have overlapping generations. For the stable age distribution, calling population size in the $t$th year $N_t$, $N_t/N_{t-1} = \lambda$ so that:

$$N_t = \lambda\, N_{t-1}.$$

But: $\qquad N_{t-1} = \lambda\, N_{t-2},$

so that: $N_t = \lambda N_{t-1} = \lambda(\lambda N_{t-2}) = \lambda^2 N_{t-2}.$

For $k$ years of population growth with a stable age distribution:

$$N_t = \lambda^k N_{t-k}. \qquad (6)$$

This is analogous to equation (1) and shows that the pattern of population growth becomes geometric once the stable age distribution is attained.

It is possible to solve for the finite rate

TABLE 8. The factor of population increase for each year for the populations shown in Table 6.

| | | | Population | | |
|---|---|---|---|---|---|
| Year | 6(a) | 6(b) | 6(c) | 6(d) | 6(e) |
| 1 | 0.5 | 3 | 1 | 0.62 | 0.25 |
| 2 | 3 | 1 | 1.42 | 1.90 | 3 |
| 3 | 1 | 1.42 | 1.26 | 1.11 | 1 |
| 4 | 1.42 | 1.26 | 1.28 | 1.36 | 1.42 |
| 5 | 1.26 | 1.28 | 1.30 | 1.28 | 1.26 |
| 6 | 1.28 | 1.30 | 1.28 | 1.28 | 1.28 |
| 7 | 1.30 | 1.28 | 1.29 | 1.30 | 1.30 |
| 8 | 1.28 | 1.29 | 1.29 | 1.28 | 1.28 |

of increase, λ, from the life-history functions. The procedure is as follows. In Tables 5 and 6, after a sufficient number of years of population growth, the original population members have all died, and the remaining members all were born in year 0 or later. The number in any age group $x$ in season $t$ is then given by $N_t(x) = N_{t-x}(0)l(x)$, i.e., by the number of birth $x$ years ago multiplied by the proportion surviving to age $x$. In order to obtain the number of births in year $t$, equation (4) is applied, but, in using the equation, $N_{t-x}(0)l(x)$ is substituted for $N_t(x)$:

$$N_t(0) = \sum_{x=1}^{\infty} N_{t-x}(0)l(x)m(x) \quad .$$

Dividing both sides of the resulting expression by $N_t(0)$ gives:

$$1 = \sum_{x=1}^{\infty} \frac{N_{t-x}(0)l(x)m(x)}{N_t(0)} \quad . \qquad (7)$$

To solve for λ from the resulting equation it is only necessary to assume that the age distribution has reached its stable form. Then as shown by equation (6), $N_t/N_{t-x} = \lambda^x$, and, since for the stable age distribution the proportions in the age groups do not change with time, $N_t(0)/N_{t-x}(0)$ must also be equal to $\lambda^x$. Taking reciprocals, it follows that $N_{t-x}(0)/N_t(0) = \lambda^{-x}$, and substituting this into equation (7) gives:

$$1 = \sum_{x=1}^{\infty} \lambda^{-x} l(x)m(x) \quad . \qquad (8)$$

By trial and error it is possible to find one and only one value of $\lambda$ such that the right-hand side of equation (8) sums to unity. For Table 4, specified to three decimal places, $\lambda = 1.288$, verifying that the rates of increase in Table 8 do tend to the finite rate of increase.

Using the calculated value of $\lambda$ and equation (5) it is possible to obtain the stable age distribution. Equation (5) is:

$$c_t(x) = \frac{N_t(x)}{\sum\limits_{y=0}^{\infty} N_t(y)} .$$

Expressing $N_t(x)$ as $N_{t-x}(0)l(x)$ and $N_t(y)$ as $N_{t-y}(0)l(y)$ gives:

$$c_t(x) = \frac{N_{t-x}(0)l(x)}{\sum\limits_{y=0}^{\infty} N_{t-y}(0)l(y)} .$$

Dividing the numerator and denominator of the right-hand side of the equation by $N_t(0)$ gives:

$$c_t(x) = \frac{N_{t-x}l(x)/N_t(0)}{\sum\limits_{y=0}^{\infty} N_{t-y}(0)l(y)/N_t(0)} ,$$

and, again by equation (6),

$$c_t(x) = \frac{\lambda^{-x}l(x)}{\sum\limits_{y=0}^{\infty} \lambda^{-y}l(y)} . \qquad (9)$$

Applying this equation for $\lambda = 1.288$ and for the values of $l(x)$ given in Table 4, gives for the stable age distribution:

$$
\begin{aligned}
c(0) &= 0.540 \\
c(1) &= 0.210 \\
c(2) &= 0.163 \\
c(3) &= 0.063 \\
c(4) &= 0.025
\end{aligned}
$$

Table 7 shows that the stable age distribution is closely approximated after 8 years of population growth, regardless of the age of the founding population member.

Since $\lambda$ is the eventual annual rate of increase expressed per head for the population, and, since this rate of increase is attained regardless of the initial age distribution, it is clear that $\lambda$ is one of the most important parameters characterizing the population and its life history. However, in describing the life history attributes of a population, ecologists ordinarily do not use $\lambda$, the finite rate of increase, but, rather, its natural logarithm:

$$r = \log_e\lambda. \qquad (10)$$

$r$ has been called the *Malthusian parameter* and the *ultimate rate of increase* (Mertz, 1970) and describes population growth once the stable age distribution is achieved. For the populations in Table 6 for which $\lambda = 1.288$, $r = 0.2528$. I shall show how $r$ is related to the *intrinsic rate of natural increase* or the *innate capacity for increase in numbers*.

Equation (10) implies: $\lambda = e^r$, where $e$ is the base of natural logarithms. Substituting this into equation (8) gives:

$$1 = \sum\limits_{x=0}^{\infty} e^{-rx}l(x)m(x) , \qquad (11)$$

a usual expression for solving for $r$ in life-history studies. An equation based on (11) has been used to solve for $r$ for populations described in Selections 1, 2, and 10 of this book.

The ultimate rate of increase of a population, $r$, is a measure of its capacity for sustained change in numbers and is given by its particular set of life-history attributes. The higher a population's $r$, the higher is this capacity; of two populations, the one with the higher $r$ is the more fit in this sense. However, the life-history attributes of the population members are influenced not only by their intrinsic biological attributes but also by their environment. In fact it is impossible to conceive of a population living without an environment. So $r$ must also express the properties of the physical and biotic environment. In general the environment in which a population has its highest $r$ is the optimal one for that population. In Selection 10 of this book, Birch describes the influence of moisture, temperature, and food quality on $r$ for various insect populations. $r$, then, is a measure of population quality and environmental attributes *taken together*.

Birch (1948) and Andrewartha and Birch

(1954) used the terms, *intrinsic rate of natural increase* and *innate capacity for increase in numbers,* to describe the ultimate rate of natural increase of a population living under a certain set of conditions. Specifically, these terms refer to the ultimate rate of natural increase "when the quantity of food, space, and animals of the same kind are kept at an optimum and other organisms of different kinds are excluded" from the environment (Andrewartha and Birch, 1954; p. 33). By "other organisms of different kinds," Andrewartha and Birch mean other organisms which might detract from the ultimate rate of natural increase; they certainly do not mean food organisms of other species which form an obligatory part of the population's way of life. The words "innate" and "intrinsic" in describing this kind of population increase refer to the fact that the population is unimpaired by the effects of crowding, shortage of food, predators, parasites, disease, and so on. In this sense $r_m$, the symbol customarily applied to the intrinsic rate of natural increase, is a maximum. Lower ultimate rates of increase would be obtained if the life-history functions, $l(x)$ and $m(x)$, were specified for suboptimal levels of crowding or if the effects of food depletion and other kinds of organisms were taken into account. When ecologists are interested in a population's physiological capacity for increase under a given set of conditions, they use the intrinsic rate of natural increase. This is the parameter estimated in Selection 1.

Besides the stable age distribution, the ultimate rate of increase, and the intrinsic rate of natural increase, other demographic concepts which emerge from our model of population growth are generation time and reproductive value. However, these topics are deferred, pending a discussion of continuously breeding populations.

### POPULATIONS OF CONTINUOUS BREEDERS

For populations of continuous breeders entirely different methods, based on integral calculus, must be used. About as simple an account of this theory as can be given appears in Lotka (1956). The most that can

be done here is to summarize some of the findings from this theory.

For populations of continuous breeders the net reproductive rate is given by an integral equation rather than a summation as discussed earlier:

$$R_0 = \int_0^\infty l(x)m(x)\,dx \quad . \qquad (12)$$

Here $l(x)$ and $m(x)$ are continuous functions, and $m(x)$ is a birth rate per head per unit time for females aged $x$. Again, if $R_0 = 1$ each female just replaces herself. If $R_0 < 1$ the ultimate population will decline, and if $R_0 > 1$, the ultimate population will increase.

As long as $l(x)$ and $m(x)$ do not change with time, populations of continuous breeders invariably attain a stable age distribution regardless of the starting conditions, and, once stabilization is achieved, the rate of population increase is given by the differential equation:

$$\frac{dN_t}{dt} = rN_t \quad , \qquad (13)$$

where $r$ is the ultimate rate of natural increase. In its integrated form the equation is:

$$N_t = N_0 e^{rt} \quad , \qquad (14)$$

where $e$ is the base of natural logarithms and $N_0$ is the population size $t$ units of time ago. Using natural logarithms equation (14) becomes:

$$\log_e N_t = \log_e N_0 + rt \quad , \qquad (15)$$

and the curve of population growth against time becomes a straight line with slope $r$.

It is customary to define a finite rate of increase, $\lambda$, the factor by which the population increases per unit time. This is obtained by replacing $t$ with 1 in equation (14), which gives:

$$N_1 = N_0 e^r = N_0 \lambda \quad .$$

Again, $\lambda$ is defined in such a way that it equals the natural logarithm of $r$, and this preserves equation (10) which was derived for seasonal breeders. It is because of the similar results obtained for seasonal and continuous breeders that either $r$ or $\lambda$ could be used to characterize the ultimate performance of seasonally breeding populations. However, $r$ is usually used.

From equation (13) the population holds its own for $r = 0$, decreases for $r < 0$, and increases for $r > 0$. In other words, from the discussion just following equation (12), $r = 0$ if $R_0 = 1$, but $r < 0$ for $R_0 < 1$ and $r > 0$ for $R_0 > 1$.

For continuous breeders the equation which defines $r$ in terms of $l(x)$ and $m(x)$ is:

$$1 = \int_0^\infty e^{-rx} l(x) m(x) \, dx \quad . \tag{16}$$

Usually, however, this equation is approximated by a sum like equation (11), and $l(x)$ and $m(x)$ are defined in terms of the length of the intervals involved in the sum. This method is illustrated in Selection 1.

Lotka (1956) gives the equations defining the age distribution and other attributes of the stable population for continuous breeders.

## GENERATION TIME

The concept of generation time, which is very simple for populations which do not develop overlapping generations, becomes difficult when generations are permitted to overlap. In fact for many purposes the concept may not be a very useful one.

A number of authors have used the following approach: In her lifetime a female is expected to produce $R_0$ daughters, where $R_0$ is the net reproductive rate. Then $R_0$ is the expected size of a generation, and generation time should be the length of time it takes for the stable population to increase by the factor $R_0$. Calling generation time $T$, we should be able to solve for this quantity as follows using equation (14),

$$N_T = N_0 e^{rT} \quad .$$

Dividing both sides of the equation by $N_0$ gives:

$$N_T/N_0 = R_0 = e^{rT} \quad .$$

Taking natural logarithms and solving for $T$ gives an expression for generation time:

$$T = \log(R_0)/r \quad . \tag{17}$$

Unfortunately, for $r = 0$ ($R_0 = 1$), this quantity is undefined. This makes this definition of generation time particularly unsatisfactory, for, certainly, the concept ought to be applicable to all populations, whether or not their size is changing.

Leslie (1966), in the most valuable statement to date on this topic, discussed two other definitions of generation time—one based on the average age of females at reproduction and the other based on the average age of mothers present in the population and in the act of reproduction. Neither definition will be wholly satisfactory for all purposes, and the discussion of generation time presented here is intended merely to show some of the difficulties involved with the concept.

## REPRODUCTIVE VALUE

The concept of reproductive value, developed by Fisher (1958), is one which emerges readily from Table 6. Since the 5 populations in Table 6 all have attained about the same annual rate of increase by year 8, their sizes relative to each other should remain about the same through subsequent years. It is clear then that population 6(d), founded with one 3-year-old, which is the largest population in year 8, will produce the largest ultimate population. Another way of saying this is that a 3-year-old is worth more than a member of any other age group. A 0-year-old [population 6(a)] and a 4-year-old [population 6(e)] are of exactly equal value and are worth less than members of any of the other age groups. From the table it would appear that a 3-year-old is worth about $10.30/5.72$ or 3.39 times as much as a 0-year-old.

Fisher's (1958) procedure for measuring reproductive value is to set the value of an individual aged 0 exactly at 1. Then, for seasonal breeders, the equation for reproductive value is:

$$v(x) = \frac{e^{rx}}{l(x)} \sum_{y=x}^\infty e^{-ry} l(y) m(y) \quad . \tag{18}$$

An extremely lucid derivation of this equation appears in MacArthur and Wilson (1967; pp. 89-92). Applying the equation to

TABLE 9. True reproductive values for members of the age groups belonging to populations tabulated in Table 6 compared to approximations derived from the total populations as of year 8. The true reproductive values are calculated from equation (18).

| | True $v(x)$ | Approximate $v(x)$ |
|---|---|---|
| 0-year-olds | 1 | — |
| 1-year-olds | 2.575 | 2.582 |
| 2-year-olds | 3.316 | 3.322 |
| 3-year-olds | 3.388 | 3.390 |
| 4-year-olds | 1 | 1.000 |

a 3-year-old for the $l(x)m(x)$ table shown in Table 4, v(3) turns out to be 3.388. This shows that the value of 3.39 obtained from Table 6 was very close to the true one. The reproductive values of all age groups and approximations calculated from Table 6 are shown in Table 9. The correspondence between the actual and approximate values is very close.

Since each member of a population has its own reproductive value which depends on its age, it is possible to calculate a total population reproductive value $V_t$. This amounts to the sum of the individual reproductive values for each of the population members:

$$V_t = \sum v(x) \quad . \tag{19}$$

all
population
members

In calculating $V_t$ for the populations in Table 6 it is important to remember that the columns for each year in the table are shown for the very instant that the newborn appear in the population. This poses difficulties. Each of the newborn is automatically assigned a reproductive value of unity, and, at the very instant of birth, each mother loses one unit of reproductive value. Therefore, there is no sharp jump in the population's total reproductive value. To compute the total reproductive value for year $t$ one may ignore the newborn and apply equation (19). This amounts to performing the calculation at the very instant before birth. Otherwise it would be permissible to count each new daughter as unity but to omit the first term in the sum

in equation (18), i.e., to perform the calculations for the instant after birth. Either procedure gives the same outcome, and I have followed the option of calculating reproductive value just before the newborn appear in the population. Then, for example, for population 6(b) for year 1, the total population reproductive value is $v(2)$ or 3.316. For year 2 the reproductive value of the total population in 6(b) is $v(1) + 0.5\, v(3) = 2.575 + 0.5(3.388) = 4.269$. Dividing $V_2$ by $V_1$, i.e., 4.269/3.316, gives 1.287 to three decimal places, which, allowing for rounding error, is equal to the finite rate of increase per year, $\lambda$. Thus, in the course of one year during which the population size remained at 3, the total reproductive value of the population increased by the factor, $\lambda$. Similarly, for each of the populations in Table 3, each and every year the total reproductive value increases by the same factor, $\lambda$. Fisher has proved for continuous breeders that

$$\frac{dV_t}{dt} = rV_t \tag{20}$$

and that this equation holds regardless of population age distribution. In other words, although population size in continuously breeding populations increases at the ultimate rate of increase only after age stabilization has occurred, total reproductive value *always* increases at the ultimate rate of increase, no matter what the population age distribution may be. For seasonal breeders the same sort of relationship holds: total reproductive value increases every season by the same factor—the factor by which the ultimate population will grow every season.

I have already shown that two populations with the same $r$, founded according to different initial conditions, will ultimately reach a ratio of population sizes given by their initial total reproductive values. For this reason total reproductive value is a better indicator of future population performance than is initial population size, and two ecologists, MacArthur (1960) and Lloyd (1964), have suggested that, for some purposes, total reproductive value is a more important measure of population quantity than is population abundance.

Goodman (1967) has suggested a somewhat different definition of reproductive value from the one used here. His definition is applicable when populations have identical $r$s but different life-history functions, $l(x)$ and $m(x)$. When this is true, equation (18) *is not* applicable.

D.B.M.

### ADDITIONAL REFERENCES*

DARWIN, J. H., AND R. M. WILLIAMS. 1964. The effect of time of hunting on the size of a rabbit

*General nontechnical references cited in this discussion are to be found in "Literature Cited" at the end of the general introduction to this section.

population. New Zealand Journal of Science 7: 341-352.

GOODMAN, L. 1967. On the reconciliation of mathematical theories of population growth. Journal of the Royal Statistical Society, Series A, *130:* 541-553.

LESLIE, P. H. 1966. The intrinsic rate of increase and the overlap of successive generations in a population of guillemots (*Uria aalge Pont.*). Journal of Animal Ecology 35: 291-301.

LLOYD, M. 1964. Weighting individuals by reproductive value in calculating species diversity. American Naturalist 98: 190-192.

MACARTHUR, R. H. 1960. On the relation between reproductive value and optimal predation. Proceedings of the National Academy of Science 46: 143-145.

SHARPE, F. R., AND A. J. LOTKA. 1911. A problem in age-distribution. Philosophical Magazine, Series 6, *21:* 435-438.

# THE INTRINSIC RATE OF NATURAL INCREASE FOR THE HUMAN LOUSE, PEDICULUS HUMANUS L.

FRANCIS C. EVANS AND FREDERICK E. SMITH

Institute of Human Biology and Department of Zoology, University of Michigan

In 1940 the late A. J. Lotka called attention to the advantages of using the intrinsic rate of natural increase, or the rate of increase per head in a population which has attained a stable age distribution, as a measure of population growth (Lotka, 1943). But curiously enough there is no reference to this important parameter in the most recent survey of progress in the field of population ecology (Hutchinson and Deevey, 1949), and only a few papers dealing with this concept have been published to date. This is no doubt due in part to the fact that calculation of the intrinsic rate of natural increase requires a knowledge of age-specific mortality and fecundity rates, and data of this sort are not common. In fact, the list of animals for which life-table information of any kind is available is an extremely short one; to those mentioned by Hutchinson and Deevey may be added the rice weevil *Calandra oryzae* (Birch, 1948) and the flour beetle *Tribolium castaneum* (Leslie and Park, 1949). In the majority of these cases, life-table data have been given for a portion of the life span only. Complete records are relatively rare, even for laboratory-reared species. To the best of our knowledge, such information has not yet been published for a parasitic organism. For these reasons, it seems desirable to make available the material presented in this paper.

Several years ago, one of the authors (F. C. E.) had the opportunity of rearing in the laboratory a considerable number of human lice, *Pediculus humanus* L. Satisfactory information about all stages of the life history was obtained in sufficient quantity to provide a complete life-table for this species as it existed under controlled conditions. The strain of louse used for this study was acquired through the kindness of Messrs. H. H. Stage and G. H. Culpepper of the Bureau of Entomology, United States Department of Agriculture. The majority of the life-table information was secured in the course of an experimental program directed by Dr. Paul Gyorgy, Department of Pediatrics, University of Pennsylvania School of Medicine, and supported by a very generous grant from the Josiah Macy, Jr. Foundation of New York. Grateful acknowledgement is made to these persons, as well as to the many members of the staff and institution of Clinton State Farms, New Jersey, who cooperated in the program. Further information on certain life history aspects was obtained from subsequent observations carried on at Haverford College, Haverford, Pennsylvania, with the assistance of Robert M. Davenport.

## METHODS AND DATA

The general features of the biology of *Pediculus humanus* are well-known and have been summarized by Buxton (1939). The life cycle consists of

the egg, three larval instars, and the adult stage. The species is an ob-
ligate parasite of man, but Culpepper (1946a) has successfully reared
through many generations a strain that fed on domestic rabbits. The human
louse can readily be maintained in the laboratory, large numbers can be
housed in a very small space, and the rapidity with which it completes its
life history makes it potentially useful as an experimental animal.

The rearing technique employed in securing the present data was patterned closely after that used by Culpepper (1944). The lice were maintained in a constant temperature cabinet at a temperature which rarely went
above 30.5° C. or below 29.5° C. and at a relative humidity which varied
between 30 and 55 per cent but which generally approached the higher
value. The conditions closely approximate those at which Culpepper (1946a)
obtained maximum average fecundity and longevity and which may be considered optimal for the species. The lice were kept in uncrowded colonies
on small (1.5 × 1.5 inches) patches of woolen cloth in glass beakers, which
were removed from the cabinet for about 15 or 20 minutes in the early
morning and for a similar period in the late afternoon to allow the insects
to feed on the arms or legs of volunteer hosts. Counts of surviving individuals in each colony were made daily, and dead lice were removed as
well as all eggs produced during the preceding 24-hour period. Each day's
egg production was kept separately and formed the basis of a subcolony of
which a number were kept for observations on larval development.

The data pertaining to duration of the several life history stages have
been summarized in terms of mean values. In all cases where it has seemed
useful to indicate the precision of the mean estimate, the standard error
($\sigma_{\bar{x}}$) has been used. The standard deviation ($\sigma_x$) is also given, to show
the extent of variation in the population.

*Adults.* The records of adult survival used to prepare the accompanying
life-table were obtained from 800 freshly emerged adult lice reared in 1947
when the temperature cabinet was being maintained at the Clinton State
Farms. These lice consisted of equal numbers of each sex and were distributed in eight colonies of 50 males and 50 females each. The basic
survival data are shown in table 1. Since the colonies were not counted
more often than once a day, it is assumed that, when first observed, mature
lice had already had on the average 0.5 days of adult life. The maximum
duration of adulthood in these colonies was 43-44 days for a male and
45-46 days for a female. The mean duration of adult life in days was
17.645 ± 0.398 for males and 17.575 ± 0.459 for females, with respective
standard deviations of 8.0 and 9.2 days. The difference between these two
means is not statistically significant.

*Eggs.* The 400 females in the eight colonies referred to above produced
a total of 32,595 eggs, or an average of 81.5 eggs per female. The total
daily production was observed for each colony, and the mean number of
eggs per female per day, recorded for the eight colonies as a whole, is also
shown in table 1. Lice of this species do not normally lay eggs on their
first day of adult life. Egg production rose steadily from less than 2 per

## TABLE 1

ADULT SURVIVORSHIP AND FECUNDITY IN *Pediculus humanus*

| Mid-point of age class, in days after emergence from larva | Number alive at mid-point of age class | | Eggs per female per day | Mid-point of age class, in days after emergence from larva | Number alive at mid-point of age class | | Eggs per female per day |
|---|---|---|---|---|---|---|---|
| | ♂♂ | ♀♀ | | | ♂♂ | ♀♀ | |
| 0.5 | 400 | 400 | 0.0000 | 24.5 | 86 | 94 | 4.6064 |
| 1.5 | 398 | 396 | 1.8686 | 25.5 | 74 | 85 | 4.3529 |
| 2.5 | 398 | 395 | 3.2557 | 26.5 | 65 | 72 | 4.4167 |
| 3.5 | 392 | 385 | 4.4324 | 27.5 | 55 | 66 | 4.7424 |
| 4.5 | 386 | 379 | 4.7256 | 28.5 | 42 | 59 | 4.7600 |
| 5.5 | 370 | 370 | 5.0541 | 29.5 | 33 | 53 | 5.4151 |
| 6.5 | 366 | 358 | 5.4665 | 30.5 | 22 | 47 | 4.7872 |
| 7.5 | 357 | 351 | 5.2336 | 31.5 | 18 | 38 | 4.8684 |
| 8.5 | 350 | 338 | 5.3757 | 32.5 | 11 | 27 | 5.4444 |
| 9.5 | 343 | 322 | 5.6491 | 33.5 | 5 | 19 | 5.7895 |
| 10.5 | 322 | 306 | 5.3725 | 34.5 | 4 | 17 | 3.6471 |
| 11.5 | 298 | 292 | 5.7534 | 35.5 | 3 | 11 | 5.2727 |
| 12.5 | 287 | 270 | 4.7778 | 36.5 | 1 | 9 | 10.1111 |
| 13.5 | 277 | 248 | 5.2984 | 37.5 | 1 | 8 | 8.0000 |
| 14.5 | 253 | 232 | 5.3405 | 38.5 | 1 | 8 | 3.3750 |
| 15.5 | 234 | 210 | 5.6333 | 39.5 | 1 | 6 | 5.6667 |
| 16.5 | 216 | 188 | 5.8457 | 40.5 | 1 | 5 | 4.4000 |
| 17.5 | 193 | 173 | 6.0578 | 41.5 | 1 | 5 | 4.4000 |
| 18.5 | 168 | 158 | 5.4747 | 42.5 | 1 | 5 | 3.0000 |
| 19.5 | 154 | 141 | 5.8794 | 43.5 | 1 | 4 | 4.2500 |
| 20.5 | 138 | 138 | 5.4420 | 44.5 | 0 | 3 | 4.3333 |
| 21.5 | 131 | 124 | 5.6694 | 45.5 | | 1 | 4.0000 |
| 22.5 | 114 | 114 | 5.0789 | 46.5 | | 0 | 0.0000 |
| 23.5 | 98 | 100 | 5.2800 | | | | |

female on the second day to more than 5 on the fifth day, maintained this level throughout most of the reproductive period, and dropped off slightly toward the close.

A total of 28,197 eggs were observed throughout the egg period and 24,730 of these, or 87.7 per cent, hatched. The duration of the egg stage was determined for 24,645 eggs, as shown in table 2. Eggs hatched in from 5 to 12 days. The mean duration in days for the egg period was 8.015 ± 0.009, with a standard deviation of 1.4 days.

*Larvae.* Four of the eight colonies provided information on larval mortality. Of 804 larvae observed throughout the larval period, 694 or 86.3 per cent matured and emerged as adults. It was not possible to keep records of individual larvae, and the duration of each of the three larval instars was not determined. In 1948, however, after the temperature cabinet had been transferred to Haverford, the interval between hatching from the egg and each of the three molts was observed for a smaller number of larvae, as shown in table 3. The mean interval in days between hatching and molting was 5.230 ± 0.038 for the first molt, 8.627 ± 0.031 for the second molt, and 12.812 ± 0.036 for the third molt. From the figures the length of each instar

TABLE 2

DURATION OF THE EGG STAGE IN *Pediculus humanus*

| Age at hatching (days) | Number of eggs which hatched |
|---|---|
| 5 | 7 |
| 6 | 3528 |
| 7 | 4259 |
| 8 | 7320 |
| 9 | 7470 |
| 10 | 1949 |
| 11 | 111 |
| 12 | 1 |

has been calculated as 5.23 days for the first, 3.40 days for the second, and 4.18 days for the third. Since the third molt gives rise directly to the adult, the mean duration of the entire larval period was 12.81 days, the standard deviation of which was only 0.67 days. In this group of larvae, the survival was 90.4 per cent, and the mortality was distributed rather uniformly over the three instars (table 3). In preparing the survivorship table, the 86.3 per cent survival figure was used, inasmuch as it was obtained from a larger series and from the same source that provided the data for eggs and adults.

### ANALYSIS OF THE DATA

Despite the care with which the observations were obtained, it was necessary to make several assumptions in setting up the mortality and fecundity

TABLE 3

SURVIVORSHIP AND DURATION OF THE LARVAL PERIOD IN *Pediculus humanus*

| Interval in days between hatching and | | Number of larvae which molted | Number beginning larval life = 377 |
|---|---|---|---|
| First molt | 4 | 53 | |
| | 5 | 184 | |
| | 6 | 116 | |
| | 7 | 10 | |
| | | | No. surviving first molt = 363 |
| Second molt | 8 | 150 | |
| | 9 | 186 | |
| | 10 | 18 | |
| | | | No. surviving second molt = 354 |
| Third molt | 12 | 115 | |
| | 13 | 176 | |
| | 14 | 50 | |
| | | | No. surviving third molt = 341 |

tables. In the first place, it was assumed that all of the eggs laid were fertile and that failure to hatch was due to embryonic mortality. It was impossible to determine time of death in the egg stage, and the total mortality for this phase of the life cycle was therefore assumed to be distributed evenly over the entire period. Similarly, the total larval mortality has been apportioned equally to each day of the larval period, since the daily mortality is not known; that such regularity in deaths probably does occur is suggested by the observed uniformity in mortality for each of the three instars. The sex of individual lice was readily distinguishable immediately after emergence as adults but could not be determined in the egg or larval stages, and it was therefore assumed that the mortality rates in these stages were equally applicable to males and to females. Finally, the assumption has been made that half of the eggs produced were female and half were male. Buxton (1939) notes that the sex ratio of the offspring of particular pairs of lice is often far from equality and that unisexual families have sometimes been reported, but there was no evidence of markedly uneven sex ratios in the many laboratory populations reared by us.

The analysis of the data follows that of Birch (1948) and Leslie and Park (1949) except that, because of the relative shortness of the life span and the fact that daily records were available, it proved unnecessary to adopt some arbitrary, larger unit for age grouping, a procedure which sacrifices a certain amount of possibly useful information. Table 4 presents the calculations. The life-table ($1_x$) function, shown in column 2, indicates the probability at birth of á female being alive at age x, when $l_0$ is taken as unity. The maternal frequency ($m_x$), given in column 3, shows the average number of female eggs produced per day by a female alive aged x. The sum of this column, 113.799, represents the gross reproduction rate, or the average number of daughter eggs that it is expected would be produced by a female living throughout the entire reproductive period. The average daily output of daughter eggs by such a female is 2.53. The sum of the fourth ($l_x m_x$) column, 30.930, is the net reproduction rate, $R_O$. It indicates that one female egg alive would on the average be replaced by approximately 31 live daughter eggs, that is, there is a 31-fold increase per generation.

The intrinsic rate of increase, r, was calculated by the method also employed by Birch and by Leslie and Park, which is reasonably accurate for comparatively low values. This method involves the use of trial values of r to find that value which will satisfy the equation $\Sigma e^{-rx}l_x m_x = 1$. Column five of table 4 shows the values of $e^{-rx}$ when r = 0.111. With this value of r, the summation of $e^{-rx}l_x m_x$ for each age in which $m_x > O$, shown in column six, proved to be 1.0027, a reasonably good approximation to the formula. (At r = 0.112, this summation was 0.9745.) The intrinsic rate of increase of *Pediculus humanus,* estimated from the data given above, may therefore be taken to be r = 0.111 per day. The mean length of a generation, given by $T = \log_e R_O/r$, was 30.92 days. A population increasing at the rate of 0.111 per individual per day would double in numbers every 6.24 days.

TABLE 4

LIFE TABLE, FECUNDITY, RATE OF INCREASE, AND STABLE AGE DISTRIBUTION
Of *Pediculus humanus*

| 1 | 2 | 3 | 4 | 5 | 6 | 7 | 8 | 9 |
|---|---|---|---|---|---|---|---|---|
| x | $l_x$ | $m_x$ | $l_x m_x$ | $e^{-rx}$ (r = .111) | $e^{-rx}l_x m_x$ | $e^{-rx}l_x$ | Stable age dist. | Per cent of total population, stable age dist. |
| **Egg** | | | | | | | | |
| 0.0 | 1.000 | | | 1.0000 | | | | |
| 0.5 | .993 | | | .9460 | | .9394 | 118.6 | |
| 1.5 | .978 | | | .8466 | | .8280 | 104.5 | |
| 2.5 | .964 | | | .7577 | | .7304 | 92.2 | |
| 3.5 | .949 | | | .6781 | | .6435 | 81.2 | |
| 4.5 | .935 | | | .6068 | | .5674 | 71.6 | 67.88 |
| 5.5 | .920 | | | .5431 | | .4996 | 63.1 | |
| 6.5 | .906 | | | .4860 | | .4403 | 55.6 | |
| 7.5 | .891 | | | .4350 | | .3875 | 48.9 | |
| 8.5 | .877 | | | .3893 | | .3414 | 43.1 | |
| **Larva** | | | | | | | | |
| 9.5 | .868 | | | .3484 | | .3024 | 38.2 | |
| 10.5 | .859 | | | .3118 | | .2678 | 33.8 | |
| 11.5 | .850 | | | .2790 | | .2372 | 29.9 | I 15.18 |
| 12.5 | .840 | | | .2497 | | .2097 | 26.5 | |
| 13.5 | .831 | | | .2235 | | .1857 | 23.4 | |
| 14.5 | .822 | | | .2000 | | .1644 | 20.8 | |
| 15.5 | .813 | | | .1790 | | .1455 | 18.4 | II 6.99 26.43 |
| 16.5 | .804 | | | .1602 | | .1288 | 16.3 | |
| 17.5 | .795 | | | .1434 | | .1140 | 14.4 | |
| 18.5 | .786 | | | .1283 | | .1008 | 12.7 | |
| 19.5 | .776 | | | .1148 | | .0891 | 11.2 | III 4.26 |
| 20.5 | .767 | | | .1027 | | .0788 | 9.9 | |
| 21.5 | .757 | | | .0919 | | .0696 | 8.8 | |
| **Adult** | | | | | | | | |
| 22.5 | .749 | 0.934 | 0.700 | .0823 | .0576 | .0616 | 7.8 | |
| 23.5 | .748 | 1.628 | 1.218 | .0736 | .0897 | .0551 | 7.0 | |
| 24.5 | .729 | 2.212 | 1.613 | .0659 | .1063 | .0480 | 6.1 | |
| 25.5 | .718 | 2.363 | 1.697 | .0590 | .1001 | .0423 | 5.3 | |
| 26.5 | .700 | 2.527 | 1.769 | .0528 | .0934 | .0369 | 4.7 | |
| 27.5 | .678 | 2.733 | 1.853 | .0472 | .0875 | .0320 | 4.0 | |
| 28.5 | .665 | 2.617 | 1.740 | .0423 | .0735 | .0281 | 3.5 | |
| 29.5 | .640 | 2.688 | 1.720 | .0378 | .0651 | .0242 | 3.1 | |
| 30.5 | .609 | 2.825 | 1.720 | .0339 | .0582 | .0206 | 2.6 | |
| 31.5 | .579 | 2.687 | 1.556 | .0303 | .0471 | .0175 | 2.2 | |
| 32.5 | .553 | 2.877 | 1.591 | .0271 | .0431 | .0150 | 1.9 | |
| 33.5 | .511 | 2.389 | 1.221 | .0243 | .0296 | .0124 | 1.6 | |
| 34.5 | .469 | 2.640 | 1.242 | .0217 | .0270 | .0102 | 1.3 | |
| 35.5 | .439 | 2.670 | 1.172 | .0194 | .0228 | .0085 | 1.1 | |
| 36.5 | .397 | 2.817 | 1.118 | .0174 | .0195 | .0069 | 0.9 | |
| 37.5 | .356 | 2.923 | 1.041 | .0156 | .0162 | .0055 | 0.7 | |
| 38.5 | .328 | 3.029 | 0.994 | .0139 | .0138 | .0046 | 0.6 | |
| 39.5 | .299 | 2.737 | 0.818 | .0125 | .0102 | .0037 | 0.5 | |
| 40.5 | .267 | 2.940 | 0.785 | .0112 | .0088 | .0030 | 0.4 | |
| 41.5 | .261 | 2.721 | 0.710 | .0100 | .0071 | .0026 | 0.3 | |
| 42.5 | .235 | 2.835 | 0.666 | .0089 | .0060 | .0021 | 0.3 | |
| 43.5 | .216 | 2.539 | 0.548 | .0080 | .0044 | .0017 | 0.2 | |
| 44.5 | .189 | 2.640 | 0.499 | .0072 | .0036 | .0014 | 0.2 | 5.69 |
| 45.5 | .178 | 2.303 | 0.410 | .0064 | .0026 | .0011 | 0.1 | |
| 46.5 | .161 | 2.176 | 0.350 | .0057 | .0020 | .0009 | 0.1 | |
| 47.5 | .136 | 2.208 | 0.300 | .0051 | .0015 | .0007 | 0.1 | |

23

TABLE 4 (*continued*)

| x | $l_x$ | $m_x$ | $l_x m_x$ | $e^{-rx}$ (r = .111) | $e^{-rx}l_x m_x$ | $e^{-rx}l_x$ | Stable age dist. | Per cent of total population, stable age dist. |
|---|---|---|---|---|---|---|---|---|
| | | | | Adult | | | | |
| 48.5 | .125 | 2.371 | 0.296 | .0046 | .0014 | .0006 | 0.1 | |
| 49.5 | .112 | 2.380 | 0.267 | .0041 | .0011 | .0005 | 0.1 | |
| 50.5 | .101 | 2.708 | 0.274 | .0037 | .0010 | .0004 | | |
| 51.5 | .089 | 2.394 | 0.213 | .0033 | .0007 | .0003 | | |
| 52.5 | .072 | 2.434 | 0.175 | .0030 | .0005 | .0002 | | |
| 53.5 | .051 | 2.722 | 0.139 | .0026 | .0004 | .0001 | | |
| 54.5 | .036 | 2.895 | 0.104 | .0024 | .0002 | .0001 | | |
| 55.5 | .033 | 1.824 | 0.060 | .0021 | .0001 | .0001 | | |
| 56.5 | .021 | 2.636 | 0.055 | .0019 | .0001 | .0000 | | |
| 57.5 | .017 | 5.056 | 0.086 | .0017 | .0001 | | | |
| 58.5 | .015 | 4.000 | 0.060 | .0015 | .0001 | | | |
| 59.5 | .015 | 1.688 | 0.025 | .0013 | .0000 | | 0.1 | |
| 60.5 | .011 | 2.833 | 0.031 | .0012 | | | | |
| 61.5 | .010 | 2.200 | 0.022 | .0011 | | | | |
| 62.5 | .010 | 2.200 | 0.022 | .0010 | | | | |
| 63.5 | .009 | 1.500 | 0.016 | .0009 | | | | |
| 64.5 | .008 | 2.125 | 0.017 | .0008 | | | | |
| 65.5 | .006 | 2.166 | 0.013 | .0007 | | | | |
| 66.5 | .002 | 2.000 | 0.004 | .0006 | | | | |
| 67.5 | .000 | 0.000 | 0.000 | | | | | |
| Sum | | 113.799 | 30.930 | | 1.0027 | 7.9204 | 1000.0 | 100.00 |

Leslie and Park point out that in the case of species having a large relative rate of increase, calculation of the stable age distribution may have little meaning, since the great increase of density that would normally occur in a limited environment would certainly alter rapidly the age-rates of death and reproduction. The material necessary for such a computation, that is, a knowledge of the survivorship ($l_x$) curve throughout the entire life span, was already at hand, however, and we have made the calculation in order to compare the type of stable age distribution for *Pediculus humanus* with those published for other insects. Values for $e^{-rx}l_x$ calculated for each age group are shown in column seven of table 4. The proportion of the total $e^{-rx}l_x$ value represented by each age group and expressed in terms of 1000 females living is then given in column eight. In summary, this stable age distribution consists of 5.69 per cent adults, 26.43 per cent larvae, and 67.88 per cent eggs. These values approximate those obtained for Calandra (Birch, 1948) and Tribolium (Leslie and Park, 1949).

### DISCUSSION

The intrinsic rate of increase of a population has been defined as the rate of increase per head under specified physical conditions and when the possible effects of increasing density do not need to be considered (Birch, 1948). For a given species, the intrinsic rates of increase under different sets of conditions should provide measures of the relative favorability of the respective environments. For different species, on the other hand, a comparison of intrinsic rates of increase obtained under different physical conditions may be extremely misleading (Leslie and Park, 1949). Nevertheless, there is presumably an upper limit to the intrinsic rate of increase for each species, and these maximal values of r should offer a basis for comparisons when one is not primarily interested in the specific conditions of the environments. If the optimal conditions for a species be defined as those under which the maximum rate of increase can be realized, and if the intrinsic rates of increase of two or more species have been measured under such conditions, then a comparison of r values should be significant regardless of what the actual physical environments were. In a laboratory experiment designed to determine the intrinsic rate of increase, it is probable that as nearly optimal conditions for development as possible will be provided, unless the experiment is also concerned with the effects of competition or some other density-dependent factor. It will be assumed in this discussion that the various values of r which are referred to were obtained under approximately optimal conditions and represent maximal or nearly maximal rates of increase.

In table 5 we have assembled those values of r which have been published for five laboratory-reared species (the short-tailed vole, *Microtus agrestis;* the laboratory rat, *Rattus norvegicus;* the flour beetle, *Tribolium castaneum;* the rice weevil, *Calandra oryzae;* and the human louse, *Pediculus humanus*), together with information pertaining to associated aspects of population growth and development. These r values vary from 0.01 to just over 0.10, a seemingly rather narrow range. Indeed, the bacteriophage $T_2$ of *Escherichia coli*, which can increase on the average 120-fold every 21 minutes (Delbrück, 1946), has an r value of 328, and it is certain that such a slowly developing species as the 17-year cicada has an r less than 0.001. The range of r values calculated from experimental life-table data is unlikely ever to be more than a small fraction of the total r spectrum. This indirect method of determining the intrinsic rate of increase is mathematically laborious and is resorted to primarily when the life span of the species is so long and the space requirements of the individual organisms are so great that direct observation is impracticable or impossible. Nevertheless, the small range of values of r which have thus far been obtained by this method provides a number of interesting comparisons.

Human rates of increase are not entirely comparable with those in table 5, for it is exceedingly difficult to evaluate and to remove the effects of density in the case of human populations. There are no data for man that are reliably density-independent, and we have therefore refrained from including human material in the comparison.

The two rodents differ sharply from the three insects in the order of magnitude of the intrinsic rate of increase, that of the latter being approximately eight times as great as that of the former. Much of this difference is evidently related to differences in the times for development, represented in table 5 by the mean length of a generation in days. It is clear that, other things being equal, growth rates and times for development, as defined above, are inversely linear. Therefore a species which lengthens its period of

TABLE 5

COMPARISON OF DATA PERTAINING TO RATE OF INCREASE FOR VARIOUS SPECIES OF RODENTS AND INSECTS

| | Species | Intrinsic rate of increase (r/day) | Mean length of generation in days (T) | Net reproduction rate ($R_O$) | Time required to double population (days) | Source of data |
|---|---|---|---|---|---|---|
| Rodents | *Microtus agrestis* | 0.0125 | 141.75 | 5.904 | 55.44 | Leslie and Ranson, 1940 |
| | *Rattus norvegicus* | 0.0147 | 217.57 | 25.66 | 47.14 | Leslie, 1945 |
| Insects | *Tribolium castaneum* | 0.101 | 55.6 | 275.0 | 6.86 | Leslie and Park, 1949 |
| | *Calandra oryzae* | 0.109 | 43.4 | 113.56 | 6.36 | Birch, 1948 |
| | *Pediculus humanus* | 0.111 | 30.92 | 30.93 | 6.24 | Evans and Smith, 1952 |

26

development may pay a price for doing so in a corresponding decrease in population growth rate. Unless increased time of development is accompanied by compensatory changes, such as lowered mortality or increased fecundity, the reduced growth rate may not be sufficient to meet the exigencies of the environment. A species with such a deficiency will become extinct.

If all of the difference in the five intrinsic rates of growth was explainable by the mean generation periods, their products should be constant. The actual values of these products, however, are as follows:

| | |
|---|---|
| *Microtus agrestis* | 1.772 |
| *Rattus norvegicus* | 3.198 |
| *Tribolium castaneum* | 5.616 |
| *Calandra oryzae* | 4.731 |
| *Pediculus humanus* | 3.432 |

These values are the natural logarithms of the net reproduction rates, which are also shown in table 5, and they suggest a further relationship affecting the intrinsic rate of increase.

The net reproduction rate as given here indicates the number of female eggs or young which would be expected under optimal conditions to replace a given female egg or young of the previous generation. A comparison of the net reproduction rates given in table 5 shows that at maximum rates of increase a female Rattus is replaced by more than four times as many individuals as is a female Microtus. The position of the graminivorous insects, with their high reproductive rates, is not surprising. The astonishing species is the louse, which under optimal conditions is replaced by approximately the same number of offspring as the rat.

A species that is well adjusted to its natural environment may be expected to maintain rather constant numbers if the environment remains constant over a reasonably long period of time. In such a case, the factors which repress population growth would counterbalance the maximum capacity for growth. It may be assumed, as a working hypothesis at least, that the maximum growth capacity of a species is the result, not of an accident, but of evolutionary process and that it represents an adjustment to the long-term requirements of its natural habitat. The implications here are (1) that the maximal value of r is held above a critical level by natural selection, and (2) that higher values, for which there would be no net positive selection, are reduced through the general economy of the organism. Under natural conditions, then, the intrinsic rate of increase will tend to be reduced to zero and the net reproduction rate to 1.0. From the population point of view, the size of the maximal r, or its distance from zero, should therefore reflect the degree to which the natural environment departs from conditions conducive to greatest growth. Similarly, the magnitude of $R_0$ measured under conditions which are optimal for maximum growth should indicate the rigorousness of the natural environment in terms of individual replacement.

To refer again to the rates in table 5, and remembering the assumption that these represent maximal or nearly maximal rates of growth, a few further comparisons can be made. Both in terms of the population and in terms of the individual, the two rodent environments would seem to be much closer to optimal than the three insect environments. Within each of the two groups, however, relations are less clear.

From the two rodent values of r, it is seen that the natural environments of the vole and the rat are nearly alike in their distances from optimal, with that of the vole population slightly closer than that of the rat population. The two values of $R_O$, however, suggest that the likelihood of a vole being born and becoming mature in its natural environment is much closer to expectancy under optimal conditions than is that of a rat. Since $R_O$ can be reduced to 1.0 not only by increased mortality but also by reduced fecundity, the comparison here concerns the likelihood of coming to exist at all as well as of survival through maturity. In view of the apparent fecundity of rats under natural conditions, it is evident that their survival must be relatively poor.

Among the three insects, the maximal intrinsic rates of growth are much alike, suggesting equivalent deviations of the natural environments from the optimal environments in terms of population survival. In terms of the individual, however, the three natural environments appear to be very different. A comparison of the $R_O$ values for the two graminivorous species indicates that the "distance" of the natural environment from optimal conditions is more than twice as great in *Tribolium castaneum* as in *Calandra oryzae*. There is a large discrepancy between the $R_O$ values of these two species and that of the louse, which seemingly belongs to another order of magnitude altogether. The low value of the net reproduction rate in *Pediculus humanus* is indeed surprising, for a high rate is usually associated with the parasitic mode of life. The indications are that the individual louse has a much better chance of surviving and propagating its kind than the individual flour beetle or rice weevil, and that its natural environment is remarkably secure.

## SUMMARY

Data on mortality, fecundity, and duration of life history stages were obtained for lice kept in uncrowded colonies at a temperature of approximately 30° C. and at a relative humidity which varied between 30 and 55 per cent. Under these conditions the intrinsic rate of natural increase, that is, the rate of increase per head in a population which has attained a stable age distribution, was calculated to be 0.111 per day for *Pediculus humanus*. In this population, one female egg alive would on the average be replaced by 30.93 live daughter eggs, and 6.24 days would be required for the population to double in numbers. A comparison of vital statistics with those already published for two species of graminivorous insects and two species of rodents, all of which are assumed to have been obtained under conditions conducive to maximum rates of growth, suggests that the natural environment of the individual human louse is a remarkably safe one.

28

## LITERATURE CITED

Birch, L. C., 1948, The intrinsic rate of natural increase of an insect population. Jour. Animal Ecol. 17: 15–26.

Buxton, P. A., 1939, The louse: an account of the lice which infect man, their medical importance and control. London: Edward Arnold & Co.

Culpepper, G. H., 1944, The rearing and maintenance of a laboratory colony of the body louse. Amer. Jour. Trop. Med. 24: 327–329.

    1946a, Rearing body lice on rabbits. Jour. Econ. Ent. 39: 660.

    1946b, Factors influencing the rearing and maintenance of a laboratory colony of the body louse. Jour. Econ. Ent. 39: 472–474.

Delbrück, M., 1946, Bacterial viruses or bacteriophages. Biol. Rev. 21: 30–40.

Hutchinson, G. E., and E. S. Deevey, Jr., 1949, Ecological studies on populations. Survey of Biological Progress 1: 325–359.

Leslie, P. H., and T. Park, 1949, The intrinsic rate of natural increase of *Tribolium castaneum* Herbst. Ecology 30: 469–477.

Leslie, P. H., 1945, On the use of matrices in certain population mathematics. Biometrika 33: 183–212.

Leslie, P. H., and R. M. Ranson, 1940, The mortality, fertility and rate of natural increase of the vole (*Microtus agrestis*) as observed in the laboratory. Jour. Animal Ecol. 9: 27–52.

Lotka, A. J., 1943, The place of the intrinsic rate of natural increase in population analysis. Proc. 8th Amer. Sci. Congr. 8: 297–313.

Reprinted from *The Genetics of Colonizing Species*, H. G. Baker and G. Ledyard Stebbins (Eds.).
Academic Press, New York, 1965, pp. 77–91.

# Selection for Colonizing Ability

R. C. LEWONTIN

DEPARTMENT OF ZOOLOGY, UNIVERSITY OF CHICAGO, CHICAGO, ILLINOIS

The problem of the optimal genetic and phenotypic characteristics of
a colonizing species can be posed at three levels of differentiation. At
the first, one may ask what the ideal colonizing species would be like
and the answer is so easy to give that it is trivial. Obviously, effective
dispersal, high somatic plasticity, and high interspecific competitive
ability are all desirable and the greatest degree of all three is most desirable. But this reduces the problem of colonizing species to a trivial
one. The best possible organism is easy to specify. At the second level
we abandon the notion of the best possible organism and ask which
among the existing genetic systems are more favorable for colonization.
Will weeds tend to be selfers rather than open-pollinators, annuals rather
than perennials, and so on? These broader questions are treated by
Stebbins, Baker, Ehrendorfer, and others in this symposium. They are
more pertinent in plants and in certain classes of lower invertebrates than
in the higher animals where a diversity of genetic systems is not so evident, although the insects, as a whole, do have a diversity of genetic
systems almost approaching that of plants.

It is the third level of variability that I would like to discuss, the
variability ordinarily available within a species, variability of a more
subtle kind whose selection does not involve a total remaking of the
species. We must realize that the possibilities for selection in a population are not unlimited, that the genetic structure of a population is the
result of a compromise among various selective exigencies so that it is
not possible, in any short time, for natural selection to cause an increase
in fitness with respect to every stage of the life cycles and every metabolic activity. An increase in fecundity may entail, in the absence of a
complete remaking of the reproductive system, a reduction in viability or
a longer development time. Thus, when we ask about the result of

natural selection in any immediate sense we must assume that only small increases in fitness can be made and that all aspects of the physiology and morphology cannot be remade drastically and independently. It is no use to point out that a *Drosophila* with a cerebrum, a vertebrate eye, and an opposable thumb would be an advantage over other *Drosophila*. That might be true, but it has nothing to do with natural selection.

In order to investigate the effects of selection for colonizing ability or selection in a colonizing species it is necessary to define colonization in a broad sense. Colonization is the establishment of a population of a species in a *geographical* or *ecological* space not occupied by that species. Rather than speaking of colonizing *species*, it is of more general interest to consider *colonizing episodes* for any species, that is, instances of colonization by some population of the species. Looked at in this way species lie in a continuum from ecologically and geographically restricted forms like the *Sequoia* to roadside weeds, from species with extremely rare colonizing episodes to those whose entire life pattern is one of colonization. For example *D. melanogaster* and *Anthonomus grandis* are rather far in the direction of colonizing species, since colonizing episodes occur every spring when the small overwintering population begins to increase in the absence of any population pressures.

This absence of population pressures is the mark of a colonizing episode and the population can be assumed to be growing exponentially with unlimited resources, at least for a short time. This does not mean that the population increases rapidly, but only that it is in the exponential growth phase and is essentially density independent.

For this reason that first part of this paper will be devoted to a consideration of the effects of selection in a population growing in an unlimited environment.

The second aspect of colonization, although not without exception, is the change in direction of selective forces that may accompany a colonizing episode. A newly formed colony is at first low in density and the individuals are in competition with individuals of *other* species, as opposed to the situation in older populations where any competition is primarily with members of the same species. In addition, the physical factors of the environment are likely to be rather different in a newly colonized area. For this reason the second part of this discussion will be concerned with the results of occasional radical alterations in selective forces on the genetic constitutions of the populations.

Finally, it is in the colonizing species that the possibilities are greatest for interdeme selection. Colonies are not always successful, perhaps usually not when they involve expansion of area and ecological tolerance. Thus many colonizing episodes must end in failure, and this means that population characteristics can be selected as a whole by the frequent extinction of whole demes. In this way questions of *optimal* genetic characteristics become important since there is a mechanism for the selection of optimal strategies.

## SELECTION OF LIFE CYCLE COMPONENTS

In an extremely interesting article in 1954 Cole discussed the effects of changing various aspects of the life cycle on the intrinsic rate of increase of a species. In particular he was concerned with major changes in life cycle phenomena such as the change to iteroparity. I should like in this paper to consider much smaller changes in life cycle phenomena such as small changes in fecundity, longevity, length of developmental period, etc., on the rate of increase. Such a study will reveal the relative selective advantages of genetic changes affecting these different life cycle phenomena. Underlying such a study is the assumption that selection cannot act on all the genes of an organism simultaneously in a major way because the available selection differential is limited and because of the physiological correlation among different aspects of the phenotype. Obviously, an animal with a higher fecundity, a greater longevity, a faster development will be at an advantage. But the real question, and thus the interesting one is "What is the relative advantage of increased fecundity of a certain amount as opposed to greater longevity?" The answer to such a question will give an insight into the direction in which populations will change during a colonizing episode.

Following our original assumption that during a colonizing episode the population is growing exponentially, the Volterra equation will hold and

$$\int_0^\infty e^{-rx} l(x) m(x) \, dx = 1 \tag{1}$$

where $r$ is the intrinsic rate of increase of the population; $l(x)$ is the probability of an individual living to age $x$ from age 0; $m(x)$ is the number of offspring produced per unit time at age $x$.

We now wish to ask how different changes in the age-specific mortality and fecundity schedules, $l(x)$ and $m(x)$, affect $r$. To do this we need a reasonably simple form of $l(x) m(x) = V(x)$, i.e., one that is integrable, and has a fairly realistic shape, yet which can be varied by the variation of relatively few, biologically meaningful parameters. A function which satisfies these criteria is a triangular $V$-function shown in Fig. 1.

$V(x)$ may be interpreted as the age specific fecundity schedule adjusted for the probability of survival to age $x$. $A$, $T$, and $W$ are the age of first reproduction, peak reproduction ("turnover point"), and last offspring, respectively. The total lifetime offspring production of an individual from birth is then given by the area under $V(x)$, that is by

$$S = \int_0^\infty V(x)\, dx = \frac{(W - A)}{2} V(T) \tag{2}$$

It will be possible with such a function to vary independently the total offspring production, $S$, and the pattern of reproduction in terms of the total length of life, age to first offspring, steepness of fecundity increase, and decrease with age, and so on. That this model is a reason-

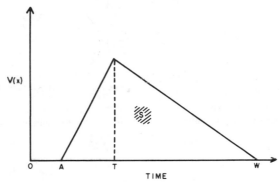

Fɪɢ. 1. Generalized triangular reproductive function, $V(x)$. $A$ is age of first offspring; $T$, turnover point; $W$, age of last offspring; $S$, total number of offspring.

able approach to real $V(x)$ curves is shown by Figs. 2–4 which show schedules for *Calandra oryzae* (Birch, 1948) and *D. serrata* (Birch *et al.* 1963). It is only the general shape we are concerned with and not the finer details of departures from linearity.

Some elementary algebra and geometry applied to Fig. 1 gives the following relationship

$$V(x) = \frac{2S(W - x)}{(W - T)(W - A)} \qquad x \geq T$$
$$V(x) = \frac{2S(x - A)}{(T - A)(W - A)} \qquad x < T \tag{3}$$

Substituting Eq. (3) in Eq. (1) gives the expression relating the rate of increase $r$ to the parameters $S$, $A$, $T$, and $W$.

$$\frac{(W - A)r^2}{2S} = \frac{1}{T - A}[e^{-rA} - e^{-rT}] + \frac{1}{W - T}[e^{-rW} - e^{-rT}] \tag{4}$$

This implicit expression can then be solved numerically for $r$ under various conditions.

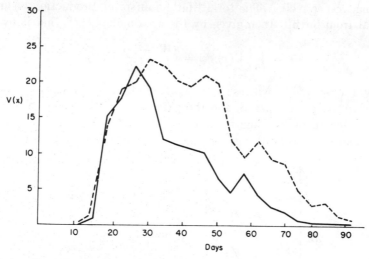

Fig. 2. Observed $V(x)$-functions for two races of *D. serrata* at 25°C. Both $V(x)$-functions give the same value of $r$ because of lack of contribution of later ages to the rate of increase.

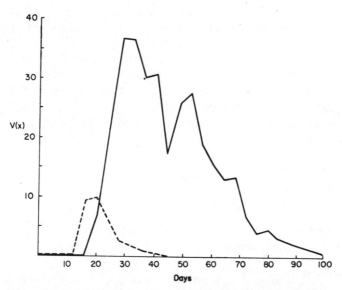

Fig. 3. Observed $V(x)$-functions for two races of *D. serrata* one at 20°C (solid line) and one at 25°C (dashed line). Both $V(x)$-functions give the same value of $r$ because of the overriding importance of leftward displacement of the dashed curve. Difference in total offspring is a factor of 10.

The results of such solutions are shown in Figs. 5–8. In each case the abcissa represents total productivity $S$ on a logarithmic scale. On the ordinate for each graph is one of the parameters $A$, $W$, or $T$. The lines connect points of equal $r$ so that each graph is really a response surface showing how $r$ decreases or increases with joint changes in $S$ and one of the other parameters. With the help of such response surfaces it is possible to answer the following sort of questions. In order to increase $r$ from 0.270 to 0.300 how much does fecundity have to be increased for

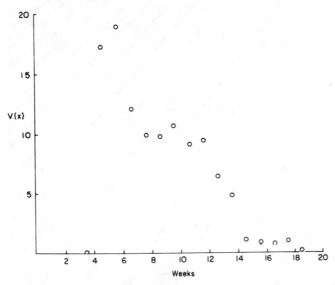

FIG. 4. Observed $V(x)$ of a beetle *Calandra oryzae* at 29°C. From Birch (1948).

different developmental rates? A decrease of how many days in time to first egg is equivalent to a doubling of fecundity? The figures are arranged in decreasing order of the effect of the time parameter variation. In Fig. 5 we see the effect of simply shifting the whole $V(x)$ schedule earlier and later without changing its shape. The dotted line represents a base configuration corresponding to $A = 12$, $T = 23$, $W = 55$ for comparison with other graphs.

We see, for example, from the upper right section that a doubling of total fecundity from 5000 to 10,000 offspring can increase the $r$ from 0.510 to 0.565 but that an equal increase would come from reducing development time (time to first egg) from 8.6 to 7.5 days. Thus one day saved in development is worth a doubling of fecundity or 5000 eggs. At the oposite end of the scale where fecundity is low a doubling of fecundity from 150 to 300 eggs will increase $r$ from 0.180 to 0.205 and this is equivalent to a 3-day shortening of development from 16.2 to 13.2 days.

Figure 6 shows the effect of varying the date of the first egg, while holding other times constant. This changes the shape of the fecundity

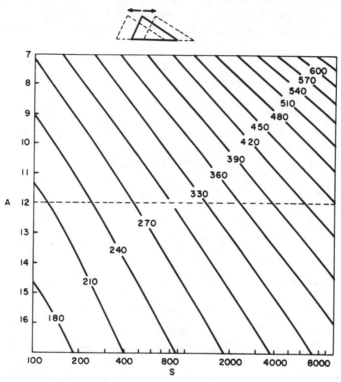

FIG. 5. Response surface showing equal $r$ lines for different total offspring numbers and different locations of the $V(x)$-function along the X axis. The dashed line corresponds to $A = 12$, $T = 23$, $W = 55$. Changes in $A$ shown on the ordinate also have equal accompanying changes in $T$ and $W$.

curve causing steeper or shallower rate of increase of fecundity. Figure 7 shows the effect of varying turnover time, while holding $A$ and $W$ constant. The changes in shape of the $V$-function here are concerned with the proportion of eggs laid before and after the turnover point. Finally, Fig. 8 shows the effect of extending the period of egg laying (changing $W$) without increasing total fecundity. As might be expected such extension actually lowers $r$ because eggs have been postponed but not increased.

To compare these four curves we can use as a reference point the intersection of the $r = 0.300$ contour with the base reference line.    The change in the number of eggs necessary to increase $r$ from 0.300 to 0.330 is the same in all cases, of course (780 eggs to 1350, nearly a doubling).

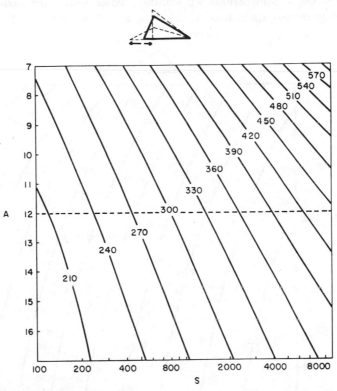

FIG. 6.    Response surface showing equal $r$ lines for different total offspring numbers and different $A$ values with $T = 23$ and $W = 55$.

The number of days needed to be equivalent to this increase in fecundity for the four cases are:

| | |
|---|---|
| 1. Rigid translation | 1.55-day decrease |
| 2. Decrease age to sexual maturity | 2.20-day decrease |
| 3. Decrease turnover age | 5.55-day decrease |
| 4. Decrease age at last egg | 21.00-day decrease |

In general the number of time units required to be equivalent to a given amount of increase in total fertility is smallest when the fertility is already high and the time short, whereas larger time changes are needed when fertility is low and time long. But the general point holds true that small absolute changes in developmental rates of the order of 10% are roughly equivalent to large increases in fertility of the order of 100%.

From these considerations we should predict that very little genetic variance in development time ought to be found in species with a history

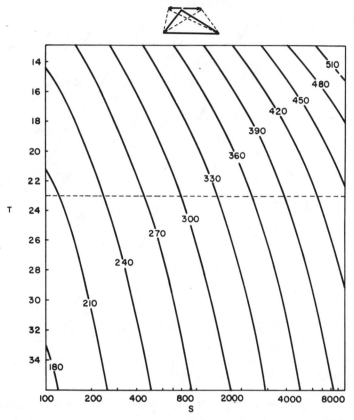

Fig. 7. Response surface showing equal $r$ lines for different total offspring numbers and different $T$ values with $A = 12$ and $W = 55$.

of colonization, whereas relatively larger amounts of variance for fecundity might be expected. Selection will have long since shortened development time, but will not have acted as efficiently on fecundity. Although there is a great deal of published information on fecundities and life tables of different genotypes in populations, there is no accompanying data on developmental rates. Information from selection ex-

periments is more difficult to interpret, and no simultaneous experiments
on selection for fecundity and developmental rate have been done.    In
*Drosophila serrata*, Birch and associates (1963) have shown that large
differences in fecundity and longevity exist between different geographical
races, whereas there are no differences between races in developmental
rate.   Tables I and II taken from that paper illustrate this point
dramatically.   Recent experiments of Dobzhansky *et al.* (1964) asso-

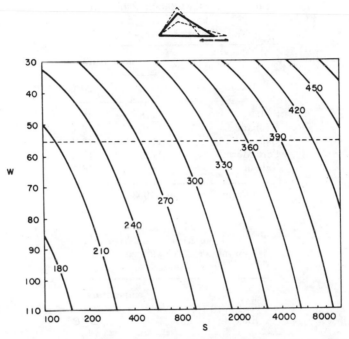

FIG. 8.   Response surface showing equal *r* lines for different total offspring numbers
and different *W* values with *A* = 12 and *T* = 23.

ciates in *D. pseudoobscura* laboratory populations show that polymorphic populations segregating for Arrowhead and Chiricahua gene arrangements have an average fecundity at 25°C of 431 eggs per female per
lifetime.   Monomorphic populations of AR and of CH give 283 and 316
eggs per female per lifetime, respectively.   The polymorphic cages then
produce females with one and one-half times the fecundity of Arrowhead
and one and one-third times the fecundity of Chiricahua monomorphic
populations.   The development times for these three populations are, respectively, 13.73, 13.85, and 14.44 days, a difference between longest and
shortest of only 5%.

More experimentation in this field is necessary, especially model experiments of natural selection under conditions of radical expansion and contraction of population size.

The models discussed thus far predict the course of natural selection on the assumption that the population is growing continuously in a den-

TABLE I

DURATION OF DEVELOPMENT IN DAYS
FROM EGG TO EMERGENCE OF ADULT
AT 25° AND 20°C IN
*Drosophila serrata*[a]

| Race | Temperature | |
|---|---|---|
| | 25°C | 20°C |
| Sydney | 11.8 | 16.4 |
| Brisbane | 11.6 | 16.0 |
| Cairns | 11.7 | 16.1 |
| Port Moresby | 11.5 | 16.4 |
| Rabaul | 11.7 | 16.0 |

[a] From Birch *et al.* (1963).

TABLE II

TOTAL NUMBER OF EGGS LAID PER
FEMALE AT 25°C AND 20°C IN
*Drosophila serrata*[a]

| Race | Temperature | |
|---|---|---|
| | 25°C | 20°C |
| Sydney | 559 | 428 |
| Brisbane | 670 | 546 |
| Cairns | 498 | 373 |
| Port Moresby | 368 | 270 |
| Rabaul | 151 | 69 |

[a] From Birch *et al.* (1963).

sity-independent fashion. Very soon the population will reach a size at which competition may become an important element in determining fitness and the question arises of how competitive ability is correlated with the intrinsic rate of increase, $r$. We know from the experiments of Lewontin (1955), Lewontin and Matsuo (1963), and others, for *Drosophila* and from the experiments of Sakai and Harper reported in this

Symposium, for plants, that competitive ability with other species or genotypes is not perfectly correlated with performance in pure stands or pure populations.  Moreover, the competitive interactions appear to be exaggerated at nonoptimal densities.  In the studies with Dobzhansky to which I have referred it was possible to compare the rates of increase of populations with changes in their intrapopulation fitnesses.  In *D. pseudoobscura* inversion heterozygotes are usually heterotic and lead to balanced polymorphism at 25°C, but not at 16°C.  In agreement with this, the rates of increase of polymorphic populations are higher than monomorphic at 25°C but not at 16°C.  The agreement is not perfect however.  Polymorphic Arrowhead-Pikes Peak populations have a higher $r$ than either monomorphic Arrowhead or Pikes Peak but, in fact, there is no heterosis in this case and the Arrowhead gene arrangement eliminates Pikes Peak.  In general, such results as well as the results of Sakai, Lewontin, and others show a reasonable positive correlation between performance in competitive and noncompetitive situations, but this correlation is far from perfect and there are many unique competition interactions.

The pertinence of these studies is that the selection on life cycle components that goes on during the logarithmic growth phase is not entirely lost to the population during the plateau of population size, but neither can it be assumed that those genotypes favored in the first phase are *necessarily* those selected during the later stages.

## SELECTION IN CHANGING ENVIRONMENTS

The second question of importance for a colonizing episode is the effect of a radically changed environment.  For successful colonization the population must be able to maintain a positive rate of increase at first and then, on the average, a rate of increase of zero.  If the genotypes in the colonizers should be such that they fail to replace themselves, at least in the new environment the colonization will fail, the "infection" will not "take."  This Symposium has given us abundant evidence of the frequent failure of colonizations, and it is certain that successful cases are a selected sample of the essentially random genetic collections that have attempted colonization.  There is then a great possibility for selection between demes, selection in the characteristics of the population as a whole.

We may then inquire what the relative probabilities of successful colonization are for populations of various genetic structures and even what the *optimal* genetic structure is for a colonizer to maintain a positive rate of increase in a new environment, while at the same time maintaining itself in the original territory of the species.  The same question can be asked over time rather than space. Given a species which is reduced sharply in numbers at more or less regular intervals by unfavorable conditions, what is the optimal genotypic structure of the population which will both guarantee its survival in low numbers during unfavorable periods and also give it a high rate of increase in favorable times and allow it to maintain very large populations at peak periods? Barring trivial solutions to this problem, like perfect homeostasis, we know really very little of an exact nature.

One example of how this problem can be attacked exactly, at least in one case, is provided by the recent work of my colleague Dr. Richard Levins. Dr. Levins has been considering the average fitness of a population through time, when environmental conditions are assumed to fluctuate either randomly or with a definite period. The particular model is as follows: There is an optimal phenotype $S_t$ which changes from generation to generation. Each genotype has a phenotype $P_i$ and the fitness of that genotype $W_i$ decreases as the square of the deviation of $P_i$ from $S_t$. That is:

$$W_{it} = 1 - (S_t - P_i)^2$$

From this definition of fitness it follows that the average fitness of the population over many generations, $\bar{W}$, is given by

$$\bar{W} = 1 - \sigma_S^2 - (\bar{S} - \bar{P})^2 - \sigma_{\bar{P_t}}^2 - \overline{\sigma_P^2} + 2\,Cov(S_t, \bar{P_t})$$

where $\sigma_S^2$ is the variance through time of the optimum, $(\bar{S} - P)$ is the difference between the mean optimum and the mean phenotype of the population through time, $\sigma_{\bar{P_t}}^2$ is the variance of mean phenotype of the populations, $\overline{\sigma_P^2}$ is the average within generation phenotypic variance, and $Cov(S_t, \bar{P_t})$ is the covariance between the mean phenotype in any generation and the optimum in that generation.

This formulation shows that the average fitness of the population is decreased by fluctuating environment ($\sigma_S^2$ and $\sigma_{\bar{P_t}}^2$), but is partly restored by any correlation between phenotype and environment, $Cov(S_t, \bar{P_t})$. This covariance is increased if the population can respond easily in its genetic composition to changing environment, but the very same genetic flexibility also increases the variance $\sigma_{\bar{P_t}}^2$ but decreases the variance $\overline{\sigma_P^2}$. The net result of all these is a balance so that an intermediate degree of genetic responsiveness may result in the highest average fitness over time. As an illustration of this balance Levins has considered, among other models, a simple one-locus case in which the phenotypic values of the genotypes *AA, Aa,* and *aa* are *a,* 0, and —*a,* respectively, and in which the average value of $S$ is 0 over long periods. As *a* grows larger, the population is more responsive to selection since gene effects are magnified.

The question is whether there is an optimal strength of gene effect. An example of the results of such investigations is given in Fig. 9 taken from Dr. Levins work. The different curves relating mean fitness $\overline{W}$ to gene effect $a$, correspond to different degrees of correlation of environment between successive generations. We see that when successive environments are strongly correlated ($r = 0.8$ or greater) then there is an optimal

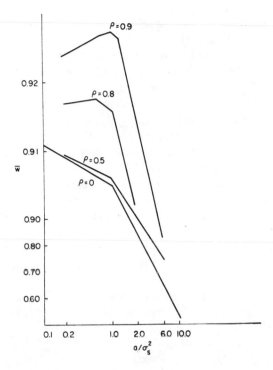

Fig. 9. Relation of average $\overline{W}$ over time to intensity of gene effect for different degrees of serial autocorrelation of the environment. Ordinate shows $\overline{W}$ and abscissa shows ratio of gene affect, $a$, to environmental variance $\sigma_s^2$.

value of $a$ about equal to the environmental variance. For smaller correlations, however, the greater the genetic flexibility the *lower* the fitness. Thus, it is far better in a poorly correlated sequence of environments not to try to track the environment but to have a constant phenotype at the average optimum. When environments are more strongly serially correlated, however, some genetic variance is desirable but not too much. We might expect to find that in environments with low serial correlation as, for example, environments which fluctuate every few generations, these would be strong canalization for characters in which intermediates have the highest fitness. In environments with longer periodicities, ten-generation periodicities corresponding to a correlation of 0.8, it is of advantage to have some genetic variance and to "track" the environment.

We would predict on the basis of such work that different genetic strategies of colonization will be evolved depending upon the statistical pattern of environment. Populations with low genetic variability for a character will more often be successful in environments requiring frequent radical alteration of phenotype, whereas populations with high genetic variability will more often leave successful colonies in environments which, although radically different from the original species range, are in themselves rather stable. A note of caution is necessary here. We do not know how general this result is, but only that it holds for characters fitting the model I have described. Nevertheless, it points the way to a quantitative analysis of the problem of the genetic conditions most conducive to successful colonization.

It may be objected that examination of the optimal genetic system is not very helpful since there is no mechanism for this optimization. There are, in fact, two such mechanisms. The first is direct selection of modifiers within the population to increase or decrease the effect of a gene. That such modifiers are easily selected is well known in *Drosophila*. Second, colonizing species are being subject to constant interdeme selection since nearly all colonizing episodes end in failure. It is at the interdeme level that optimal strategies can be selected, but it must be remembered that the precision of such selection is bound to be less than for intrademe selection.

It is my hope that the methods of analysis of population strategies illustrated by the work of Levins and by Lewontin (1961) can be used generally for the solution of such evolutionary problems.

### REFERENCES

Birch, L. C. (1948). The intrinsic rate of natural increase of an insect population. *J. Animal Ecol.* **17,** 15–26.

Birch, L. C., Dobzhansky, Th., Elliott, P., and Lewontin, R. C. (1963). Relative fitness of geographic races of *Drosophila serrata*. *Evolution* **17,** 72–83.

Cole, L. (1954). The population consequences of life history phenomena. *Quart. Rev. Biol.* **29,** 103–137.

Dobzhansky, Th., Lewontin, R. C., and Pavlovsky, D. (1964). The capacity for increase in chromosomally polymorphic and monomorphic populations of *D. pseudoobscura*. *Heredity* **19,** 597–614.

Lewontin, R. C. (1955). The effects of population density and composition on viability in *D. melanogaster*. *Evolution* **9,** 27–41.

Lewontin, R. C. (1961). Evolution and the theory of games. *J. Theoret. Biol.* **1,** 382–403.

Lewontin, R. C., and Matsuo, Y. (1963). Interaction of genotypes determining viability in *D. busckii*. *Proc. Natl. Acad. Sci. U. S.* **49,** 270–278.

# THE
# AMERICAN NATURALIST

| Vol. 100 | January-February, 1966 | No. 910 |

## POPULATION STABILITY AND LIFE HISTORY PHENOMENA

### W. W. MURDOCH*

Bureau of Animal Population, University of Oxford, England

### INTRODUCTION

The numbers of individuals in natural populations are bound to fluctuate; however, mechanisms for resisting violent fluctuations and enhancing stability may evolve, if they are compatible with natural selection at the level of the individual. A reason why such evolution should occur has been given by Hutchinson (1954): large fluctuations are dangerous for a species since they may lead to oversaturation of the environment and to very low densities which increase the probability of at least local extinction through chance events. Since natural environments are not constant, selection for stabilizing mechanisms means selection for the capacity in members of the population for changing responses to a varying environment.

This paper concerns the possible existence of such a stabilizing mechanism in invertebrates whose adults have the capacity to survive and to reproduce in more than one breeding season. The proposed mechanism functions through a relationship between breeding and survival whereby the survival of adults, especially females, is inversely related to their previous reproductive activities. It has been studied in a group of beetles belonging to the family Carabidae.

A detailed presentation and analysis of the results discussed here have been made in a previous paper (Murdoch, in press), and, consequently, methods will be mentioned only briefly and only a summary of the relevant results will be given.

### GENERAL ECOLOGY OF THE BEETLES

The populations of the beetles studied are virtually confined to the deep litter layer of marshes and fens. These habitats are isolated and well-defined, the species are virtually flightless, dispersal mechanisms appear to be poorly developed, and movements of animals into and out of the populations were negligible. Three populations of *Agonum fuliginosum* and, in two of the marshes, populations of *A. thoreyi* were studied from 1961 to

*Present address: Department of Biological Sciences, University of California, Santa Barbara, California.

spring 1963 in marshes near Oxford, England. These populations are designated 1, 2, and 3. The beetles breed once a year, from May to late July,
and during this time may produce 50 to 100 eggs (Briggs, 1957). They have
three larval instars in summer, then pupate and emerge in autumn. From
then until the following spring the adults hibernate.

A typical pattern of adult mortality emerged during the study. Mortality
is severe during the breeding season, variable from early July to early
winter, then low, both in old adults and new adults emerged in fall, during
winter until the onset of breeding the following spring. Evidence from enclosed experimental populations suggests that the high mortality (up to
80%) in the breeding season was due to predation by small mammals. The
mortality from July to winter is our main concern here.

## ESTIMATION OF REPRODUCTIVE RATE

Eggs were not found in the field and therefore estimating reproductive
rates in this manner was impossible; since only one female could be induced to lay eggs in the laboratory, in spite of a number of attempts to set
up breeding colonies, this method could not be used either. The number of
mature eggs present in females taken from the field has been used as an
estimate of egg laying rate in lieu of direct measurements. The use of this
method involves an assumption, so far untested, that the rate at which a female lays eggs is directly proportional to the number of mature eggs it contains. Several lines of evidence suggest that the assumption is valid (Murdoch, 1965).

## TEST OF THE HYPOTHESIS

The survival from spring to winter 1961 of adult *A. fuliginosum* in the
two main populations, 1 and 2, was low (about 5%), following high mean
mature egg numbers of $7.0 \pm 1.4$ and $9.5 \pm 0.9$, respectively, in spring. On
the other hand, Dawson (1957 unpubl.) recorded percentages of 17% to 68%
of old adult *A. fuliginosum* in several overwintering populations during two
successive winters, suggesting that survival to winter of adults alive in
spring was high. The only other obvious difference between these two
sets of data was that females in Dawson's study had produced fewer eggs;
the mean mature egg number was approximately four per female, 24% of all
females examined ($n = 53$) in the breeding season having no mature eggs
compared with only 5% (1 in 25) in the present study. On this basis the
hypothesis was set up that, other mortality factors being of equal intensity,
the survival of adult females from one breeding season to the next is inversely proportional to their preceding reproductive rates. Since survival
over winter appeared to be high, and old and new adults survive equally at
that time (see also Dawson, 1957), survival from spring to fall or early
winter becomes crucial.

The hypothesis was partially tested in a field experiment in 1962. In
May, adult beetles were placed in mesh enclosures containing litter from
which all other species of Carabidae were excluded, and these were in turn
placed among the litter at marsh 1. The categories in the experiment were

TABLE 1.

Survival of female (classes 1, 2 and 4) and male (class 3) *A. fuliginosum* in a field experiment in 1962. Note: The "initial number" decreases where replicates were lost.

| Class | Initial no. per bag | | July | | | | September | | | |
|---|---|---|---|---|---|---|---|---|---|---|
| | | | No. surviving / Initial no. | | % survival | | No. surviving / Initial no. | | % survival | |
| | ♀ | ♂ | ♀ | ♂ | ♀ | ♂ | ♀ | ♂ | ♀ | ♂ |
| 1 | 2 | 2 | 16/18 | ... | 89 | ... | 5/14 | ... | 36 | ... |
| 2 | 4 | ... | 35/40 | ... | 88 | ... | 20/28 | ... | 72 | ... |
| 3 | ... | 4 | ... | 19/40 | ... | 48 | ... | 9/32 | ... | 28 |
| 4 | 4 | 4 | ... | ... | ... | ... | 12/16 | ... | 75 | ... |

as shown in Table 1; all but class 4 started out with 10 replicates but several were lost, probably owing to small mammal predation. The important comparison is between class 1, the control, and class 2, the prediction being that females without males will survive to September better than females with males. Since the effects of breeding are likely to be cumulative, differences in survival between classes 1 and 2 would be expected to appear towards the end of the breeding season, i.e., July. It can be seen that survival to early July was similar in these two classes but that females on their own survived from July to September better than did females with males. The difference between the survival rates in the two classes only marginally fails to be significant at the 95% level ($\chi^2 - 3.57$, $P \sim 0.06$), an encouraging result for such small numbers of animals. That the decline in female survival after the breeding season is due in some way to interaction with males during the breeding season is supported by the high survival between July and September of females, previously kept without males but placed with males in July (class 4). The difference in female survival over the latter period between classes 2 and 4 is statistically insignificant ($\chi^2 = .064$, $.9 > P > .75$).

This experiment has not sorted out the effects on females of "interactions with males" from those of egg development and oviposition. Females on their own develop some eggs, but probably do so more slowly than females kept with males (Norris, 1934; Smith, 1959) and interaction with males may well be an important factor in reduced survival (cf. Lloyd and Park, 1962). It is interesting to note that during the breeding season a group of males survived worse than males with females ($\chi^2 = 5.177$, $P < .05$), and much worse than a group of females ($\chi^2 = 9.55$, $P < .01$). Possibly something akin to the "homosexual rape" between males in Tribolium, as suggested by Lloyd and Park, occurs.

The hypothesis is more difficult to test in natural populations since mortality factors vary in their intensity from time to time and place to place. However, the natural populations studied in sufficient detail in 1962 fulfilled the predictions based on the hypothesis. In *A. fuliginosum* the mean mature egg number in May and June in population 1 was significantly lower ($t = 3.56$, $P < .01$) than that in population 2, there being no data from population 1 in July that year. The corresponding survivorships from May to winter were 26% in 1 and 6% in 2. The difference between the survivorships of classes 1 and 2 (females with males and females alone) in the experiment occurred from early July, and survival over this period was different in the two natural populations also, being at least 65% in 1 and between 10% and 25% in 2.

The results from the experiment, the two populations discussed above, and several others studied are summarized in Table 2. It can be seen that for all instances for which evidence is available the prediction of high old adult survival following poor breeding is fulfilled.

TABLE 2.

Summary of the relation between reproduction and survival in several populations.

| Type of population | Species | Population no. | Breeding status or mean mature egg no. | Estimated survival (%) May-winter |
|---|---|---|---|---|
| Experimental | A. fuliginosum | ... | breeding | 36 |
|  |  | ... | non-breeding | 72 |
| Natural | A. fuliginosum | 1 | 3.2 ± 0.6 (May-June) | 25 |
|  |  | 2 | 6.0 ± 0.6 (May-June) | 6 |
|  | A. fuliginosum | 2 | 6.2 ± 0.5 (May-July) | 6 |
|  |  | 3 | 3.7 ± 0.6 (May-July) | 48 |
|  | A. thoreyi | 2 | 4.7 ± 1.3 | 14 |
|  |  | 3 | 0.9 ± 0.5 | 30–60 |

## DISCUSSION

From laboratory studies it appears that the relationship between breeding and survival outlined above may be fairly widespread in insects, for example in some Carabidae (Burgess and Collins, 1911), in Tribolium (Mertz, D. personal communication), in a Lepidopteran (Norris, 1934), in the cockroach Periplanata (Comfort, 1956) and in Drosophila (Smith, 1959).

### Population stability

It is easy to see how, in the carabids in years of poor breeding, the increased survival of old adults might help to prevent a decline in numbers. There is empirical evidence that this is the case in some natural populations (Murdoch, *op. cit.*; Dawson, 1957). Van der Drift (1951), Schjøtz-Christensen (1961) and Tipton (1960) found carabids breeding in their second season. Thus survival of old adults to at least a second breeding season may well be an important factor in carabid populations and in some instances might be essential for the persistence of a population. Although it is difficult to tell old from young females once breeding is in progress, there seems no doubt that females breed in their second season. Thus distinguishably old females were found to have mature and developing eggs in this study, and Burgess and Collins (1911) concluded that old *Calasoma sycophanta* (Carabidae) females actually reproduced better than did first year females.

The significance of the mechanism in the dynamics of a population, and the manner in which it might enhance stability may be clarified by a brief discussion of other aspects of the beetles' biology. First, in general, under a given light and temperature regime reproductive rate is a function of food supply; and in this study oviposition rate, as measured by mature egg number, was found to bear a direct relationship to food supply (Murdoch, *op. cit.*). Secondly, adults can live without food for several weeks during the breeding season. Finally, adults can exist together at very high densities without any increased mortality. From these observations the following relationship between food supply, breeding and survival is suggested: when the food supply is sufficient and the reproductive rate is high, many young are produced and old adults die; when food is scarce, breeding is reduced, during the breeding season adults survive well on little food and survival after breeding is high. The mechanism is thus one which buffers the population against the effect of a temporary food shortage during the breeding season, or against any other factor causing a temporary reduction in breeding.

As suggested by Hutchinson (1954), fluctuations may arise due to the time lag in the response of negative feed-back mechanisms and he suggests that this lag is best reduced "by making natality less density dependent so that the burden of regulation is placed on mortality." In the mechanism described above natality remains sensitive to population and environmental pressures, but is so linked to adult mortality that the two processes are affected at the same time by certain important factors, such as food supply, thus reducing the lag effect without relying solely on mortality for stabilization.

*Life history phenomena*

The results discussed above are relevant also to a theoretical argument presented by Cole (1954). He has shown that in an annual species, where $B$ = the number of offspring in a "litter," the intrinsic rate of increase ($r$) can be defined as $r = 1n(B)$. Clearly this assumes no mortality before reproduction and is the maximum possible rate of increase. Taking the most extreme case of repeated reproduction, i.e., parental immortality, $r = 1n(B + 1)$. Thus "for an annual species, the absolute gain in the (maximum possible) intrinsic population growth which could be achieved by changing to the perennial reproductive habit would be exactly equivalent to adding one individual to the average litter size" (my parenthesis). Cole further states that in species where the litter size is large and the pre-reproductive life is relatively short, such as in those discussed in this paper, the gain will be very small. Cole states that in such cases "it seems probable that a change in life history which would add 1 to the litter size would be more likely to occur than a change permitting repeated reproduction, which in many cases would necessitate adjustments to survive several seasons of dormancy." However, in the species described here, many individuals of a group of insects generally considered annuals have reproduced in two or more seasons, which would seem contrary to ex-

pectations based on the argument put forward above by Cole. A more realistic view of population phenomena might remove the apparent inconsistency; thus potential variations in the maximum possible intrinsic rate of
growth may not be important in the actual growth or maintenance of a population. In this instance the probability of an adult's surviving to a subsequent breeding season may be greater than that of an egg's surviving and
developing into a breeding adult by then, so that survival to another breeding season adds more to population growth than adding one to the "litter"
size, a factor not taken into consideration in calculating the maximum possible intrinsic growth. Thus it appears that sometimes, in spite of Cole's
*a priori* reasoning, it may be of selective advantage for a species with a
large litter size and short pre-reproductive life to retain the potentiality for
survival to more than one breeding season.

## SUMMARY

The hypothesis was tested that, other mortality factors being of equal
intensity, the survival of adult female Carabidae, from near the end of one
breeding season to the start of the next, is inversely proportional to the
amount of reproduction done in that first breeding season. It is suggested
that this is one of the compensatory mechanisms leading to population stability in Carabidae and may be widespread in other insects. It is pointed
out that the expected influence of natural selection upon life history phenomena may be quite different when actual, rather than potential, population changes are considered.

## ACKNOWLEDGMENTS

I wish to thank Mr. C. S. Elton, my Doctoral supervisor, for his continual
encouragement and timely advice, and for reading and criticizing the manuscript. I am grateful to various members of the staff and visitors to the
Bureau of Animal Population who read early drafts of some sections. I
also wish to thank Dr. P. H. Leslie for advice on statistics and Mr. D. A.
Kempson for technical help and advice. The study was carried out while I
received a Nature Conservancy Studentship and, for some months, a grant
from Corpus Christi College, Oxford. Oxford University Chest and Blen-
heim Park Estate kindly gave the permission to visit the study areas.

## LITERATURE CITED

Briggs, J. B. 1957. Some experiments on control of ground beetle damage
    to strawberry. Ann. Rep. E. Malling Res. Sta. 1956, p. 142–145.
Burgess, A. F., and C. W. Collins. 1911. *Calosoma sycophanta*: its life
    history, behaviour, and successful colonization in New England.
    Bull. U. S. Dept. Agric. Bur. Entomolol. No. 101.
Cole, L. C. 1954. The population consequences of life history phenomena.
    Quart. Rev. Biol. 29: 103–137.
Comfort, A. 1956. The biology of senescence. Routledge & Paul, London.
    257 p.
Dawson, N. 1957. The ecology of fenland Carabidae. Unpubl. D.Phil.
    thesis, Cambridge Univ.

Hutchinson, G. E. 1954. Notes on oscillatory populations. J. Wildlife Manage. 18: 107–109.

Lloyd, M., and T. Park. 1962. Mortality resulting from interactions between adult flour beetles in laboratory cultures. Physiol. Zool. 35: 330–347.

Murdoch, W. W. 1965. Aspects of the population dynamics of some Carabidae. J. Anim. Ecol. (In press)

Norris, M. J. 1934. Contributions towards the study of insect fertility III. Adult nutrition, fecundity, and longevity in the genus *Ephestia* (Lepidoptera, Phycitidae). Proc. Zool. Soc. London, p. 333–360.

Schjøtz-Christensen, B. 1961. Forplantningsbiologien hos *Amara infima* Dft. og *Harpalus neglectus* Serv. Flora og Fauna 67: 8–18.

Smith, J. M. 1959. The rate of ageing in *Drosophila sudobscura*. *In* Ciba Foundation: Colloquia on Ageing 5: 269–280.

Tipton, J. D. 1960. Some aspects of the biology of the beetles *Nebria brevicollis* (F.) and *Feronia caerulescens* (L.) with particular reference to diurnalism and population fluctuations. Unpubl. Ph.D. thesis, Reading University.

Van der Drift, J. 1951. Analysis of the animal community in a beech forest floor. Meded. Inst. Toegep. Biol. Onderz. Nat. No. 9, 168 p.

# THE
# AMERICAN NATURALIST

| Vol. 102 | September-October, 1968 | No. 927 |

## PATTERN IN LIFE HISTORY AND THE ENVIRONMENT[1]

### GARTH I. MURPHY

Department of Oceanography, University of Hawaii, Honolulu, Hawaii 96822

### INTRODUCTION

The purpose of this paper is to examine the relationship of a particular life-history phenomenon, iteroparity (Cole, 1954), with respect to the competitive ability of populations in an environment that causes variations in reproductive success. Cole's paper generates a paradox: that is, under many circumstances, if not most, iteroparity is the least effective way to enhance the intrinsic rate of increase $r$. Yet it is widespread! One must assume, then, that under some circumstances iteroparity bestows a competitive advantage to the organism. In this paper I hope to show that under the conditions of uncertain survival of pre-reproductives and relatively stable survival of reproductives, iteroparity is advantageous, both with respect to competition between species (interspecific competition) and competition within a freely interbreeding population (intraspecific competition).

Certain aspects of this paper are an extension of a computer study (Murphy, 1967) that was directed to evaluating the effect of reduced iteroparity (through fishing mortality) on an exploited fish population. The results showed that a level of fishing which should have been acceptable, insofar as the average ability of the fished population to grow was concerned, induced serious population fluctuations when reproductive success was allowed to vary randomly with an amplitude similar to that observed in the Pacific sardine population. This problem, especially as it relates to the probability of extinction, was treated analytically by Holgate (1967) with compatible results.

### A QUALITATIVE STATEMENT

It is common knowledge that many long-lived organisms (e.g., redwood trees) reproduce over many years but only rarely reproduce successfully. The usual explanation is that the habitat is completely occupied and only on occasion is there space in which a seedling can become established.

Contribution No. 306, Hawaii Institute of Marine Biology, University of Hawaii.

The argument I wish to advance is that there is evolutionary pressure toward just this type of life-history pattern. Evolutionary pressure for long life, late maturity, and many reproductions may be generated either by an environment in which density-independent factors cause wide variation in the survival of pre-reproductives or by an environment that is biologically inhospitable to pre-reproductives because of intense competition with the reproductives. Conversely, either high or variable adult mortality will tend to generate evolutionary pressure toward early reproduction, high fecundity, and few reproductions, or only one reproduction.

Evidence for the dynamic significance of the interdependence of life-history features was developed by Beverton (1963), who made a comparative study of herring-like fishes with respect to the potential yield per recruit, that is, the expectation of harvest per individual that reached maturity. The three parameters considered were longevity, growth, and age at first maturity. He concluded that these three factors, broadly speaking, interact in a compensatory way, so that "longevity . . ., growth . . . , maturation form a consistent pattern that results in similar response to fishing pressure from a wide range of stocks which might, at first sight, seem to have very different dynamic characteristics."

An evolutionary argument to rationalize Beverton's observations can be easily erected by proposing that longevity is fundamentally a function of predation. Larger size, assuming homologous organisms, reduces predation dangers in obvious ways, but, of course, has a limit dependent upon the distribution of food resources. Assuming the largest possible size is desirable, it follows that it is advantageous to achieve that size in the shortest possible time. The most obvious way to accomplish this is to postpone first reproduction. The converse is that the consequence of heavy predation is short life, precluding attainment of large size, requiring early maturity and probably a higher birth rate, and increasing the possibility of mortality from physiological exhaustion, as well as further inhibiting attainment of large size.

The evolutionary advantage of escaping predation by attaining a larger size and, hence, having an opportunity to reproduce more often is intuitively attractive, but, as already indicated, this advantage is superficially incompatible with the consequences of the intrinsic rate of natural increase, $r$, as defined by Lotka's equation (1):

$$1 = \int_0^\infty e^{-rx} l(x) m(x)\, dx, \tag{1}$$

where $r$ is the intrinsic rate of increase of the population, $l(x)$ is the probability of an individual living to age $x$ from age 0, and $m(x)$ is the number of offspring produced per unit time at age $x$. Clearly, an earlier-reproducing, shorter-lived, more fecund population would tend to have the higher $r$ and should tend to win in competition, and, if there were a common gene pool, the short-lived genotype would tend to dominate.

However, this is not necessarily so. In the balance of this paper I will show that, at least under some circumstances, variable reproductive success can reverse the expectation in a competition model and in a simple genetic model.

## COMPETITION BETWEEN TWO POPULATIONS

The logistic approach to competition (and other population problems) has often been criticized because of its assumptions. Accordingly, competition was examined in the context of Ricker's (1954) reproduction equation, further elaborated in Ricker (1958, p. 263). This has the advantage of modeling at least one explicit form of reproductive compensation (cannibalism), and it lends itself readily to numerical evaluation schedules that take into account the major life-history parameters, such as growth, mortality, and age-specific fecundity, without violating any of the assumptions of the model.

The set of simultaneous competition equations based on the Ricker model is:

$$R' = P'e^{(E'-P'-aP'')/M'}$$

$$R'' = P''e^{(E''-P''-bP')/M''},$$

(2)

where $P$ = population size; $R$ = reproduction per generation; $E$ = population size at replacement or equilibrium reproduction; $M$ = population size at absolute maximum reproduction; $'$, $''$ denote population 1 and 2, respectively; $a$ = interaction coefficient, population 2 on population 1, assumed positive; and $b$ = interaction coefficient, population 1 on population 2, assumed positive. (Interaction is assumed to be qualitatively the same as the effect of the population on itself.)

Algebraic evaluation of the outcome of competition is easiest if equations (2) are converted to the form:

$$\ln \frac{R'}{P'} = \frac{E' - P' - aP''}{M'}$$

$$\ln \frac{R'}{P''} = \frac{E'' - P' - bP'}{M''}.$$

(3)

From equations (3) a set of statements analogous to the statements derived from logistic theory can be erected:

a) $E' > aE''$, $E'' < bE'$: $P'$ wins.
b) $E' < aE''$, $E'' > bE'$: $P''$ wins.
c) $E' > aE''$, $E'' > bE'$: coexistence.
d) $E' < aE''$, $E'' < bE'$: one or the other wins, depending on initial numbers.

These outcomes are identical to those of logistic theory if $E$ is regarded as analogous to the asymptotic population value of logistic theory. In the most interesting case, coexistence, the equilibrium levels of the two competing systems can be solved for by setting $R/P$ in equations (3) equal to 1 (the condition that must prevail at equilibrium), and solving simultaneously for $P'$ and $P''$.

Predation can be introduced in a way exactly analogous to Gause's (1934) system of introducing predation to the logistic set of equations. First, it is necessary to compute a fraction which represents the reduction in fecundity over the expected life span as a result of the increased mortality. The natural logarithm of this fraction $c$ is introduced as follows:

$$R' = P'e^{[(E'-P'-aP'')/M']-c'}$$

$$R'' = P''e^{[(E''-P''-bP')/M'']-c''}$$

(4)

The equations analogous to equations (3) for evaluating the outcomes are:

$$\ln \frac{R'}{P'} = \frac{E' - P' - aP'' - c'M'}{M'}$$

$$\ln \frac{R''}{P''} = \frac{E'' - P'' - bP' - c''M''}{M''},$$

(5)

and the outcome statements, assuming $c' = c''$, are:

$a'$) $E' > (aE'' + c'M')$,   $E'' < (bE' + c''M'')$: $P'$ wins.
$b'$) $E' < (aE'' + c'M')$,   $E'' > (bE' + c''M'')$: $P''$ wins.
$c'$) $E' > (aE'' + c'M')$,   $E'' > (bE' + c''M'')$: coexistence.
$d'$) $E' < (aE'' + c'M')$,   $E'' < (bE' + c''M'')$: depends on initial numbers.

The most interesting aspect of having introduced nonselective predation is that the new decision statements now involve the quantity $M$, which is inversely (but not necessarily simply) related to the quantity $r$ in equation (1) (Murphy, 1967). Nonselective predation leads to reversal of the expected outcome in some cases; that is, it is obvious from the series of statements, $a$ to $c$, that the species with the highest $E$ value, which can be interpreted as the species making most efficient use of the resources, wins, unless special interaction coefficients are invoked. In the second set of statements, $a'$ to $d''$, the outcome can be reversed under conditions of equal predation, the species with the higher $r$ (lower $M$) winning. Again, this set of equations functions in a way analogous to logistic competition equations in a steady environment.

Computer simulation (Table 1) was used to test the effect of variable reproductive success on the outcomes predicted by the steady-state equations. The basic computational scheme was a straightforward extension of that embodied in Ricker (1954). The life-history parameters used for the two competing populations approximate real populations $M$ for example sardines and anchovies in the California Current system (Murphy, 1966) $M$ but with some simplifications (Table 1)

TABLE 1

SUMMARY OF POPULATION STRUCTURE AND PARAMETERS USED IN
THE COMPUTER SIMULATION

| | POPULATION 1 | | | POPULATION 2 | | |
|---|---|---|---|---|---|---|
| AGE | Relative $l(x)$ | Relative $m(x)$ | Distribution of Reproduction | Relative $l(x)$ | Relative $m(x)$ | Distribution of Reproduction |
| 2... | 1.000 | 0.000 | ... | 1.000 | 2.211 | .553 |
| 3... | 0.670 | 1.992 | .334 | .449 | 2.211 | .248 |
| 4... | 0.449 | 1.992 | .224 | .202 | 2.211 | .112 |
| 5... | 0.301 | 1.992 | .150 | .091 | 2.211 | .050 |
| 6... | 0.202 | 1.992 | .101 | .041 | 2.211 | .023 |
| 7... | 0.135 | 1.992 | .067 | .018 | 2.211 | .010 |
| 8... | 0.091 | 1.992 | .045 | .008 | 2.211 | .004 |
| 9... | 0.061 | 1.992 | .030 | ... | ... | ... |
| 10... | 0.041 | 1.992 | .020 | ... | ... | ... |
| 11... | 0.027 | 1.992 | .013 | ... | ... | ... |
| 12... | 0.018 | 1.992 | .009 | ... | ... | ... |

NOTE.—For population 1, $\Sigma\, l(x)m(x) = 4 = R_0$ (reproduction per generation); $E = 10,000$; $M = 7,213$; $r = .3188$ (equation 1). For population 2, $\Sigma\, l(x)m(x) = 4 = R_0$; $E = 8,696$; $M = 6,272$; $r = .5472$ (equation 1).

The long-lived population has an instantaneous natural mortality co-efficient of 0.4; the short-lived, 0.8. The relative size of the two populations was determined by assuming that a finite amount of energy comes into the system, that it takes 10 energy units to replace one unit lost (death by predation), and that maintenance energy is 10 times the standing crop per unit time.

The equilibrium level ($E$) of the first population was arbitrarily set at 10,000 individuals, which, because of the energy scheme, sets the equilibrium level of the second population at 8,696 individuals.

Additional conventions are that all growth ends at age 2 and is identical for both populations; that population 1 first reproduces at age 3 and population 2 at age 2; and that only mature adults are involved in the interaction. The reproduction per generation $R_0$ was set at 4.0 for both populations, which defines the two $m(x)$ schedules, as fecundity is assumed proportional to size. With these numbers in hand, both $M$ and $r$, the remaining parameters, can be easily calculated. The system is designed to simplify simulation testing of the effect of variability on reproduction, and yet to preserve the features of real world life-history patterns essential to the problem.

As might be expected from the competition equations, when the two populations are set in competition with interaction coefficients equal to unity at starting densities of 1,000 individuals each and no environmental variability, population 2 (which has the higher $r$) increases more rapidly than population 1 (long-lived, lower $r$) and then falls off to extinction as population 1 continues to grow. The relative trends closely resemble commonly reproduced figures of *Tribolium* competition experiments such as Fig. 10.10 B in Andrewartha and Birch (1954).

In order to test whether the outcome could be altered by random variability in reproductive success, the iteration coefficients were altered ($a = 0.82$ and $b = 1.13$) so that there was coexistence with the steady state, steady environment level of the long-lived population (No. 1) at 2,364, and of the short-lived population at 6,757. Uniformly distributed random factors having a mean of unity and with four-, eight-, and sixteenfold variation (highest divided by lowest) were introduced after time period 26, at which point the two populations, each started at 1,000 units, had nearly reached equilibrium (2,898 and 6,314). The results are shown in Fig 1.

The data points in Fig. 1 are 20-year means. The only matters of interest that they obscure are the occasional reverses that are the result of a long series of favorable reproduction years. Reversal occurred twice in the sixteenfold record and more often in the others. For example, there were seven years during which the short-lived were more abundant than the long-lived in the last 50 years of the fourfold record. However, considering that the built-in dynamics of the system are such that the short-lived form in the absence of random variation in reproduction would be almost three times as abundant, there has been clear demonstration of the value of iteroparity. Factors drawn from normal distributions were also tested and gave the same general results, though they of course tended to be, on the average, less severe in effect because of their more marked central tendency.

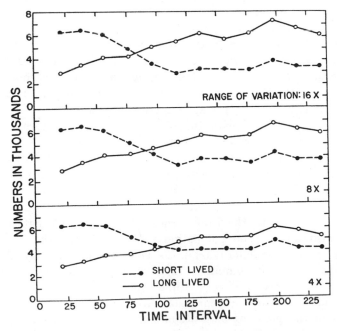

Fig. 1.—The result of applying reproductive uncertainty in computer simulation of competing populations.

## GENETIC MODELS

Demonstration of the competitive superiority of long life and multiple reproduction does not necessarily mean that there will be selective pressure within populations toward iteroparity. In order to explore this problem, very simple genetic models were developed. The first consisted of a simple two-allele system with a closely linked fecundity gene which was not, in itself, subject to selection. The homozygote *AA* reproduces at one time interval after birth and then dies after producing three times as many gametes as *aa*. The heterozygotes produce twice as many gametes as *aa* and die after one reproduction at one time unit after birth. Homozygotes *aa* produce one-third as many gametes as *AA* at each reproduction but are longer-lived, reproducing at both time units 1 and 2 after birth. Gametes are assumed to be mixed randomly at the time of reproduction.

The maximum population size was arbitrarily set at 10,000 units. The population at each time period consists of the carry-overs (*aa*), together with the new additions to the population resulting from the reproduction of the previous period. The relative composition of the new recruits was determined by the usual binomial expansion, after determining the relative numbers of *A* and *a* gametes produced by the parental stock.

In the absence of environmental variations, the absolute number of progeny was, in each instance, simply 10,000 minus the carry-over. That is, it was assumed that the habitat was filled completely each time period by the new recruits. In the system just described, the gene pool was cleansed of the *a* (long life) allele in 32 time periods when started with 1,000 *AA* and 3,000 *aa* homozygotes.

The scheme for random variation is quite simple. The rule is that on a random basis years are assigned a value of 1.0 or 0.1 with respect to the fraction of the presumably expected recruits that would be added to the subsequent population. That is, if there were, under normal circumstances (unity reproduction), room for 4,000 recruits in the population, only 400, distributed in accordance with the binomial expansion, were allowed in the poor year. In this trial, the population was initiated as before, and at time interval 12, the gene pool was cleansed of *A* (short life, high fecundity). Inspection of the particular sequence of random factors employed suggests that this period (12 intervals) was somewhat shorter than the mean expectation. A second trial required 25 intervals to eliminate *A*.

A second model with the same genetic rules but different population rules was also tested. The population rules were that the environment was saturated at 10,000 individuals as before. Each individual was allowed to produce a finite number of zygotes which is a simple multiple of the 3:2:1 gamete ratio. This multiple will be called the reproduction factor. During a favorable year, the entire production of zygotes was allowed up to the point of saturation. For a poor year, only 0.1 of the zygotes were allowed. Thus, there are two limits instead of only one on each succeeding generation: the absolute ability of the population to increase, as well as the vacant places in the habitat. As before, each population was initiated with 1,000 *AA* individuals and 3,000 *aa*.

In the case of a reproduction factor of 1.0 and no random variation (full reproduction), the population was all *AA* in 32 periods. With random variation, it was all *a* in 19 periods. When the reproduction factor was 1.3, the population was all *AA* in 32 periods with full reproduction each period. With random variation (same series of numbers), the population was all *aa* in 34 periods. With the zygote factor raised to 2.0 and full reproduction each period, *AA* won in 32 periods. With random variation, *AA* also won, but 53 periods were required. The functional reason for this is that the general fecundity was raised so high that the random variation in reproductive success was ineffective most of the time, that is, the saturation limit usually prevailed as when there was no variation.

The second model, in contrast to the first, does not have a built-in mechanism precluding extinction (the problem considered by Holgate, 1967). In order to be certain that the random factors would not by themselves drive *AA* to extinction, thus generating a misleading experiment, pure populations of *AA* and *aa* were subjected to the same set of factors. Both populations survived 60 periods under the smallest reproduction factor (1.0).

As a final test, random numbers were abandoned and a simple alternation of good and bad years was tried. With the reproduction factor at 1.0, *aa* won in 22 periods. When the pattern was alternating sets of two good years and two poor, *aa* won in 21 periods.

It seems clear from the competition and genetic trials that under conditions of relatively stable adult mortality and unstable infant mortality and competition there can be selection for long life and multiple reproduction. If the gene pools were not randomly mixed during each reproductive period, the result would still hold, as the population competition model would then apply.

Some data relative to the arguments we have just considered are available. The material in Table 2 has been assembled from the sources indicated. All of the populations are abundant, schooling, plankton-feeding forms. Of

TABLE 2

SUMMARY OF REPRODUCTION PARAMETERS

| Population | Age at First Maturity | Reproductive Span | Variation in Spawning Success (Highest/Lowest) |
|---|---|---|---|
| Herring (Atlanta-Scandian) | 5–6* | 18† | 25 ×* |
| Herring (North Sea) | 3–4–5* | 10† | 9 ×* |
| Pacific sardine | 2–3‡ | 10‡ | 10 ×‡ |
| Herring (Baltic) | 2–3* | 4* | 3 ×* |
| Anchovy (Peru) | 1§ | 2§ | 2 ×§ |

* Hempill (1963).
† Estimated from data in Beverton (1963).
‡ Murphy (1966).
§ Murphy (1966), Saetersdal, Tsukayama, and Alegre (1965).

the tabulated data, age at first reproduction is reasonably firm. Reproductive span is less firm because the life span in the absence of exploitation generally has not been directly observed. Variation in spawning success is even less firm, in part because the records are of different length and in part because such data with population held constant are generally not available. Despite these difficulties, the trend, Fig. 2, is so marked that it would require large revisions in the estimates of the parameters to alter the general conclusion.

It is of some interest to note that the Peruvian anchovy reproduces in the Peruvian Current in winter, possibly the most stable oceanographic situation in the world (El Niño occurs in summer); and the Atlanta-Scandian herring stock reproduces in the Polar Front region, possibly the most unpredictable environment in the world ocean.

The conclusions from these data and the foregoing model studies are consolidated in Figure 3. The upper left-hand box (long life, steady reproduction) is at first sight the most desirable quarter. We have, however, been considering zooplankton feeding fishes that serve as forage for larger carnivores. Any significant population of that type would soon be driven to short-life steady reproduction by predation pressure. The instability of the population in the lower left-hand quarter would of course tend to preclude the development of very great predation pressure, or, if it did develop, the population and the predators would both be unobservable because of extinction (see Murphy, 1967).

## DISCUSSION

Cole (1954) anticipated the essence of this paper when he wrote, on page 120 (regarding tapeworms and redwood trees), "With so large a litter size one wonders if iteroparity in this case may not represent something other than an adaptation for increasing biotic potential." Certainly these two forms are extremes in the sense that the adult leads a very safe life and the opportunities for the young are precarious and variable. The two cases

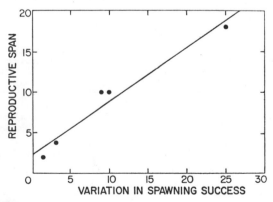

FIG. 2.—Relationship between reproductive uncertainty and reproductive span in certain fishes. Data from Table 2.

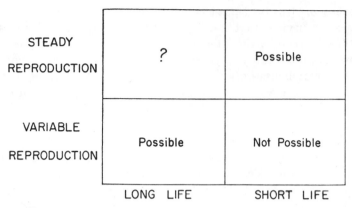

F<small>IG</small>. 3.—Summary of arguments with respect to marine fishes.

also represent two extremes in that variation in survival of tapeworm zygotes is essentially independent of the adult population, while variation in survival of *Sequoia* is very much dependent on the density of the adult population.

With some success in rationalizing one class of pattern in life history at hand, it is useful to attempt to extend the reasoning. The simplest possible extension is to consider organisms with a relatively safe, juvenile existence (e.g., periodic cicadas) and an uncertain adult existence. The pressures will be toward single reproduction and high birth rate. Perhaps this is the rationalization for the origin of the pattern in Pacific salmonids. Those that do not die a mandatory physiological death after spawning (e.g., the migratory trout) have a trivial survival to future spawnings, despite their large size (ca. 10 lb.). For example, Shapovalov and Taft (1954) list the number that spawns 2, 3, and 4 times as 15%, 2%, and 0.1 % respectively, of those spawning once. A slight increase in the number of eggs at first spawning would easily restore the lost biotic potential. The habit of many species of salmonids of maturing (first or final) at different ages might represent a way of retaining some of the advantages of iteroparity without sacrificing the birth rate.

Cody (1966) has considered another aspect of the general problem, clutch size in birds. We should determine whether his observations are relevant to the propositions advanced in this paper; that is, whether they can be explained on the basis of uncertainty in survival from zygote to maturity, and survival of adults to subsequent reproductions. The general idea advanced by Cody that there is a competitive advantage accruing to organisms that increase the carrying capacity of the habitat is inherent in logistic competition equations and the Ricker competition equation presented herein. Clutch size is, of course, only one of the triumvirate of important life-history parameters, and, in itself, is not even relevant. What is relevant at the first level is the number of eggs that survive to maturity in the absence of density-dependent mortality, and, at the second level, the variations in survival that can be directly related to the size of the adult population. It seems axiomatic that small clutch size must be associated with low adult mortality (and longevity), high survival to maturity, or both. Large clutch size must be associated with either high adult mortality, high infant mortality, or both. This suggests that, rather than considering an undefined stability, it might be fruitful to investigate stability with respect to survival from zygote to first maturity, apart from survival after first maturity.

The basic difficulty with Cody's argument, however, is that the genetic pressure in a "stable" situation, which for the moment we can take to mean unvarying infant and adult mortality, will tend to favor early maturity and high birth rates, possibly involving short life. This was demonstrated in the simple genetic models presented earlier. However, stable juvenile and adult mortality inevitably tends to result in populations that are near the carrying capacity of the habitat, immediately introducing the type of uncertainty in the survival of zygote to maturity exemplified by the redwoods. This, in turn, places a premium on longevity, requiring a probable reduction in birth rate so that more energy can be devoted to assuring longevity. Excessive nest predation, as discussed by Cody, introduces another type of uncertainty in survival from zygote to first maturity. If nest predation is actually reduced by having smaller clutch sizes, as suggested by Cody, it would represent a secondary selective factor. What is missing is reliable data on adult longevity. Presumably, the benign climate reduces the expectation of death from abiotic factors, and certainly many tropical birds are long-lived, for example, parrots.

Cody's argument becomes tenuous in the instance of islands. His data on temperate islands can be easily explained within the context of his framework, but perhaps more easily by invoking the advantage of iteroparity in a population near saturation (the redwood case). The data from tropical islands suggests that next predation has nothing to do with the general situation in the tropics; rather, that the situation there is simply the result of uncertainty of survival from zygote to first maturity, generated by populations at, or near, saturation.

Cody's data and explanations for hole nesters are somewhat incomprehensible on the basis of both his arguments and mine. A more direct explanation is that they are a special case in which the resource in short supply is the hole itself. It seems certain that selection for larger clutch size will result, with or without adult longevity, if the adult population is constantly below saturation, that is, if a situation exists analogous to the general temperate situation.

There are, of course, other mechanisms for formally achieving the benefits of iteroparity. One is the habit, already mentioned, of members of a single cohort of Pacific salmon (e.g., *Onychorynchus nerka*) reproducing at different ages, though all die after a single reproduction. Also relevant are plant seeds that do not germinate until external signals are optimum—for example, heavy enough wetting to insure that the seedling will live to re-produce (Cohen, 1967).

## CONCLUSIONS

It can be concluded that uncertainty in survival from zygote to first maturity, from whatever source, generates selective pressure for iteroparity (longer life), which may entrain pressure for reduced energy allocation for reproduction in order to insure longer life. The stability of tropical faunas, therefore, might be simply a reflection of the relatively long lives of the individual members of the community and their relatively low birth rates. Longevity can, of course, be achieved by means other than devoting less energy to reproduction. Changes in structure and intelligence will also contribute. There is, then, a simple, mechanistic explanation for the tropics being the central zone insofar as the main line of animal evolution is concerned. In the temperate zones, in contrast, the constraint of uncertain adult and zygote survival places a premium on high $r$, which does not preclude evolution but does introduce restrictive conditions. Similarly, it seems less likely that achieving iteroparity by means other than long life will be conducive to important evolutionary advances in the adult form.

## SUMMARY

The possibility that iteroparity may be an evolutionary response to uncertain survival from zygote to first maturity is examined in a competition model and a genetic model. The competition model used is an alternative to the logistic model and is based on the Ricker formulation of population growth. The genetic model is a straightforward two-allele system. Both models show clear advantage in iteroparity if there is uncertainty from zygote to first maturity. Illustrative material on marine plankton-feeding fishes suggests the modeling is realistic. Consideration of other evidence suggests the approach may contribute to understanding the dynamics of evolution.

## ACKNOWLEDGMENTS

Miss Dianne Budde wrote the competition computer program. The University of Hawaii Computer Center furnished free time. The genetic models were evaluated on a Wang Loci 2ab desk computer. The demonstration of the ideas in this paper was considerably improved after a discussion with Monte Lloyd, who insisted that a genetic model would have to be included.

### LITERATURE CITED

Andrewartha, H. G., and L. C. Birch, 1954. The distribution and abundance of animals. Univ. Chicago Press. xv + 782 p.

Beverton, R. J. H. 1963. Maturation, growth, and mortality of clupeid and engraulid stocks in relation to fishing, p. 44–67. *In* B. B. Parrish [ed.], Contrib. to herring symp. 1961. Vol. 154. Rapports et Procès-Verbaux des Réunions, Conseil Perm. Int. pour l'Exploration de la Mer. Copenhagen.

Cody, M. L. 1966. A general theory of clutch size. Evolution 20(2):174–184.

Cohen, D. 1967. Optimizing reproduction in a randomly varying environment when a correlation may exist between the conditions at the time a choice has to be made and the subsequent outcome. J. Theoretical Biol. 16:1–14.

Cole, Lamont C. 1954. The population consequences of life history phenomena. Quart. Rev. Biol. 29(2):103–137.

Gause, G. F. 1934. The struggle for existence. Williams and Wilkins, Baltimore. vii + 163 p.

Hemphill, G. 1963. The causes of changes in recruitment, p. 44–67. *In* B. B. Parrish [ed.], Contrib. to herring symp. 1961. Vol. 154. Rapports et Procès-Verbaux des Réunions, Conseil Perm. Int. pour l'Exploration de la Mer. Copenhagen.

Holgate, P. 1967. Population survival and life history phenomena. J. Theoretical Biol. 14:1–10.

Murphy, G. I. 1965. Preliminary analysis of the population dynamics of the Peruvian anchovy. Rep. to Inst. del Mar del Peru. Mimeographed. p. 1–21.

———. 1966. Population biology of the Pacific sardine (*Sardinops caerulea*). California Acad. Sci., Proc. 4th Ser. 34(1):1–84.

———. 1967. Vital statistics of the Pacific sardine (*Sardinops caerulea*) and the population consequences. Ecology 48(5):731–736.

Ricker, W. E. 1954. Stock and recruitment. J. Fisheries Res. Board Canada 11(5):559–623.

———. 1958. Handbook of computation for biological statistics of fish populations. Fisheries Res. Board Canada Bull. 119:1–300.

Saetersdal, G., Tsukayama, I., and Alegre, B. 1965. Fluctuaciones en la abundancia aparente del stock de anchoveta en 1959–1962. Inst. del Mar del Peru Bull. 1(2):35–103.

Shapovalov, L., and A. C. Taft. 1954. The life histories of the steelhead rainbow trout (*Salmo gairdneri gairdneri*) and silver salmon (*Oncorhynchus kisutch*). California Dep. of Fish and Game Fish Bull. 98:1–375.

Reprinted from the Proceedings of the National Academy of Sciences
Vol. 49, No. 2, pp. 270-278.   February, 1963.

# INTERACTION OF GENOTYPES DETERMINING VIABILITY IN DROSOPHILA BUSCKII*

BY R. C. LEWONTIN AND YOSHIRO MATSUO†

DEPARTMENT OF BIOLOGY, UNIVERSITY OF ROCHESTER, NEW YORK

Communicated by Theodosius Dobzhansky, December 12, 1962

It is well known that the relative fitnesses of genotypes in a population are influenced by the physical factors of the environment.   There is an increasing body of experimental evidence to show that the biotic components of the environment, especially the density and genotypic composition of the population, also may have effects on relative fitness.   The literature on the effect of larval density on viability in *Drosophila* is quite extensive.[1-5] The result of these experiments was that the relative viabilities of competing genotypes vary with density and that, in general, very high densities exaggerate differences between genotypes. Less work has been done, however, on the interesting question of how relative frequencies of different genotypes may affect the fitnesses. There is some indirect evidence that fitnesses of inversion types may be a function of frequency in natural populations.[6] In laboratory populations, there is clear evidence of changes in relative fitness of inversion with changing frequency.[7, 8] A specific test of whether genotypes may interact to give fitnesses not predictable from their performance in pure culture was made by Lewontin[1] and the lack of predictability was confirmed in those experiments.

This previous experiment was designed to survey a large number of genotypes to look for the phenomena of interaction. No genotype was really well studied, however. Of particular interest is the question of whether there are any regularities in the interaction between genotypes. The experiments reported in this paper are designed to take a closer look at interaction in a few genotypes by using a greater range of densities and a greater variety of mixture proportions than in previous experiments. In this way a norm of reaction for viability can be described with respect to two components of biotic environment: density and proportion.

*Experimental Methods and Design.*—Newly hatched first instar larvae varying in age from 1 to 7 hr were collected and placed in 25 mm × 45 mm shell vials containing 4 cc of Krivshenko's medium. This medium is made up in the following proportions: 1000 cc water, 10 gm agar, 80 gm corn meal, 50 gm dry brewers yeast, 100 gm white Karo sirup, and 6 gm linseed meal. No live yeast was added to the vials.

Five stocks of *D. busckii* were used. These were Acme-A (a wild-type stock) and four mutant strains white (w), claret (cl), cut (ct) and yellow (y). The experiments consisted in testing the viability of each mutant strain in pure culture and in various mixed proportions with the wild-type strain. The design for each of the mutant series was the same. The densities used were 2, 8, 32, 128, 256, and 512 *total* larvae per vial. At each *total* density the following series of mixtures were used: 100% Acme; 75% Acme:25% mutant; 50% Acme:50% mutant; 25% Acme:75% mutant; 100% mutant. At a total density of 2 larvae only the pure cultures and the 50:50 mixture were possible.

The number of replicates for each density is given in Table 1. Because of the large size of the experiment it was not possible to make up all densities and all mixtures of a given mutant series on the same day. One fifth of all replicates of a given mutant series were made up on a given day. That is 5, 2, 2, 1, 1, and 1 vials respectively of the increasing densities were made up and this was repeated 5 times to make up the full set.

Emerging adults were counted and classified every day and the vials were kept until four successive days yielded no flies. The temperature was 25°C throughout.

*Results of the Experiments.*—The results are summarized in Figures 1, 2, 3, and 4. In each figure, part A shows the survival of the wild type, Acme-A, at each density for each of the mixture combinations. Part B of each figure shows the survival of the mutant. There are absolute, not relative survival proportions.

*General effect of density:* Every experiment shows the same general norm of reac-

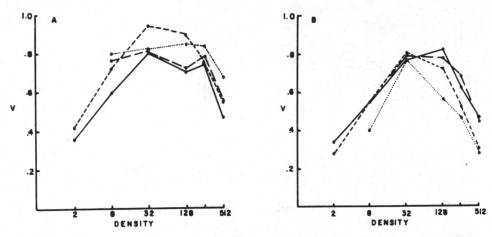

FIG. 1.—Absolute viabilities of Acme-A and *white*.  A. solid line: 100% Acme;  long dashes: 75% Acme;  short dashes: 50% Acme;  dots: 25% Acme.  B. solid line: 100% *white*;  long dashes: 75% *white*;  short dashes: 50% *white*;  dots: 25% *white*.

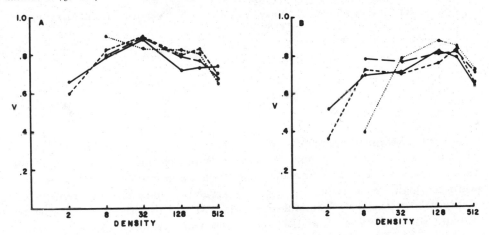

FIG. 2.—Absolute viabilities of Acme-A and *claret*.  See Figure 1 for meaning of lines.

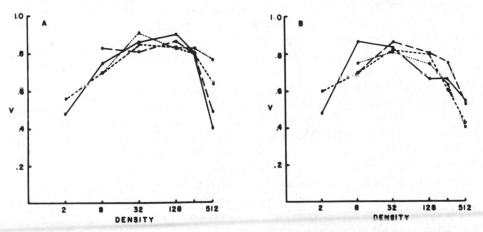

FIG. 3.—Absolute viabilities of Acme-A and *cut*.  See Figure 1 for meaning of lines.

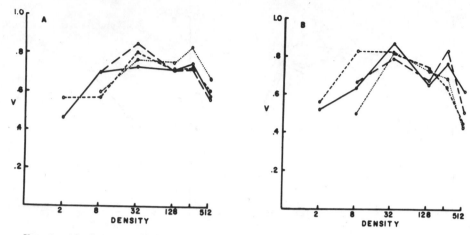

FIG. 4.—Absolute viabilities of Acme-A and *yellow*. See Figure 1 for meaning of lines.

TABLE 1

NUMBERS OF REPLICATES AND TOTAL NUMBERS OF LARVAE TESTED IN EACH MIXTURE AT
DIFFERENT DENSITIES

| Total density | Replicate vials per mixture | No. of mixtures | Total vials | Total larvae tested |
|---|---|---|---|---|
| 2 | 25 | 3 | 75 | 150 |
| 8 | 10 | 5 | 50 | 400 |
| 32 | 10 | 5 | 50 | 1600 |
| 128 | 5 | 5 | 25 | 3200 |
| 256 | 5 | 5 | 25 | 6400 |
| 512 | 5 | 5 | 25 | 12800 |

tion of survival with respect to density. All the curves are concave downward with a peak of viability at intermediate densities. Both high and low densities result in lower survival. The mutant *claret* (Fig. 2) shows an optimum density shifted toward the high end, between 128 and 256 larvae per vial and an extremely low viability at low densities. The mutant *cut* (Fig. 3) is at the other extreme with an optimum density between 8 and 32 larvae per vial. Acme-A, *yellow* and *white* are intermediate between these two extreme types, but in all cases both high and low densities are deleterious. Thus, we have a very clear confirmation of the observations of Lewontin.[1] It has been pointed out[3] that the undercrowding effect in these earlier experiments may have been due to conditioning of the food for yeast growth by the action of the larvae since live yeast was used. It must be that the "cooperative" action of the larvae in the present experiments lies elsewhere than in conditioning the food for yeast growth, since no live yeast is added.

*General effect of varying composition:* The next question is whether the absolute viability of each mutant and Acme-A is altered at a given density by the presence of a different genotype in the same vial. From Figure 1a it is clear that the viability of *white* is lower at most densities when competing with Acme-A (broken lines) than it is in pure culture (solid line). The reverse is true for Acme-A (Fig. 1b). Here a mixture with *white* increases the viability of Acme-A. The increase in Acme-A viability in mixture is more consistent than the decrease in *white* viability. Sixteen out of sixteen mixed viabilities of Acme were greater than or equal to the pure viability at the comparable density. In the case of *white*, only eleven out of sixteen values were lowered by mixture. On the other hand the viabilities of *white* show a kind of consistency lacking in the case of Acme. The viability curve for the 25% *white*: 75% Acme-A mixture lies below that for the 50:50 mixture, which in turn lies below the 75:25 mixture. The 75:25 mixture is not different from the pure *white* (Fig. 1*b*). Thus, as the proportion of white larvae increases, the absolute viability of *white* increases in a regular fashion.

In both the *yellow* series (Fig. 4) and the *claret* series (Fig. 2) the viability of Acme-A is generally shifted upward in mixtures from the viability of pure Acme-A, but this is not as striking or consistent as in the *white* series. In neither of these series is the mutant genotype consistently changed in viability by mixture. Finally, in the *cut* series there is no apparent general effect of composition on viability of either mutant or Acme-A genotypes.

*Interaction of density and composition:* It is, unfortunately, a very difficult matter to test statistically either the general effect of density or the general effect of composition in these experiments. This is because, by the very nature of the experiments, the replication variance of each determination is different. The replication variance at a density of 2 larvae per vial is on the average 20 times that for the highest density, 512 larvae per vial.

This difficulty of testing is not really a serious one in judging the results of the general effects of density and composition. The effect of density as seen in the previous section is so consistent, that there is not the slightest doubt of its reality. When we turn to the general effects of composition, there is no consistency over all experiments, but certain patterns are so clear as to leave no doubt as to their reality. In the *white* series, for example, there can be no doubt of the consistency of the general effect of composition on the viability of both mutant and wild-type genotypes. For the other mutants, there is no obvious general effect. What is possible, however, is to examine the effect of composition *within* each density and to test the reality of any observed differences by a conventional analysis of variance. For example, at a density of 512 larvae per vial both the *cut* genotype and the Acme-A genotype are affected by mixture (Fig. 3). The same applies to the *claret* series (Fig. 2) while for the *yellow* series only the mutant is consistently affected at the density of 512.

The result of tests for the effect of mixture on viability are shown in Table 2. The table gives the F values resulting from a series of one-factor analyses of variance testing whether the variation observed among the viabilities of different mixtures *within* each density is significantly greater than the variation among replicate vials. The upper figure of each pair refers to the viability of Acme-A in the series, the lower figure to the viabilities of mutants. Out of the 48 F values, 11 correspond to a probability of 5% or less, and 26 F values are greater than unity. Of the 11 significant F tests, 5 are at the density of 512 larvae per vial. Looked at in another way, at densities of 256 and 512, 15 out of 16 tests gave F values greater than unity and, of these, 7 were significant at the 5% level or better. All this points to the fact that there is a real effect of composition at the higher densities while there is none apparent at the lower densities by the criterion of the analysis of variance. The analysis is not very powerful at lower densities, however. Low densities have, *ipso facto*, a very large replication variance which makes detection of composition effects very difficult. For example, it is obvious that in the *white* series mixed cultures were *consistently* different in viability of Acme-A from pure cultures at the lowest densities as well as the highest (Fig. 1*a*).

TABLE 2

F Ratios from Analyses of Variance Testing the Significance of Variation in Viability Due to Mixture Proportions

| Series | | 2 | 8 | 32 | Density 128 | 256 | 512 |
|---|---|---|---|---|---|---|---|
| White | A | 0.240 | 1.080 | 2.445* | 1.088 | 1.597 | 3.958‡ |
| | *w* | 0.274 | 0.547 | 0.171 | 4.140‡ | 2.781* | 3.097† |
| Claret | A | 0.244 | 0.809 | 0.452 | 0.685 | 1.645 | 1.042 |
| | *cl* | 1.535 | 2.453* | 0.593 | 0.567 | 2.411* | 1.392 |
| Cut | A | 0.663 | 0.654 | 2.369* | 1.000 | 0.081 | 10.302‡ |
| | *ct* | 1.822 | 0.889 | 0.354 | 0.276 | 1.420 | 2.359* |
| Yellow | A | 0.622 | 0.474 | 1.235 | 0.039 | 1.702 | 1.232 |
| | *y* | 0.092 | 1.512 | 0.404 | 0.171 | 1.656 | 3.846‡ |

\* Prob $\cong$ 0.05.
† Prob $\cong$ 0.025.
‡ Prob $\cong$ 0.01.

In summary, then, at high densities there is a clear effect of mixture proportion on the viability of both components of the mixture; while at low densities there is a clear dependence in some cases, as in the *white* series, but the evidence is equivocal for other mutant series.

*Relative Viabilities.*—The real interest of these experiments is not in the absolute viabilities of the genotypes but in their relative viabilities.

For example, Figure 2 shows that, in pure culture at a density of 512 larvae per vial, Acme-A has a higher absolute viability (0.741) than *claret* (0.652). But all of the mixed cultures show a depression of Acme-A and an increase in *claret* to the extent that *claret* actually has a higher viability than Acme-A when these genotypes are in direct competition. The results of such comparisons for all the mutant series are shown in Figures 5, 6, 7, and 8. The heavy solid line, in each case, is the *predicted* relative viability of Acme-A calculated as the absolute viability of Acme-A in pure culture divided by the absolute viability of the mutant in pure culture. The broken lines show the *observed* relative viabilities of Acme-A calculated from the vials in which the two genotypes were actually in competition.

The most striking case is that of the *white* series (Fig. 5). The predicted relative viabilities of Acme-A show no particular trend with density and on the average over densities Acme-A has a slight predicted advantage ($\bar{V} = 1.038$). In actual competition, however, Acme-A was far superior to *white* and this superiority changed in a regular way with density and composition. At both high and low densities, Acme-A is far better in competition with *white* than was predicted from pure culture experiments, while at intermediate density, especially at 32 larvae per vial, the prediction and observation agree fairly closely. Moreover, at the three highest densities, the order of relative viabilities corresponds to the proportion of Acme-A in the mixture. Below the density of 32, however, the relationship is not consistent, although the 75% Acme-A mixture remains the best. It is interesting that this U-shaped curve of viability against density has its minimum at 32 larvae per vial which is the optimum density for survival of both Acme-A and *white*. That is, the relative viability curves are the inverse of the absolute viability curves.

The other mutant series show less dramatic but related phenomena. The *claret* series (Fig. 6) shows a downward slope of predicted relative viability with

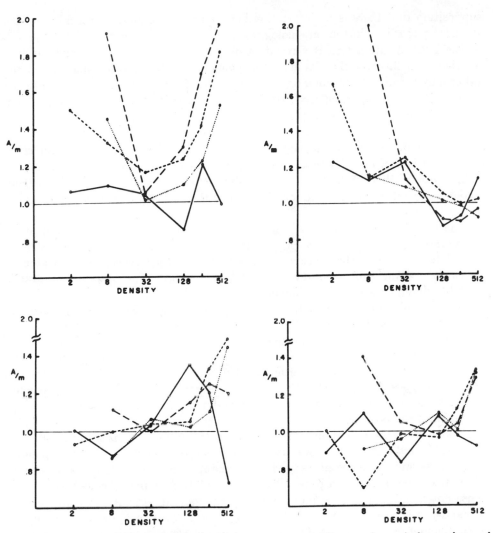

FIGS. 5–8.—*Solid lines:* predicted viability from pure cultures. *Long dashes:* observed viability in 75% Acme cultures. *Short dashes:* observed viability in 50% Acme cultures. *Dots:* observed viability in 25% Acme cultures.

density. The observed curves agree with the predicted curve except at the two lowest densities where Acme-A performs much better than predicted, while at the highest density the relative viabilities of Acme-A and *claret* are reversed by mixture. Again the deviation from prediction is most marked at an extreme, non-optimum density.

While the *claret* series shows the left limb of the *white* series U-shaped relationship, the *cut* series (Fig. 7) shows the right limb of this relation. Here, agreement with prediction from pure culture is again at a density of 32 and the only real deviation is at 512 larvae per vial.

*Implications of the results:* The supposition that one can predict the relative viabilities of genotypes from their absolute viabilities in pure culture is really a supposition that there is no interaction between these genotypes in exploiting the resources; that is, that they are biologically independent of each other.

One kind of interaction is a result of direct interference of one genotype with another. In this case the viability of one genotype will decrease while that of the other either remains the same or increases. All of our cases of interaction are of this sort. What is particularly important is whether it is possible to predict from the results of pure culture experiments which will be the stronger competitor in such an interaction. In this case we expect the general form of the curve relating viability to density to be the same in all mixtures. This is the case for the *claret* series. It is as if one genotype were more efficient in using the resources available than another; this difference in efficiency shows up more clearly when the two genotypes are in active competition for the resource than when there is only intra-group competition.

The other three mutant series, however, show interactions that are not at all predictable from pure culture performance. Both *yellow* and *cut* series show a complete reversal of the relative predicted fitness in active competition at high densities. *White* shows no reversal but the unexpected appearance of drastic viability differences where no difference at all would have been predicted.

The general implications of these findings are several. First, it is not possible to make general statements about the relative viabilities of genotypes from a knowledge of those viabilities at a particular density of composition. However, predictability is reasonably good at *optimal* densities. Second, from a population genetic standpoint, the relative fitnesses of genotypes change as the frequencies of these genotypes change so that the course of natural selection cannot be predicted without a knowledge of the full norm of reaction of the genotypes with respect to density and composition.

Finally, from the evolutionary standpoint, such interactions as seen at high densities in the *cut* and *yellow* series raise the question of the relation between population fitness and genotype fitness. Since Acme-A in pure culture has a lower viability than the mutants in pure culture, a population of pure Acme-A is in some sense not as fit as a population of pure mutant individuals. At least the load of larval death is greater. Nevertheless, the presence of Acme-A and mutants in the same population results in a dramatic increase in Acme-A viability above that of the mutants. As a result the mutants will be eliminated. We then have the paradox that a population will evolve toward a lower *absolute* fitness, even though the value of intra-population fitness, $\overline{W}$, seems to be increasing. Thus, natural selection does not assure that the fitness of the population, as a whole, will be increased.

*Summary.*—The larval viability of four mutant strains and one wild-type strain of *Drosophila busckii* were tested over a range of densities and proportional mixtures of wild-type and mutant. Densities ranged from 2 to 512 larvae per vial and mixtures consisted of 100% mutant; 75% mutant; 25% wild type; 50%:50%, 25%:75% and 100% wild-type. The results were: (1) For all strains the highest viability is at an intermediate density, not at the lowest. (2) For a given density, especially at high density, the proportion of the two genotypes in the mixture was important in determining viability. (3) Relative viabilities observed in mixtures agreed with predicted viabilities from pure cultures at intermediate (optional densities) but deviated strongly at high and low densities.   (4) The genotype with higher viability in pure culture often had lower viability in mixed culture.   The implication of this last observation is that the absolute fitness of a population may not have any relation to the direction of genetic change in that population, and that the population may evolve to a lower state of absolute fitness.

* This research was supported by Grant RG-6222 from the Division of Research Grants of the National Institutes of Health.

† Training Grant Fellow supported by National Institutes of Health Training Grant to the Department of Biology, University of Rochester.

[1] Lewontin, R. C., *Evolution*, **9**, 27–41 (1955).
[2] Birch, L. C., *Evolution*, **9**, 389–399 (1955).
[3] Boggild, O., and J. Keiding, *Oikos*, **9**, 1–21 (1958).
[4] Bakker, K., *Arch. Neerl. de Zool.*, **14**, 200–281 (1961).
[5] Moree, R., and J. R. King, *Genetics*, **46**, 1735–1752 (1961).
[6] Lewontin, R. C., and M. J. D. White, *Evolution*, **14**, 116–129 (1960).
[7] Levene, H., O. Pavlovsky, and Th. Dobzhansky, *Evolution*, **8**, 335–349 (1954).
[8] Spiess, E. B., *Evolution*, **11**, 84–93 (1957).

Reprinted from EVOLUTION 12: 504–511. December, 1958

# NATURAL SELECTION IN WATER SNAKES (*NATRIX SIPEDON* L.) ON ISLANDS IN LAKE ERIE

JOSEPH H. CAMIN AND PAUL R. EHRLICH

*Chicago Academy of Sciences, Chicago, Illinois* [1]

Received February 26, 1958

Although in recent years laboratory selection has become a commonplace, natural selection operating in wild populations has been quite difficult to document. Much of the published work has been inconclusive (see summary in Robson and Richards, 1936, for early work) or open to controversy (e.g., Lamotte, Cain and Sheppard, and Sedlmair on *Cepaea*). The present study analyzes all available data on color pattern variation in the water snakes of the Lake Erie islands. These data appear to illustrate a situation in which migration and strong selection pressure combine to give a relatively clear-cut picture of differential elimination of color pattern types from a population.

The uniform medium-gray color of the majority of adult water snakes inhabiting the islands in the western part of Lake Erie (as opposed to the "normal" dark banded type) was first noted by Morse (1904). In 1937 Conant and Clay described the island population as a separate subspecies *Natrix sipedon insularum*, differing from typical *sipedon* primarily in the large percentage of unbanded or weakly banded individuals. In 1954 Camin, Triplehorn and Walter compared the frequencies of various pattern types in wild-caught juveniles with those of the adult population and found a statistically significant decrease in the proportion of banded individuals from the juvenile to the adult population. In the present paper these previous data are reanalyzed and integrated with additional data, principally on frequencies of pattern types in

litters, in order to present a picture of the entire post-natal selection for pattern type.

## MATERIALS AND METHODS

Data from Middle Island are from the collections of Camin, Triplehorn and Walter made in 1949 and Camin and Ehrlich in 1957. Litter data from the Bass Complex islands are from the collections of Camin in 1948 and Camin and Ehrlich in 1957. All other data are from Conant and Clay (1937).

Conant and Clay originally divided the continuous variation in pattern types arbitrarily into four classes A–D (see figure 1), A being unbanded and D being typical banded *N. sipedon sipedon*. For greater precision, Camin *et al.* added the intermediate categories ab, bc and cd. These latter categories are employed here when comparison with Conant and Clay's data is not required. Where necessary for statistical tests, categories were lumped as follows: A = A + ab, B = B, C = bc + C, D = cd + D. A + B and C + D were lumped where the tests required only two classes of individuals. For convenience in the discussion to follow, "banded" and "unbanded" will be used to describe the two halves of the pattern spectrum (e.g., when referring to the effects of migration of "unbanded" individuals, we are including types ab and B snakes, which actually do show some light banding).

"Bass Complex" refers to North Bass, Middle Bass, South Bass, Green and Rattlesnake Islands. Middle-Pelee refers to Middle and Pelee Islands. "Peninsular mainland" refers to collections from Port

[1] Present address of both authors: Department of Entomology, University of Kansas, Lawrence, Kansas.

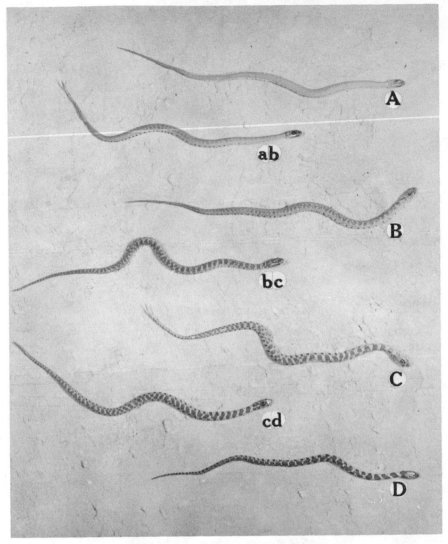

FIG. 1. Pattern types of island water snakes.

Clinton, Lakeside, Marblehead and Catawba Peninsula (all Ohio).

All pregnant females were isolated and their litters, including those stillborn, were scored as to pattern type. There was no sign of a correlation between pattern type and live birth.

There is no evidence that there is any change in pattern type from birth to maturity. Both Conant and Camin have kept individuals of *N. s insularum* in captivity over periods of several years without noticing any change in pattern.

Individuals of all pattern types have been recorded from the adult population.

### DESCRIPTION OF THE ISLANDS

The Lake Erie islands (fig. 2) vary in area from less than one acre to about fifteen square miles. The islands are wooded, and with a few exceptions (such as a large marsh on Middle Bass) they have little or no inland water. In general the water snakes are confined to the peripheries of the islands where they sub-

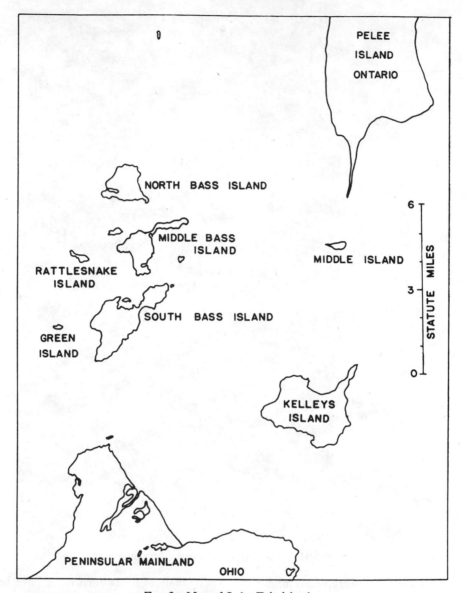

Fig. 2. Map of Lake Erie islands.

sist in large part on *Necturus* and storm-killed fish (Conant, 1951 and unpublished observations). The peripheries of the islands consist of flat limestone rocks (see Conant, 1951, Pl. 26, fig. 1), limestone cliffs or limestone pebble beaches.

The highest point on the islands is on South Bass (about 70 feet above lake level). Middle Island is approximately 15 feet above lake level at its highest.

GEOGRAPHIC VARIATION

As can be seen from the histograms (fig. 3), there is considerable geographic variation in pattern type. All the Ontario mainland snakes were typically banded *sipedon* and the peninsular mainland samples contained a very few unbanded individuals. The difference between the Ontario and Peninsular

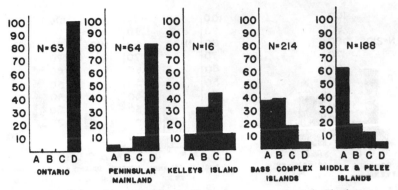

FIG. 3. Geographic variation (ordinates—per cent of total; abscissas—pattern types).

samples was not significant by Fisher's exact probability test (P = .123).

The sample from Kelleys I. contains a significantly greater proportion of banded individuals than that from the Bass Complex (chi-square, .01 > P > .001) and the Bass Complex sample has a significantly larger proportion of banded individuals than the one from Middle-Pelee (chi-square, P << .001).

Camin and other biologists in the area have frequently observed snakes swimming several miles from the nearest shore. This would indicate that there is considerable mainland-island and inter-island migration. A major factor in maintaining the geographic variation would appear to be this pattern of migration. Whereas South Bass and Kelleys Islands would probably receive about equal numbers of banded mainland migrants, South Bass doubtless receives additional migrants from the more northerly members of the Bass Complex. Because of their greater distance from shore, these northern islands of the Bass Complex would receive fewer typical *sipedon* migrants from the mainland and thus have populations with a lower proportion of banded individuals. The unbanded southward migrants could account for the fact that South Bass (as well as the Bass Complex as a whole) has a lower proportion of banded individuals than does Kelleys.

Similarly the relative isolation from the mainland of Middle and Pelee Islands could account for the greater proportions of unbanded individuals in their populations.

EVIDENCE OF SELECTIVE ELIMINATION

Figure 4 shows by histograms the pattern type frequencies of Bass Complex litters and adults and Middle Island litters, juveniles and adults.

The "raw" litter data are presented by histograms in figures 5 and 6. In these figures, the type classification of the female parent is indicated by a vertical line topped by the ♀ symbol. It is interesting to note that in all but one litter the female was of a class closer to the unbanded extreme of the distribution than was the median class of the offspring. A number of genetic explanations could account for this phenomenon, but without further data an hypothesis would have no value.

Because of the restrictions placed on the data by the fact that the litters are samples from the sample of the total gene pool carried by their parents (a type of cluster sampling), it is immediately apparent that simple chi-square analysis would not give a legitimate test of the apparent differences in type frequencies between the litter and adult populations. The young are not mutually independent samplings from the population of young, as the adults are from the adult population; on the contrary, phenotypes of dif-

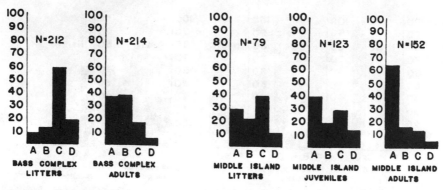

FIG. 4. Comparisons of young and adults (ordinates—per cent of total; abscissas—pattern types).

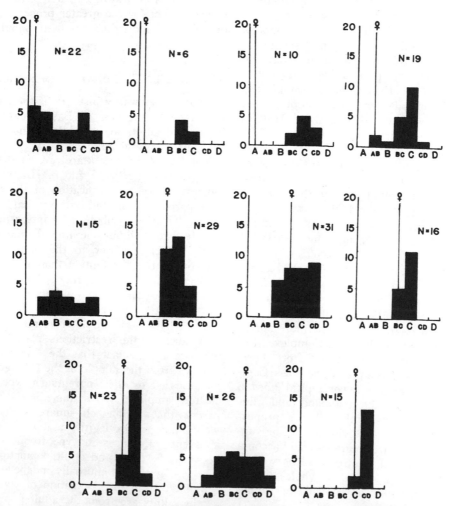

FIG. 5. Distribution of pattern types in Bass Complex litters (ordinates—number of individuals).

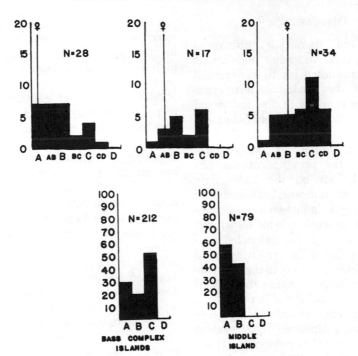

FIG. 6. 1st row: Distribution of pattern types in Middle Island litters (ordinates—number of individuals); 2nd row: Litters classified by female parent type (ordinates—per cent of total).

ferent individuals in the same litter present considerable correlation.

Using a formula [1] for the most conservative estimate of the variance of $\hat{p}$ (an

[1] Mr. David W. Calhoun, biometrician with G. D. Searle and Co., has contributed the following derivation: A simple upper limit for the variance of $\hat{p}$ can be obtained as follows. As a model let us assume each litter is associated with a probability, p, that any individual will be of type "A or B." The individuals making up a single litter form a binomial sample with parameter p. The values of p for different litters may be different, the distribution of these p's for the population of litters being unknown. Assume, finally, that litter size does not depend on p. Then the variance of $\hat{p}$, the proportion of type "A or B" in the pooled sample from all litters, has the form

$$\text{Var } (\hat{p}) = A\Sigma n^2/(\Sigma n)^2 + B/(\Sigma n)$$

where the n's are the individual litter sizes, A is the true variance (unknown) of the distribution of p's among litters and B is the average of the binomial variances pq for individual litters. Neither A nor B can exceed 0.25, and they cannot both assume this value, no matter what the distribution of p. Therefore

$$\text{Var } (\hat{p}) < 0.25[\Sigma n^2/(\Sigma n)^2 + 1/(\Sigma n)].$$

estimate of the parametric proportion of types $A + B$) in the litter populations, and the binomial variance for the adult populations, the significance of the differences between the litter and adult populations was tested using the Fisher-Behrens test with infinite and 213 degrees of freedom. It was found that the Bass Complex litter population was significantly different ($P < .001$) from the Bass Complex adult population.

The Middle Island litter population was not found to be significantly different from the Middle Island adult population. This failure to demonstrate a statistically significant difference is doubtless due to the insufficient sampling (3 litters only) of the litter population, since the similarly constituted wild-caught juvenile population is significantly different from the adult population (chi-square; $P < .01$).

## DISCUSSION

The observed significant differences between the young and adult populations can only be accounted for by differential elimination of the banded pattern types or by pattern changes in the individual snakes. The evidence is overwhelmingly in favor of the former hypothesis.

There are a number of possible explanations for the presence of the unbanded populations on the Lake Erie islands. The environmental conditions of the islands might induce purely phenotypic changes in snakes which matured there. The fact that the unbanded pattern types are found in the litters, and the evidence indicating no change in pattern type of individual snakes throughout life would seem to obviate this possibility.

A high proportion of unbanded pattern types might be maintained by migration from other unbanded populations. However, all known *N. sipedon* populations that could possibly supply migrants are made up of typical banded snakes.

For the frequency of unbanded genotype to be maintained by mutation alone in the observed populations would require directed mutation at a rate far above that known for any locus ever studied in any organism, even if it is assumed that color pattern is a single factor trait.

Genetic drift is not indicated as a factor in maintaining the high frequency of unbanded individuals on the islands for two reasons: First, the snakes are extremely abundant on the islands (seven collectors captured about 400 *N. sipedon* on Middle Island in five hours in 1949; three collectors captured 234 in four hours on South Bass in 1935) so that there is no reason to believe that their effective population size on any of the larger islands would approach the level at which drift would be an important factor. Second, the pattern trend is towards unbanded individuals on all the islands, which indicates a systematic pressure rather than random drift.

Therefore, by a process of elimination, selection alone can reasonably account for the presence of populations with a high proportion of unbanded individuals on the islands.

Although it is not essential to the case in point, the source of the selection pressure is of considerable interest. To the human eye, the unbanded snakes are very effectively cryptically colored when they are on the flat limestone rocks of the island peripheries. In contrast, the banded individuals are highly conspicuous. It seems likely that a visual predator is one of the principal selective influences. Gulls are abundant around the islands and experiments by the authors (carried on with the cooperation of the Lincoln Park Zoo) indicated that gulls would eat young water snakes. Other likely predators are herons (which are abundant in the area), raptors, and (recently) man.

Whatever the selective agents are, it appears that the establishment of a genetic system producing essentially 100% unbanded individuals has been prevented by a continual influx of "banded" genes brought into the island gene pools by a steady flow of mainland immigrants. This balance between strong selection and migration pressures has produced a situation which lends itself extraordinarily well to analysis. Unfortunately the presence of some migrant individuals makes it impossible to determine the exact composition of the non-migrant (selected) adult population.

On examining the works of Conant and Clay (1937) and Conant (1951) it becomes apparent that, in the problem at hand, the subspecies approach has tended to obscure a significant biological problem. Snakes of intermediate pattern types were considered to be intergrades between two distinct biological entities and some of the dynamic aspects of the situation were not considered. This should not be construed as criticism of Conant and Clay, whose careful and detailed analysis has made possible the present study.

It should be noted that as long ago as 1942, Dunn pointed out the value of snakes and other reptiles for studies of selection in operation. It is hoped that this line of investigation will not continue to be neglected.

## SUMMARY

Data are presented indicating postnatal selection for pattern type in water snakes (*Natrix sipedon*) on the islands of Lake Erie. Strong selection, demonstrable without regard to selective agent, has produced a shift towards unbanded pattern types on the islands, while constant migration from the mainland has maintained "banded" genes in the island gene pools. These antagonistic pressures have produced a situation unusually amenable to analysis.

## ACKNOWLEDGMENTS

We wish to thank the following individuals for aid on various aspects of the work: David W. Calhoun, Skokie, Illinois; Roger Conant, Philadelphia Zoological Garden; Henry S. Dybas, Chicago Natural History Museum; Howard K. Gloyd, Chicago Academy of Sciences; Robert W. Hull, Northwestern University; Ernst Mayr, Harvard University; R. Marlin Perkins, Lincoln Park Zoo, Chicago; Loren S. Putnam, Ohio State University; George B. Rabb, Brookfield Zoological Garden, Brookfield, Illinois; and Edward S. Thomas, Ohio State Museum. We would also like to acknowledge the assistance of our wives, Emily F. Camin and Anne H. Ehrlich, in the preparation of the manuscript and figures.

## LITERATURE CITED

CAIN, A. J., AND P. M. SHEPPARD.[2] 1954. Natural selection in *Cepaea*. Genetics, **39**: 89–116.

CAMIN, JOSEPH H., CHARLES A. TRIPLEHORN AND HAROLD J. WALTER. 1954. Some indications of survival value in the type "A" pattern of the island water snakes of Lake Erie. Chicago Acad. Sci. Nat. Hist. Misc., no. 131, 3 pp.

CONANT, ROGER. 1951. Reptiles of Ohio (second edition). University of Notre Dame Press, 284 pp.

——, AND WILLIAM M. CLAY. 1937. A new subspecies of water snake from islands in Lake Erie. Occ. Papers Univ. Michigan Mus. Zool., no. 346, 9 pp.

DUNN, EMMETT REID. 1942. Survival value of varietal characters in snakes. American Naturalist, **76**: 104–109.

LAMOTTE, M.[2] 1951. Recherches sur la structure génétique des populations naturelles de *Cepaea nemoralis* (L.). Bull. Biol. France, Suppl. **35**: 1–239.

MORSE, MAX. 1904. Batrachians and reptiles of Ohio. Proc. Ohio State Acad. Sci., **4**: 95–144.

ROBSON, G. C., AND O. W. RICHARDS. 1936. The Variation of Animals in Nature. Longmans, Green and Co., 425 pp.

SEDLMAIR, H.[2] 1956. Verhaltens-, Resistenz- und Gehäuseunterschiede bei den polymorphen Banderschnecken *Cepaea hortensis* (Müll.) und *Cepaea nemoralis* (L.). Biol. Zentralblatt, **75**: 281–313.

[2] These references selected from the extensive literature on the question of selection in *Cepaea*.

REPRINT No. 603 from *Animal Behaviour*, **14**, 2–3, April/July, 1966

*Anim. Behav.*, 1966, **14**, 332–339

# MATING SUCCESS AND GENOTYPE FREQUENCY IN *DROSOPHILA*

By LEE EHRMAN

*The Rockefeller University, New York City*

Petit (1958) found that the mating success of two classical mutants of *Drosophila melanogaster*, *Bar* and *white*, depends on their frequencies in relation to the wild-type. In a mixture of *Bar* and wild-type flies, *Bar* males are less successful in mating; their disadvantage is, however, reduced when only few of them are present, and increases as their frequency in relation to wild-type males becomes greater. With *white*, the mating success is greater when *white* males are rare or are predominant, and least when this proportion in the population is between 40 and 80 per cent. Ehrman, Spassky, Pavlovsky & Dobzhansky (1965) found a similar situation in experiments with *Drosophila pseudoobscura*. Experimental populations, kept in population cages, were started in each generation with twenty pairs of flies from one cage, to which were added five pairs of 'migrants' from another cage. The flies were selected for positive or for negative geotaxis in a specially constructed maze (Hirsch, 1961). Some cage populations originally contained flies monomorphic for the AR gene arrangement in their third chromosomes, and other populations were monomorphic for CH chromosomes. When the donor population was CH and the recipient AR, the frequency of CH chromosomes increased far more rapidly than expected on the basis of other experiments started with equal numbers of AR and CH. The mating success of the carriers of CH and AR chromosomes was then studied by observing them in special chambers, constructed according to Elens & Wattiaux (1964) and discussed and photographed by Ehrman (1965). With equal numbers of females and males of both karyotypes random mating was observed. With twenty pairs of one and five pairs of the other karyotype, the rarer one had a distinct advantage. The advantages and disadvantages were reversed when the frequencies were reversed.

The above findings were entirely unexpected to us. Preferential mating correlated with frequency may evidently be of considerable importance in evolutionary processes. The present communication describes experiments designed to obtain further evidence that might throw light on this phenomenon. It should be treated as a progress report, since it is realized that much more work will be needed to understand the ethological basis as well as the genetic and evolutionary consequences of preferential mating. Sexual discrimination is a trial-and-error affair among the drosophilids observed here. Males will court females (sometimes, even other males) of any species and will try to repeat courting and mating. The acceptance is controlled mainly by the female, and so are other 'turning points' in the courtship–mating–insemination sequence, such as termination of the mount. The females have three sperm-storing organs and will only mate a second time if their supply of stored sperm is diminished (Manning, 1962). For a description of the courtship and mating behaviour in *Drosophila pseudoobscura*, see Spieth (1952); (for a pictorial description, Ehrman & Strickberger, 1960; Ehrman, 1964).

## Materials and Methods

The ARrowhead and CHiricahua populations utilized here have been described in detail by Ehrman *et al.* (1965); the section of Table I in the present article, labelled 'AR Mather, 16° *v.* 25°C' refers to this one particular population grown at either of these two temperatures to test for possible mating advantages induced by raising flies in different environments.

The Tree Line stock was a composite one made up from five strains homozygous for this gene arrangement collected at Mather, California. TL was selected because it is rare, occurring at a frequency of about 10 per cent in the population of the Mather locality. Similarly, the STandard stock is also a composite of five strains collected at Mather. Standard, however, is not rare in nature. The mutant Delta ($\triangle$) is an autosomal dominant affecting wing venation, lethal when homozygous; orange (or.) is an autosomal recessive affecting eye colour. Both mutants have good viability and are easy to classify.

All of the above are *Drosophila pseudoobscura*. Two strains of *Drosophila paulistorum* were tested; one from Cantareira Sâo Paulo, Brazil, belonging to the Andean-South Brazilian race of the species (item 24, Dobzhansky & Spassky, 1959), and the other from Simla, Trinidad, a member of the same race (item 17, Dobzhansky, Ehrman, Pavlovsky & Spassky, 1964b).

The technique of direct observation of mating used here has been devised by Elens & Wattiaux (1964), and employed by Ehrman (1965) and Ehrman *et al.* (1965). This method is superior to the old 'male-choice' technique for several reasons, the most important of which is that it permits the observation of four types of mating, i.e. A♀ × A♂, A♀ × B♂, B♀ × A♂, B♀ × B♂. It is also possible to record the time when each mating occurs, and its sequence among the other matings.

Females and males, aged separately for at least 3 days, are introduced into a chamber, and are observed at 6 min intervals for approximately 6 hr. Most of the matings take place within the first hour, when the observations are spaced at 4 min intervals or less. To make the flies from different strains distinguishable through the glass of the observation chamber (with the aid of a 4× hand lens), the margin of one wing is clipped in one of the strains; the strains marked and unmarked are alternated in successive runs. The wing clipping is done in lightly etherized flies, which are then left to recover for at least 24 hr before being placed in the observation chamber, the transfer being made without etherization.

### Results

Table I summarizes the results of the experiments in which a total of twenty-four or twenty-five pairs (twenty-five females and twenty-five males) of *Drosophila pseudoobscura* were introduced into each observation chamber. They belonged to two different strains, or to the same strain raised under two different conditions, denoted as A and B. The columns in the table headed 'A' and 'B' give the numbers and the nature of the strains used. Several runs were made for each experiment. The four columns headed 'Matings' report the numbers of each of the four possible kinds of mating observed in a given experiment. The columns 'Have Mated' show the numbers of the females and the males of each kind which were observed to mate; a female can mate only once during the period of observation, while a male can mate several times. The columns 'Chi-squares' test the significance of the observed deviations in the numbers of the matings from what would be expected on the assumption of randomness, i.e. on the assumption that the probability of a fly mating is independent of what other flies of the same sex and

species are present in the observation chambers. These Chi-squares have one degree of freedom, making the deviation from randomness of 3·841 significant at the 5 per cent level, and 6·635 at the 1 per cent level. Calculations based on the performance of the females have been omitted where almost 100 per cent of them have mated once during the course of the observations. The rare type mating advantage, if it exists in the females tested here, is much smaller than that recorded in males (see Ehrman *et al.*, 1965); even if only the first half of the matings are considered, few significant Chi-squares for the rare type females are obtained.

The lines Nos. 1–6 in Table I report the experiments in which some of the flies observed came from strains derived from ancestors collected originally at Mather, California ('Cal.'), and others at Austin, Texas. All flies were homozygous for the AR gene arrangement in their third chromosomes. With twelve pairs of California and twelve pairs of Texas flies per chamber, no significant deviation from randomness of mating is observed. With twenty California and five Texas pairs, the Texas males are significantly more successful in mating than are California males, and this is even more striking when the ratio is twenty-three California : two Texas. With twenty Texas : five California, not only the California males but also California females mate more often than do the Texas flies. The ratio ten California : fifteen Texas confers a small, but still significant, advantage on California males, despite their somewhat lower frequency. With the exception of this last observation, then, results confirm and extend the findings of Ehrman *et al.* (1965) on the mating advantages of the genotypes which are less frequent than other genotypes in the observation chambers.

The mating advantage appears to be a property of minority males, and only rarely and to a lesser extent of minority females. Experiments were accordingly arranged in which the observation chambers contained twenty-five California females, twenty-three California males and two Texas males. The matings observed (in six runs) were: Cal. ♀ × Cal. ♂ = 102; Cal. ♀ × Texas ♂ = 18.

In other eight runs, the chambers contained twenty-five Texas females; twenty-three Texas and two California males, and the matings observed were: Texas ♀ × Texas ♂ = 86; Texas ♀ × Cal. ♂ = 19.

Table I. Numbers of Matings Recorded in Observation Chambers Containing Two Kinds of *D. pseudoobscura*

| No. | A | B | Runs | A♀×A♂ | A♀×B♂ | B♀×A♂ | B♀×B♂ | A♀ | B♀ | A♂ | B♂ | χ² ♂ |
|---|---|---|---|---|---|---|---|---|---|---|---|---|
| | **Pair per chamber** | | | **Matings** | | | | **Have mated** | | | | |
| 1 | 12 Cal. | 12 Texas | 7 | 29 | 21 | 26 | 28 | 50 | 54 | 55 | 49 | 0·35 |
| 2 | 20 Cal. | 5 Texas | 6 | 57 | 27 | 13 | 12 | 84 | 25 | 70 | 39 | 16·96 |
| 3 | 5 Cal. | 20 Texas | 7 | 13 | 17 | 26 | 48 | 30 | 74 | 39 | 65 | 19·91 |
| 4 | 23 Cal. | 2 Texas | 5 | 73 | 20 | 4 | 4 | 93 | 8 | 77 | 24 | 34·75 |
| 5 | 2 Cal. | 23 Texas | 10 | 4 | 8 | 26 | 62 | 12 | 88 | 30 | 70 | 65·76 |
| 6 | 10 Cal. | 15 Texas | 11 | 16 | 44 | 23 | 46 | 60 | 69 | 39 | 90 | 5·13 |
| AR Mather, 16° *v*. 25° | | | | | | | | | | | | |
| 7 | 12–16° | 12–25° | 8 | 44 | 18 | 28 | 28 | 62 | 56 | 72 | 46 | 5·72 |
| 8 | 20–16° | 5–25° | 6 | 67 | 18 | 15 | 1 | 85 | 16 | 82 | 19 | 0·09 |
| 9 | 5–16° | 20–25° | 6 | 11 | 12 | 21 | 57 | 23 | 78 | 32 | 69 | 8·61 |
| 10 | 23–16° | 2–25° | 10 | 67 | 29 | 13 | 3 | 96 | 16 | 80 | 32 | 64·26 |
| 11 | 2–16° | 23–25° | 9 | 3 | 11 | 20 | 72 | 14 | 92 | 23 | 83 | 27·02 |
| Raised separately | | | | | | | | | | | | |
| 12 | 12 + | 12 or. | 7 | 40 | 5 | 30 | 27 | 45 | 57 | 70 | 32 | 14·16 |
| 13 | 20 + | 5 or. | 6 | 64 | 10 | 14 | 12 | 74 | 26 | 78 | 22 | 0·25 |
| 14 | 5 + | 20 or. | 8 | 7 | 8 | 38 | 47 | 15 | 85 | 45 | 55 | 39·06 |
| 15 | 23 + | 2 or. | 7 | 85 | 11 | 6 | 1 | 96 | 7 | 91 | 12 | 1·87 |
| 16 | 2 + | 23 or. | 8 | 6 | 5 | 31 | 71 | 11 | 102 | 37 | 76 | 94·27 |
| Raised together | | | | | | | | | | | | |
| 17 | 12 + | 12 or. | 8 | 43 | 2 | 43 | 12 | 45 | 55 | 86 | 14 | 51·84 |
| 18 | 20 + | 5 or. | 8 | 78 | 11 | 14 | 5 | 89 | 19 | 92 | 16 | 1·82 |
| 19 | 5 + | 20 or. | 9 | 16 | 4 | 39 | 42 | 20 | 81 | 55 | 46 | 74·94 |
| 20 | 23 + | 2 or. | 8 | 104 | 2 | 9 | 7 | 106 | 11 | 113 | 4 | 3·34 |
| 21 | 2 + | 23 or. | 7 | 7 | 7 | 37 | 50 | 14 | 87 | 44 | 57 | 173·38 |
| Raised separately | | | | | | | | | | | | |
| 22 | 12 + | 12△ | 5 | 32 | 23 | 29 | 24 | 55 | 53 | 61 | 47 | 1·81 |
| 23 | 20 + | 5△ | 4 | 64 | 16 | 14 | 6 | 80 | 20 | 78 | 22 | 0·25 |
| 24 | 5 + | 20△ | 5 | 12 | 12 | 40 | 45 | 24 | 85 | 52 | 57 | 52·30 |
| 25 | 23 + | 2△ | 5 | 80 | 21 | 7 | 3 | 101 | 10 | 87 | 24 | 27·98 |
| 26 | 2 + | 23△ | 5 | 3 | 7 | 27 | 72 | 10 | 99 | 30 | 79 | 56·55 |

**Table I** *continued*

| No. | Pair per chamber A | Pair per chamber B | Runs | A♀×A♂ | A♀×B♂ | B♀×A♂ | B♀×B♂ | A♀ | B♀ | A♂ | B♂ | $\chi^2$ ♂ |
|---|---|---|---|---|---|---|---|---|---|---|---|---|
| | | | | Matings | | | | Have mated | | | | |
| Raised together | | | | | | | | | | | | |
| 27 | 12 + | 12△ | 5 | 26 | 28 | 33 | 19 | 54 | 52 | 59 | 47 | 1·36 |
| 28 | 20 + | 5△ | 4 | 63 | 17 | 14 | 6 | 80 | 20 | 77 | 23 | 0·56 |
| 29 | 5 + | 20△ | 4 | 10 | 10 | 45 | 35 | 20 | 80 | 55 | 45 | 76·56 |
| 30 | 23 + | 2△ | 6 | 76 | 17 | 7 | 5 | 93 | 12 | 83 | 22 | 23·93 |
| 31 | 2 + | 23△ | 5 | 6 | 6 | 28 | 80 | 12 | 108 | 34 | 86 | 67·41 |
| 32 | 12 ST | 12 TL | 6 | 48 | 16 | 21 | 30 | 64 | 51 | 69 | 46 | 4·60 |
| 33 | 20 ST | 5 TL | 7 | 63 | 26 | 16 | 13 | 89 | 29 | 79 | 39 | 12·56 |
| 34 | 5 ST | 20 TL | 5 | 9 | 10 | 24 | 57 | 19 | 81 | 33 | 67 | 10·56 |
| 35 | 23 ST | 2 TL | 6 | 74 | 26 | 5 | 4 | 100 | 9 | 79 | 30 | 56·55 |
| 36 | 2 ST | 23 TL | 6 | 2 | 8 | 19 | 81 | 10 | 100 | 21 | 89 | 18·38 |

In both cases the rare males are involved in more matings than expected by chance (Chi-squares 7·99 and 14·39 respectively for the two experiments).

The question that now logically presents itself is whether the mating advantage of a rare form requires that the rare and the common types be genetically different. Flies of Texas origin (AR gene arrangement in the third chromosomes) were made to oviposit at room temperature, and then some cultures were allowed to develop at 16°C and others at 25°C. When equal numbers (twelve pairs) of the flies developed at both temperatures were placed in observation chambers (line 7, Table I), the males brought up at the lower temperature were significantly more successful in mating. This advantage was erased when the males developed at the higher temperature were a minority of 5 : 20 (line 8), and became a pronounced disadvantage with a ratio of 2 : 23 (line 10). On the contrary, the flies developed at the lower temperature increased their mating advantage when they became a minority (lines 9 and 11). The flies brought up at the lower temperature are on the average larger in size and more vigorous than those developed at the higher temperature. This makes the greater mating success of the former when the two are equal in frequencies not unexpected (Ewing, 1961). The dependence of the mating success on frequency is, however, an unexpected and interesting finding.

Experiments were made comparing the mating success of the flies raised together from egg to adult in the same culture bottle on the same culture medium, and of flies raised in different cultures. For this purpose, inseminated females of the mutant orange (bright-red eyes, a third chromosome recessive), and of the wild-type (several strains, all with the ST gene arrangement, from Mather, California, intercrossed) were allowed to oviposit, of course without males, together in the same cultures, or separately in different cultures. When the flies hatched, they were selected and aged as usual, and their behaviour was studied in the observation chambers. When orange and wild-type are equally numerous the orange males are much inferior in mating success to the wild-type males (lines 12 and 17, Table I). This is analogous to the lowered mating success of the males raised at the high temperature (line 7). And again, just as with the males raised at the high temperature, the mating disadvantage of the orange males is removed when they become a minority 5 : 20 (lines 13 and 18) or 2 : 23 (lines 15 and 20). The advantage of the wild-type males is, on the contrary, accentuated when they are a minority (lines 14, 16, 19 and 21). There is, however, no appreciable difference between the flies developed together (lines 17–21) and those raised in separate cultures (lines 12–16).

It seems desirable to test the independence of the mating success from the medium in which flies develop from egg to the adult stage by using a mutant which does not adversely affect the mating propensity when present in equal numbers with the wild-type. The mutant orange does, as we have seen, produce such an effect. The third-chromosome dominant mutant Delta ($\triangle$), is more suitable; its use was suggested by Professor R. C. Lewontin, University of Chicago. Being lethal when homozygous, Delta cultures produce mutant as well as wild-type individuals as sibs. On the other hand, the wild-type segregants can be bred by themselves in separate cultures, yielding only wild-type progeny. Observation chambers with twelve pairs of Delta and an equal number of wild-type flies show uniform mating success in both sexes. This is independent of whether the two kinds of flies were raised together or separately (lines 22 and 27, Table I). When Delta : wild-type ratio is 1 : 4, the mating is still uniform (lines 23 and 28), but with a ratio of 2 : 23 Delta males have a very significant advantage (lines 25 and 30). When wild-type is a minority, the males are strikingly successful in mating (lines 24, 29, 26, 31). No difference is observed between mating success of flies developed in the same or in different cultures (compare lines 22–26 with the corresponding combinations in the lines 27–31).

The remainder of Table I (lines 32–36) reports the results of testing flies with standard (ST) and with Tree Line (TL) give arrangements in the third chromosomes of the Mather, California population. The rationale of this experiment is as follows. In nature the ST chromosomes have much higher frequencies than TL (Dobzhansky et al., 1964a). It is then possible that TL flies may be at a disadvantage in mating compared to ST flies. Such differences between Drosophila pseudoobscura karyotypes have been demonstrated in certain other strains by Spiess

& Langer (1964). Indeed, in chambers with equal numbers of ST and TL flies significantly more of the former than of the latter have mated (line 32). Yet, both ST males (lines 34 and 36) and TL males (lines 33 and 35) are preferred as mates when they are a minority.

In an attempt to find out how widespread mating advantages of minority males may be, experiments have been made with two strains of the Andean–South Brazilian race of *Drosophila paulistorum* coming respectively from São Paulo, Brazil, and from Simla, Trinidad. These are nearly the geographic extremes of the distribution region of this race. With twelve pairs of each strain in the observation chamber (Table II, line 1), the intra-strain matings (A × A and B × B) greatly outnumber the inter-strain ones (A × B and B × A). The joint isolation index, computed according to the method of Malogolowkin, Simmons & Levene (1965) is $0.69 \pm 0.07$, a very pronounced ethological isolation. The question at issue is now this: Does the rarity of the males of a given strain help to overcome the ethological isolation between the strains? The data in Table II suggest a negative answer; the only significant Chi-square in Table II is in line 4, where the males of the Trinidad strain seem to have been more successful than expected for their numbers.

Two more experiments can be reported in the present communication, designed to explore the possible causes of the mating advantages of the minority class males. As shown above, the mating success of a class of males does not depend on whether these males were raised in the same cultures with their potential mates or in different cultures. This makes it improbable that the sensory cue involved may be acquired from the environment in which the individuals develop between the egg and the adult stages.

**Table II. Numbers of Matings Recorded in Observation Chambers Containing *D. paulistorum* from São Paulo, Brazil (A), and from Simla, Trinidad (B)**

| No. | Pairs per chamber A | B | Runs | Matings A♀×A♂ | A♀×B♂ | B♀×A♂ | B♀×B♂ | Have mated A♀ | B♀ | A♂ | B♂ | Chi-squares ♀ | ♂ |
|---|---|---|---|---|---|---|---|---|---|---|---|---|---|
| 1 | 12 | 12 | 6 | 40 | 4 | 12 | 45 | 44 | 57 | 52 | 49 | 1·68 | 0·90 |
| 2 | 20 | 5 | 7 | 68 | 12 | 12 | 10 | 80 | 22 | 80 | 22 | 0·16 | 0·16 |
| 3 | 5 | 20 | 7 | 17 | 10 | 9 | 68 | 27 | 77 | 26 | 78 | 2·31 | 1·63 |
| 4 | 23 | 2 | 7 | 85 | 7 | 2 | 8 | 92 | 10 | 87 | 15 | 0·45 | 6·23 |
| 5 | 2 | 23 | 6 | 4 | 6 | 4 | 108 | 10 | 112 | 8 | 114 | 0·00 | 0·34 |

The possibility that this cue may come from the adult flies themselves must be considered. One experiment used a 'double chamber' technique. Two regular observation chambers are used, separated only by a cheesecloth partition, which forms the ceiling of the lower and the floor of the upper chamber. The two chambers are taped and tied securely together. In the upper chamber five pairs of some 'rare' type, A, and twenty pairs of a 'common' type, B, are introduced. In the lower chamber about fifteen pairs of the 'rare' type are introduced, as nearly as possible simultaneously. Matings occur in both the lower and the upper chambers, but only the matings in the latter are recorded in the usual manner. Observations of the behaviour of the flies in single chambers are used as controls. The double chambers and the control chambers are run, of course, simultaneously or nearly so. *Drosophila pseudoobscura* strains with AR and with CH third chromosomes, selected for positive or for negative geotaxis, were used as experimental animals. The mating success of the males of these strains has been shown by Ehrman *et al.* (1965) to be frequency dependent, the rare type enjoying an advantage.

The results are reported in Table III. Lines 2 and 4 show the outcomes of the control experiments, in single chambers. As before, the minority type males are involved in very significantly more matings than would be expected from their frequencies. The Chi-squares are large enough to have negligible probabilities of being due to chance. The mating advantage of the 'rare' males disappears in double chambers (lines 1 and 3); here these males are no longer a real minority, because many males of the same kind are

present under the cheesecloth partition in the lower chamber.

Another experimental technique is to use a single observation chamber twice in succession, with as little time as possible between the two runs. For the first run, the chamber contained about fifteen pairs of AR flies selected for the positive, or for the negative geotaxis (lines 5 and 6 in Table III). After about 1 hr, these flies were discarded, five pairs of AR and twenty pairs of CH flies introduced into the chamber, and observed as usual. Comparison of the control and experimental runs (lines 2 and 5, and 4 and 6 respectively) shows that the mating advantages of the rare type males persist, although perhaps weakened in comparison with the controls.

Finally, the possibility, however remote, had to be ruled out that the mating success of the flies is somehow influenced by marking them. In many experiments one of the types was marked by notching one of its wings, to make it recognizable. In successive runs the kind of flies so marked was alternated. Wild-type flies (segregants from the cultures of the mutant Delta) were taken, some of them had one of their wings notched and the other entire. Then observation chambers received groups of twenty-three pairs which were designated as 'common' and two pairs which were designated as 'rare'. Either the 'common' (C), or the 'rare' (R) flies had wings notched. In five runs the results obtained were as follows: C ♀ × C ♂ = 87; C ♀ × R ♂ = 5; R ♀ × C ♂ = 7; R ♀ × R ♂ = 2.

The Chi-squares for the deviations from the uniform mating success are 0·109 for the females and 0·163 for the males. Neither comes close to being significant. Notching of a wing does not make any difference in mating success.

**Table III. Numbers of Matings Recorded in 'Double Chambers' (items 1 and 3), in Single Control Chambers (items 2 and 4), and in Chambers Previously Occupied (items 5 and 6)**

| No. | Pairs per chamber | | Runs | Matings | | | | Have mated | | | | Chi-square ♂ |
|---|---|---|---|---|---|---|---|---|---|---|---|---|
| | A | B | | A♀×A♂ | A♀×B♂ | B♀×A♂ | B♀×B♂ | A♀ | B♀ | A♂ | B♂ | |
| 1 | 5 AR+ | 20 CH+ | 5 | 9 | 15 | 12 | 84 | 24 | 96 | 21 | 99 | 0·47 |
| 2 | 5 AR+ | 20 CH+ | 5 | 18 | 7 | 34 | 63 | 25 | 97 | 52 | 70 | 39·02 |
| 3 | 5 AR− | 20 CH− | 5 | 4 | 15 | 14 | 79 | 19 | 93 | 18 | 94 | 1·08 |
| 5 | 5 AR− | 20 CH− | 5 | 14 | 11 | 34 | 55 | 25 | 89 | 48 | 66 | 34·81 |
| 5 | 5 AR+ | 20 CH+ | 5 | 10 | 15 | 35 | 63 | 25 | 98 | 45 | 78 | 21·15 |
| 6 | 5 AR− | 20 CH− | 5 | 10 | 15 | 26 | 74 | 25 | 100 | 36 | 89 | 6·05 |

## Discussion

The experiments of Petit (1958) on *Drosophila melanogaster*, of Ehrman *et al.* (1965), and those described in the present communication on *D. pseudoobscura*, have brought to light a most interesting phenomenon. When two kinds of males are present in an environment, the mating success of each kind depends upon its frequency in relation to the other kind. Within the range of frequencies investigated, the rare male mates relatively more frequently than the common males.

This is true with strains with different chromosomes, strains of different geographic origins, mutant versus wild-type flies, and flies of the same strain raised in different environments (different temperatures). This is, however, not true of the strains of *D. paulistorum* of different geographic origin which show an incipient ethological isolation.

If the mating success of the representatives of a given genotype is greater when it is rare than when it becomes common, important genetic and evolutionary consequences might follow. A greater mating success confers upon the genotype a higher Darwinian fitness. This fitness will, however, decrease as the frequency increases, until an equilibrium is established. This mechanism, if at all frequent in a species, will cause the population of that species to be highly polymorphic. The polymorphism will be balanced even if the heterozygous genotypes do not possess an advantage compared to the homozygotes.

The physiological basis of the mating advantage of rare forms is quite obscure.[*] In *Drosophila*, the females are believed to be responsible for 'choosing' their mating partners, while the males are more nearly promiscuous and attempt to court, or at least to investigate, individuals of about their size irrespective of strain, species, and even sex. The numbers of courtships observed in the mating chambers are considerably greater than the numbers of copulations. Although a few females copulate with the first male that approaches them, others are courted several times. It is therefore possible that the females acquire some information concerning the relative frequencies of the different kinds of available males before they finally accept one. The cues involved are, however, unclear. The experiment with the 'double chamber', described above, suggests that either auditory, or olfactory, or a combination of both kinds of stimuli may be involved. More conclusive evidence can, however, be obtained only by further experiments, which are being planned. It is evidently also important to know whether the dependence of the mating success on the frequency is widespread or we just happened to choose materials in which it is observed. If it is widespread, the phenomenon will have to be given a serious consideration as an evolutionary agent.

An indication that this type of mating preference does indeed exist in higher animals has been provided by Professor Konrad Lorenz, who kindly permits me to quote from his letter: 'We have repeatedly seen in our greylag goose colony that males start to court with explosive suddenness a female that has been absent from the colony for a few months or who is a perfect stranger. We have had a dramatic example of this happening a few weeks ago when fifteen greylags coming from another colony arrived in Seewiesen. Four of our ganders started to court three of the strange females with the explosive suddenness of 'falling in love'. One of them even deserted his former mate to do so, a thing extremely rare in greylag geese . . . where . . . the choice of mate lies with the male rather than with the female.' Professor Lorenz also states, 'Of course I believe that this phenomenon is quite widespread among higher animals. I suspect that the extremely variable song of some songbirds is selected for by the female's tendency of being more strongly attracted by a song which is "somehow different".'

## Summary

The mating success of different strains of *Drosophila pseudoobscura* and *D. paulistorum* has been studied in Elens–Wattiaux observation chambers. When two kinds of females and of males are present, the mating success depends upon their relative frequencies. The less frequent kind, especially of males, is more successful in mating. In *D. pseudoobscura* this is so when strains with different chromosomes, of different geographic origins, mutant *v.* wild-type flies, and flies raised at different temperatures are tested. The frequency effect is not observed with two sexually isolated strains of *D. paulistorum*. The mating advantage fostered by rarity may increase the genetic diversity on the population concerned.

## Acknowledgments

This work was supported in part by Contract No. AT-(30-1)-3096, U.S. Atomic Energy Commission.

[*] Now see *Evolution*, **23**, 59–64, on "The sensory basis of mate selection in Drosophila."

The author was in receipt of U.S. Public Health Service Research Career Development Award 1K3 HD-9033-01.

## REFERENCES

Dobzhansky, Th., Anderson, W. W., Pavlovsky, O., Spassky, B. & Wills C. J. (1964a). Genetics of natural populations. XXXV. A progress report on genetic changes in populations of *Drosophila pseudoobscura* in the American southwest. *Evolution*, **18**, 164–176.

Dobzhansky, Th., Ehrman, L., Pavlovsky, O. & Spassky, B. (1964b). The superspecies *Drosophila paulistorum*. *Proc. natn. Acad. Sci. U.S.A.*, **51**, 3–9.

Dobzhansky, Th. & Spassky, B. (1959). *Drosophila paulistorum*, a cluster of species in *statu nascendi*. *Proc. natn. Acad. Sci. U.S.A.*, **45**, 419–428.

Ehrman, L. (1964). Courtship and mating behavior as a reproductive isolating mechanism in Drosophila. *Am. Zool.*, **4**, 147–153.

Ehrman, L. (1965). Direct observation of sexual isolation between allopatric and between sympatric strains of the different *Drosophila paulistorum* races. *Evolution*, **19**, 459–464.

Ehrman, L., Spassky, B., Pavlovsky, O. & Dobzhansky, Th. (1965). Sexual selection, geotaxis, and chromosomal polymorphism in experimental populations of *Drosophila pseudoobscura*. *Evolution*, **19**, 337–346.

Ehrman, L. & Strickberger, W. (1960). Flies mating: a pictorial record. *Nat. Hist.*, **69**, 28–33.

Elens, A. A. & Wattiaux, J. M. (1964). Direct observation of sexual isolation. *Drosoph. Inf. Serv.*, **39**, 118–119.

Ewing, A. W. (1961). Body size and courtship behavior in *Drosophila melanogaster*. *Anim. Behav.*, **9**, 93–99.

Hirsch, J.[*] (1961). Sign of taxis as a property of the genotype. *Science, N.Y.*, **22**, 835–836.

Malogolowkin-Cohen, Ch., Solima-Simmons, A. & Levene, H. (1965). A study of sexual isolation between certain strains of *Drosophila paulistorum*. *Evolution*, **19**, 95–103.

Manning, A. (1962). A sperm factor affecting the receptivity of *Drosophila melanogaster* females. *Nature, Lond.*, **194**, 252–253.

Petit, C. (1958). Le déterminisme génétique et psychophysiologique de la compétition sexuelle chez *Drosophila melanogaster*. *Bull. biol. Fr. Belg.*, **92**, 1–329.

Spiess, E. B. & Langer, B. (1964). Mating speed control by gene arrangements in *Drosophila pseudoobscura* homokaryotypes. *Proc. natn. Acad. Sci. U.S.A.*, **51**, 1015–1019.

Spieth, H. T. (1952). Mating behavior within the genus *Drosophila* (Diptera). *Bull. Am. Mus. nat. Hist.*, **99**, 395–474.

(*Received* 22 *November* 1965; *Ms. number*: A388)

[*] and Erlenmeyer-Kimling, L.

## APPENDIX

Professor E. B. Spiess, University of Pittsburgh, has permitted me to include the following data, collected in February 1964. The data are relevant here because the species tested, *Drosophila persimilis*, is a very close relative—a sibling species, of *D. pseudoobscura*. Also, the technique was similar to the one employed above: twenty males and twenty females were observed mating in a chamber. Here, however, only the ratio of the two types of male was altered, the females were always ten Klamath and ten Whitney (KL and WT are two autosomal inversions in *D. persimilis* which are always present in the homozygous condition in these experiments). Professor Spiess observed each chamber for 1 hr and ran six chambers for each ratio tested. The inversions were distinguished by the appropriately marked wings of their carriers. He presents his data as the number of males that have mated out of the number of males of that karyotype available.

| WT/KL ♂ Ratio | ♂♂ mated | |
|---|---|---|
| | KL | WT |
| 9/1 | 0·50 | 0·51 |
| 8/2 | 0·54 | 0·48 |
| 7/3 | 0·42 | 0·63 |
| 6/4 | 0·15 | 0·67 |
| 5/5 | 0·15 | 0·67 |
| 4/6 | 0·15 | 0·54 |
| 3/7 | 0·33 | 0·72 |
| 2/8 | 0·20 | 0·88 |
| 1/9 | 0·34 | 0·83 |

Clearly, KL males are doing proportionately better when they are rare; reciprocally, WT has a greater success in mating when it is rare.

Reprinted from the Proceedings of the National Academy of Sciences
Vol. 44, No. 11, pp. 1136–1141.   November, 1958.

# INCREASE IN FITNESS IN EXPERIMENTAL POPULATIONS RESULTING FROM HETEROSIS

## By Hampton L. Carson

DEPARTMENT OF ZOÖLOGY, WASHINGTON UNIVERSITY, ST. LOUIS, MISSOURI

*Communicated by Th. Dobzhansky, September 19, 1958*

*Introduction*—A local population of a species, or deme, consists of an array of individual genotypes.   At any one time level, the deme represents the active evolutionary interface between the hereditary material and the environment. Genetic novelties due to new mutations or recombinations are automatically tested when the deme is under natural selection.   If a genetic change improves the fitness of its carriers, natural selection may be expected to reproduce the change differentially.   The result is adaptive evolution.

The experiments here described represent an attempt to study the process of adaptation directly.   The equivalent of one gamete of foreign genetic material is introduced into an experimental population having a size which is held by natural selection in equilibrium with a rigidly controlled and limited environment.   Although the environment is unchanged, this introduction is followed by an immediate threefold increase in the population size.   Such an increase, occurring as it does under continual strong natural selection, reflects a corresponding increase in the biological efficiency of the group under the specific environmental conditions embodied in the experiment.   The evidence is strong that this increase is due to immediate contributions to fitness made by new heterotic combinations formed in the populations.

*Materials and Methods.*—Two strains of *Drosophila melanogaster* were used. The first of these, hereafter referred to as "se ss ro," is a laboratory stock homozygous for five third-chromosome recessives. These are: sepia (se), spineless (ss), kidney (k), ebony-sooty (e$^s$), and rough (ro). The second strain used was the wild-type Oregon-R.

Each experimental population was maintained in a chamber made of an ordinary glass shell vial (95 × 25 mm.) to which a tube of cellulose acetate of the same size and diameter as the shell vial is attached by cellophane tape. The chamber of the latter tube contains a small platform of blotting paper. The unit is closed at the end with cotton. The glass vial contains 9.5 cc. of a carefully prepared uniform cornmeal-Karo-agar medium. Ten grams of granulated agar-agar are dissolved in 200 cc. tap water, then 33 cc. dark Karo (maize) syrup are added. While stirring, 115 gm. of yellow cornmeal (maize; Quaker Oats Co.) mixed with 400 cc. cold water are added. After adding 500 cc. more water, the mixture is boiled for at least 5 minutes or until the total volume is exactly 1,100 cc. Under some atmospheric conditions it is necessary to add a small amount of water after 5 minutes of boiling in order that the final volume will be 1,100 cc. Just before pouring 9.5 cc. of medium into each shell vial, 10 cc. of a 10 per cent solution of Tegosept in 70 per cent alcohol are added. The population food must be made in a small vessel and stirred constantly to keep it uniform in consistency. This food is prepared twice a week and kept under refrigeration. It is prepared for use by yeasting the surface with 10 mg. of Fleischmann's fresh dry yeast, moistened with one drop of distilled water. A strip of absorbent paper toweling, 15 × 75 mm., is doubled and pushed down into the food cake to the bottom of the vial.

Populations are begun in such chambers and a new vial substituted for the old at exact intervals, so that the population of flies in the tube has access to each food cake for 48 hours only. After being exposed to three consecutive such food vials, the entire adult population is etherized lightly, weighed, and counted on the same day and at the same hour each week. The flies are then immediately replaced, together with any newly hatched flies (see below), in the chamber. A clean cellulose acetate "supervial" is used each week; this change is also made on the counting day. The vial with which the population has contact immediately after counting is left in position for 24 hours only. This latter vial is then discarded, or the eggs therein used for samples, and a new cycle of three consecutive 48-hour periods is instituted.

The three 48-hour vials from each week are plugged tightly with cotton and kept separately from the adult population; no further yeast or moisture is added. All young flies hatching from these vials are collected onto unyeasted food at least every 2 days. Twice a week (once in addition to the day on which the population is counted) such accumulated hatching flies are etherized lightly, weighed, counted, and added to the adult population. Vials are not discarded until all flies have emerged. The system thus maintains a closed vial population the size of which is in equilibrium with the food source as soon as the weekly deaths are equal to the weekly additions. The basic design is similar to that used by Buzzati-Traverso,[1] except that in the present case the total mass of the adult population and the young hatching flies are measured each week.  All experiments were carried out at 25.5°C.; the mean generation time under the strong selective conditions is long, approximately 14 days.

*The Experiments.*—A base control population (C-1, Table 1) of se ss ro was

## TABLE 1

SIZE AND PRODUCTION OF EXPERIMENTAL POPULATIONS OF *Drosophila melanogaster* AT EQUILIBRIUM

| POPULATION | WEEKS AT EQUILIBRIUM | POPULATION SIZE | | PRODUCTION | |
|---|---|---|---|---|---|
| | | Mean No. Individuals per Week | Mean Wet Weight (Mg. per Week) | Mean No. Individuals per Week | Mean Wet Weight (Mg. per Week) |
| *Controls:* | | | | | |
| C-1 se ss k eˢ ro Feb.–Oct. '57 | 32 | 161.6 ± 6.4 | 90.3 ± 3.0 | 100.8 ± 4.4 | 48.4 ± 1.9 |
| C-2 se ss k eˢ ro Dec. '57–Apr. '58 | 20 | 158.9 ± 8.4 | 88.4 ± 2.9 | 65.5 ± 5.1 | 29.1 ± 2.4 |
| C-3 se ss k eˢ ro Dec. '57–Apr. '58 | 20 | 154.4 ± 4.4 | 88.7 ± 2.0 | 61.0 ± 3.3 | 27.6 ± 1.5 |
| C-4 Oregon-R May–Sep. '58 | 16 | 380.2 ± 16.1 | 226.4 ± 8.1 | 150.5 ± 9.2 | 84.2 ± 5.2 |
| C-5 Oregon-R May–Sep. '58 | 16 | 330.5 ± 17.6 | 190.4 ± 9.8 | 151.6 ± 11.0 | 82.7 ± 6.8 |
| *Experimentals:* | | | | | |
| E-1 se ss k eˢ ro with *n* Oregon autosomes Mar.–Aug. '58 | 20 | 457.4 ± 13.7 | 292.5 ± 9.1 | 171.0 ± 10.6 | 91.0 ± 5.9 |
| E-2 se ss k eˢ ro with *n* Oregon autosomes Mar.–Aug. '58 | 20 | 502.6 ± 14.9 | 318.6 ± 8.9 | 201.1 ± 14.4 | 105.2 ± 8.0 |

begun on January 2, 1957, using 50 female and 50 male flies from stock.  On October 7, 1957, this population was divided into four replicates (C-2,C-3,E-1, and E-2, Table 1).  After equilibrium was again reached in these four replicates, one young, wild-type male was introduced into each of the two experimental populations (E-1 and E-2) on December 23, 1957.  These males were $F_1$'s from a cross of an Oregon-R male by an se ss ro female taken from the population into which the male was subsequently introduced.  The male which was put into population E-1 lived for approximately 21 days; the male in population E-2 lived for 14 days. No flies were introduced into the controls, C-2 and C-3.  Control populations C-4 and C-5, made up from Oregon-R stock, were established on February 22, 1958.

Table 1 summarizes the size and production of these seven populations after inspection of the data indicated that the population in question was no longer systematically rising and was thus at approximate equilibrium.  Each figure in the table represents the mean size or production of the population over a period of consecutive weeks.  Both the mean number of individuals and the mean wet weight, with their respective standard errors, are given.  Figures 1 and 2 show the progressive changes in population size (weight) and production (weight), respectively, following the addition of single males to experimental populations E-1 and E-2 (*solid lines*). Figure 3 shows the change in frequency of three of the five types of mutant homozygotes (i.e., se/se, ro/ro, ss/ss) which are formed in the populations following the introduction of the males. The data given in Figure 3 are based on counts of the entire population; the two replicates were essentially similar, and the data have been combined. Free recombination of all third-chromosome genes was observed, and $e^s/e^s$ and k/k homozygotes were likewise present throughout the course of the experiment. Fifteen generations after introduction of their wild-type alleles, all three of the five types of mutant genes which were closely followed remained in the population in substantial frequency, as indicated by the frequency of the homozygous classes observed. Estimates of gene frequencies for these three genes, based on the square roots of the frequency of the homozygous classes after 15 generations, are as follows: ro = 53.4 per cent, se = 25.3 per cent, and ss = 12.3 per cent.

*Discussion.*—Introduction of a single set of haploid autosomes (and a Y chromosome) derived from Oregon-R stock into equilibrated populations of se ss ro has resulted in a greater than threefold increase in the size of the population. The number of individuals is approximately trebled, whereas the increase in weight is even greater, being about a factor of 3.5. It follows that an increase both in number of individuals and in size of individual organisms has occurred. Comparable increases in production are likewise observed. These changes occur, in the absence of any environmental change, in an explosive fashion in about three generations. The improvement not

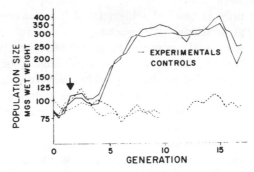

Fig. 1.—Increase in size of two experimental populations of *Drosophila melanogaster* (*solid lines*) following introduction of a single haploid set of autosomes into each of them (*at arrow*).

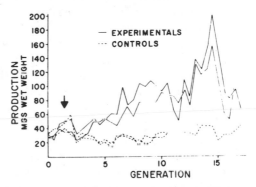

Fig. 2.—Increase in production (milligrams flies wet weight hatched per week) of two populations of *Drosophila melanogaster* (*solid lines*) following introduction of a single haploid set of autosomes into each of them (*arrow*).

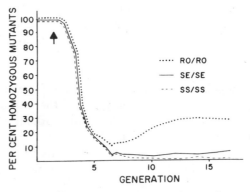

Fig. 3.—Change in frequency of mutant phenotypes in the two experimental populations shown in Figs. 1 and 2. The arrow indicates the point at which the single males were added.

only is quickly achieved but has not been observed to undergo breakdown in 15 generations. These changes in population size and production are concurrent with, and appear to be correlated directly with, a drop in the frequency of the third-chromosome recessives which were being followed. These genes (at least se, ss, and ro) have quickly assumed what appear to be balanced intermediate gene frequency levels. Such behavior is to be expected in at least four of these genes (se, ss, e, and ro). Considerable evidence exists in the literature to suggest that these genes regularly display heterosis in experimental populations, that is, each tends to persist at a fairly high gene frequency, in some cases for 70 generations or more, and is apparently not being progressively eliminated.[2-6] The present experiments indicate that heterosis is not only present but may immediately serve to improve fitness in the population as indicated by the correlated sharp rise in the population size and production (i.e., the biological efficiency of the group).

The improvement found cannot be due to the simple "covering-up" by dominance of the deleterious effects caused by the mutant genes or polygene segments of the se ss ro stock. This is evident from the fact that the polymorphic experimental populations (E-1 and E-2) show heterosis in that they transgress, in their size and thus fitness, not only the se ss ro controls but the donor Oregon-R populations as well (Table 1). The relative contributions of different genes to this heterosis cannot, of course, be ascertained in these experiments. Indeed, there is no reason to believe that the wild-type alleles of the particular oligogenes followed as markers are any more important in this than any of the many other uncontrolled polygene groups introduced in the same male.

The immediacy of the effect and the rapidity of the assumption of a higher level of fitness leads one to conclude that coadaptation could not have entered into this adjustment. Rather, the salutary effects of simple hybrid vigor (= luxuriance) involving possibly a large number of autosomal loci can apparently be immediately exploited by a population and be retained without immediate breakdown. Evidently, natural selection accomplishes this through the prompt development of balanced polymorphism. Whether this heterosis is maintained indefinitely and whether coadaptation may ultimately serve as a basis of further improvement are interesting points to be left to future study of these same populations.

*Summary.*—Introduction of a single set of haploid autosomes into an experimental population which is equilibrated by natural selection results in an approximately threefold rise in the collective size and production of the population. The environment is rigidly controlled throughout. The biomass of the experimental populations transgresses also the level maintained by that control population which was used as a donor of the introduced wild-type chromosomes. The data suggest that simple heterosis without coadaptation (= luxuriance) may indeed contribute directly to fitness. Natural selection appears not only to prevent the breakdown of the immediate heterosis but also to maintain it through favoring the development of balanced polymorphism.

I am most grateful to Mrs. Marian Stalker for preparing the figures and to Mrs. Kyoko Kato, Miss Carole Guze, and Miss Karen Alt for painstaking and faithful technical assistance.  This work was supported by a grant from the National Science Foundation.

[1] A. A. Buzzati-Traverso, *Heredity*, **9**, 153, 1955.
[2] P. L'Heritier and G. Tessier, *Compt. rend.*, **124**, 882, 1937.
[3] H. Kalmus, *J. Genet.*, **47**, 58, 1945.
[4] G. Tessier, *Compt. rend. acad. sci.*, **124**, 676, 1788, 1947.
[5] W. E. Kerr and S. Wright, *Evolution*, **8**, 293, 1954.
[6] M. Susman and H. L. Carson, *Am. Naturalist* (in press).

Reprinted from the Proceedings of the National Academy of Sciences
Vol. 57, No. 4, pp. 893–898. April, 1967.

# PLANT POISONS IN A TERRESTRIAL FOOD CHAIN*

By Lincoln P. Brower, Jane Van Zandt Brower, and Joseph M. Corvino

DEPARTMENT OF BIOLOGY, AMHERST COLLEGE, AMHERST, MASSACHUSETTS

*Communicated by G. E. Hutchinson, February 2, 1967*

Abundant evidence indicates that the primary adaptive role of secondary plant substances is the defense against herbivorous vertebrates and invertebrates.[1,2] Of even greater evolutionary interest, however, is the important ecological theory that certain herbivores have evolved the ability to sequester noxious molecules from their food plants which they in turn use to deter their own predators.[1] This paper will present the results of experiments designed to test this theory for a food chain involving milkweed plants (Asclepiadaceae), the monarch butterfly (*Danaus plexippus* L.), whose larvae eat the leaves of these plants, and the blue jay (*Cyanocitta cristata bromia* Oberholser), an omnivorous bird.

1. *Experimental Design.*—The monarch butterfly was used because of its unpalatability to avian predators, and because of the close larval food plant association of the entire subfamily, Danainae, with the classically poisonous plant families, Asclepiadaceae and Apocyanaceae.[1–3] These plants contain digitalis-like cardiac glycosides which are of extreme potency as vertebrate heart toxins.[1,4–6]

In order to test the molecular-sequestering hypothesis, it is of great importance that the insect be holometabolous to show definitively that the plant poisons are assimilated by the adult. In contrast, hemimetabolous insects such as grasshoppers could utilize gut storage of the plant material. Furthermore, in the absence of complete metamorphosis in terrestrial insects, the adult food is likely to be the same as or similar to that of the nymph, with the result that the imago is not a pristine entity as far as food intake is concerned. Use of the monarch butterfly avoided these complications.

Our rationale in attempting to demonstrate that the food plant is the source of unpalatability involved the selection of a strain of monarch butterflies that would feed upon a plant belonging to a nonpoisonous group. Cabbage (*Brassica oleraceae* L., Cruciferae[7]) was chosen because it is not known[4,8] to contain the characteristic cardiac glycosides of the milkweeds and because it is easily grown in a greenhouse. It would be possible, then, to compare the effect upon individual birds of first feeding them cabbage-reared insects, and then milkweed-reared ones. Thus each bird would serve as its own control. Our prediction was that the cabbage-reared butterflies would be palatable, whereas those reared on milkweed would not. Our first experiment (birds 1–5) compared the palatibility of the cabbage-reared monarchs with that of monarchs reared on *Asclepias curassavica* L., a species known to contain several cardiac glycosides.[9–11]

The second experiment (birds 6–8) was carried out to test the palatability of monarchs reared on a taxonomically distant species of the asclepiadaceous plant *Gonolobus rostratus* (Vahl), Roemer and Schultes.[12] Climbing in habit, this plant genus is very different from *Asclepias*, and occurs widely in the New World tropics.[13] One species (*Gonolobus laevis* Michx.), upon which the monarch has been reported,[14] occurs as far north as Pennsylvania.[15] (In Trinidad, West Indies, August 5, 1964, Arima Valley, we found a third instar larva of the monarch on *G. rostratus*, though here *Asclepias curassavica* is clearly its preferred food plant.)    The plan was to feed the birds as before on cabbage-reared monarchs and then to test them on the *Gonolobus*-reared ones,[16] our prediction being that the latter would be extremely unpalatable.

2.    *Methods and Materials.*—The original stock of monarch butterflies was obtained in Florida[17] during March 1965, and was maintained for 20 generations on *Asclepias curassavica* at our Amherst College laboratory.    This stock was crossed with another from Florida after 8 generations, and the material used in the experiment was accumulated from the ninth through the fifteenth generations of this amalgamated stock.

The *A. curassavica* plants were grown from seeds obtained in the vicinity of Mayaro, Trinidad, West Indies, and also from cuttings of these plants.    It is possible that some of the seedlings came from three plants of unknown origin, although all are unquestionably *A. curassavica*.

Selection of a cabbage-eating strain in early 1966 was difficult.    Young first instar larvae were removed from *A. curassavica* plants upon which the females had oviposited and were placed in small plastic containers[18] on cabbage leaves taken from 1- to 3-in.-high seedlings.    All the larvae refused to eat, and died.    A second approach was made by painting the cabbage leaves with a crude ether extract of *A. curassavica* leaves.    Some first instar larvae ate these leaves, and three ultimately reached the fourth instar but ceased feeding.    They were returned to *A. curassavica*, upon which they completed development.    These three were mated *inter se* but produced no fertile eggs and were therefore bred to individuals that had been reared on *A. curassavica*.    Numerous fertile eggs resulted and upon hatching were divided into two groups.    Group 1 was left on *A. curassavica* and reared through all stages on it.    Group 2 was transferred onto cabbage which was now (and subsequently) *not* painted with the ether extract.    Larvae in this group developed slowly on the exclusive cabbage diet, with high mortality particularly from the fourth instar to the pupal stage.    Although a few adults were obtained, none was fertile.

To continue the line, fourth instar cabbage larvae were transferred back to *A. curassavica* to complete their development normally.    Matings of these transfers among themselves and also with siblings from group 1 produced eggs for the next generation that were similarly subdivided, and so on, allowing the maintenance of the cabbage-eating strain for five generations.

Exclusively cabbage-fed (except for the possible ingestion of a small amount of *A. curassavica* during the first instar prior to putting the insects on cabbage) larvae, prepupae, and adults were frozen in a deep freezer and accumulated over the five generations along with comparable material fed on an exclusive *A. curassavica* diet. The only difference between the two was that because of continued attempts to breed them, the cabbage-reared adults were one to several days old, whereas the *Asclepias*-reared ones were always frozen before they were 48 hours old.

In the experiments, we fed each jay one of three stages of monarchs:    fifth instar larvae, prepupae (very late fifth instar larvae, which had evacuated their gut contents), or adult males.    All material was thawed to room temperature before being presented to the birds.

The blue jays were caught in the wild (in Franklin County, Massachusetts) by mist netting and were stored in our aviary for a few days to several weeks before use.

The sex of the birds was not determined.   The four jays of the first experiment were placed in individual cages in the laboratory and given the experimental food manually, as described previously.[3]   Preliminary experiments established that although the birds freely accepted mealworms, all initially refused cabbage-reared monarch larvae on sight.   This reluctance was overcome by an extreme food deprivation schedule:  birds were restored to their regular diet only when they accepted the cabbage-reared monarchs.   Of six birds, two died of starvation before eating and four (birds 1–4) were tested.   With birds 5–8, new automatic feeders[19] were employed which obviated the long deprivation period.

The experiments with birds 1–4 were conducted from March 19 to April 13, 1966, using fourth instar larvae for two birds, prepupae for one bird, and the bodies of adult male butterflies (from which wings and legs had been removed) for one bird. The experiments with birds 5–8, using adult male butterflies, were carried out in December 1966.   All five birds receiving adult male monarchs were initially broken in on similarly prepared adult males of *Anartia amalthea* (L.), a known palatable Nymphaline species.[1]   The visible behavior of each bird was recorded in writing for at least 30 minutes after it had eaten all the experimental insects, or, if some material was left, for 30 minutes after it stopped eating.

Birds 1–5 were given one half of their total cabbage-reared monarchs on day 1, followed by the remaining half on day 2.   On day 3 they were given the *Asclepias* material.   On a final day, all five birds were given mealworms as a terminal control insect.   Birds 6–8 were fed all individuals in each monarch category on separate days.   Bird 6 received its mealworms on a final day, whereas birds 7 and 8 were given theirs three hours after receiving the *Asclepias*-reared monarchs.

3.   *Results.*—Once the birds overcame their initial hesitancy to attack the cabbage-reared monarchs, they ate rapidly with no signs of unpalatability or sickness whether larvae, prepupae, or adult males (birds 1–6, Table 1).   Their reaction to these, following ingestion, was virtually indistinguishable from that after eating mealworms.

In great contrast to the cabbage-fed monarchs, those reared on *Asclepias curassavica* caused all eight birds to become sick.   Ingestion of these was followed uniformly by violent retching and vomiting of the partially digested insects and fluid (Table 1).   Other less objective indications of unpalatability included excessive billwiping, crouching, alternate fluffing and flattening of the feathers, erratic movements about the cage, jerky movements of head, wings, and thoracic regions, partial closure of the eyes, eating of sand, twitching, and a generally sick appearance.   The range of time for vomiting to occur following ingestion of the first *Asclepias*-reared insect was from 8 minutes and 10 seconds to 14 minutes and 30 seconds (Table 1). Recovery from the vomiting and return to a normal appearance seemed complete from approximately 20 minutes to 1 hour following ingestion of the first insect.

The results obtained with *Gonolobus*-reared butterflies were contrary to prediction: bird 6 found them as palatable as the cabbage-reared ones.   Because of this, it was possible to substitute *Gonolobus*-monarchs for cabbage ones that were in short supply (birds 7 and 8).   Both of these birds likewise avidly ate four *Gonolobus*-monarch males with no ill effects.

It is shown in Table 1 (bird 5) that vomiting was even caused by the ingestion of less than one *Asclepias*-reared male.   The minimum number of cabbage-reared

TABLE 1
FREQUENCY AND TIME ELAPSED BEFORE VOMITING IN BLUE JAYS FOLLOWING INGESTION OF
MONARCH BUTTERFLIES REARED ON THREE LARVAL FOOD PLANTS

| | No. offered | No. eaten | Vomiting frequency* | Time before vomiting† |
|---|---|---|---|---|
| *Bird 1.* (larvae) | | | | |
| Cabbage-fed‡ | 10 | 10 | 0 | — |
| *Asclepias curassavica*-fed | 5 | 3 | 9 | 9' 20" |
| Mealworms | 5 | 5 | 0 | — |
| *Bird 2.* (larvae) | | | | |
| Cabbage-fed‡ | 10 | 9 | 0 | — |
| *Asclepias curassavica*-fed | 5 | 2 | 5 | 14' 30" |
| Mealworms | 5 | 5 | 0 | — |
| *Bird 3.* (prepupae) | | | | |
| Cabbage-fed‡ | 8 | 8 | 0 | — |
| *Asclepias curassavica*-fed | 4 | 1 | 3 | 14' 00" |
| Mealworms | 4 | 4 | 0 | — |
| *Bird 4.* (adults) | | | | |
| Cabbage-fed‡ | 4 | 4 | 0 | — |
| *Asclepias curassavica*-fed | 2 | 1.5 | 9 | 11' 30" |
| Mealworms | 2 | 2 | 0 | — |
| *Bird 5.* (adults) | | | | |
| Cabbage-fed‡ | 4 | 4 | 0 | — |
| *Asclepias curassavica*-fed | 2 | 0.75 | 5 | 12' 00" |
| Mealworms | 4 | 4 | 0 | — |
| *Bird 6.* (adults) | | | | |
| Cabbage-fed | 2 | 2 | 0 | — |
| *Gonolobus rostratus*-fed | 4 | 4 | 0 | — |
| *Asclepias curassavica*-fed | 2 | 1.5 | 4 | 13' 00" |
| Mealworms | >5 | >5 | 0 | — |
| *Bird 7.* (adults) | | | | |
| *Gonolobus rostratus*-fed | 4 | 4 | 0 | — |
| *Asclepias curassavica*-fed | 2 | 2 | 7 | 8' 10" |
| Mealworms | >5 | >5 | 0 | — |
| *Bird 8.* (adults) | | | | |
| *Gonolobus rostratus*-fed | 4 | 4 | 0 | — |
| *Asclepias curassavica*-fed | 2 | 1.25 | 6 | 10' 00" |
| Mealworms | >5 | >5 | 0 | — |

\* During 30-min period following ingestion.
† Measured from time first insect was eaten.
‡ First half given on day 1, second half on day 2.

males ingested on one day was nearly three times this amount, while for the *Gonolobus*-reared ones, this difference was more than fivefold. Because of this, and because of the uniformity of the results for all eight birds, statistical treatment of the data is obviated.

4. *Discussion.*—The results of this experiment establish that the unpalatability of the monarch butterfly is causally related to the species of plant ingested by the larvae. What is not certain, however, is whether the unpalatability is caused by molecules taken directly from the plants. It is possible that the cabbage-reared monarchs are palatable because cabbage has within it chemical substances to which the monarch butterfly is not adapted and which disrupt its metabolism, thereby preventing the insect from synthesizing its noxious properties. Cabbage is not a food plant of the monarch butterfly in its natural environment, and the ones we did manage to rear on it had high mortality in the later stages and no fertile adults were produced; clearly, their metabolism was abnormal when they were reared on this plant. Consequently, the cabbage-feeding experiment *per se* does not prove the molecular-sequestering hypothesis. However, *Gonolobus* is a genus in the Asclepiadaceae that is normally fed upon by the monarchs in nature, and it is therefore

very unlikely that the metabolism of the butterfly would be disturbed when eating this plant. Why, then, were the *Gonolobus*-reared monarchs palatable?

At the outset of our experiment, we had made the general assumption that all asclepiad plants contain cardiac glycosides.[20] We now know that this is not true: Professor Th. Reichstein, of Basel University, has chemically analyzed dried leaves of our *Gonolobus rostratus* plants and found them to be devoid of cardiac glycosides.[21] In contrast, *Asclepias curassavica* contains at least seven different cardiac poisons.[9-11] Thus our experiments narrow down the association of unpalatability in the monarch to those asclepiad plants containing these compounds, as opposed to those lacking them.

Further support for the molecular-sequestering hypothesis has been provided by Parsons.[22] With material from our Trinidad laboratory, he has produced chemical and pharmacological evidence that adult monarch butterflies reared on *Asclepias curassavica* definitely contain at least three cardiac poisons. Moreover, the case is made stronger by the fact that cardiac glycosides have a steroid nucleus,[6] and insects are, as far as is known, unable to synthesize steroids.[23] Further work on the chemical identity of the poisons in the butterflies and the plants is in progress.[24]

While it is now extremely likely that these butterflies do obtain the poisonous molecules from the milkweeds, final disproof of their synthesis by the butterflies can only be achieved by radioactive labeling studies of the biosynthetic and transfer pathways of the cardiac glycosides in both the plants and the insects.

The fact that the palatability of the monarch butterfly can vary according to the food plant that its larvae ingested may at last resolve the controversy over the theory of warning coloration. The basis of this argument has largely been the conflicting evidence on the palatability of butterflies to vertebrate predators among which the monarch has been a principal subject.[25] Our new evidence provides a basis for reinvestigating the relative frequencies of palatable and unpalatable members of the same species in the same and in different geographic areas where alternative foods are available.

Finally, on the basis of this experiment, we offer an additional theoretical category of mimicry: *automimicry*. Here, a species has a palatability polymorphism resulting from the larval food plant selected by the ovipositing female. As such, palatable insects are perfect visual mimics of the unpalatable members of their own species.

5. *Summary.*—(1) By the selection of a strain of cabbage-eating monarch butterfly larvae, *Danaus plexippus*, it has been possible to show experimentally that this nonpoisonous food plant renders larvae, prepupae, and adult monarchs palatable to blue jays. (2) Monarchs reared on *Asclepias curassavica*, a natural food plant known to contain heart poisons, caused the same birds to vomit, even following the ingestion of less than one adult. (3) Another asclepiad plant (*Gonolobus rostratus*), lacking cardiac toxins, proved to produce fully palatable adults. (4) It was concluded that the unpalatability of the monarch butterfly is causally related to the species of plant ingested by the larvae. Although direct transfer of poisonous molecules from plant to insect is strongly suggested, radioactive labeling would provide the only direct proof. (5) The discovery of an intraspecific palatability polymorphism in the monarch butterfly prompts us to advance a new theoretical category of mimicry: *automimicry*.

This paper is dedicated to Professor Harold H. Plough.

We are grateful to G. E. Hutchinson for criticizing the manuscript, to E. B. Ford, F.R.S., for his enthusiastic support of this study, to Professor Th. Reichstein for chemically analyzing the *Gonolobus* leaves, and to M. Rothschild for discussion. Jocelyn Crane and Richard Archbold provided much material support, and Judith Myers helped us obtain stocks. For help in rearing the butterflies and plants, we wish to thank Winifred Sayer, Warren McAvoy, and Susan Latham. And to Juan Hernandez, our most competent field assistant in Trinidad, we are indeed indebted.

* This research was supported by National Science Foundation grants 20152 and GB4924.

[1] Brower, L. P., and J. V. Z. Brower, *Zoologica*, **49**, 137 (1964).

[2] Ehrlich, P. R., and P. H. Raven, *Evolution*, **18**, 586 (1965).

[3] Brower, J. V. Z., *Evolution*, **12**, 32 (1958).

[4] Hoch, J. H., *A Survey of the Cardiac Glycosides and Genins* (Columbia: University of South Carolina Press, 1961), 93 pp.

[5] Moe, G. K., and A. E. Farah, in *The Pharmacological Basis of Therapeutics* (New York: Macmillan, 1965), 3rd ed., p. 665.

[6] Gero, A., in *Drill's Pharmacology in Medicine*, ed. J. R. DiPalma (New York: McGraw-Hill, 1965), 3rd ed., p. 567.

[7] Burpee Seed Co., "Golden Acre" and "Earliana" varieties.

[8] Reichstein, Th., personal communication, March 28, 1966.

[9] Tschesche, R., D. Forstmann, and V. K. M. Rao, *Chem. Ber.*, **91**, 1204 (1958).

[10] Tschesche, R., G. Snatzke, and G. Grimmer, *Naturwissenschaften*, **46**, 263 (1959).

[11] Kupchan, S. M., J. R. Knox, J. E. Kelsey, and J. A. S. Renauld, *Science*, **146**, 1685 (1964).

[12] Identified by A. A. Bullock of the Royal Botanic Gardens, Kew, England (personal communication, April 13, 1966); the plant was erroneously called *G. broadwayi*, in *Flora of Trinidad and Tobago*, by R. O. Williams and E. E. Cheesman (Port-of-Spain, Trinidad: Guardian Commercial Printery, 1947), vol. 2, pt. 3, p. 173.

[13] Willis, J. C., *A Dictionary of the Flowering Plants and Ferns* (Cambridge: University Press, 1931), 6th ed., p. 297.

[14] Urquhart, F. A., *The Monarch Butterfly* (Toronto: University of Toronto Press, 1960), p. 106.

[15] Britton, N. L., and A. Brown, *An Illustrated Flora of the Northern United States, Canada, and the British Possessions* (New York: The New York Botanical Garden, 1947), vol. 3, 2nd ed., p. 36.

[16] Grown at Amherst College from seeds of a single pod collected in the Northern Range of Trinidad, W.I.

[17] Brower, L. P., *Ecology*, **42**, 76 (1961); at Area no. 1.

[18] Brower, L. P., J. V. Z. Brower, and F. P. Cranston, *Zoologica*, **50**, 1 (1965).

[19] Motor-powered rotary feeders with 12 cups appearing sequentially per revolution with approximately a 1-min exposure for each cup.

[20] According to Hoch,[4] members of at least eight genera of the Asclepiadaceae contain cardiac poisons: *Asclepias, Calotropis, Cryptostegia, Gomphocarpus, Menabea, Pachycarpus, Periploca,* and *Xysmalobium*.

[21] Personal communication, June 20, 1966.

[22] Parsons, J. A., *J. Physiol.*, **178**, 290 (1965).

[23] Gilmour, D., *Biochemistry of Insects* (New York: Academic Press, 1961), p. 32.

[24] Reichstein, Th., L. P. Brower, J. v. Euw, M. Rothschild, and J. A. Parsons, in preparation.

[25] Refs. 1 and 3, and Brower, L. P., *Ecology*, **43**, 181 (1962) vs. Urquhart;[14] Sheppard, P. M., *J. Lepidopterists' Soc.*, **19**, 227 (1965) vs. Petersen, B., *J. Lepidopterists' Soc.*, **18**, 165 (1964).

# II

# Distribution and Abundance

## DISTRIBUTION

The distribution of species was first studied on a geographic scale. Wallace (1876) and Schimper (1903) were the founders of the study of geographic distribution of animals and plants; more recent summaries are those of Hesse, Allee, and Schmidt (1937), Ekman (1953), Good (1964), Gleason and Cronquist (1964), Darlington (1957, 1965), and MacArthur and Wilson (1967). Within their geographic range, populations are located in particular habitats, and within these are usually aggregated into clumps of individuals. On this local scale, methods for measuring the kind and degree of spatial pattern, or dispersion, have been extensively studied. These methods have been summarized by Grieg-Smith (1964) and Southwood (1966).

Once the distribution of a species has been described, the next question is: what are the factors determining the distribution? In the books listed above, many hypotheses have been proposed to account for the geographic limits of a species, but none has been tested experimentally. Probably the most promising line of evidence comes from the transplanting of species to new locations. Thousands of species have been introduced, accidentally or deliberately, into new locations by winds and water currents in the distant past, or more recently, and at an increasing rate, by man. These experiments have shown that many species can live beyond their "natural" boundaries (Elton, 1958). However, many of these species have been moved without their enemies and competitors into areas disturbed by man. Few introduced species have become successfully established in natural communities (Harper, 1965). This suggests that if a species is not bounded by an uninhabitable environment (such as dry land to a fish), or stopped by a barrier to natural dispersal, its boundary is probably determined by competitors or enemies, rather than by purely physical factors. However no systematic experiments have yet been published which show, conclusively, which factors determine the limits of a geographic range of a species.

Dispersal, the mass movement of organisms, has been studied in certain groups of animals (birds, locusts, aphids, fish) and plants (seeds, pollen, phytoplankton). Studies of geographic dispersal are summarized in the books listed earlier and in Wolfenbarger (1946) and Southwood (1962).

Factors limiting the distribution of local populations are somewhat easier to determine. Measurement of the physical and chemical environment within and outside local aggregations may give indications of the kind and intensity of factors setting the local boundaries (Platt and Griffiths, 1964). Probably the best example of this is the determination of local distribution by soil characteristics, such as wetness and physical and chemical proportions (Oosting and Billings, 1942).

On the other hand the boundaries are often more abrupt than any changes in the physical environment, suggesting either that the physical limiting factor is transient (such as fire), or that biotic agencies may be limiting. Thus a predator may eliminate all individuals outside a safe refuge (Brooks and Dodson, 1965; Macan, 1965; Connell, 1970), or one species may displace a competitor completely from part of its habitable range (Connell, Selection 12; Muller, et al., Selection 13).

Within the area inhabited by a population, various patterns are possible. Individuals are seldom distributed randomly. Aggregation is the general rule, since some parts of the area are usually less suitable than others; within the aggregation, interference or aggression between individuals may cause them to be spaced rather uniformly, as in territorial birds (Howard, 1920; Nice, 1941), marine invertebrates (Connell, 1963) or plants (Pielou, Selection 11).

One school of thought regards the study of the distribution of species as inseparable from a study of abundance. Andrewartha and Birch (1954) feel that since the point where abundance declines to zero is also the limit of distribution, a study of the factors which determine when $r$ becomes negative will also reveal what limits the distribution of the species.

## ABUNDANCE

We distinguish here, rather arbitrarily, two sorts of approaches to questions of abundance. The first kind focuses on the single population and examines other aspects of the biotic and physical environment as they seem to become important to that population. The second kind of study examines interactions between populations and often focuses on processes or mechanisms which presumably underlie many situations. Clearly the approaches are not mutually exclusive and reflect mainly a difference in emphasis.

Ecologists ask a variety of questions about the numbers of organisms in populations. Of field populations they may ask: What prevents indefinite increase, that is, what limits populations? What causes most of

the observed fluctuations in time? Are populations stable and, if so, what factors or mechanisms contribute to their stability? Do local populations frequently become extinct? More generally, they may ask, what determines the numbers of organisms in populations in different places and at different times. It is unfortunately true that studies concerned with the control and regulation of populations have not generated much in the way of clear and unambiguous general theory. Discussions of theory are contained in Andrewartha (1961), Chitty (1960), Christian and Davies (1964), Lack (1966), Pimentel (1961), Solomon (1964), Richards (1961), and Wynne-Edwards (1962). The Cold Spring Harbor Symposium Volume 22 brings together a number of points of view, as do various volumes of the Annual Review of Entomology from 1960 onward. The following series of articles discusses various points of view concerning generalizations about population control: Hairston, Smith, and Slobodkin (1960), Murdoch (1966), Ehrlich and Birch (1967) and Slobodkin, Smith, and Hairston (1967). Questions such as those asked above lead to various kinds of studies. The most straightforward, though by no means technically the easiest approach, is to count the numbers of organisms in an area over an extended period of time and, where possible, to measure the mortality of different life stages, to assign causes to these mortalities, and to determine changes in birth rates and movements into and out of the population. Examples of such "life table" studies can be found in Morris (1963), Klomp (1966), and Perrins (1965). These studies vary in completeness, but even the most thorough, for example Morris (1963), are incomplete in several important respects. In fact, the latter study is an excellent illustration of how difficult it is to obtain a complete analysis of causal mechanisms by analyzing populations in nature. A valuable analytical tool which has evolved in these studies is "key factor" analysis (Morris, 1959; Varley and Gradwell, 1960; and Southwood, 1967). This allows one to pinpoint these environmental factors which, on the basis of correlation, "explain" various fractions of the observed variability in numbers through time. For several insect populations (e.g., Davidson and Andrewartha, 1958 and Klomp, 1966) the main key factor has been shown to be the weather, though Morris (1959) showed that parasitism by other insects was the important key factor in the black-headed budworm. Southwood (1966) contains a useful summary of various types of analyses of field data, as well as of many other topics in ecology.

In general, field experiments are difficult to do, but can be a powerful tool when combined with descriptive field studies. Selection 16 is an example. The study of population regulation, in particular, seems to have suffered from the absence of a conceptual framework which would have allowed an experimental approach (Nicholson, 1954 and Andrewartha, 1961, Chapter 9). A study of regulation concerns itself with mechanisms tending to return a population to an "equilibrium" value. There is disagreement as to whether or not regulation is widespread or important in nature (Andrewartha and Birch, 1954 and Ehrlich and Birch, 1967), but in populations where it is thought to occur, an experiment suggested by Nicholson (1957) provides new possibilities for analysis. In this experiment the density of parts of the population is either increased or decreased and one then studies the population to see if its various parts converge to the same density. Such convergence provides evidence for regulation (Solomon, 1964; Eisenberg, 1966). Another example of the use of field experiments in analyzing population dynamics can be found in Krebs (1966). Where experiments are impossible a great deal may be learned by comparing different populations (for example, Chitty, 1960).

An obvious response to the difficulties of field studies is to work in the laboratory. This is particularly advantageous when an investigator wants to concentrate his efforts on elucidating population mechanisms rather than accumulating historical records of the behavior of field populations. While such work has the advantage that experiments can be controlled, adequately repli-

cated, and analyzed accurately, it clearly suffers from the disadvantage of not being "natural." There is an enormous amount of literature on laboratory studies and we refer here to the major kinds of studies and only a few references. In general there are two types of studies. The first, we can call populational (Park, 1948 and Selection 21). Here either one or several species are maintained as populations under different treatments and are followed through time. The second type of study might be called analytical. These studies often are experiments of shorter duration and generally involve studying some process or mechanism outside of a strict population context. This type of experiment frequently is used to analyze relationships which emerge from field data.

Populational studies of single species are exemplified by the work of Gause (1964) on microorganisms and protozoa, Park, et al. (1964) and Mertz (1969) on *Tribolium,* Frank (Selection 17) and Slobodkin (1954 and 1960) on *Daphnia,* Slobodkin (1964) and Stiven (1959) on *Hydra,* and Southwick (1955) on small mammals.

Two major topics concerning interactions between populations are predation and competition. Various aspects of a mathematical theory of predation have been developed by Lotka (1956), Volterra (1931), Nicholson and Bailey (1935), and Leslie and Gower (1960). These authors have modeled the changes in numbers of prey and predator (or insect parasitoid) through time. (A parasitoid lays its eggs in the eggs or early stages of other organisms, generally other insects, and the young parasitoid develops in the body of the host and eventually kills it.) The first two authors developed the classical predator-prey equations which were examined experimentally by Gause (1964), using simple organisms. Nicholson and Bailey introduced time lags into the system, while Leslie developed stochastic models of predator-prey systems. This theoretical framework has given rise to a number of studies of populations of prey and predators (or parasitoids) in the laboratory, including those of Huffaker (1966), Utida (1950), Flanders (1968), and Salt (1967).

A recent development follows from the

simple observation that the amount of predation caused by a population is the number of prey killed per predator times the number of predators present. Both components can change in response to prey density and have been called, respectively, the functional and numerical response (Solomon, 1949). Holling (1965) has taken this analytical approach to predation and developed models of the functional response and has done experimental studies (Selection 19). Burnett (1964) and Takahashi (1968) also have done experiments on this problem and much of the recent work is summarized by Salt (1967). Field studies include Buckner and Turnock (1965). Predatory behavior in the presence of several prey species has been studied by Ivlev (1961), Landenberger (1968), and Murdoch (1969).

Few field analyses of predation are available. Some of the best are in the literature on applied ecology. For example Huffaker and Kennett (1966) have shown the efficacy of pest control by predators and parasites. Brooks and Dodson (1965) and Macan (1965) discuss the effects of fish predation on the composition of plankton. These studies, like that of Connell (1970), suggest that predators sometimes eliminate a species from most of its potentially inhabitable range, rather than control it at a low level. Predators may also influence the age structure of a prey population (Connell, 1961a, 1970).

Interspecies competition also has a classical mathematical theory (Gause, 1964), and again Leslie and Gower (1958) have examined stochastic models. A great deal of laboratory work has been done by Park and his co-workers (Park, Leslie, and Mertz, 1964), by Frank (1957), and by Harper (1967). Slobodkin (1964) has gone a stage further and combined a study of competition (between *Hydra* spp.) and predation. This paper includes a demonstration of a theoretical statement by Gause (1964) that predation can stabilize the outcome of competition. Predation may also prevent competitive exclusion by reducing the populations of the competitors so that resources are no longer limiting, as discussed by Connell (1961b) and Paine (1966).

Field work on competition has generally taken two forms. First, the role of competition in determining the distribution and abundance of species has been studied by observation, and occasionally by experiment (Connell, 1961b; Istock, 1966; Debach, 1966). This kind of study, together with mathematical and laboratory studies, has generated discussions of the role of competition in nature and the generality of "Gause's hypothesis" or the "competitive exclusion principle" (Hardin, 1960; DeBach, 1966). Second, these considerations have stimulated studies of the characteristics of potentially competing species and the role of competition in evolution. Examples are Hutchinson (1959) and Schoener (1965). These studies of "character displacement" and other aspects of competition clearly influence the kind of ideas which have been developed about the structure of communities, a subject which is taken up in Section III of this book.

J.H.C.<br>W.W.M.

### LITERATURE CITED

ANDREWARTHA, H. G. 1961. *Introduction to the Study of Animal Populations.* Phoenix Science Series. Univ. of Chicago Press, Chicago. 281 pp.

ANDREWARTHA, H. G., AND L. C. BIRCH. 1954. *The Distribution and Abundance of Animals.* Univ. of Chicago Press, Chicago. 782 pp.

BROOKS, J. L., AND S. I. DODSON. 1965. Predation, body size, and composition of plankton. Science *150:* 28-35.

BUCKNER, C. H., AND W. J. TURNOCK. 1965. Avian predation on the larch sawfly, *Pristiphora erichsonii* (Htg.), (Hymenoptera: Tenthridinidae). Ecology *46:* 223-236.

BURNETT, T. 1964. Host larval mortality in an experimental host-parasite population. Canadian Journal of Zoology *42:* 745-765.

CHITTY, D. 1960. Population processes in the vole and their relevance to general theory. Canadian Journal of Zoology *38:* 99-113.

CHRISTIAN, J. J., AND D. E. DAVIES. 1964. Endocrines, behavior, and population. Science *146:* 1550-1560.

CONNELL, J. H. 1961a. Effects of competition, predation by *Thais lapillus* and other factors on natural populations of the barnacle *Balanus balanoides.* Ecological Monographs *31:* 61-104.

CONNELL, J. H. 1963. Territorial behavior and dispersion in some marine invertebrates. Research in Population Ecology 5: 87-101.

CONNELL, J. H. 1970. A predator-prey system in the marine intertidal region. I. *Balanus glandula* and several predatory species of *Thais*. Ecological Monographs 40:(1).

DARLINGTON, P. J., JR. 1957. *Zoogeography: The Geographical Distribution of Animals*. Wiley, New York. 675 pp.

DARLINGTON, P. J., JR. 1965. *Biogeography of the Southern End of the World*. Harvard Univ. Press, Cambridge. 236 pp.

DAVIDSON, J., AND H. G. ANDREWARTHA. 1958. The influence of rainfall, evaporation and atmospheric temperature on fluctuations in the size of a natural population of *Thrips imaginis* (Thysanoptera). Journal of Animal Ecology 17: 200-222.

DEBACH, P. 1966. The competitive displacement and coexistence principles. Annual Review of Entomology 11: 183-212.

EHRLICH, P. R., AND L. C. BIRCH. 1967. The "balance of nature" and "population control." American Naturalist 101: 97-107.

EISENBERG, R. M. 1966. The regulation of density in a natural population of the pond snail, *Lymnaea elodes*. Ecology 47: 889-906.

EKMAN, S. P. 1953. *Zoogeography of the Sea*. Sidgwick, London. 417 pp.

ELTON, C. S. 1958. *The Ecology of Invasions by Animals and Plants*. Wiley, New York. 181 pp.

FLANDERS, S. E. 1968. Mechanisms of population homeostasis in *Anagasta* ecosystems. Hilgardia 39: 367-404.

FRANK, P. W. 1957. Coactions in laboratory populations of two species of *Daphnia*. Ecology 38: 510-519.

GAUSE, G. F. 1964. *The Struggle for Existence*. Hafner, New York. 163 pp.

GLEASON, H. A., AND A. CRONQUIST. 1964. *The Natural Geography of Plants*. Columbia Univ. Press, New York. 420 pp.

GOOD, R. 1964. *The Geography of the Flowering Plants*. 3rd ed. Wiley, New York. 518 pp.

GRIEG-SMITH, P. 1964. *Quantitative Plant Ecology*. Butterworths, Washington. 256 pp.

HAIRSTON, N. G., F. E. SMITH, AND L. B. SLOBODKIN. 1960. Community structure, population control, and competition. American Naturalist 94: 421-425.

HARDIN, GARRETT. 1960. The competitive exclusion principle. Science 131: 1292-1297.

HARPER, JOHN L. 1965. Establishment, aggression, and cohabitation in weedy species. In *The Genetics of Colonizing Species*. H. G. Baker and G. L. Stebbins, Eds. Academic Press, New York. pp. 243-265.

HARPER, J. L. 1967. A Darwinian approach to plant ecology. Journal of Animal Ecology 36: 495-518.

HESSE, RICHARD, W. C. ALLEE, AND K. P. SCHMIDT. 1937. *Ecological Animal Geography*. Wiley, New York. 597 pp.

HOLLING, C. S. 1965. The functional response of predators to prey density and its role in mimicry and population regulation. Memoirs of the Entomological Society of Canada 45: 5-60.

HOWARD, H. E. 1920. *Territory in Bird Life*. Atheneum, New York. 239 pp.

HUFFAKER, C. B. 1966. Competition for food by a phytophagous mite. Hilgardia 37: 533-567.

HUFFAKER, C. B., AND C. E. KENNETT. 1966. Studies of two parasites of Olive Scale *Parlatoria oleae* (Colvée): IV. Biological control of *Parlatoria oleae* (Colvée) through the compensatory action of two introduced parasites. Hilgardia 37: 283-335.

HUTCHINSON, G. E. 1959. Homage to Santa Rosalia, or why are there so many different kinds of animals. The American Naturalist 93: 145-159.

ISTOCK, C. A. 1966. Distribution, coexistence, and competition of whirligig beetles. Evolution 20: 211-233.

IVLEV, V. S. 1961. *Experimental Ecology of the Feeding of Fishes*. Yale Univ. Press, New Haven.

KLOMP, H. 1966. The dynamics of a field population of the pine looper, *Bupalis piniarius* L. (Lep. Geom.). Advances in Ecological Research 3: 207-305.

KREBS, C. J. 1966. Demographic changes in fluctuating populations of *Microtus californicus*. Ecological Monographs 36: 239-273.

LACK, D. 1966. *Population Studies of Birds*. Oxford Univ. Press, Oxford. 341 pp.

LANDENBERGER, D. E. 1968. Studies on selective feeding in the Pacific starfish *Pisaster* in Southern California. Ecology 49: 1062-1075.

LESLIE, P. H., AND J. C. GOWER. 1958. The properties of a stochastic model for two competing species. Biometrika 45: 316-330.

LESLIE, P. H., AND J. C. GOWER. 1960. The properties of a stochastic model for the predator-prey type of interaction between two species. Biometrika 47: 219-234.

LOTKA, A. J. 1956. *Elements of Mathematical Biology*. Dover, New York. 465 pp.

MACAN, T. T. 1965. Predation as a factor in the ecology of water bugs. Journal of Animal Ecology 34: 691-698.

MACARTHUR, R. H., AND E. O. WILSON. 1967. *The Theory of Island Biogeography*. Princeton Univ. Press, Princeton, N.J. 203 pp.

MERTZ, D. B. 1969. Age distribution and abundance in populations of flour beetles. I. Experimental studies. Ecological Monographs 39: 1-31.

MORRIS, R. F. 1959. Single-factor analysis in population dynamics. Ecology 40: 580-588.

MORRIS, R. F. (Ed.). 1963. The dynamics of epidemic spruce budworm populations. Memoirs of the Entomological Society of Canada 31: 1-332.

MURDOCH, W. W. 1966. "Community structure, population control, and competition"—a critique. American Naturalist 100: 219-226.

MURDOCH, W. W. 1969. Switching in general predators: experiments on predator specificity and stability of prey populations. Ecological Monographs *39:*(4).

NICE, M. M. 1941. The role of territory in bird life. American Midland Naturalist *26:* 441-487.

NICHOLSON, A. J. 1954. An outline of the dynamics of animal populations. Australian Journal of Zoology *2:* 9-65.

NICHOLSON, A. J. 1957. Comments on paper of T. B. Reynoldson. Cold Spring Harbor Symposium on Quantitative Biology *22:* 326.

NICHOLSON, A. J., AND V. A. BAILEY. 1935. The balance of animal populations. Part I. Proceedings of the Zoological Society of London 1935. 551-598.

OOSTING, H. J., AND W. D. BILLINGS. 1942. Factors affecting vegetational zonation on coastal dunes. Ecology *23:* 131-142.

PAINE, R. T. 1966. Food web complexity and species diversity. American Naturalist *100:* 65-75.

PARK, T. 1948. Experimental studies of interspecies competition. I. Competition between populations of the flour beetles *Tribolium confusum* Duval and *Tribolium castaneum* Herbst. Ecological Monographs *18:* 265-308.

PARK, T., P. H. LESLIE, AND D. B. MERTZ. 1964. Genetic strains and competition in populations of *Tribolium*. Physiological Zoology *37:* 97-162.

PERRINS, C. M. 1965. Population fluctuations and clutch size in the great tit, *Parus major* L. Journal of Animal Ecology *34:* 601-647.

PIMENTEL, D. 1961. Animal population regulation by the genetic feed-back mechanism. American Naturalist *95:* 65-79.

PLATT, R. B., AND J. F. GRIFFITHS. 1964. *Environmental Measurement and Interpretation.* Reinhold Publishing Corp., New York. 235 pp.

RICHARDS, O. W. 1961. The theoretical and practical study of natural insect populations. Annual Review of Entomology *6:* 147-162.

SALT, G. W. 1967. Predation in an experimental protozoan population (*Woodruffia-Paramecium*). Ecological Monographs *37:* 113-144.

SCHIMPER, A. F. W. 1903. *Plant Geography Upon a Physiological Basis* (Translated by W. R. Fisher). Clarendon Press, Oxford. (1960 ed., H. R. Engelmann, Weinheim). 839 pp.

SCHOENER, T. W. 1965. The evolution of bill size differences among sympatric congeneric species of birds. Evolution *19:* 189-213.

SLOBODKIN, L. B. 1954. Population dynamics in *Daphnia obtusa* Kurtz. Ecological Monographs *24:* 69-88.

SLOBODKIN, L. B. 1960. Ecological energy relationships at the population level. American Naturalist *94:* 213-236.

SLOBODKIN, L. B. 1964. Experimental populations of Hydrida. Journal of Animal Ecology, a symposium supplement *33:* 131-148.

SLOBODKIN, L. B., F. E. SMITH, AND N. G. HAIRSTON. 1967. Regulation in terrestrial ecosystems and the implied balance of nature. American Naturalist *101:* 109-123.

SOLOMON, M. E. 1949. The natural control of animal populations. Journal of Animal Ecology *18:* 1-35.

SOLOMON, M. E. 1964. Analysis of processes involved in the natural control of insects. Advances in Ecological Research *2:* 1-58.

SOUTHWICK, C. H. 1955. The population dynamics of confined house mice supplied with unlimited food. Ecology *36:* 212-225.

SOUTHWOOD, T. R. E. 1962. Migration of terrestrial arthropods in relation to habitat. Biological Reviews *37:* 171-214.

SOUTHWOOD, T. R. E. 1966. *Ecological Methods.* Methuen, London. 391 pp.

SOUTHWOOD, T. R. E. 1967. The interpretation of population change. Journal of Animal Ecology *36:* 519-529.

STIVEN, A. E. 1959. The relationship between size, budding rate, and growth efficiency in three species of *Hydra*. Researches on Population Ecology *7:* 1-15.

TAKAHASHI, F. 1968. Functional response to host density in a parasitic wasp, with reference to population regulation. Researches on Population Ecology *10:* 54-68.

UTIDA, S. 1950. On the equilibrium state of the interacting population of an insect and its parasite. Ecology *31:* 165-175.

VARLEY, G. C., AND G. L. GRADWELL. 1960. Key factors in population studies. Journal of Animal Ecology *29:* 399-401.

VOLTERRA, V. 1931. In translation in Chapman, R. N., *Animal Ecology*. McGraw-Hill, New York. 464 pp.

WALLACE, A. R. 1876. *The Geographical Distribution of Animals.* 1962 ed. Hafner, New York.

WOLFENBARGER, D. O. 1946. Dispersion of small organisms. American Midland Naturalist *35:* 1-152.

WYNNE-EDWARDS, V. C. 1962. *Animal Dispersion in Relation to Social Behavior.* Oliver and Boyd, Edinburgh. 653 pp.

Reprinted from *Ecology*, Vol. 34, No. 4, October, 1953

# EXPERIMENTAL BACKGROUND TO THE STUDY OF THE DISTRIBUTION AND ABUNDANCE OF INSECTS

## I. THE INFLUENCE OF TEMPERATURE, MOISTURE AND FOOD ON THE INNATE CAPACITY FOR INCREASE OF THREE GRAIN BEETLES.[1]

L. C. Birch

*Zoology Department, University of Sydney*

## INTRODUCTION

It is well known that in nature many species of insects vary in numbers from place to place at any one time, and in any one place their numbers fluctuate with the seasons. They tend to increase in numbers in favourable places or if we consider their numbers in one place they tend to increase during favourable seasons and to decrease during unfavourable seasons. Distribution from place to place and abundance at different times are two aspects of the one fundamental problem.

Other things being equal species which can increase in numbers rapidly during the favourable periods will be more abundant than those which increase in numbers slowly. Thompson (1939) was aware of this and he pointed out that "the complex of factors which actually affect control in the case of any one species differs in composition from point to point and year to year in the area of distribution." Davidson and Andrewartha (1948) were able to identify the major factors determining numbers of *Thrips imaginis* in South Australia as they fluctuated from season to season. In any one year the number reached was a race against time, depending chiefly upon the extent of the favourable season. On the average the physical environment remained favourable for too short a period for the insects to increase to a point where competition became important. The complex of factors causing fluctuations in this and other natural populations can only be discovered by the ecologist who is prepared to study the natural population of insects in the field. Nevertheless, certain concepts derived from laboratory experiments can form a useful background for such field studies.

One such concept is the innate capacity a species has to increase in numbers. A species which has a high capacity for increasing in numbers may reach larger numbers in favourable situations (or in favourable seasons) than the species with a low capacity for increase. In a previous paper (Birch 1948) reasons were given for choosing, as the most appropriate measure of an insect's innate capacity for increase, the index which Lotka (1925) called "the intrinsic rate of natural increase."

The intrinsic rate of natural increase $(r)$ is the infinitesimal rate of increase which a population of *stable age distribution* would have when growing in a constant environment in which space was unlimited:

$$\frac{dN}{dt} = rN.$$

or in the integrated form:

$$N_t = N_o e^{rt}$$

where $N_o$ is the number of animals at time zero and $N_t$ is the number of animals at time $t$.

The *stable age distribution* is a particular sort of age distribution; its characteristics have been discussed elsewhere (e.g. Lotka 1925, Birch 1948), and need not be discussed at this point.

Notwithstanding the fact that natural populations never possess a stable age distribution nor a stable environment the innate capacity for increase $(r)$ is a very useful concept for background experimental studies on distribution and abundance of animals in the field. In this

[1] This investigation was aided by a grant from the Commonwealth Research Grant to the University of Sydney.

paper it is shown how the magnitude of $r$ may be influenced by temperature, moisture and food in the case of three grain beetles. All other components of the environment of these beetles have been kept constant, including the density of insects in the grain, which has been kept constant at an optimum in all experiments.

The effect of temperature and moisture on the innate capacity for increase $r$ has been studied on the two beetles *Calandra oryzae* L. (small strain) and *Rhizopertha dominica* Fab. The study has covered the whole range of temperature and the greater part of the range of moisture within which these species can survive. The reason for the choice of species in this set of experiments is that *R. dominica* is typically a "tropical" species compared to *C. oryzae* which occurs in colder regions. It was hoped that this study might form a basis for understanding the different distribution and abundance of two such different species.

The effect of food (wheat and maize) on the intrinsic rate of natural increase has been studied on the two beetles *C. oryzae* (small strain) and *C. oryzae* (large strain) and at one combination of temperature (29.1°C) and relative humidity (70%). The two beetles are not inter-fertile and so they are really true sibling species though they have not yet been described as separate species (Birch 1944). The reason for choosing them in this experiment with different foods is that the small strain commonly occurs in stored wheat in Australia, but it has not been found in stored maize. On the other hand the large strain commonly occurs in maize but it has not been found in stored wheat. Yet both species breed in either wheat or maize in the laboratory. It was hoped that a study of the influence of food on their relative capacities for increase might throw some light on their distribution and abundance or at any rate serve as a basis for such studies. The temperature and moisture chosen for the experiments were within the optimum for the two beetles.

By means of studies on these three beetles I hope to show in this and subsequent papers how a knowledge of the innate capacity for increase and the way it is influenced by various components of the environment can contribute to an understanding of the distribution and abundance of animals.

The use of the intrinsic rate of natural increase in defining precisely tolerance ranges and therefore the limits to distribution of a species is dealt with in some detail. Only one aspect of its use in problems of abundance within the zone of tolerance is considered in this paper and that is when the only limiting factor to increase is the time available in which conditions are favourable for increase in numbers. The influence of crowding, both by the same and other species on the rate of increase is a consideration of subsequent papers. In those more complex conditions the index $r$ may serve still as a valuable basis for study.

## EXPERIMENTAL PROCEDURE AND RESULTS

The insects used in all experiments were obtained from stock cultures which had been maintained for several months under constant conditions. Cultures of both strains of *C. oryzae* were kept at 29.1° C and 70% relative humidity in both wheat and maize; *R. dominica* was cultured at 32.3° C and 70% relative humidity in wheat. The temperature of experiments was controlled to ±0.1° C. Humidity was kept constant with saturated salt solutions and also with sulphuric acid solutions of appropriate concentration.

The intrinsic rate of natural increase of the three species under various experimental conditions has been determined from three sets of experimental data: the life table or $l_x$ table, the duration of development of the immature stages and the age schedule of female births or $m_x$ data. The life table gives the proportions of individuals alive at the beginning of arbitrarily chosen age intervals from birth to the death of the last individual in the population. The age schedule of female births is the number of female births (or eggs laid which would develop into females if they survived to maturity) for each parental age group such as one, two and three weeks of age. For any particular age group of pivotal age $x$, $m_x$ is the number of female births. In the case of the insects used in these experiments $m_x$ is the weekly number of eggs divided by two since only half the eggs are destined to become females. The insect is conveniently considered to be of zero age as a newly laid egg. The age of the newly emerged adult can therefore only be known when the duration of the immature stages of egg, larva, prepupa and pupa is known.

The procedure used for determining the life table and the age schedule of fecundity is given together with the results in the following subsections. The combination of these data to give the intrinsic rates of natural increase of the insects is given in the later section.

### The Life Table

In estimating the intrinsic rate of natural increase over a wide range of temperature and humidity it was not necessary to determine the adult life table for every temperature and humidity studied. Preliminary estimates of $r$ at different temperatures and humidities indicated that differences in the adult life tables made little difference to the value of $r$ when the total mortality of the immature stages was greater than 50 per cent. It was necessary, of course, to determine the mortality of the immature stages under all combinations of temperature, moisture, and food for which values of $r$ were required. This information is shown in columns three of Tables III, IV and V. Some of the data were obtained from Birch (1945a), the rest of the data were obtained by the same procedure described in this earlier paper. On the basis of these data on mortality of immature stages the following set of conditions was selected for determining the life tables of adults:

| Species | Temp.° C | Relative humidity | Grain |
|---|---|---|---|
| C. oryzae (small strain) | 29.1 | 70 | Wheat |
| C. oryzae (small strain) | 29.1 | 70 | Maize |
| C. oryzae (small strain) | 32.3 | 70 | Wheat |
| C. oryzae (large strain) | 29.1 | 70 | Wheat |
| C. oryzae (large strain) | 29.1 | 70 | Maize |
| R. dominica | 32.3 | 70 | Wheat |

A total of 800 newly emerged adults (0-15 hours old) was used in each experimental determination of a life table. The beetles were obtained from stock cultures which had been kept for several months at the same temperature and humidity and with the same food as in the experiment. Each lot of 800 adults was divided into 20 replicates of 40 insects, each in 12 grams of grain. This was equivalent to a density of one insect per 10 grains of wheat and one insect per 0.8 grains of maize. Because of the difficulty of sexing the living beetles no attempt was made to sex the beetles until after they had died in the experiment.

The insects and grain were kept in 4" x 1" glass tubes covered at the open end with phosphor-bronze gauze. These were kept in incubators at a constant temperature and humidity. The tubes were examined weekly for dead insects; these were then removed, sexed and counted. Throughout the experiment the population density in each tube was kept constant, so far as possible, by replacing dead insects with living ones from the highest-numbered tube, to bring the others back to a total of 40 insects per tube. Thus the number of tubes became reduced during the experiments but the density of insects remained reasonably constant. At two-weekly intervals the grain was completely replaced with new grain.

Since the beetles were not sexed at the beginning of the experiments the sexes were not represented by exactly the same numbers. The only serious inequality of numbers occured in the experiments with the small strain of C. oryzae in wheat and in maize where final analysis revealed about twice as many females as males. Previous workers on insect life tables

TABLE I. The mean length of life in weeks of adults of three grain beetles at 70% relative humidity.

| Species | Temp. °C | Food | Male | | | Female | | |
|---|---|---|---|---|---|---|---|---|
| | | | Mean | s.d. | C.V. | Mean | s.d. | C.V. |
| C. oryzae (Small Strain)............ | 29.1 | Wheat | 16.58 | 7.27 | 44 | 17.05 | 6.86 | 40 |
| C. oryzae (Small Strain)............ | 29.1 | Maize | 28.93 | 11.14 | 39 | 23.18 | 7.85 | 34 |
| C. oryzae (Small Strain)............ | 32.3 | Wheat | 10.78 | 5.44 | 50 | 10.70 | 3.87 | 36 |
| C. oryzae (Large Strain)............ | 29.1 | Wheat | 19.63 | 7.73 | 39 | 18.13 | 7.23 | 40 |
| C. oryzae (Large Strain)............ | 29.1 | Maize | 25.22 | 10.83 | 43 | 18.33 | 8.37 | 46 |
| R. dominica..................... | 32.3 | Wheat | 19.67 | 5.03 | 26 | 17.21 | 5.91 | 34 |

s.d.=standard deviation.          C.V.=coefficient of variability.

have adopted the practice of keeping the sexes separate. This was not done in these experiments as we wished to know the length of life of the insects under the sorts of conditions existing in a laboratory culture. For the purposes of estimating $r$ we are only interested in the life table of the female but the life table of the male has also been determined because of its general interest.

The mean length of life of adults is shown in Table I; the coefficients of variability are of the usual order for such data. Males had a greater longevity than females in four out of six experiments. In the remaining two experiments the longevity of the two sexes was about the same. These results are discussed below. The longevity of both strains of C. oryzae is greater in maize than in wheat with the exception of the female of the large strain which has about the same mean length of life in wheat and in maize. The rela-

tive increase in longevity in maize is greatest for males and is greatest for the male of the small strain which lives 12 weeks longer in maize; this is a surprisingly large increase.

The life tables are shown in Table II and in Figures 1 to 6 (complete lines).

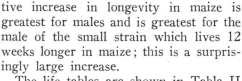

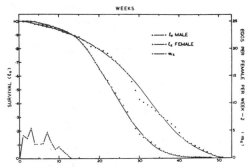

FIG. 2. The adult survival rate and the fecundity of the small strain of Calandra oryzae at 29.1° C in maize of 13% moisture content. The $l_x$ curves show the life tables of adults. The $m_x$ curve shows the number of eggs laid per female per week ÷ 2.

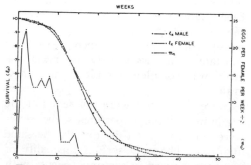

FIG. 1. The adult survival rate and the fecundity of the small strain of Calandra oryzae at 29.1° C in wheat of 14% moisture content. The $l_x$ curves show the life tables of adults. The $m_x$ curve shows the number of eggs laid per female per week ÷ 2.

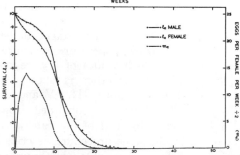

FIG. 3. The adult survival rate and the fecundity of the small strain of Calandra oryzae at 32.3° C in wheat of 14% moisture content. The $l_x$ curves show the life tables of adults. The $m_x$ curves show the number of eggs laid per female per week ÷ 2.

TABLE II. Life tables of adult grain beetles. The figures in the body of the table show the proportion of beetles alive ($l_x$) at the beginning of each age interval $x$. (See Figs. 1-6.)

| Species | C. oryzae Small strain | | C. oryzae Small strain | | C. oryzae Small strain | | C. oryzae Large strain | | C. oryzae Large strain | | R. dominica | |
|---|---|---|---|---|---|---|---|---|---|---|---|---|
| Temperature °C | 29.1 | | 29.1 | | 32.3 | | 29.1 | | 29.1 | | 32.3 | |
| Humidity % | 70 | | 70 | | 70 | | 70 | | 70 | | 70 | |
| Food | Wheat | | Maize | | Wheat | | Wheat | | Maize | | Wheat | |
| No. of Insects | 205 | 543 | 205 | 550 | 388 | 373 | 300 | 517 | 304 | 443 | 352 | 372 |
| Age in Weeks | Male | Female | Male | Female | Male | Female | Male | Female | Male | Female | Male | Female |
| 0 - 1 | 1.000 | 1.000 | 1.000 | 1.000 | 1.000 | 1.000 | 1.000 | 1.000 | 1.000 | 1.000 | 1.000 | 1.000 |
| 1 - 2 | .993 | .996 | .998 | 1.000 | .950 | .976 | .995 | 1.000 | .996 | .995 | 1.000 | .997 |
| 2 - 3 | .987 | .991 | .995 | 1.000 | .902 | .954 | .994 | .999 | .992 | .988 | 1.000 | .988 |
| 3 - 4 | .975 | .983 | .987 | .999 | .864 | .937 | .988 | .999 | .983 | .978 | 1.000 | .978 |
| 4 - 5 | .969 | .978 | .979 | .996 | .846 | .926 | .977 | .992 | .974 | .968 | .999 | .969 |
| 5 - 6 | .959 | .971 | .971 | .987 | .816 | .905 | .959 | .983 | .961 | .954 | .998 | .966 |
| 6 - 7 | .955 | .961 | .964 | .976 | .785 | .882 | .939 | .970 | .955 | .938 | .994 | .958 |
| 7 - 8 | .945 | .942 | .959 | .965 | .744 | .853 | .926 | .959 | .950 | .914 | .990 | .949 |
| 8 - 9 | .937 | .921 | .953 | .958 | .707 | .819 | .916 | .940 | .946 | .891 | .985 | .935 |
| 9 - 10 | .911 | .887 | .946 | .953 | .650 | .754 | .902 | .918 | .937 | .866 | .977 | .922 |
| 10 - 11 | .873 | .848 | .933 | .946 | .568 | .644 | .884 | .890 | .924 | .839 | .968 | .906 |
| 11 - 12 | .818 | .797 | .921 | .936 | .478 | .504 | .855 | .851 | .907 | .807 | .953 | .879 |
| 12 - 13 | .759 | .748 | .913 | .922 | .388 | .365 | .815 | .799 | .887 | .771 | .937 | .837 |
| 13 - 14 | .697 | .692 | .906 | .905 | .318 | .248 | .775 | .750 | .860 | .733 | .915 | .778 |
| 14 - 15 | .634 | .644 | .895 | .887 | .263 | .170 | .745 | .694 | .836 | .688 | .894 | .707 |
| 15 - 16 | .550 | .579 | .883 | .861 | .221 | .108 | .716 | .639 | .807 | .634 | .839 | .624 |
| 16 - 17 | .483 | .529 | .860 | .830 | .178 | .068 | .685 | .578 | .784 | .583 | .760 | .545 |
| 17 - 18 | .419 | .478 | .841 | .793 | .139 | .037 | .648 | .523 | .756 | .536 | .659 | .477 |
| 18 - 19 | .385 | .410 | .816 | .747 | .102 | .020 | .603 | .467 | .731 | .498 | .584 | .434 |
| 19 - 20 | .312 | .385 | .803 | .695 | .073 | .013 | .556 | .403 | .708 | .447 | .522 | .391 |
| 20 - 21 | .243 | .324 | .793 | .646 | .050 | .009 | .503 | .342 | .679 | .402 | .475 | .351 |
| 21 - 22 | .181 | .265 | .782 | .602 | .032 | .005 | .456 | .293 | .637 | .349 | .418 | .301 |
| 22 - 23 | .159 | .226 | .764 | .564 | .026 | .004 | .414 | .260 | .595 | .307 | .358 | .254 |
| 23 - 24 | .145 | .197 | .736 | .518 | .023 | .003 | .376 | .235 | .556 | .266 | .297 | .196 |
| 24 - 25 | .129 | .169 | .707 | .472 | .020 | .002 | .340 | .212 | .523 | .235 | .237 | .150 |
| 25 - 26 | .109 | .129 | .678 | .427 | .014 | .001 | .280 | .185 | .489 | .203 | .167 | .097 |
| 26 - 27 | .098 | .097 | .648 | .382 | .006 | .000 | .218 | .160 | .457 | .172 | .105 | .060 |
| 27 - 28 | .088 | .078 | .618 | .336 | .002 | .... | .162 | .135 | .425 | .144 | .054 | .029 |
| 28 - 29 | .080 | .068 | .553 | .269 | .000 | .... | .136 | .109 | .398 | .126 | .003 | .015 |
| 29 - 30 | .070 | .059 | .491 | .215 | .... | .... | .120 | .088 | .370 | .105 | .016 | .010 |
| 30 - 31 | .062 | .049 | .426 | .171 | .... | .... | .109 | .071 | .350 | .088 | .012 | .005 |
| 31 - 32 | .055 | .038 | .405 | .152 | .... | .... | .075 | .059 | .336 | .071 | .010 | .003 |
| 32 - 33 | .049 | .028 | .386 | .133 | .... | .... | .040 | .045 | .317 | .063 | .008 | .001 |
| 33 - 34 | .044 | .018 | .369 | .116 | .... | .... | .009 | .032 | .289 | .058 | .004 | .000 |
| 34 - 35 | .041 | .010 | .343 | .094 | .... | .... | .004 | .024 | .254 | .051 | .001 | |
| 35 - 36 | .037 | .003 | .315 | .070 | .... | .... | .003 | .020 | .217 | .042 | .000 | |
| 36 - 37 | .031 | .000 | .291 | .048 | .... | .... | .003 | .015 | .189 | .033 | | |
| 37 - 38 | .023 | .... | .272 | .037 | .... | .... | .003 | .010 | .161 | .027 | | |
| 38 - 39 | .017 | .... | .247 | .029 | .... | .... | .002 | .005 | .147 | .020 | | |
| 39 - 40 | .013 | .... | .223 | .020 | .... | .... | .001 | .003 | .121 | .014 | | |
| 40 - 41 | .012 | .... | .181 | .013 | .... | .... | .000 | .001 | .099 | .008 | | |
| 41 - 42 | .010 | .... | .145 | .010 | .... | .... | .... | .000 | .071 | .006 | | |
| 42 - 43 | .010 | .... | .115 | .008 | .... | .... | .... | .... | .057 | .005 | | |
| 43 - 44 | .010 | .... | .101 | .006 | .... | .... | .... | .... | .041 | .004 | | |
| 44 - 45 | .010 | .... | .088 | .005 | .... | .... | .... | .... | .032 | .030 | | |
| 45 - 46 | .010 | .... | .072 | .004 | .... | .... | .... | .... | .024 | .002 | | |
| 46 - 47 | .009 | .... | .059 | .002 | .... | .... | .... | .... | .018 | .002 | | |
| 47 - 48 | .005 | .... | .044 | .001 | .... | .... | .... | .... | .011 | .001 | | |
| 48 - 49 | .002 | .... | .029 | .000 | .... | .... | .... | .... | .004 | .001 | | |
| 49 - 50 | .000 | .... | .015 | .... | .... | .... | .... | .... | .001 | .000 | | |
| 50 - 51 | .... | .... | .005 | .... | .... | .... | .... | .... | .000 | | | |
| 51 - 52 | .... | .... | .000 | | | | | | | | | |

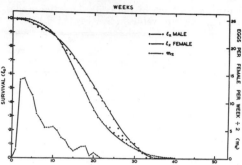

FIG. 4. The adult survival rate and the fecundity of the large strain of *Calandra oryzae* at 29.1° C in wheat of 14% moisture content. The $l_x$ curves show the life tables of adults. The $m_x$ curves show the number of eggs laid per female per week ÷ 2.

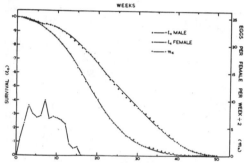

FIG. 5. The adult survival rate and the fecundity of the small strain of *Calandra oryzae* at 29.1° C in maize of 13% moisture content. The $l_x$ curves show the life tables of adults. The $m_x$ curves show the number of eggs laid per female per week ÷ 2.

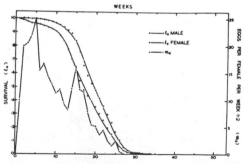

FIG. 6. The adult survival rate and the fecundity of *Rhizopertha dominica* at 32.3° C in wheat of 14% moisture content. The $l_x$ curves show the life tables of adults. The $m_x$ curves show the number of eggs laid per female per week ÷ 2.

They were constructed from the weekly records of deaths of males and females.

Weekly survival is represented as a fraction of unity, hence survival at birth is represented by 1 and zero survival by 0. The data were smoothed by obtaining three weekly moving averages. It is these values which are shown in the tables and figures. Free-hand curves have been drawn through the plotted points but the three-weekly moving averages were used in the subsequent calculation of $r$. There seemed to be no particular merit in fitting mathematical expressions to the life tables and so this was not done.

Figures 1 to 6 show that the death rate of the adult was initially low in all experiments. It reached a maximum about the middle of the life span and decreased again towards the end of the life span. This is quite typical of a number of life tables of animals (c.f. Deevey 1947). In contrast *Tribolium confusum* (Pearl, Park, and Miner 1941) and the black widow spider (Deevey and Deevey 1945) are characterized by heavy mortality in the early life of the adult.

### Age-specific Fecundity Rates

The number of eggs laid per female during each week of life has been determined for each combination of temperature and moisture shown in Tables III, IV, and V. The way in which this information was obtained has been described by Birch (1945b). It is only necessary to add that the fecundity of *C. oryzae* was determined at a density of one insect per ten grains of wheat and one insect per fifteen grains of maize. Ten pairs of insects were used in each experiment. With *R. dominica* twenty-five pairs were used at a density of one insect in four grains. Since fecundity was not very much greater at densities lower than these (Birch 1945b) we can safely assume that the rates correspond reasonably closely with those at the optimum density.

The age-specific fecundity rates for the six sets of conditions under which life tables were also obtained are shown in Figures 1-6. The data for the remaining experiments are not shown in detail since

TABLE III. Showing the effect of temperature and moisture on the innate capacity of the small strain of *C. oryzae* to increase in numbers in wheat. (Data in last column shown in Fig 8.)

| Temp. °C | Percent moisture content of wheat | Percent[1] mortality immature stages | Total[2] number of eggs laid per female | Duration[3] of development egg to adult (weeks) | Mean length of a generation in weeks (T) | Rate of multiplication per generation (R$_0$) | Intrinsic rate of natural increase (r) | | Finite rate of increase per female per week (λ) |
|---|---|---|---|---|---|---|---|---|---|
| | | | | | | | Approximate estimate | Accurate estimate | |
| 13.0 | 14 | 100 | 0 | . . . | . . . | 0 | − ∞ | − ∞ | 0 |
| 15.2 | 14 | 75 | 1/week | 32.9 | 39.2 | 1.23 | 0.005 | 0.005 | 1.007 |
| 18.2 | 14 | 12 | 4/week | 15.5 | 20.4 | 17.32 | 0.133 | 0.140 | 1.15 |
| 23.0 | 14 | 10 | 266 | 6.1[5] | 10.6 | 96.58 | 0.360 | 0.430 | 1.54 |
| 25.5 | 14 | 7 | 384 | 4.9 | 7.6 | 101.30 | 0.500 | 0.605 | 1.83 |
| 29.1 | 14 | 10 | 344 | 4.0 | 6.4 | 134.18 | 0.560 | 0.772 | 2.15 |
| 32.3 | 14 | 65 | 197 | 4.1 | 6.9 | 31.38 | 0.424 | 0.501 | 1.65 |
| 33.5 | 14 | 75 | 27 | 9.4 | 10.4 | 3.38 | 0.120 | 0.120 | 1.13 |
| 34.0 | 14 | 97 | . . | . . . | . . . | . . . . . | . . . . . | . . . . . | . . . . |
| 35.0 | 14 | 100 | 5 | . . . | . . . | 0 | − ∞ | − ∞ | 0 |
| 15.2 | 12 | 100 | 0 | . . . | . . . | 0 | − ∞ | − ∞ | 0 |
| 23.0 | 12 | 40[4] | 80 | 5.7 | 9.9 | 20.31 | 0.280 | 0.303 | 1.35 |
| 29.1 | 12 | 36[4] | 75 | 4.3 | 7.5 | 20.79 | 0.349 | 0.406 | 1.50 |
| 33.5 | 12 | 88 | 20 | 9.4 | 10.7 | 1.14 | 0.001 | 0.001 | 1.00 |
| 34.0 | 12 | 100 | 0 | . . . | | 0 | − ∞ | − ∞ | 0 |
| 15.2 | 11 | 100 | 0 | . . . | . . . | 0 | − ∞ | − ∞ | 0 |
| 18.2 | 11 | 86 | 21 | 16.1 | 19.5 | 1.30 | 0.013 | 0.013 | 1.10 |
| 25.5 | 11 | 64 | 72 | 5.2 | 8.5 | 13.81 | 0.279 | 0.310 | 1.36 |
| 29.1 | 11 | 38 | 66 | 4.4 | 8.3 | 17.98 | 0.310 | 0.350 | 1.42 |
| 33.5 | 11 | 97 | 0 | . . . | . . . | 0 | − ∞ | − ∞ | 0 |
| 18.2 | 10.5 | 99 | 0 | . . . | . . . | 0 | − ∞ | − ∞ | 0 |
| 25.5 | 10.5 | 88 | 16 | 5.7 | 8.6 | 1.77 | 0.067 | 0.067 | 1.07 |
| 29.1 | 10.5 | 76 | 10 | 4.3 | 7.1 | 0.75 | − 0.041 | −0.041 | 0.96 |
| 32.3 | 10.5 | 100 | . . | . . . | . . . | 0 | − ∞ | − ∞ | 0 |
| 15-35 | 10.0 | 100 | . . | . . . | . . . | 0 | − ∞ | − ∞ | 0 |

[1] Data from Birch (1945a).      [2] Data from Birch (1945b).      [3] Data from Birch (1945c).
[4] Interpolated from Birch (1945d).      [5] Interpolated from Birch (1945c).

they are extensive and of little interest except as a step in the estimation of *r*. Instead the total number of eggs is shown in column 4 of Tables III, IV, and V.

From Figures 1-6 (especially Figs. 2 and 5) and the data summarised in Table VI, it would appear that the last egg was always laid long before the last female died. But the $l_x$ and $m_x$ curves may not be compared in this way because the former are based on samples of 400 insects and the latter on samples of 10 female *Calandra* and 25 female *Rhizopertha*. The larger sample, by virtue of its size alone, is more likely to include long-lived individuals.

### THE INNATE CAPACITY FOR INCREASE

In order to calculate the innate capacity for increase *r* it is necessary to

know: (a) the life-table, (b) the duration of development of the immature stages, (c) the age specific fecundity rates. These data are not given in full for all the conditions of temperature and humidity studied because that would be cumbersome. Complete information is given for six examples; these are shown in Figures 1-6 and Tables III, IV, and V. The rest of the data given in Tables III, IV, and V are sufficient to indicate how the components of *r* vary with temperature, moisture and food.

A number of useful indices besides *r* have been calculated from these data. Methods of estimation have been given in full by Birch (1948) and these are repeated in outline below.

The intrinsic rate of natural increase *r*,

TABLE IV. Showing the effect of temperature and moisture on the innate capacity of *R. dominica* to increase in numbers in wheat. (Data in last column shown in Fig. 8.)

| Temp. °C | Percent moisture content of wheat | Percent[1] mortality immature stages in sound grain | Total[2] number of eggs laid per female | Duration[3] of development egg to adult (weeks) | Mean length of a generation in weeks (T) | Rate of multiplication per generation (R$_0$) | Intrinsic rate of natural increase (r) Approximate estimate | Intrinsic rate of natural increase (r) Accurate estimate | Finite rate of increase per female per week (λ) |
|---|---|---|---|---|---|---|---|---|---|
| 18.3 | 14 | 100 | 38+ | ... | ... | 0 | − ∞ | − ∞ | 0 |
| 29.0 | 14 | 26 | 288[4] | 4.6 | 7.6 | 97.05 | 0.439 | 0.578 | 1.78 |
| 32.3 | 14 | 21[4] | 573[5] | 4.0 | 7.0 | 123.39 | 0.517 | 0.686 | 1.99 |
| 34.0 | 14 | 22 | 415 | 3.5 | 6.5 | 141.69 | 0.562 | 0.762 | 2.14 |
| 38.2 | 14 | 86 | 97 | 5.2 | 7.1 | 8.04 | 0.288 | 0.294 | 1.34 |
| 38.6 | 14 | 100 | ... | ... | ... | 0 | − ∞ | − ∞ | 0 |
| 18.3 | 11 | 100 | 45 | ... | ... | 0 | − ∞ | − ∞ | 0 |
| 22.0 | 11 | 89 | 181 | 13.4 | 19.6 | 7.83 | 0.120 | 0.105 | 1.11 |
| 38.2 | 11 | 91 | 113 | 6.6 | 8.7 | 4.55 | 0.174 | 0.174 | 1.19 |
| 38.6 | 11 | 100 | ... | ... | ... | 0 | − ∞ | − ∞ | 0 |
| 22.0 | 10 | 100 | 132 | 13.4 | ... | 0 | − ∞ | − ∞ | 0 |
| 26.0 | 10 | 85 | 256 | 5.1 | 12.0 | 18.58 | 0.216 | 0.243 | 1.28 |
| 34.0 | 10 | 77 | 295 | 5.0 | 8.9 | 30.00 | 0.334 | 0.383 | 1.47 |
| 36.0 | 10 | 88 | 172 | 5.6 | 9.6 | 12.15 | 0.238 | 0.261 | 1.30 |
| 38.2 | 10 | 100 | 52 | 6.6 | ... | 0 | − ∞ | − ∞ | 0 |
| 30.0 | 9 | 100 | ... | ... | ... | 0 | − ∞ | − ∞ | 0 |
| 34.0 | 9 | 98 | 315 | 5.0 | 8.7 | 16.38 | 0.280 | 0.321 | 1.38 |
| 36.0 | 9 | 100 | 160 | 5.6 | ... | 0 | − ∞ | − ∞ | 0 |
| 18-38 | 8 | 100 | ... | ... | ... | 0 | − ∞ | − ∞ | 0 |

[1] Data from Birch (1945a).   [2] Data from Birch (1945b) except 29.1° and 32.3°C at 14 p.c. moisture content.
[3] Data from Birch (1945c).   [4] Interpolated from Birch (1945d).   [5] Additional experimental estimate.

TABLE V. Showing the effect of food (wheat and maize) on the innate capacity for increase of the small and large strains of *C. oryzae* at 29.1° C and 70% relative humidity. At this humidity wheat had a moisture content of 14% and maize had a moisture content of 13%.

| Strain | Food | Percent mortality immature stages in grain | Total number of eggs per female | Duration of development, egg to adult (weeks) | Mean length of a generation in weeks (T) | Rate of multiplication per generation (R$_0$) | Mean duration of life of adult female in weeks | Intrinsic rate of natural increase (r) Approximate estimate | Intrinsic rate of natural increase (r) Accurate estimate | Finite rate of increase per female per week (λ) |
|---|---|---|---|---|---|---|---|---|---|---|
| Small | Wheat | 10 | 344[1] | 4.0 | 6.4 | 134.18 | 17.05 | 0.560 | 0.772 | 2.15 |
| Small | Maize | 13 | 70 | 5.0 | 8.2 | 30.53 | 23.18 | 0.348 | 0.417 | 1.52 |
| Large | Wheat | 10 | 208[1] | 4.4 | 8.0 | 89.43 | 18.13 | 0.436 | 0.564 | 1.76 |
| Large | Maize | 34.6 | 154 | 4.9 | 8.8 | 46.71 | 18.33 | 0.359 | 0.436 | 1.55 |

[1] Segrove (1951) records a higher total fecundity of the large strain compared with the small strain in England in wheat at 25°C and 70 % relative humidity.

(Columns 8 and 9, Tables III and IV; Columns 9 and 10, Table V):

An accurate estimate of *r* was obtained from the following relationship:

$$\int_0^\infty e^{-rx} l_x m_x dx = 1$$

TABLE VI. The relation between length of life of females and the ages at which 50% and 100% of eggs were laid.

| Species | Temp. °C | Food | Percentage of females alive in the longevity experiments | |
|---|---|---|---|---|
| | | | At age when 50 p.c. of eggs had been laid in fecundity experiment | At age when last egg had been laid in fecundity experiment |
| C. oryzae (small strain).......... | 29.1 | Wheat | 98 | 64 |
| C. oryzae (small strain).......... | 29.1 | Maize | 99 | 94 |
| C. oryzae (small strain).......... | 32.3 | Wheat | 93 | 37 |
| C. oryzae (large strain).......... | 29.1 | Wheat | 99 | 29 |
| C. oryzae (large strain).......... | 29.1 | Maize | 95 | 69 |
| R. dominica................... | 32.3 | Wheat | 94 | 15 |

where $l_x$ is the proportion of individuals alive at the beginning of the age interval $x$ and $m_x$ is the number of female births for the particular age group of pivotal age $x$.

An approximate short-cut estimate of $r$ (see Birch 1948) is also shown in Tables III, IV, and V but this method is only of sufficient accuracy when $r$ has a low value not exceeding about 0.200 (see Columns 8 and 9, Tables III and IV; Columns 9 and 10, Table V).

The finite rate of increase per female per week ($\lambda$), (last column, Tables III, IV, and V):

The finite rate of increase is the multiplication per female per week which a population of stable age distribution would have when increasing in a constant environment in which space was unlimited. $\lambda$ is derived from the intrinsic rate of increase $r$ by the following relationship:

$$\lambda = \text{antilog }_e r.$$

We shall use $\lambda$ as our expression of the innate capacity for increase rather than $r$ since it is an easier concept for the non-mathematical ecologist to grasp. A ready conversion of $r$ to $\lambda$ covering the values given in Tables III, IV, and V is given in Figure 7.

The multiplication per generation ($R_0$), (Column 7, Tables III, IV, and V):

$$R_0 = \Sigma \, l_x \, m_x$$

The mean length of a generation ($T$), (Column 6, Tables III, IV, and V).

$$T = \frac{\log_e R_0}{r}$$

*The effect of temperature and moisture on the finite rate of increase of the small strain of* C. oryzae *and* R. dominica.

The finite rates of increase ($\lambda$) of C. oryzae and R. dominica which are shown in the final columns of Tables III and IV have been plotted in Figure 8. The points on the graph indicate the combinations of temperature and moisture for which values of $\lambda$ have been obtained. To avoid confusion the actual values of $\lambda$ at these points are not shown but isopleths have been drawn through points of equal value of $\lambda$. The lines show the way in which temperature and moisture differentially affect the innate capacity for increase of the two species.

For each species there is a particular zone of temperature and moisture within which the capacity for increase is great-

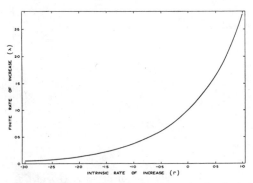

FIG. 7. The relationship between the intrinsic rate of natural increase $r$ and the finite rate of natural increase $\lambda$. ($\lambda =$ antilog$_e r$)

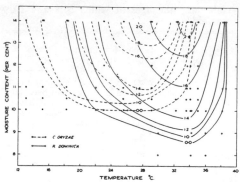

FIG. 8. The finite rate of increase (λ) of *Calandra oryzae* (small strain) and *Rhizopertha dominica* living in wheat of different moisutre contents and at different temperatures. (See final columns of Tables III and IV.)

est. This is the zone within the isopleth λ = 2. There is also a zone beyond which no increase can occur at all: this is defined by the isopleth λ = 1 (*r* = 0). When λ = 1 the species cannot increase but it could maintain its numbers from generation to generation. The isopeth for λ = 0 (*r* = − ∞) defines the zone in which no insects of reproductive age would be added to the population because the death rate of immature stages is 100%. Between the zero isopleth and the isopleth for unity (*r* is negative) the death rate exceeds the birth rate and although some eggs are laid the death rate is so high that the population eventually dies out. The rate at which it dwindles is directly proportional to the value of λ.

Some indication of the relative importance of birth rate and death rate in determining any particular value of λ in these experiments can be gained from a glance at the columns for total fecundity (column 4) and death rate (column 3) in Tables III and IV. For example, *R. dominica* invariably continued to lay some eggs under conditions in which none of the eggs survived. This is true of *C. oryzae* at some temperatures in wheat of 14% moisture content, but in drier wheat a temperature which caused 100% mortality in the immature stages also prevented adults from laying any eggs.

Various deductions can be made from Figure 8 about the possible distribution

and abundance of the two species. It is clear that *R. dominica* can invade drier and hotter wheat than can *C. oryzae*. On the other hand *C. oryzae* can increase in numbers in wheat which is so cold that *R. dominica* cannot survive. The relative geographic distribution of the two species will therefore be related to the relative positions of the zero boundaries in Figure 8.

The known distribution of the two species in nature confirms these deductions. For example *R. dominica* is virtually absent from the coldest state of Australia (Tasmania) whereas *C. oryzae* is quite common there. *R. dominica,* on the other hand has been known to become a serious pest in the warmer mainland when wheat was stored for periods of a year or more (Wilson 1945).

The area within the isopleth λ = 1 (Fig. 8) defines the zones of temperature and moisture which are tolerable for survival of populations of these insects. Theoretically numbers could increase indefinitely at any combination of temperature and moisture within this boundary provided other factors of the environment were not limiting. But the rate at which numbers increased within this zone would vary tremendously depending upon the particular value of λ. It would be fastest when λ was a maximum.

The effect of temperature and moisture

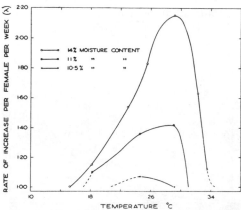

FIG. 9. The finite rate of increase (λ) of *Calandra oryzae* living in wheat of different moisture contents and at different temperatures. (See final columns of Table III.)

on the innate capacity for increase of *C. oryzae* in the tolerable zone is shown in Figure 9. In wheat of 14% moisture content there is a curvilinear relationship between temperature and the innate capacity for increase, the curve drops sharply after it reaches a peak. The theoretical number of individuals at the end of *n* weeks is given by $\lambda^n$. For example, at 15.2° C one female would give rise to $(1.007)^{10} = 2$ females and 2 males. In the same time at 29.1° C one female would give rise to $(2.15)^{10} = 2014$ females and the same number of males. In other words in 10 weeks at 29.1° C the population would be 2000 times greater than it would be in the same time at 15.2° C.

Similar comparisons might be made between the two species in the same environment. Figure 8 shows that in wheat of 14% moisture content *C. oryzae* has a greater innate capacity for increase than *R. dominica* at all temperatures up to 31° C. At 31° C the value of $\lambda$ is the same for both species ($\lambda = 1.8$), but at temperatures higher than 31° C *R. dominica* has a greater innate capacity for increase than *C. oryzae*. As the moisture content of wheat drops *R. dominica* gains the ascendency at lower temperatures. This is shown in Figure 8 by the way in which the intersections of isopleths for the same value of $\lambda$ are further to the left at the lower moisture contents. This information is summarised in Table VII which shows the combinations of temperature and moisture at which the isopleths for values of $\lambda$ from 1 to 1.8 intersect in Figure 8.

The importance of small differences in temperature on the relative rates of increase of populations of the two species is illustrated in the following examples for insects living in wheat of 14% moisture content:

> In 10 weeks at 29.1° C one female of *R. dominica* gives rise to $(1.78)^{10} = 319$ females.
>
> In 10 weeks at 29.1°C one female of *C. oryzae* gives rise to $(2.14)^{10} = 2014$ females.

TABLE VII. Showing combinations of temperature and moisture at which *R. dominica* and the small strain of *C. oryzae* have the same innate capacity for increase ($\lambda$). (See Fig. 8).

| Finite rate of increase ($\lambda$) | Temp. °C | Moisture content % of wheat |
|---|---|---|
| 1.8 | 30.0 | 10.3 |
| 1.6 | 28.3 | 12.0 |
| 1.4 | 24.5 | 11.7 |
| 1.2 | 21.5 | 12.8 |
| 1.0 | 23.5 | 13.0 |

> In 10 weeks at 32.3° C one female of *R. dominica* gives rise to $(2.0)^{10} = 1024$ females.
>
> In 10 weeks at 32.3° C one female of *C. oryzae* gives rise to $(1.65)^{10} = 150$ females.

In these examples an increase of 3.2° C causes a threefold increase in numbers of *R. dominica* but a 13-fold decrease in numbers of *C. oryzae*.

We have discussed the way in which the innate capacity for increase varies for the two species within the zone of tolerance (*i.e.*, where $\lambda$ exceeds unity). Species do not, of course, go on increasing indefinitely in nature at these rates. This does not necessarily mean that this information is of little use as a guide to possible abundance of different species in nature. Its possible application can be illustrated by a hypothetical model. We might imagine a situation in which food and space were relatively unlimited but the time during which temperature, moisture and other factors were favourable for increase (*i.e.*, $\lambda$ exceeded 1) was limited to a short period in each year. During this favourable period a species which had a high value of $\lambda$ would reach higher numbers than one which had a low value of $\lambda$. It would be called a common species by comparison. In this simplified model we would expect presence and absence of a species to be related to its innate capacity for increase and within its range of tolerance commonness and rareness would be related to the innate capacity for increase. This model is, of course, an abstraction from nature. There, all sorts of factors operate together to determine abundance. But it may nevertheless represent one important aspect of what happens in some natural populations.[1]

### The effect of food on the finite rate of increase of the small and large strains of C. oryzae.

The small and large strains of C. oryzae both breed readily in maize as well as in wheat in laboratory cultures, although the small strain appears to be confined to wheat and the large strain confined to maize in field stores of grain. It would seem that the type of food has some influence on distribution and abundance. The innate capacity for increase of the two species in both sorts of grain has therefore been determined as basic data for studying this problem.

The information necessary for the estimation of $r$ (and $\lambda$) was obtained for both beetles in wheat and maize at 29.1° C at a relative humidity of 70%. At this humidity wheat had a moisture content of 14% and maize had a moisture content of 13%. There was thus a difference in moisture content of the two sorts of grain as well as a difference in quality. The method of obtaining the information for the estimation of $r$ (and $\lambda$) was the same as that already described. The results are shown in Figures 1, 2, 4 and 5, and in Table V. The last column of the table shows the innate capacity for increase expressed as the finite rate of increase $\lambda$.

The small strain has a much higher innate capacity for increase in wheat than in maize. The large strain has also a higher innate capacity for increase in wheat compared with maize but the difference is much smaller. Comparison of the two beetles in the same sort of grain shows that the small strain has a higher innate capacity for increase than the large strain in wheat. But in maize the reverse is true; the large strain has a higher innate capacity for increase than the small strain. In other words, under the conditions of these experiments, maize favours

---

[1] Since writing this a nice example has been provided by Howe (1953).

the large strain and wheat favours the small strain. We would, of course, need much more information than this from which to draw any conclusions about distribution and abundance, but this much information does suggest that at a favourable temperature and humidity the large strain would have an initial advantage over the small strain in maize and vice versa in wheat. Other factors may also work in the direction of favouring the small strain in wheat and the large strain in maize and some of these are being investigated.

Since Table V and Figures 1, 2, 4 and 5 give the components of birth rate and death rate which determine the values of $\lambda$, they can be used to indicate which components of the innate capacity for increase are largely responsible for the differences in $\lambda$ shown in the last column of Table V. For example, the reduction of $\lambda$ for the small strain in maize as compared with wheat is primarily due to a tremendous reduction in the number of eggs laid in maize (Figs. 1 and 2, Table V column 4), and the slower development of the immature stages in maize (Table V column 5). The mortality of the immature stages is about the same in both grains but it is surprising to find that the length of life of adults is greater in maize than in wheat (Table V column 8).

We have already pointed out that the reduction in the value of $\lambda$ for the small strain in maize compared with wheat is greater than the corresponding comparison for the large strain. This is primarily due to the greater reduction of fecundity of the small strain in maize. The reduction in fecundity of the large strain in maize is so much less that the large strain has a higher value of $\lambda$ despite its higher mortality.

These differences of the innate capacities of the two strains in wheat and maize are recorded in the absence of any additional data which might explain them. The reduction of fecundity in maize is possibly due to its greater hardness and the difficulty of boring oviposition holes into the hard surface. But this possibility has not yet been investigated.

## Acknowledgments

Dr H. G. Andrewartha of the Waite Institute, University of Adelaide, kindly read the manuscript and made a number of valuable suggestions much to its improvement. Thanks are due to Miss W. Doran for technical assistance in the experiments and in making the figures.

## Conclusion and Summary

Although numerous studies have been made on the various components of birth rate and death rate of insects and other animals, this appears to be the first in which all the components of birth rate and death rate necessary for the estimation of the innate capacity for increase have been determined over the complete range of temperature tolerable and over a wide range of moisture. Data are given on the precise effect of temperature and moisture on the innate capacity for increase of the small strain of *C. oryzae* and *R. dominica* at an optimum density of insects in wheat. Data are also provided on the effect of wheat and maize on the innate capacity for increase of the large and small strains of *C. oryzae*.

The significance of this information is that it provides background experimental data for studies on distribution and abundance.

The limits of distribution of the beetles are determined, so far as temperature and moisture are concerned, by the combinations of temperature and moisture beyond which the finite rate of increase ($\lambda$) is less than 1 (the intrinsic rate of increase $r$ is negative).

Within the zone of temperature and moisture tolerable for the insects, their abundance, under certain circumstances, may be related to the innate capacity for increase (expressed either as $\lambda$ or $r$.). Only certain aspects of this larger problem are considered in this paper, in particular the relationship between $\lambda$ and abundance when the limiting factor for increase is the length of time during which

conditions are favourable for increase (*i.e.,* when $\lambda$ is greater than 1). When time is the only limiting factor then we would expect to find a relationship between abundance and the value of $\lambda$. Other factors such as crowding, parasites and competitors are a further complication; some of these factors are considered in a forthcoming paper.

Data on the innate capacity for increase of *C. oryzae* and *R. dominica* show that the temperatures tolerable for increase are lower for *C. oryzae* than *R. dominica*. *R. dominica* can also tolerate drier wheat. This corresponds with the known distribution of these species in Australia.

The two strains of *C. oryzae* can breed in wheat and in maize in the laboratory, but the large strain has only been found in maize and the small strain has only been found in wheat in stores in the field. At a favourable temperature and humidity (29.1° C and 70% relative humidity) in the laboratory, the innate capacity for increase of the small strain is greater than that of the large strain. But the reverse is true in maize. This may be one of a number of factors which combine to make the small strain common in wheat and the large strain common in maize.

From tables showing birth rates (age-specific fecundity rates) and death rates (the adult life table and mortality rates of immature stages) it can be seen how temperature, moisture and food influence the components of the innate capacity for increase. The combinations of temperature and moisture which result in a drastic reduction in birth rate also cause a drastic increase in death rate. The influence of food appears to be different. Maize causes a great reduction in birth rate compared with wheat in both strains of *C. oryzae* but the increase in the death rate is quite small for the small strain though appreciable for the large strain. The combined effect is that the small strain has a much higher innate capacity for increase in wheat than in maize. The large strain has a slightly higher innate capacity for increase in wheat as compared with maize.

Some data additional to that necessary for the estimation of the innate capacity for increase have been provided in this paper. The complete life tables of adult males and females were determined under six different sets of conditions, although only the life table of the female during her egg laying life is required for the estimation of $\lambda$. In four out of six experiments males had a greater longevity than females. This result contrasts with previous studies on longevity of other insects where males have been shown to have a shorter life than females (*e.g.*, Deevey 1947; Pearl, Park, and Miner 1941). But in these latter experiments males and females were kept separately. In the experiments described in this paper they were kept together and under these circumstances females lay many more eggs than do virgin females. It is possible that the extra drain on the resources imposed by egg-laying shortens the life of the female compared to what it would be for a virgin female.

The longevity of the small strain of *C. oryzae* was much greater in maize than in wheat. The same was true of males of the large strain. But there was little difference in longevity of females of the large strain in wheat and maize.

Whereas longevity was increased in maize the fecundity of the small and large strains of *C. oryzae* was very much less in maize than in wheat. This is possibly due to the greater hardness of maize and the consequent difficulty in boring oviposition holes. Comparison of the life table and the fecundity table suggests that a large proportion of females lived for weeks after they would have laid their last eggs. This result may, however, be an artifact since smaller numbers of insects were used in obtaining the age-fecundity data compared with large numbers used in obtaining the life table.

## REFERENCES

Birch, L. C. 1944. Two strains of *Calandra oryzae* L. (Coleoptera). Aust. J. Exp. Biol. & Med. Sci., 22: 271-275.

————. 1945a. The mortality of the immature stages of *Calandra oryzae* L (small strain) and *Rhizopertha dominica* Fab in wheat of different moisture contents. Aust. J. Exp. Biol. and Med. Sci., 23: 141-145.

————. 1945b. The influence of temperature, humidity and density on the oviposition of the small strain of *Calandra oryzae* L and *Rhizopertha dominica* Fab. Aust. J. Exp. Biol. and Med. Sci., 23: 197-203.

————. 1945c. The influence of temperature on the development of the different stages of *Calandra oryzae* L and *Rhizopertha dominica* Fab. Aust. J. Exp. Biol. and Med. Sci., 23: 29-35.

————. 1945d. A contribution to the ecology of *Calandra oryzae* and *Rhizopertha dominica* Fab. (Coleoptera) in stored wheat. Trans. Roy. Soc. South Aust., 69: 140-149.

————. 1948. The intrinsic rate of natural increase of an insect population. J. Animal Ecol., 17: 15-26.

Davidson, J. and H. G. Andrewartha. 1948. The influence of rainfall, evaporation and atmospheric temperature on fluctuations in the size of a natural population of *Thrips imaginis* (Thysanoptera). J. Animal Ecol. 17: 200-222.

Deevey, G. B., and E. S. Deevey. 1945. A life table for the black widow. Trans. Conn. Acad. Arts and Sci., 36: 115-134.

Deevey, E. S. 1947. Life tables for natural populations of animals. Quart. Rev. Biol., 22: 283-314.

Howe, R. W., 1953. Studies on beetles of the family Ptinidae VIII. The intrinsic rate of increase of some Ptinid beetles. Ann. Appl. Biol., 40: 121-134.

Lotka, A. J. 1925. Elements of physical biology. Baltimore: Williams & Wilkins.

Pearl, R., T. Park, and J. R. Miner. 1941. Experimental studies on the duration of life. XVI. Life tables for the flour beetle *Tribolium confusum* Duval. Amer. Nat., 75: 5-19.

Segrove, F. 1951. Oviposition behaviour in the two strains of the rice weevil, *Calandra oryzae*. Linn (Coleoptera, Curculionidae). J. Exp. Biol., 28: 281-297.

Thompson, W. R. 1939. Biological control and the theories of the interactions of populations. Parasitology, 31: 299-388.

Wilson, F. 1945. The control of insect pests in Victorian Bulk Wheat Depots. Journ. C.S.I.R., 18: 103-109.

Reprinted from *J. Ecol.* **48**, 575-584, October 1960

# A SINGLE MECHANISM TO ACCOUNT FOR REGULAR, RANDOM AND AGGREGATED POPULATIONS

By E. C. PIELOU

*West Summerland, British Columbia*

*(With one Figure in the Text)*

## I. INTRODUCTION

In studying the spatial arrangement of natural populations of plants it has been customary to distinguish three types of distribution or pattern: random, aggregated and regular. The individuals of a species are said to be at random if the position of each individual plant is independent of that of all the others; aggregated populations are those in which there is a tendency for the individuals of the species to occur in clumps; and in regular populations the plants are more evenly spaced than they would be were they distributed according to chance.

Aggregated populations have been found to be very common in nature and two causes have been suggested for this aggregation (Feller 1943). On the one hand seeds may fall at random over an area but if the habitat is not homogeneous the proportion germinating and thriving will vary from site to site so that the density is high in some sites and low in others. On the other hand the habitat may be homogeneous but the individual plants may occur in family groups owing to the fact that they reproduce vegetatively or by seeds with small radius of dispersal. Feller (1943) has shown that it is impossible, by statistical methods alone, to distinguish between these two causes of aggregation; in any case, both might well be operating simultaneously.

Regular populations appear to be extremely rare. According to Greig-Smith (1957) a regular pattern would be expected to occur if the members of a population were so abundant that they competed with each other for the available space. A frequency table obtained by quadrat-sampling such a population should be well graduated by a binomial series, as was done, for instance, by Student (1907) who considered the distribution of yeast cells in the squares of a haemacytometer.

Several frequency functions have been used to graduate the results obtained by quadrat-sampling aggregated populations, those most favoured being the negative binomial (Greenwood & Yule 1920, Bliss & Fisher 1953), Neyman's type A (Neyman 1939, Archibald 1948) and Thomas's double Poisson (Thomas 1949, Archibald 1950). In none of these, however, is the necessarily finite size of the individual plants taken into account. In studying aggregated plant populations allowance for the effects of plant size appears to have been made only by Skellam (1952) who calculated a distribution based on the assumption that clumps of plants (of the species being investigated) occurred at random but *within* a clump the individuals exhibited a positive binomial distribution owing to the effects of competition. This series has since been named the Poisson Binomial by McGuire, Brindley & Bancroft (1957).

E. C. Pielou is now with the Department of Biology, Queen's University, Kingston, Ontario.

There seems, then, to have been a fundamental difference of approach to the study of regular and of aggregated populations. In the former case the finite size of the plants has been taken into account whereas in the latter it has been disregarded. Further, as will be shown later, a dense population of plants of appreciable size will be regular only if the range in size of the plants is small.

It seemed of interest, therefore, to consider what type of distribution might be shown by a population of large, long-lived plants, reproducing by seed, such as forest trees. It was assumed that the seeds were distributed independently of each other in space and sequentially in time over a homogenous area, and grew into trees of various sizes as would happen in nature. In making synthetic models of such a population the further assumptions were made that each 'tree' would have a circular root system with the trunk at the centre and that no other tree could establish itself within the area already pre-empted by the root system of an earlier arrival. The diameters of the root systems were allowed to vary between pre-assigned limits. It will be shown that this mechanism can give rise to regular, random or aggregated populations, the type obtained depending on both the density and the range of size of the circles representing the root systems.

## II. Model Populations

### (1) *Construction of the models*

In making model populations the range of size for the circles ('root systems') was first chosen. Points ('seeds') were then placed at random on a sheet of graph paper by means of random co-ordinates and around each, as it was placed, a circle was drawn. Each circle was made as large as the available space allowed (that is, it was not allowed to overlap previously drawn circles) subject to the restriction that its radius must lie between the pre-assigned limits. Any point falling within a previously drawn circle, or so close to one that a circle centred on it would have a radius smaller than the minimum permitted, was deleted. Three sets of models were made, each on a sheet of 400 sq. units. In the set A the radii of the circles ranged from 0·2 to 0·7 units; in set B from 0·1 to 1·0 units; and in set C from 0·1 to 2·0 units. Within each set populations of various densities were constructed and the suffixes attached to the capital letter denoting each set shows the density of that model. Thus $A_1$ was the least dense model of Set A.

### (2) *Quadrat-sampling of the models*

To determine the type of distribution of the models, each was sampled with randomly thrown square quadrats. The figure recorded for each quadrat was the number of circle-*centres* (representing centres of 'tree trunks') inside it. Two sizes of quadrat were used on all but two of the models; on these, three sizes of quadrat were used. The quadrats were thrown down at random rather than being placed in a grid because of the finite size of the individuals forming the populations. Had the quadrats been contiguous a populous one would necessarily have had sparsely filled ones adjacent to it since the circles whose centres lay in the populous quadrat would have overlapped the adjacent quadrats. Throwing the quadrats at random ensured their mutual independence. In all cases 100 quadrats were used and the area sampled was 324 sq. units as a one unit wide border around each sheet was ignored.

As a preliminary test of each population's pattern the variance/mean ratios of the quadrat results were calculated. The expected value of this ratio in a random population is unity and its standard error is $\sqrt{2/(n-1)}$ (Greig-Smith 1957). Thus with $n = 100$ and using a 5% significance level values of variance/mean less than 0·716 indicate regularity of the population, values between the limits 0·716 and 1·284 indicate randomness and values greater than 1·284 aggregation. The results of these tests are given in Table 1.

Table 1. *The Variance/mean ratio (V/m) obtained by sampling each model with* 100 *quadrats*

| Model | 4·41 sq. unit quadrats | | 1·96 sq. unit quadrats | | 1·00 sq. unit quadrats | |
|---|---|---|---|---|---|---|
| | mean | V/m | mean | V/m | mean | V/m |
| $A_1$ | 2·27 | 0·527 | 1·00 | 0·480 | | |
| $A_2$ | 2·59 | 0·472 | 1·16 | 0·564 | | |
| $A_3$ | 3·13 | 0·368 | 1·26 | 0·343 | | |
| $A_4$ | 3·77 | 0·429 | 1·71 | 0·401 | | |
| $A_5$ | 4·60 | 0·309 | 2·18 | 0·499 | | |
| $B_1$ | 2·66 | 0·573 | 1·36 | 0·669 | | |
| $B_2$ | 3·94 | 0·745* | 1·85 | 0·512 | | |
| $B_3$ | 4·75 | 0·566 | 2·10 | 0·519 | | |
| $B_4$ | 5·76 | 0·632 | 2·58 | 0·746* | 1·32 | 0·650 |
| $B_5$ | 6·90 | 0·601 | 3·03 | 0·953* | 1·73 | 1·027* |
| $B_6$ | | | 3·75 | 0·903* | 1·87 | 1·002* |
| $B_7$ | | | 4·20 | 1·081* | 2·18 | 0·884* |
| $C_1$ | 2·54 | 1·405** | 1·25 | 1·046* | | |
| $C_2$ | 3·40 | 1·865** | 1·28 | 1·423** | | |
| $C_3$ | 4·56 | 2·304** | 2·19 | 1·760** | | |

\* V/m test indicates that the model is random.
\*\* V/m test indicates that the model is aggregated.

As may be seen, the models of set A remained regular even though the density was increased until the sheet was almost filled. With set B, however, in which the permitted range of circle size was larger, the variance/mean ratio increased with increasing density until for high densities it did not differ significantly from unity, suggesting that these populations were random. In the set C, that with the largest range of circle sizes, apparently aggregated populations were finally obtained, and the degree of aggregation increased with increasing density. This aggregation resulted from the crowding of small, late-placed circles in the gaps between the large circles placed on the sheet first. Fig. 1 shows part of model $C_3$ in which this type of pattern may be observed.

Those models for which the variance/mean test indicated a regular pattern were not tested further. Population $B_5$, which appeared random from this test with the two smaller quadrat sizes used, was then tested by fitting Poisson series to the observed frequency tables. The results are given in full in Table 2.

Clearly the observations are very well fitted by the Poisson series. It follows that if quadrat sampling only were used (provided the quadrats were not too large) this population would be indistinguishable from a truly random one made by placing points of infinitesimal size independently of one another on the sheet.

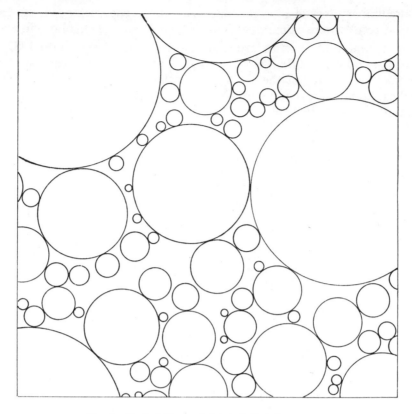

Fig. 1. Part of the model population $C_3$.

It has often been noticed (Archibald 1948) that in natural aggregated populations quadrat sampling will give a low proportion of quadrats containing a single individual compared with a random population of the same density. However, in the model populations for which the variance/mean ratio significantly exceeded unity the opposite was true in all but one case as shown in Table 3.

Table 2. *Comparisons of quadrat results from model* $B_5$ *and Poisson series having the same means*

| Quadrat size = 1·96 sq. units Mean = 3·03 | | | Quadrat size = 1·00 sq. units Mean = 1·73 | | |
|---|---|---|---|---|---|
| | Frequency | | | Frequency | |
| Individuals per quadrat | Observed | Expected | Individuals per quadrat | Observed | Expected |
| 0 | 7 } | 19·48 | 0 | 17 | 17·75 |
| 1 | 11 } | | 1 | 32 | 30·67 |
| 2 | 22 | 22·18 | 2 | 27 | 26·51 |
| 3 | 23 | 22·39 | 3 | 15 | 15·29 |
| 4 | 18 | 16·96 | 4 | 5 } | |
| 5 | 10 | 10·28 | 5 | 2 } | 9·78 |
| 6 | 6 } | 8·71 | 6 | 2 } | |
| 7 | 3 } | | | | |

$$\chi^2 = 0.212$$
$$P(\chi^2/4) > 0.99$$

$$\chi^2 = 0.727$$
$$P(\chi^2/3) = 0.8\text{-}0.9$$

## (3) *Tests based on distance-measurements*

One of the populations that seemed random (from the variance/mean test) and two that seemed aggregated, namely $B_5$, $C_2$ and $C_3$ respectively, were subjected to tests based on distance measurements. Two such tests were used.

In the first, 100 random points were placed on each model (not in the excluded one unit wide border) and the distance from each point to the individual nearest it

Table 3. *Comparison of the observed proportions of one-individual quadrats in the aggregated models, with the proportions expected in random populations of the same means*

| Model | Quadrat size (sq. units) | Mean number of individuals per quadrat | Proportion of quadrats with one individual | |
|---|---|---|---|---|
| | | | Observed | Expected |
| $C_1$ | 4·41 | 2·54 | 0·29 | 0·20 |
| $C_2$ | 1·96 | 1·28 | 0·31 | 0·36 |
| $C_2$ | 4·41 | 3·40 | 0·28 | 0·11 |
| $C_3$ | 1·96 | 2·19 | 0·30 | 0·24 |
| $C_3$ | 4·41 | 4·56 | 0·22 | 0·05 |

measured; (hereafter the word 'individual' will be used to denote the centre of one of the circles of which the populations consisted). Denoting by $\overline{\omega}_p$ the mean of the squares of these distances, $\alpha_p = \pi D \overline{\omega}_p$ was then calculated, where $D$ is the density independently known. If the population is random $\alpha_p$ has an expected value of $(n-1)/n^*$ and $2n\alpha_p$ is distributed like $\chi^2$ with $2n$ degrees of freedom (Pielou 1959). A value of $\alpha_p$ significantly greater than expectation indicates aggregation, and significantly less, regularity.

If, and only if, a population is truly random, the results obtained by measuring from random individuals to their nearest neighbours are indistinguishable from the results of measuring from random points to their nearest individuals. So an alternative test consists in calculating $\alpha_i = \pi D \overline{\omega}_i$ where $\overline{\omega}_i$ is the mean of the squares of individual-to-neighbour distances. As before, the expected value of $\alpha_i$ in a random population is $(n-1)/n^*$ but a larger value denotes regularity and a

Table 4. *Comparison of $\alpha_p$ and $\alpha_i$ for three of the models*

(The number in brackets after each entry is $n$, the number of distances measured.)

| | Model | | |
|---|---|---|---|
| | $B_5$ | $C_2$ | $C_3$ |
| $\alpha_p$ | 0·835 (100) | 1·121 (100) | 1·210 (100) |
| $\alpha_i$ | 1·663 (262) | 1·472 (260) | 1·345 (182) |

smaller value aggregation. If a population is aggregated in the sense that it consists of clumps of individuals, but if at the same time the within-clump distribution is regular owing to the finite size of the individuals, the $\alpha_p$ test should reveal the large-scale clumping and the $\alpha_i$ test the small-scale regularity. In applying the $\alpha_i$ test to the models distances were measured from all individuals in model $C_2$; in the more populous models $B_5$ and $C_3$ distances were measured from all the individuals on half the sheet. In all cases, as with the quadrat sampling, a border one unit wide around each sheet was excluded to avoid possible edge effects.

The results of these tests are shown in Table 4. It will be seen that $\alpha_i$ indicated

---

* M. D. Mountford, in a more recent article, "On E. C. P.'s index of non-randomness," *J. Ecol.*, **49**, 271–275 (1961), corrected this error. The correct value should be 1, not $(n-1)/n$.

regularity in all three models; this resulted from the fact that an individual's distance from its nearest neighbour could never be less than the diameter of the smallest circles in the population. It is also noteworthy that the $\alpha_p$ test is less sensitive to aggregation than the variance/mean ratio obtained by quadrat sampling. The value of $\alpha_p$ for $C_3$ is only just significant of aggregation at the 5 % level and for $C_2$ this test indicates randomness although the variance/mean test had shown it was aggregated.

### (4) *Discussion of findings on the models*

The results of all the tests taken together show that if a population is built up in the manner suggested it may be random, regular or aggregated, the type depending on both the size-range of the circles and the density. Moreover, different tests will lead to different conclusions. In any case, the trichotomy into 'regular', 'random' and 'aggregated' populations is meaningless and to determine whether this mechanism is responsible, in part at least, for the pattern of a natural population, other tests must be sought.

It was obvious, for instance, that in the models the distance from an individual to its nearest neighbour was positively correlated with the sum of the radii of the individual and the neighbour; the distance could never be less than the sum of the radii, and if the two circles were touching was equal to the sum. Evidence for such correlation was sought in a natural population of *Pinus ponderosa* Laws. Further study of the models seemed unrewarding owing to the three very artificial assumptions made in constructing them: that each individual occupied a perfect circle; that the maximum and minimum possible sizes were the same for each circle and that each would grow to occupy the whole available space instantaneously.

### III. A *PINUS PONDEROSA* POPULATION

#### (1) *Description of the population*

The natural population investigated consisted of *P. ponderosa* Laws. individuals forming an open woodland free of undergrowth. No other tree species was present. *P. ponderosa* is a common pine at low altitudes in the dry interior valleys of British Columbia, and, owing to the aridity of its habitat, never forms dense stands. In the area studied the sizes of the individual trees were very variable, the trunk circumferences ranging from 5 to 261 cm. It was most noticeable that the largest trees usually occupied the centres of open spaces, whereas the small trees occurred in clumps.

The area of the chosen tract was found by mapping it and was 4055 sq. m. There was a total of 148 trees in it so the tree-density was 0·0365/sq. m. The very few trees of less than 2 m height were ignored and treated as not belonging to the population.

#### (2) *Correlation between inter-tree distances and tree sizes*

From every tree the distance (in centimetres) to its nearest neighbour was measured and also the circumferences of the trunks at 1·5 m from the ground of the tree forming the origin of measurement and its neighbour. The sum of these two circumferences formed the variate whose correlation with distance to nearest neighbour was determined. Ideally one would take as variate the sum of the radii of the two root systems concerned but since measurement of these was not possible it was believed that the relation between trunk circumference (and hence radius) and root system radius was sufficiently linear for the former to be used in place of the latter. Both may be regarded as lineal measures of a tree's size.

It frequently happened (for ninety-two of the 148 trees) that the nearest neighbour relationship was reflexive; that is, a tree was the nearest neighbour of its own nearest neighbour. In those cases a particular set of readings was recorded twice, once when the first tree of the pair was used as origin of measurement and again when its neighbour was so used. When this happened *both* sets of readings were used in subsequent calculations.

The distributions of the tree-to-neighbour distances, and also of the sum of the trunk circumferences of each tree and its neighbour were both strongly skewed, so logarithms of these variates were taken to render their distributions symmetrical, before the correlation coefficient was calculated. The observed correlation coefficient of the log. variates was 0·416. For $n = 148$ this is highly significant of a correlation between the variates (Fisher 1954) and strongly supports the hypothesis that the pattern of the population resulted, in part at least, from competition among the individual trees.

### (3) *Quadrat sampling of the population*

To quadrat sample the population 100 random points were placed in the area by means of random co-ordinates and each point formed the centre of a circular quadrat of radius 4·5 m and area 63·6 sq. m. The number of trees was counted in a circular quadrat swept out by rotating a 4·5 m tape about one of its ends which was fixed at the random point. Only those trees the centres of whose trunks fell within a quadrat were counted as belonging to that quadrat.

The frequency table obtained had a variance/mean ratio of 1·954 indicating that the population was aggregated. The mean was 2·68 trees per quadrat and the number of quadrats containing one tree only was twenty in a sample of 100. The expected number of one-plant quadrats (in a sample of 100) in a random population of the same density is eighteen. Clearly then, the aggregation was not of the common type in which the proportion of one-plant quadrats is much less than in a random population. In this respect the *P. ponderosa* population ressembled the synthetic models.

### (4) *Tests based on distance measurements*

The $\alpha_p$ test (based on point-to-nearest-tree distances) and the $\alpha_i$ test (based on tree-to-nearest-neighbour distances) were both applied to the natural population.

To obtain data for the $\alpha_p$ test, point-to-nearest-tree distances were measured from each of the 100 quadrat centres. The population density was already known since the area had been measured and the number of trees in it counted. A value of $\alpha_p$ of 1·312 was obtained and this significantly exceeds random expectation thus agreeing with the quadrat results in showing that the population was aggregated.

In applying the $\alpha_i$ test the distances, already measured, from every tree in the population to its neighbour were used so that $n = 148$. (As before, when each of a pair of trees was the nearest neighbour of the other, the same distance was recorded twice.) The value of $\alpha_i$ was 1·121 which would normally be taken to mean that the population was random. However, using a sample of tree-to-neighbour distances, another test for randomness may be applied. Thus, in a truly random population, not only would $\alpha_i$ be close to $(n-1)/n^*$ but also the distribution of $r$, the tree-to-neighbour distances, would be well graduated by the frequency function $2\lambda r e^{-\lambda r^2}$ where $\lambda$ is the mean number of trees per circle of unit radius (*see* Morisita 1954 and Skellam's appendix to Hopkins 1954). Accordingly this frequency function was fitted to the observations with the results shown in Table 5.

Table 5. *Comparison of the observed distribution of tree-to-nearest-neighbour distances in the* Pinus ponderosa *population with that expected in a random population of the same density*

$D = 0.0365$ trees per sq. metre
$\lambda = 0.11465$ trees per $\pi$ sq. metres

| Distance to nearest neighbour cm | Frequency | |
|---|---|---|
| | Observed | Expected |
| 0—50 | 13 | 4·19 |
| 51—100 | 17 | 11·85 |
| 101—150 | 34 | 17·62 |
| 151—200 | 21 | 20·78 |
| 201—250 | 9 | 21·28 |
| 251—300 | 17 | 19·55 |
| 301—350 | 8 | 16·40 |
| 351—400 | 5 | 12·70 |
| 401—450 | 3 | 9·12 |
| 451—500 | 7 | 6·10 |
| >500 | 14 | 8·42 |

The fit is poor and it is clear that the numbers of very short (less than 2 m) and of very long (more than 5 m) distances exceed expectation, while there are comparatively few intermediate distances. These two departures from expectation have cancelled each other out producing a value of $\overline{\omega}_i$ (the mean of the squares of the tree-to-neighbour distances), and hence of $\alpha_i$, indistinguishable from that which would be obtained from a random population of the same density. The numerous short distances are, in fact, those measured within clumps of small trees; the long distances are those from isolated giant trees to their neighbours.

## (5) *Discussion of field results*

The marked correlation between the distance separating two trees, on the one hand, and the sum of their circumferences on the other, shows conclusively that the pines in the population investigated were competing with each other for the available space. It therefore seems certain that the mechanism described in the Introduction was responsible, at least in part, for the population's pattern.

Another similarity between the 'aggregated' models and the natural population was that, in both, the observed proportions of one-individual quadrats was *not* less than would be expected in random populations of the same densities. This is in marked contrast to the results that have frequently been obtained by investigators (*e.g.* Archibald 1948) studying aggregated populations of herbaceous plants. I believe this to result from the fact that many such herbs populations consist almost wholly of clumps of several individuals while isolated individuals are rare, whereas in the pine population investigated there were many large, isolated trees in addition to the clumps of small ones. The presence of these isolated trees also accounts for the observed distribution of tree-to-nearest-neighbour distances and the discrepant results of the $\alpha_p$ and $\alpha_i$ tests.

It seemed unlikely that the pattern of the pine population resulted wholly from the mechanism described since not all the large spaces among the trees had an isolated giant tree in the middle.

It is interesting to note that the proportion of trees for which the nearest neighbour relation was reflexive was 0·6216 and thus almost identical with the proportion (0·6215) to be expected in a random population (*see* Clark & Evans 1955).

### IV. CONCLUSIONS

Although the mechanism described can, by itself, cause a population to be aggregated there seems to be no method of determining whether a particular population's aggregation results solely from this cause. Part of the aggregation might result from the two other recognized causes, reproductive clumping and heterogeneity of habitat. However, in any aggregated population, before invoking variability of undetectable habitat factors in a seemingly homogeneous area as an explanation, it seems reasonable to give due weight to the obvious heterogeneity caused by the presence of the population members themselves. Indeed, if variability of habitat factors unconnected with the presence of the population were the sole cause of its aggregation, and intra-specific competition was not operating, one would expect the trees in the 'good' areas to be not only more numerous, but also bigger, than those in the 'bad' areas. This would result in negative correlation between distance-to-neighbour values on the one hand, and the sum of the circumference of each tree and its neighbour on the other.

A consideration of this mechanism also does much to explain the extreme rarity of regular populations in nature. The experiments with models showed that regular populations resulted only when the size-range of the circles was small, or if the range were large, only at fairly low densities. But at low densities intraspecific competition would be unimportant and when two plants chanced to begin growth close together there would be adequate space for the root systems, which would be unsymmetrical, of both.

### V. SUMMARY

1. It is possible for a single mechanism of population growth to account for regular, random and aggregated populations. If, in a uniform habitat:

(*a*) the spatial pattern of germinating seeds is random,

(*b*) they thrive only if their root systems occupy ground not already occupied by earlier colonizers; and

(*c*) the size to which they grow depends on the space available to them: then application of the tests commonly used to detect randomness or departures from it may give any of the three possible results (regularity, randomness or aggregation), 'aggregation' being indicated when the size-range of the plants, and the density, are great enough.

2. Where this mechanism is operating one finds a positive correlation between the distance from a plant to its nearest neighbour and the sum of some measure of the sizes of the root systems (*e.g.* sum of the trunk circumferences) of the two plants between which distance was measured.

G JE.

3. This mechanism also explains the rarity of regular populations in nature. The study of model populations shows that with circular 'plants' a regular pattern is obtained only when there is a small range of possible circle diameters, or, if the range is large, when the density is low. But in a natural population of low density, intraspecific competition, the only conceivable cause of regular spacing, would be comparatively unimportant.

## REFERENCES

ARCHIBALD, E. E. A. (1948). Plant populations, I. A new application of Neyman's contagious distribution. *Ann. Bot. Lond.*, N.S. **12**, 221-35.

ARCHIBALD, E. E. A. (1950). Plant populations, II. The estimation of the number of individuals per unit area of species in heterogeneous plant populations. *Ann. Bot. Lond.*, N.S. **14**, 7-21.

BLISS, C. I. & FISHER, R. A. (1953). Fitting the negative binomial distribution to biological data. *Biometrics*, **9**, 176-200.

CLARK, P. J. & EVANS, F. C. (1955). On some aspects of spatial pattern in biological populations. *Science*, **121**, 397-8.

FELLER, W. (1943). On a general class of contagious distributions. *Ann. Math. Statist.*, **14**, 389-400.

FISHER, R. A. (1954). *Statistical Methods for Research Workers.* 12th ed. London.

GREENWOOD, M. & YULE, G. U. (1920). An inquiry into the nature of frequency distributions representative of multiple happenings with particular reference to the occurrence of multiple attacks of disease or of repeated accidents. *J. Roy. Stat. Soc.*, **83**, 255-79.

GREIG-SMITH, P. (1957). *Quantitative Plant Ecology.* London.

HOPKINS, B. (1954). A new method for determining the type of distribution of plant individuals. *Ann. Bot. Lond. N.S.* **18**, 213-27.

McGUIRE, J. U., BRINDLEY, T. A. & BANCROFT, T. A. (1957). The distribution of European corn borer larvae, *Pyrausta nubilalis* (Hbn.) in field corn. *Biometrics*, **13**, 65-78.

MORISITA, M. (1954). Estimation of population density by spacing method. *Mem. Fac. Sci. Kyushu Univ.*, **E.1**, 187-97.

NEYMAN, J. (1939). On a new class of 'contagious' distributions, applicable in entomology and bacteriology. *Ann. Math. Statist.*, **10**, 35-57.

PIELOU, E. C. (1959). The use of point-to-plant distances in the study of the pattern of plant populations. *J. Ecol.*, **47**, 607-13.

SKELLAM, J. G. (1952). Studies in statistical ecology. I, Spatial pattern. *Biometrika*, **39**, 346-62.

'STUDENT' (1907). On the error of counting with a haemacytometer. *Biometrika*, **5**, 351-60.

THOMAS, M. (1949). A generalization of Poisson's binomial limit for use in ecology. *Biometrika*, **36**, 18-25.

*(Received 27 July 1959)*

Reprinted from *Ecology*, Vol. 42, No. 4, Autumn, 1961

# THE INFLUENCE OF INTERSPECIFIC COMPETITION AND OTHER FACTORS ON THE DISTRIBUTION OF THE BARNACLE *CHTHAMALUS STELLATUS*

Joseph H. Connell

*Department of Biology, University of California, Santa Barbara, Goleta, California*

## Introduction

Most of the evidence for the occurrence of interspecific competition in animals has been gained from laboratory populations. Because of the small amount of direct evidence for its occurrence in nature, competition has sometimes been assigned a minor role in determining the composition of animal communities.

Indirect evidence exists, however, which suggests that competition may sometimes be responsible for the distribution of animals in nature. The range of distribution of a species may be decreased in the presence of another species with similar requirements (Beauchamp and Ullyott 1932, Endean, Kenny and Stephenson 1956). Uniform distribution is space is usually attributed to intraspecies competition (Holme 1950, Clark and Evans 1954). When animals with similar requirements, such as 2 or more closely related species, are found coexisting in the same area, careful analysis usually indicates that they are not actually competing with each other (Lack 1954, MacArthur 1958).

In the course of an investigation of the animals of an intertidal rocky shore I noticed that the adults of 2 species of barnacles occupied 2 separate horizontal zones with a small area of overlap, whereas the young of the species from the upper zone were found in much of the lower zone. The upper species, *Chthamalus stellatus* (Poli) thus settled but did not survive in the lower zone. It seemed probable that this species was eliminated by the lower one, *Balanus balanoides* (L), in a struggle for a common requisite which was in short supply. In the rocky intertidal region, space for attachment and growth is often extremely limited. This paper is an account of some observations and experiments designed to test the hypothesis that the absence in the lower zone of adults of *Chthamalus* was due to interspecific competition with *Balanus* for space. Other factors which may have influenced the distribution were also studied. The study was made at Millport, Isle of Cumbrae, Scotland.

I would like to thank Prof. C. M. Yonge and the staff of the Marine Station, Millport, for their help, discussions and encouragement during the course of this work. Thanks are due to the following for their critical reading of the manuscript: C. S. Elton, P. W. Frank, G. Hardin, N. G. Hairston, E. Orias, T. Park and his students, and my wife.

### Distribution of the species of barnacles

The upper species, *Chthamalus stellatus*, has its center of distribution in the Mediterranean; it reaches its northern limit in the Shetland Islands, north of Scotland. At Millport, adults of this species occur between the levels of mean high water of neap and spring tides (M.H.W.N. and M.H.W.S.: see Figure 5 and Table I). In southwest England and Ireland, adult *Chtham-*

*alus* occur at moderate population densities throughout the intertidal zone, more abundantly when *Balanus balanoides* is sparse or absent (Southward and Crisp 1954, 1956). At Millport the larvae settle from the plankton onto the shore mainly in September and October; some additional settlement may occur until December. The settlement is most abundant between M.H.W.S. and mean tide level (M.T.L.), in patches of rock surface left bare as a result of the mortality of *Balanus*, limpets, and other sedentary organisms. Few of the *Chthamalus* that settle below M.H.W.N. survive, so that adults are found only occasionally at these levels.

*Balanus balanoides* is a boreal-arctic species, reaching its southern limit in northern Spain. At Millport it occupies almost the entire intertidal region, from mean low water of spring tides (M.L.W.S.) up to the region between M.H.W.N. and M.H.W.S. Above M.H.W.N. it occurs intermingled with *Chthamalus* for a short distance. *Balanus* settles on the shore in April and May, often in very dense concentrations (see Table IV).

The main purpose of this study was to determine the cause of death of those *Chthamalus* that settled below M.H.W.N. A study which was being carried on at this time had revealed that physical conditions, competition for space, and predation by the snail *Thais lapillus* L. were among the most important causes of mortality of *Balanus balanoides*. Therefore, the observations and experiments in the present study were designed to detect the effects of these factors on the survival of *Chthamalus*.

## METHODS

Intertidal barnacles are very nearly ideal for the study of survival under natural conditions. Their sessile habit allows direct observation of the survival of individuals in a group whose positions have been mapped. Their small size and dense concentrations on rocks exposed at intervals make experimentation feasible. In addition, they may be handled and transplanted without injury on pieces of rock, since their opercular plates remain closed when exposed to air.

The experimental area was located on the Isle of Cumbrae in the Firth of Clyde, Scotland. Farland Point, where the study was made, comprises the southeast tip of the island; it is exposed to moderate wave action. The shore rock consists mainly of old red sandstone, arranged in a series of ridges, from 2 to 6 ft high, oriented at right angles to the shoreline. A more detailed description is given by Connell (1961). The

other barnacle species present were *Balanus crenatus* Brug and *Verruca stroemia* (O. F. Muller), both found in small numbers only at and below M.L.W.S.

To measure the survival of *Chthamalus,* the positions of all individuals in a patch were mapped. Any barnacles which were empty or missing at the next examination of this patch must have died in the interval, since emigration is impossible. The mapping was done by placing thin glass plates (lantern slide cover glasses, $10.7 \times 8.2$ cm, area 87.7 cm²) over a patch of barnacles and marking the position of each *Chthamalus* on it with glass-marking ink. The positions of the corners of the plate were marked by drilling small holes in the rock. Observations made in subsequent censuses were noted on a paper copy of the glass map.

The study areas were chosen by searching for patches of *Chthamalus* below M.H.W.N. in a stretch of shore about 50 ft long. When 8 patches had been found, no more were looked for. The only basis for rejection of an area in this search was that it contained fewer than 50 *Chthamalus* in an area of about 1/10 m². Each numbered area consisted of one or more glass maps located in the 1/10 m². They were mapped in March and April, 1954, before the main settlement of *Balanus* began in late April.

Very few *Chthamalus* were found to have settled below mid-tide level. Therefore pieces of rock bearing *Chthamalus* were removed from levels above M.H.W.N. and transplanted to and below M.T.L. A hole was drilled through each piece; it was then fastened to the rock by a stainless steel screw driven into a plastic screw anchor fitted into a hole drilled into the rock. A hole ¼" in diameter and 1" deep was found to be satisfactory. The screw could be removed and replaced repeatedly and only one stone was lost in the entire period.

For censusing, the stones were removed during a low tide period, brought to the laboratory for examination, and returned before the tide rose again. The locations and arrangements of each area are given in Table I; the transplanted stones are represented by areas 11 to 15.

The effect of competition for space on the survival of *Chthamalus* was studied in the following manner: After the settlement of *Balanus* had stopped in early June, having reached densities of 49/cm² on the experimental areas (Table I) a census of the surviving *Chthamalus* was made on each area (see Figure 1). Each map was then divided so that about half of the number of

TABLE I. Description of experimental areas*

| Area no. | Height in ft from M.T.L. | % of time sub-merged | POPULATION DENSITY: NO./CM² IN JUNE, 1954 | | | Remarks |
|---|---|---|---|---|---|---|
| | | | *Chthamalus*, autumn 1953 settlement | | All barnacles, undisturbed portion | |
| | | | Undisturbed portion | Portion without *Balanus* | | |
| MHWS............ | +4.9 | 4 | — | — | — | — |
| 1................ | +4.2 | 9 | 2.2 | — | 19.2 | Vertical, partly protected |
| 2................ | +3.5 | 16 | 5.2 | 4.2 | — | Vertical, wave beaten |
| MHWN............ | +3.1 | 21 | — | — | — | — |
| 3a............... | +2.2 | 30 | 0.6 | 0.6 | 30.9 | Horizontal, wave beaten |
| 3b............... | " | " | 0.5 | 0.7 | 29.2 | "      "      " |
| 4................ | +1.4 | 38 | 1.9 | 0.6 | — | 30° to vertical, partly protected |
| 5................ | +1.4 | " | 2.4 | 1.2 | — | "   "   "   "   " |
| 6................ | +1.0 | 42 | 1.1 | 1.9 | 38.2 | Horizontal, top of a boulder, partly protected |
| 7a............... | +0.7 | 44 | 1.3 | 2.0 | 49.3 | Vertical, protected |
| 7b............... | " | " | 2.3 | 2.0 | 51.7 | "      " |
| 11a.............. | 0.0 | 50 | 1.0 | 0.6 | 32.0 | Vertical, protected |
| 11b.............. | " | " | 0.2 | 0.3 | — | "      " |
| 12a.............. | 0.0 | 100 | 1.2 | 1.2 | 18.8 | Horizontal, immersed in tide pool |
| 12b.............. | " | 100 | 0.8 | 0.9 | — | "      "      "      " |
| 13a.............. | −1.0 | 58 | 4.9 | 4.1 | 29.5 | Vertical, wave beaten |
| 13b.............. | " | " | 3.1 | 2.4 | — | "      "      " |
| 14a.............. | −2.5 | 71 | 0.7 | 1.1 | — | 45° angle, wave beaten |
| 14b.............. | " | " | 1.0 | 1.0 | — | "      "      "      " |
| MLWN............ | −3.0 | 77 | — | — | — | — |
| MLWS............ | −5.1 | 96 | — | — | -. | — |
| 15................ | +1.0 | 42 | 32.0 | — | -- | *Chthamalus* of autumn, 1954 set-tlement; densities of Oct., 1954. |
| 7b................ | +0.7 | 44 | 5.5 | 3.7 | — | |

* The letter "a" following an area number indicates that this area was enclosed by a cage; "b" refers to a closely adjacent area which was not enclosed. All areas faced either east or south except 7a and 7b, which faced north.

*Chthamalus* were in each portion. One portion was chosen (by flipping a coin), and those *Balanus* which were touching or immediately surrounding each *Chthamalus* were carefully removed with a needle; the other portion was left untouched. In this way it was possible to measure the effect on the survival of *Chthamalus* both of intraspecific competition alone and of competition with *Balanus*. It was not possible to have the numbers or population densities of *Chthamalus* exactly equal on the 2 portions of each area. This was due to the fact that, since *Chthamalus* often occurred in groups, the *Balanus* had to be removed from around all the members of a group to ensure that no crowding by *Balanus* occurred. The densities of *Chthamalus* were very low, however, so that the slight differences in density between the 2 portions of each area can probably be disregarded; intraspecific crowding was very seldom observed. Censuses of the *Chthamalus* were made at intervals of 4-6 weeks during the next year; notes were made at each census of factors such as crowding, undercutting or smothering which had taken place since the last examination. When necessary, *Balanus* which had grown until they threatened to touch the *Chthamalus* were removed in later examinations.

To study the effects of different degrees of immersion, the areas were located throughout the tidal range, either *in situ* or on transplanted stones, as shown in Table I. Area 1 had been under observation for 1½ years previously. The effects of different degrees of wave shock could not be studied adequately in such a small area

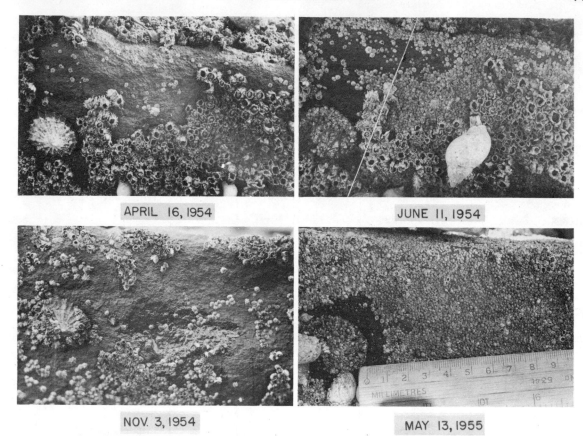

APRIL 16, 1954

JUNE 11, 1954

NOV. 3, 1954

MAY 13, 1955

Fig. 1. Area 7b. In the first photograph the large barnacles are *Balanus,* the small ones scattered in the bare patch, *Chthamalus.* The white line on the second photograph divides the undisturbed portion (right) from the portion from which *Balanus* were removed (left). A limpet, *Patella vulgata,* occurs on the left, and predatory snails, *Thais lapillus,* are visible.

of shore but such differences as existed are listed in Table I.

The effects of the predatory snail, *Thais lapillus,* (synonymous with *Nucella* or *Purpura,* Clench 1947), were studied as follows: Cages of stainless steel wire netting, 8 meshes per inch, were attached over some of the areas. This mesh has an open area of 60% and previous work (Connell 1961) had shown that it did not inhibit growth or survival of the barnacles. The cages were about 4 × 6 inches, the roof was about an inch above the barnacles and the sides were fitted to the irregularities of the rock. They were held in place in the same manner as the transplanted stones. The transplanted stones were attached in pairs, one of each pair being enclosed in a cage (Table I).

These cages were effective in excluding all but the smallest *Thais.* Occasionally small *Thais,* ½ to 1 cm in length, entered the cages through gaps at the line of juncture of netting and rock surface. In the concurrent study of *Balanus* (Con-

nell 1961), small *Thais* were estimated to have occurred inside the cages about 3% of the time.

All the areas and stones were established before the settlement of *Balanus* began in late April, 1954. Thus the *Chthamalus* which had settled naturally on the shore were then of the 1953 year class and all about 7 months old. Some *Chthamalus* which settled in the autumn of 1954 were followed until the study was ended in June, 1955. In addition some adults which, judging from their large size and the great erosion of their shells, must have settled in 1952 or earlier, were present on the transplanted stones. Thus records were made of at least 3 year-classes of *Chthamalus.*

## Results

### The effects of physical factors

In Figures 2 and 3, the dashed line indicates the survival of *Chthamalus* growing without contact with *Balanus.* The suffix "a" indicates that the area was protected from *Thais* by a cage.

In the absence of *Balanus* and *Thais,* and protected by the cages from damage by water-borne objects, the survival of *Chthamalus* was good at all levels. For those which had settled normally on the shore (Fig. 2), the poorest survival was on the lowest area, 7a. On the transplanted stones (Fig. 3, area 12), constant immersion in a tide pool resulted in the poorest survival. The reasons for the trend toward slightly greater mortality as the degree of immersion increased are unknown. The amount of attached algae on the stones in the tide pool was much greater than on the other areas. This may have reduced the flow of water and food or have interfered directly with feeding movements. Another possible indirect effect of increased immersion is the increase in predation by the snail, *Thais lapillus,* at lower levels.

*Chthamalus* is tolerant of a much greater degree of immersion than it normally encounters. This is shown by the survival for a year on area 12 in a tide pool, together with the findings of Fischer (1928) and Barnes (1956a), who found that *Chthamalus* withstood submersion for 12 and 22 months, respectively. Its absence below M.T.L. can probably be ascribed either to a lack of initial settlement or to poor survival of newly settled larvae. Lewis and Powell (1960) have suggested that the survival of *Chthamalus* may be favored by increased light or warmth during emersion in its early life on the shore. These conditions would tend to occur higher on the shore in Scotland than in southern England.

The effects of wave action on the survival of *Chthamalus* are difficult to assess. Like the degree of immersion, the effects of wave action may act indirectly. The areas 7 and 12, where relatively poor survival was found, were also the areas of least wave action. Although *Chthamalus* is usually abundant on wave beaten areas and absent from sheltered bays in Scotland, Lewis and Powell (1960) have shown that in certain sheltered bays it may be very abundant. Hatton (1938) found that in northern France, settlement and growth rates were greater in wave-beaten areas at M.T.L., but, at M.H.W.N., greater in sheltered areas.

At the upper shore margins of distribution *Chthamalus* evidently can exist higher than *Balanus* mainly as a result of its greater tolerance to heat and/or desiccation. The evidence for this was gained during the spring of 1955. Records from a tide and wave guage operating at this time about one-half mile north of the study area showed that a period of neap tides had coincided with an unusual period of warm calm weather in April so that for several days no water, not even waves, reached the level of Area 1. In the period

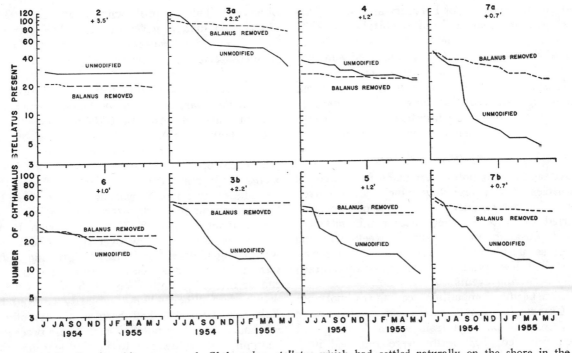

FIG. 2. Survivorship curves of *Chthamalus stellatus* which had settled naturally on the shore in the autumn of 1953. Areas designated "a" were protected from predation by cages. In each area the survival of *Chthamalus* growing without contact with *Balanus* is compared to that in the undisturbed area. For each area the vertical distance in feet from M.T.L. is shown.

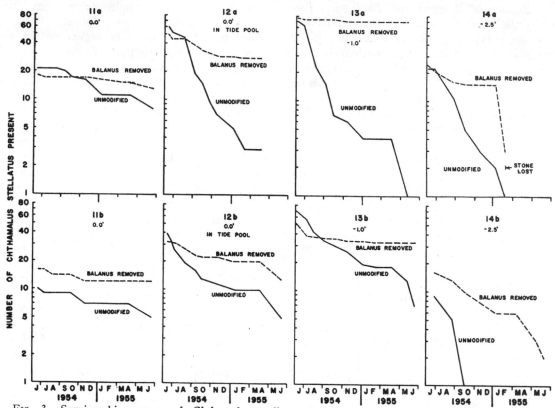

FIG. 3. Survivorship curves of *Chthamalus stellatus* on stones transplanted from high levels. These had settled in the autumn of 1953; the arrangement is the same as that of Figure 2.

between the censuses of February and May, *Balanus* aged one year suffered a mortality of 92%, those 2 years and older, 51%. Over the same period the mortality of *Chthamalus* aged 7 months was 62%, those 1½ years and older, 2%. Records of the survival of *Balanus* at several levels below this showed that only those *Balanus* in the top quarter of the intertidal region suffered high mortality during this time (Connell 1961).

### Competition for space

At each census notes were made for individual barnacles of any crowding which had occurred since the last census. Thus when one barnacle started to grow up over another this fact was noted and at the next census 4-6 weeks later the progress of this process was noted. In this way a detailed description was built up of these gradually occurring events.

Intraspecific competition leading to mortality in *Chthamalus* was a rare event. For areas 2 to 7, on the portions from which *Balanus* had been removed, 167 deaths were recorded in a year. Of these, only 6 could be ascribed to crowding between individuals of *Chthamalus*. On the undisturbed portions no such crowding was observed. This accords with Hatton's (1938) observation that he never saw crowding between individuals of *Chthamalus* as contrasted to its frequent occurrence between individuals of *Balanus*.

Interspecific competition between *Balanus* and *Chthamalus* was, on the other hand, a most important cause of death of *Chthamalus*. This is shown both by the direct observations of the process of crowding at each census and by the differences between the survival curves of *Chthamalus* with and without *Balanus*. From the periodic observations it was noted that after the first month on the undisturbed portions of areas 3 to 7 about 10% of the *Chthamalus* were being covered as *Balanus* grew over them; about 3% were being undercut and lifted by growing *Balanus*; a few had died without crowding. By the end of the 2nd month about 20% of the *Chthamalus* were either wholly or partly covered by *Balanus*; about 4% had been undercut; others were surrounded by tall *Balanus*. These processes continued at a lower rate in the autumn and almost ceased during the later winter. In the spring *Balanus* resumed growth and more crowding was observed.

In Table II, these observations are summarized for the undistributed portions of all the areas. Above M.T.L., the *Balanus* tended to overgrow the *Chthamalus,* whereas at the lower levels, undercutting was more common. This same trend was evident within each group of areas, undercutting being more prevalent on area 7 than on area 3, for example. The faster growth of *Balanus* at lower levels (Hatton 1938, Barnes and Powell 1953) may have resulted in more undercutting. When *Chthamalus* was completely covered by *Balanus* it was recorded as dead; even though death may not have occurred immediately, the buried barnacle was obviously not a functioning member of the population.

TABLE II. The causes of mortality of *Chthamalus stellatus* of the 1953 year group on the undisturbed portions of each area

| Area no. | Height in ft from M.T.L. | No. at start | No. of deaths in the next year | PERCENTAGE OF DEATHS RESULTING FROM: | | | |
|---|---|---|---|---|---|---|---|
| | | | | Smothering by *Balanus* | Undercutting by *Balanus* | Other crowding by *Balanus* | Unknown causes |
| 2......... | +3.5 | 28 | 1 | 0 | 0 | 0 | 100 |
| 3a........ | +2.2 | 111 | 81 | 61 | 6 | 10 | 23 |
| 3b........ | " | 47 | 42 | 57 | 5 | 2 | 36 |
| 4......... | +1.4 | 34 | 14 | 21 | 14 | 0 | 65 |
| 5......... | +1.4 | 43 | 35 | 11 | 11 | 3 | 75 |
| 6......... | +1.0 | 27 | 11 | 9 | 0 | 0 | 91 |
| 7a........ | +0.7 | 42 | 38 | 21 | 16 | 53 | 10 |
| 7b........ | " | 51 | 42 | 24 | 10 | 10 | 56 |
| 11a....... | 0.0 | 21 | 13 | 54 | 8 | 0 | 38 |
| 11b....... | " | 10 | 5 | 40 | 0 | 0 | 60 |
| 12a....... | 0.0 | 60 | 57 | 19 | 33 | 7 | 41 |
| 12b....... | " | 39 | 34 | 9 | 18 | 3 | 70 |
| 13a....... | −1.0 | 71 | 70 | 19 | 24 | 3 | 54 |
| 13b....... | " | 69 | 62 | 18 | 8 | 3 | 71 |
| 14a....... | −2.5 | 22 | 21 | 24 | 42 | 10 | 24 |
| 14b....... | " | 9 | 9 | 0 | 0 | 0 | 100 |
| Total, 2–7.. | — | 383 | 264 | 37 | 9 | 16 | 38 |
| Total, 11–14.. | — | 301 | 271 | 19 | 21 | 4 | 56 |

In Table II under the term "other crowding" have been placed all instances where *Chthamalus* were crushed laterally between 2 or more *Balanus,* or where *Chthamalus* disappeared in an interval during which a dense population of *Balanus* grew rapidly. For example, in area 7a the *Balanus,* which were at the high population density of 48 per cm², had no room to expand except upward and the barnacles very quickly grew into the form of tall cylinders or cones with the diameter of the opercular opening greater than

that of the base. It was obvious that extreme crowding occurred under these circumstances, but the exact cause of the mortality of the *Chthamalus* caught in this crush was difficult to ascertain.

In comparing the survival curves of Figs. 2 and 3 within each area it is evident that *Chthamalus* kept free of *Balanus* survived better than those in the adjacent undisturbed areas on all but areas 2 and 14a. Area 2 was in the zone where adults of *Balanus* and *Chthamalus* were normally mixed; at this high level *Balanus* evidently has no influence on the survival of *Chthamalus.* On Stone 14a, the survival of *Chthamalus* without *Balanus* was much better until January when a starfish, *Asterias rubens* L., entered the cage and ate the barnacles.

Much variation occurred on the other 14 areas. When the *Chthamalus* growing without contact with *Balanus* are compared with those on the adjacent undisturbed portion of the area, the survival was very much better on 10 areas and moderately better on 4. In all areas, some *Chthamalus* in the undisturbed portions escaped severe crowding. Sometimes no *Balanus* happened to settle close to a *Chthamalus,* or sometimes those which did died soon after settlement. In some instances, *Chthamalus* which were being undercut by *Balanus* attached themselves to the *Balanus* and so survived. Some *Chthamalus* were partly covered by *Balanus* but still survived. It seems probable that in the 4 areas, nos. 4, 6, 11a, and 11b, where *Chthamalus* survived well in the presence of *Balanus,* a higher proportion of the *Chthamalus* escaped death in one of these ways.

The fate of very young *Chthamalus* which settled in the autumn of 1954 was followed in detail in 2 instances, on stone 15 and area 7b. The *Chthamalus* on stone 15 had settled in an irregular space surrounded by large *Balanus.* Most of the mortality occurred around the edges of the space as the *Balanus* undercut and lifted the small *Chthamalus* nearby. The following is a tabulation of all the deaths of young *Chthamalus* between Sept. 30, 1954 and Feb. 14, 1955, on Stone 15, with the associated situations:

| | |
|---|---|
| Lifted by *Balanus* | : 29 |
| Crushed by *Balanus* | : 4 |
| Smothered by *Balanus* and *Chthamalus* | : 3 |
| Crushed between *Balanus* and *Chthamalus* | : 1 |
| Lifted by *Chthamalus* | : 1 |
| Crushed between two other *Chthamalus* | : 1 |
| Unknown | : 3 |

This list shows that crowding of newly settled *Chthamalus* by older *Balanus* in the autumn mainly takes the form of undercutting, rather than of smothering as was the case in the spring. The reason for this difference is probably that the *Chthamalus* are more firmly attached in the spring so that the fast growing young *Balanus* grow up over them when they make contact. In the autumn the reverse is the case, the *Balanus* being firmly attached, the *Chthamalus* weakly so.

Although the settlement of *Chthamalus* on Stone 15 in the autumn of 1954 was very dense, 32/cm², so that most of them were touching another, only 2 of the 41 deaths were caused by intraspecific crowding among the *Chthamalus*. This is in accord with the findings from the 1953 settlement of *Chthamalus*.

The mortality rates for the young *Chthamalus* on area 7b showed seasonal variations. Between October 10, 1954 and May 15, 1955 the relative mortality rate per day $\times$ 100 was 0.14 on the undisturbed area and 0.13 where *Balanus* had been removed. Over the next month, the rate increased to 1.49 on the undisturbed area and 0.22 where *Balanus* was absent. Thus the increase in mortality of young *Chthamalus* in late spring was also associated with the presence of *Balanus*.

Some of the stones transplanted from high to low levels in the spring of 1954 bore adult *Chthamalus*. On 3 stones, records were kept of the survival of these adults, which had settled in the autumn of 1952 or in previous years and were at least 20 months old at the start of the experiment. Their mortality is shown in Table III; it was always much greater when *Balanus* was not removed. On 2 of the 3 stones this mortality rate was almost as high as that of the younger group. These results suggest that any *Chthamalus* that managed to survive the competition for space with *Balanus* during the first year would probably be eliminated in the 2nd year.

Censuses of *Balanus* were not made on the experimental areas. However, on many other areas in the same stretch of shore the survival of *Balanus* was being studied during the same period (Connell 1961). In Table IV some mortality rates measured in that study are listed; the *Balanus* were members of the 1954 settlement at population densities and shore levels similar to those of the present study. The mortality rates of *Balanus* were about the same as those of *Chthamalus* in similar situations except at the highest level, area 1, where *Balanus* suffered much greater mortality than *Chthamalus*. Much of this mortality was caused by intraspecific crowding at all levels below area 1.

TABLE III. Comparison of the mortality rates of young and older *Chthamalus stellatus* on transplanted stones

| Stone No. | Shore level | Treatment | Number of *Chthamalus* present in June, 1954 | | % mortality over one year (or for 6 months for 14a) of *Chthamalus* | |
|---|---|---|---|---|---|---|
| | | | 1953 year group | 1952 or older year groups | 1953 year group | 1952 or older year groups |
| 13b | 1.0 ft below MTL | *Balanus* removed | 51 | 3 | 35 | 0 |
| | | Undisturbed | 69 | 16 | 90 | 31 |
| 12a | MTL, in a tide pool, caged | *Balanus* removed | 50 | 41 | 44 | 37 |
| | | Undisturbed | 60 | 31 | 95 | 71 |
| 14a | 2.5 ft below MTL, caged | *Balanus* removed | 25 | 45 | 40 | 36 |
| | | Undisturbed | 22 | 8 | 86 | 75 |

TABLE IV. Comparison of annual mortality rates of *Chthamalus stellatus* and *Balanus balanoides**

| Area no. | *Chthamalus stellatus*, autumn 1953 settlement | | |
|---|---|---|---|
| | Height in ft from M.T.L. | Population density: no./cm² June, 1954 | % mortality in the next year |
| 1.............. | +4.2 | 21 | 17 |
| 3a............. | +2.2 | 31 | 72 |
| 3b............ | " | 29 | 89 |
| 6.............. | +1.0 | 38 | 41 |
| 7a............. | +0.7 | 49 | 90 |
| 7b............. | " | 52 | 82 |
| 11a............. | 0.0 | 32 | 62 |
| 13a............. | −1.0 | 29 | 99 |
| 12a............. | (tide pool) | 19 | 95 |
| *Balanus balanoides*, spring 1954 settlement | | | |
| 1 (top).......... | +4.2 | 21 | 99 |
| 1:Middle Cage 1.. | +2.1 | 85 | 92 |
| 1:Middle Cage 2.. | " | 25 | 77 |
| 1:Low Cage 1.... | +1.5 | 26 | 88 |
| Stone 1.......... | −0.9 | 26 | 86 |
| Stone 2.......... | " | 68 | 94 |

* Population density includes both species. The mortality rates of *Chthamalus* refer to those on the undisturbed portions of each area. The data and area designations for *Balanus* were taken from Connell (1961); the present area 1 is the same as that designated 1 (top) in that paper.

In the observations made at each census it appeared that *Balanus* was growing faster than *Chthamalus*. Measurements of growth rates of the 2 species were made from photographs of the areas taken in June and November, 1954. Barnacles growing free of contact with each other were measured; the results are given in Table V. The growth rate of *Balanus* was greater than that of *Chthamalus* in the experimental areas; this agrees with the findings of Hatton (1938) on the shore in France and of Barnes (1956a) for continual submergence on a raft at Millport.

TABLE V. Growth rates of *Chthamalus stellatus* and *Balanus balanoides*. Measurements were made of uncrowded individuals on photographs of areas 3a, 3b and 7b. Those of *Chthamalus* were made on the same individuals on both dates; of *Balanus*, representative samples were chosen

|  | CHTHAMALUS | | BALANUS | |
|---|---|---|---|---|
|  | No. measured | Average size, mm. | No. measured | Average size, mm. |
| June 11, 1954................ | 25 | 2.49 | 39 | 1.87 |
| November 3, 1954............... | 25 | 4.24 | 27 | 4.83 |
| Average size in the interval....... | | 3.36 | | 3.35 |
| Absolute growth rate per day x 100 | | 1.21 | | 2.04 |

After a year of crowding the average population densities of *Balanus* and *Chthamalus* remained in the same relative proportion as they had been at the start, since the mortality rates were about the same. However, because of its faster growth, *Balanus* occupied a relatively greater area and, presumably, possessed a greater biomass relative to that of *Chthamalus* after a year.

The faster growth of *Balanus* probably accounts for the manner in which *Chthamalus* were crowded by *Balanus*. It also accounts for the sinuosity of the survival curves of *Chthamalus* growing in contact with *Balanus*. The mortality rate of these *Chthamalus*, as indicated by the slope of the curves in Figs. 2 and 3, was greatest in summer, decreased in winter and increased again in spring. The survival curves of *Chthamalus* growing without contact with *Balanus* do not show these seasonal variations which, therefore, cannot be the result of the direct action of physical factors such as temperature, wave action or rain.

Seasonal variations in growth rate of *Balanus* correspond to these changes in mortality rate of *Chthamalus*. In Figure 4 the growth of *Balanus* throughout the year as studied on an intertidal panel at Millport by Barnes and Powell (1953), is compared to the survival of *Chthamalus* at about the same intertidal level in the present study. The increased mortality of *Chthamalus* was found to occur in the same seasons as the in-

creases in the growth rate of *Balanus*. The correlation was tested using the Spearman rank correlation coefficient. The absolute increase in diameter of *Balanus* in each month, read from the curve of growth, was compared to the percentage mortality of *Chthamalus* in the same month. For the 13 months in which data for *Chthamalus* was available, the correlation was highly significant, $P = .01$.

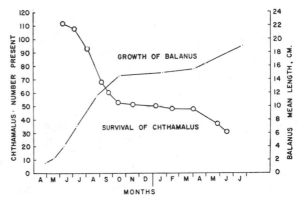

FIG. 4. A comparison of the seasonal changes in the growth of *Balanus balanoides* and in the survival of *Chthamalus stellatus* being crowded by *Balanus*. The growth of *Balanus* was that of panel 3, Barnes and Powell (1953), just above M.T.L. on Keppel Pier, Millport, during 1951-52. The *Chthamalus* were on area 3a of the present study, one-half mile south of Keppell Pier, during 1954-55.

From all these observations it appears that the poor survival of *Chthamalus* below M.H.W.N. is a result mainly of crowding by dense populations of faster growing *Balanus*.

At the end of the experiment in June, 1955, the surviving *Chthamalus* were collected from 5 of the areas. As shown in Table VI, the average size was greater in the *Chthamalus* which had grown free of contact with *Balanus;* in every case the difference was significant ($P < .01$, Mann-Whitney U. test, Siegel 1956). The survivors on the undisturbed areas were often misshapen, in some cases as a result of being lifted on to the side of an undercutting *Balanus*. Thus the smaller size of these barnacles may have been due to disturbances in the normal pattern of growth while they were being crowded.

These *Chthamalus* were examined for the presence of developing larvae in their mantle cavities. As shown in Table VI, in every area the proportion of the uncrowded *Chthamalus* with larvae was equal to or more often slightly greater than on the crowded areas. The reason for this may be related to the smaller size of the crowded *Chthamalus*. It is not due to separation, since *Chthamalus* can self-fertilize (Barnes and Crisp

TABLE VI. The effect of crowding on the size and presence of larvae in *Chthamalus stellatus,* collected in June, 1955

| Area | Treatment | Level, feet above M T L | Number of *Chthamalus* | Diameter in mm | | % of individuals which had larvae in mantle cavity |
|------|-----------|------|------|---------|-------|------|
| | | | | Average | Range | |
| 3a...... | Undisturbed | 2.2 | 18 | 3.5 | 2.7-4.6 | 61 |
| "...... | *Balanus* removed | " | 50 | 4.1 | 3.0-5.5 | 65 |
| 4....... | Undisturbed | 1.4 | 16 | 2.3 | 1.8 3.2 | 81 |
| "....... | *Balanus* removed | " | 37 | 3.7 | 2.5-5 1 | 100 |
| 5....... | Undisturbed | 1.4 | 7 | 3.3 | 2.8-3.7 | 70 |
| "....... | *Balanus* removed | " | 13 | 4.0 | 3.5-4.5 | 100 |
| 6....... | Undisturbed | 1.0 | 13 | 2.8 | 2.1-3.9 | 100 |
| "....... | *Balanus* removed | " | 14 | 4.1 | 3.0-5.2 | 100 |
| 7a & b.. | Undisturbed | 0.7 | 10 | 3.5 | 2.7-4.5 | 70 |
| " .. | *Balanus* removed | " | 23 | 4.3 | 3.0-6.3 | 81 |

TABLE VII. The effect of predation by *Thais lapillus* on the annual mortality rate of *Chthamalus stellatus* in the experimental areas*

| Area | Height in ft from M.T.L. | % mortality of *Chthamalus* over a year (The initial numbers are given in parentheses) | | | | | |
|------|------|------|------|------|------|------|------|
| | | a: Protected from predation by a cage | | | b: Unprotected, open to predation | | |
| | | With *Balanus* | Without *Balanus* | Difference | With *Balanus* | Without *Balanus* | Difference |
| Area 3.. | +2.2 | 73 (112) | 25 (96) | 48 | 89 (47) | 6 (50) | 83 |
| Area 7.. | +0.7 | 90 ( 42) | 47 (40) | 43 | 82 (51) | 23 (47) | 59 |
| Area 11.. | 0 | 62 ( 21) | 28 (18) | 34 | 50 (10) | 25 (16) | 25 |
| Area 12 . | 0† | 100 ( 60) | 53 (50) | 47 | 87 (39) | 59 (32) | 28 |
| Area 13.. | −1.0 | 98 ( 72) | 9 (77) | 89 | 90 (69) | 35 (51) | 55 |

*The records for 12a extend over only 10 months; for purposes of comparison the mortality rate for 12a has been multiplied by 1.2.
†Tide pool.

1956). Moore (1935) and Barnes (1953) have shown that the number of larvae in an individual of *Balanus balanoides* increases with increase in volume of the parent. Comparison of the cube of the diameter, which is proportional to the volume, of *Chthamalus* with and without *Balanus* shows that the volume may be decreased to ¼ normal size when crowding occurs. Assuming that the relation between larval numbers and volume in *Chthamalus* is similar to that of *Balanus,* a decrease in both frequency of occurrence and abundance of larvae in *Chthamalus* results from competition with *Balanus.* Thus the process described in this paper satisfies both aspects of interspecific competition as defined by Elton and Miller (1954): "in which one species affects the population of another by a process of interference, i.e., by reducing the reproductive efficiency or increasing the mortality of its competitor."

### The effect of predation by Thais

Cages which excluded *Thais* had been attached on 6 areas (indicated by the letter "a" following the number of the area). Area 14 was not included in the following analysis since many starfish were observed feeding on the barnacles at this level; one entered the cage in January, 1955, and ate most of the barnacles.

*Thais* were common in this locality, feeding on barnacles and mussels, and reaching average population densities of 200/m² below M.T.L. (Connell 1961). The mortality rates for *Chthamalus* in cages and on adjacent areas outside cages (indicated by the letter "b" after the number) are shown on Table VII.

If the mortality rates of *Chthamalus* growing without contact with *Balanus* are compared in and out of the cages, it can be seen that at the upper levels mortality is greater inside the cages,

at lower levels greater outside. Densities of *Thais* tend to be greater at and below M.T.L. so that this trend in the mortality rates of *Chthamalus* may be ascribed to an increase in predation by *Thais* at lower levels.

Mortality of *Chthamalus* in the absence of *Balanus* was appreciably greater outside than inside the cage only on area 13. In the other 4 areas it seems evident that few *Chthamalus* were being eaten by *Thais*. In a concurrent study of the behavior of *Thais* in feeding on *Balanus balanoides,* it was found that *Thais* selected the larger individuals as prey (Connell 1961). Since *Balanus* after a few month's growth was usually larger than *Chthamalus,* it might be expected that *Thais* would feed on *Balanus* in preference to *Chthamalus.* In a later study (unpublished) made at Santa Barbara, California, *Thais emarginata* Deshayes were enclosed in cages on the shore with mixed populations of *Balanus glandula* Darwin and *Chthamalus fissus* Darwin. These species were each of the same size range as the corresponding species at Millport. It was found that *Thais emarginata* fed on *Balanus glandula* in preference to *Chthamalus fissus.*

As has been indicated, much of the mortality of *Chthamalus* growing naturally intermingled with *Balanus* was a result of direct crowding by *Balanus.* It therefore seemed reasonable to take the difference between the mortality rates of *Chthamalus* with and without *Balanus* as an index of the degree of competition between the species. This difference was calculated for each area and is included in Table VII. If these differences are compared between each pair of adjacent areas in and out of a cage, it appears that the difference, and therefore the degree of competition, was greater outside the cages at the upper shore levels and less outside the cages at the lower levels.

Thus as predation increased at lower levels, the degree of competition decreased. This result would have been expected if *Thais* had fed upon *Balanus* in preference to *Chthamalus*. The general effect of predation by *Thais* seems to have been to lessen the interspecific competition below M.T.L.

## DISCUSSION

"Although animal communities appear qualitatively to be constructed as if competition were regulating their structure, even in the best studied cases there are nearly always difficulties and unexplored possibilities" (Hutchinson 1957).

In the present study direct observations at intervals showed that competition was occurring under natural conditions. In addition, the evidence is strong that the observed competition with *Balanus* was the principal factor determining the local distribution of *Chthamalus*. *Chthamalus* thrived at lower levels when it was not growing in contact with *Balanus*.

However, there remain unexplored possibilities. The elimination of *Chthamalus* requires a dense population of *Balanus*, yet the settlement of *Balanus* varied from year to year. At Millport, the settlement density of *Balanus balanoides* was measured for 9 years between 1944 and 1958 (Barnes 1956b, Connell 1961). Settlement was light in 2 years, 1946 and 1958. In the 3 seasons of *Balanus* settlement studied in detail, 1953-55, there was a vast oversupply of larvae ready for settlement. It thus seems probable that most of the *Chthamalus* which survived in a year of poor settlement of *Balanus* would be killed in competition with a normal settlement the following year. A succession of years with poor settlements of *Balanus* is a possible, but improbable occurrence at Millport, judging from the past record. A very light settlement is probably the result of a chance combination of unfavorable weather circumstances during the planktonic period (Barnes 1956b). Also, after a light settlement, survival on the shore is improved, owing principally to the reduction in intraspecific crowding (Connell 1961); this would tend to favor a normal settlement the following year, since barnacles are stimulated to settle by the presence of members of their own species already attached on the surface (Knight-Jones 1953).

The fate of those *Chthamalus* which had survived a year on the undisturbed areas is not known since the experiment ended at that time. It is probable, however, that most of them would have been eliminated within 6 months; the mortality rate had increased in the spring (Figs. 2

and 3), and these survivors were often misshapen and smaller than those which had not been crowded (Table VI). Adults on the transplanted stones had suffered high mortality in the previous year (Table III).

Another difficulty was that *Chthamalus* was rarely found to have settled below mid tide level at Millport. The reasons for this are unknown; it survived well if transplanted below this level, in the absence of *Balanus*. In other areas of the British Isles (in southwest England and Ireland, for example) it occurs below mid tide level.

The possibility that *Chthamalus* might affect *Balanus* deleteriously remains to be considered. It is unlikely that *Chthamalus* could cause much mortality of *Balanus* by direct crowding; its growth is much slower, and crowding between individuals of *Chthamalus* seldom resulted in death. A dense population of *Chthamalus* might deprive larvae of *Balanus* of space for settlement. Also, *Chthamalus* might feed on the planktonic larvae of *Balanus;* however, this would occur in March and April when both the sea water temperature and rate of cirral activity (presumably correlated with feeding activity), would be near their minima (Southward 1955).

The indication from the caging experiments that predation decreased interspecific competition suggests that the action of such additional factors tends to reduce the intensity of such interactions in natural conditions. An additional suggestion in this regard may be made concerning parasitism. Crisp (1960) found that the growth rate of *Balanus balanoides* was decreased if individuals were infected with the isopod parasite *Hemioniscus balani* (Spence Bate). In Britain this parasite has not been reported from *Chthamalus stellatus*. Thus if this parasite were present, both the growth rate of *Balanus*, and its ability to eliminate *Chthamalus* would be decreased, with a corresponding lessening of the degree of competition between the species.

### The causes of zonation

The evidence presented in this paper indicates that the lower limit of the intertidal zone of *Chthamalus stellatus* at Millport was determined by interspecific competition for space with *Balanus balanoides*. *Balanus*, by virtue of its greater population density and faster growth, eliminated most of the *Chthamalus* by directing crowding.

At the upper limits of the zones of these species no interaction was observed. *Chthamalus* evidently can exist higher on the shore than *Balanus* mainly as a result of its greater tolerance to heat and/or desiccation.

The upper limits of most intertidal animals are probably determined by physical factors such as these. Since growth rates usually decrease with increasing height on the shore, it would be less likely that a sessile species occupying a higher zone could, by competition for space, prevent a lower one from extending upwards. Likewise, there has been, as far as the author is aware, no study made which shows that predation by land species determines the upper limit of an intertidal animal. In one of the most thorough of such studies, Drinnan (1957) indicated that intense predation by birds accounted for an annual mortality of 22% of cockles (*Cardium edule* L.) in sand flats where their total mortality was 74% per year.

In regard to the lower limits of an animal's zone, it is evident that physical factors may act directly to determine this boundary. For example, some active amphipods from the upper levels of sandy beaches die if kept submerged. However, evidence is accumulating that the lower limits of distribution of intertidal animals are determined mainly by biotic factors.

Connell (1961) found that the shorter length of life of *Balanus balanoides* at low shore levels could be accounted for by selective predation by *Thais lapillus* and increased intraspecific competition for space. The results of the experiments in the present study confirm the suggestions of other authors that lower limits may be due to interspecific competition for space. Knox (1954) suggested that competition determined the distribution of 2 species of barnacles in New Zealand. Endean, Kenny and Stephenson (1956) gave indirect evidence that competition with a colonial polychaete worm, (*Galeolaria*) may have determined the lower limit of a barnacle (*Tetraclita*) in Queensland, Australia. In turn the lower limit of *Galeolaria* appeared to be determined by competition with a tunicate, *Pyura,* or with dense algal mats.

With regard to the 2 species of barnacles in the present paper, some interesting observations have been made concerning changes in their abundance in Britain. Moore (1936) found that in southwest England in 1934, *Chthamalus stellatus* was most dense at M.H.W.N., decreasing in numbers toward M.T.L. while *Balanus balanoides* increased in numbers below M.H.W.N. At the same localities in 1951, Southward and Crisp (1954) found that *Balanus* had almost disappeared and that *Chthamalus* had increased both above and below M.H.W.N. *Chthamalus* had not reached the former densities of *Balanus* except

at one locality, Brixham. After 1951, *Balanus* began to return in numbers, although by 1954 it had not reached the densities of 1934; *Chthamalus* had declined, but again not to its former densities (Southward and Crisp 1956).

Since *Chthamalus* increased in abundance at the lower levels vacated by *Balanus,* it may previously have been excluded by competition with *Balanus*. The growth rate of *Balanus* is greater than *Chthamalus* both north and south (Hatton 1938) of this location, so that *Balanus* would be likely to win in competition with *Chthamalus*. However, changes in other environmental factors such as temperature may have influenced the abundance of these species in a reciprocal manner. In its return to southwest England after 1951, the maximum density of settlement of *Balanus* was 12 per cm²; competition of the degree observed at Millport would not be expected to occur at this density. At a higher population density, *Balanus* in southern England would probably eliminate *Chthamalus* at low shore levels in the same manner as it did at Millport.

In Loch Sween, on the Argyll Peninsula, Scotland, Lewis and Powell (1960) have described an unusual pattern of zonation of *Chthamalus stellatus*. On the outer coast of the Argyll Peninsula *Chthamalus* has a distribution similar to that at Millport. In the more sheltered waters of Loch Sween, however, *Chthamalus* occurs from above M.H.W.S. to about M.T.L., judging the distribution by its relationship to other organisms. *Balanus balanoides* is scarce above M.T.L. in Loch Sween, so that there appears to be no possibility of competition with *Chthamalus,* such as that occurring at Millport, between the levels of M.T.L. and M.H.W.N.

In Figure 5 an attempt has been made to summarize the distribution of adults and newly settled larvae in relation to the main factors which appear to determine this distribution. For *Balanus* the estimates were based on the findings of a previous study (Connell 1961); intraspecific competition was severe at the lower levels during the first year, after which predation increased in importance. With *Chthamalus,* it appears that avoidance of settlement or early mortality of those larvae which settled at levels below M.T.L., and elimination by competition with *Balanus* of those which settled between M.T.L. and M.H.W.N., were the principal causes for the absence of adults below M.H.W.N. at Millport. This distribution appears to be typical for much of western Scotland.

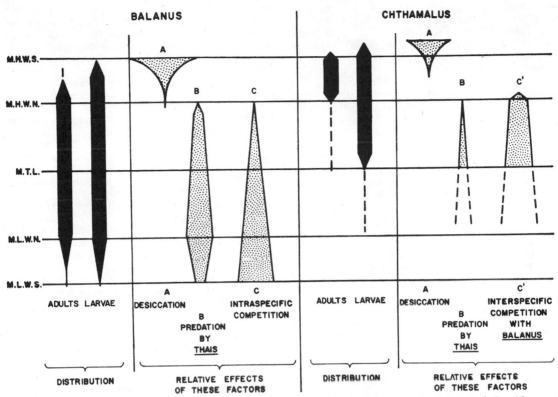

Fig. 5. The intertidal distribution of adults and newly settled larvae of *Balanus balanoides* and *Chthamalus stellatus* at Millport, with a diagrammatic representation of the relative effects of the principal limiting factors.

## SUMMARY

Adults of *Chthamalus stellatus* occur in the marine intertidal in a zone above that of another barnacle, *Balanus balanoides*. Young *Chthamalus* settle in the *Balanus* zone but evidently seldom survive, since few adults are found there.

The survival of *Chthamalus* which had settled at various levels in the *Balanus* zone was followed for a year by successive censuses of mapped individuals. Some *Chthamalus* were kept free of contact with *Balanus*. These survived very well at all intertidal levels, indicating that increased time of submergence was not the factor responsible for elimination of *Chthamalus* at low shore levels. Comparison of the survival of unprotected populations with others, protected by enclosure in cages from predation by the snail, *Thais lapillus*, showed that *Thais* was not greatly affecting the survival of *Chthamalus*.

Comparison of the survival of undisturbed populations of *Chthamalus* with those kept free of contact with *Balanus* indicated that *Balanus* could cause great mortality of *Chthamalus*. *Balanus* settled in greater population densities and grew faster than *Chthamalus*. Direct observations at each census showed that *Balanus* smothered, undercut, or crushed the *Chthamalus*; the greatest mortality of *Chthamalus* occurred during the seasons of most rapid growth of *Balanus*. Even older *Chthamalus* transplanted to low levels were killed by *Balanus* in this way. Predation by *Thais* tended to decrease the severity of this interspecific competition.

Survivors of *Chthamalus* after a year of crowding by *Balanus* were smaller than uncrowded ones. Since smaller barnacles produce fewer offspring, competition tended to reduce reproductive efficiency in addition to increasing mortality.

Mortality as a result of intraspecies competition for space between individuals of *Chthamalus* was only rarely observed.

The evidence of this and other studies indicates that the lower limit of distribution of intertidal organisms is mainly determined by the action of biotic factors such as competition for space or predation. The upper limit is probably more often set by physical factors.

### References

Barnes, H. 1953. Size variations in the cyprids of some common barnacles. J. Mar. Biol. Ass. U. K. **32**: 297-304.

————. 1956a. The growth rate of *Chthamalus stellatus* (Poli). J. Mar. Biol. Ass. U. K. **35:** 355-361.

————. 1956b. *Balanus balanoides* (L.) in the Firth of Clyde: The development and annual variation of the larval population, and the causative factors. J. Anim. Ecol. **25:** 72-84.

———— **and H. T. Powell.** 1953. The growth of *Balanus balanoides* (L.) and *B. crenatus* Brug. under varying conditions of submersion. J. Mar. Biol. Ass. U. K. **32:** 107-128.

———— **and D. J. Crisp.** 1956. Evidence of self-fertilization in certain species of barnacles. J. Mar. Biol. Ass. U. K. **35:** 631-639.

**Beauchamp, R. S. A. and P. Ullyott.** 1932. Competitive relationships between certain species of freshwater Triclads. J. Ecol. **20:** 200-208.

**Clark, P. J. and F. C. Evans.** 1954. Distance to nearest neighbor as a measure of spatial relationships in populations. Ecology **35:** 445-453.

**Clench, W. J.** 1947. The genera *Purpura* and *Thais* in the western Atlantic. Johnsonia **2,** No. 23: 61-92.

**Connell, J. H.** 1961. The effects of competition, predation by *Thais lapillus,* and other factors on natural populations of the barnacle, *Balanus balanoides.* Ecol. Mon. **31:** 61-104.

**Crisp, D. J.** 1960. Factors influencing growth-rate in *Balanus balanoides.* J. Anim. Ecol. **29:** 95-116.

**Drinnan, R. E.** 1957. The winter feeding of the oystercatcher (*Haematopus ostralegus*) on the edible cockle (*Cardium edule*). J. Anim. Ecol. **26:** 441-469.

**Elton, Charles and R. S. Miller.** 1954. The ecological survey of animal communities: with a practical scheme of classifying habitats by structural characters. J. Ecol. **42:** 460-496.

**Endean, R., R. Kenny and W. Stephenson.** 1956. The ecology and distribution of intertidal organisms on the rocky shores of the Queensland mainland. Aust. J. mar. freshw. Res. **7:** 88-146.

**Fischer, E.** 1928. Sur la distribution geographique de quelques organismes de rocher, le long des cotes de la Manche. Trav. Lab. Mus. Hist. Nat. St.-Servan **2:** 1-16.

**Hatton, H.** 1938. Essais de bionomie explicative sur quelques especes intercotidales d'algues et d'animaux. Ann. Inst. Oceanogr. Monaco **17:** 241-348.

**Holme, N. A.** 1950. Population-dispersion in *Tellina tenuis* Da Costa. J. Mar. Biol. Ass. U. K. **29:** 267-280.

**Hutchinson, G. E.** 1957. Concluding remarks. Cold Spring Harbor Symposium on Quant. Biol. **22:** 415-427.

**Knight-Jones, E. W.** 1953. Laboratory experiments on gregariousness during setting in *Balanus balanoides* and other barnacles. J. Exp. Biol. **30:** 584-598.

**Knox, G. A.** 1954. The intertidal flora and fauna of the Chatham Islands. Nature Lond. **174:** 871-873.

**Lack, D.** 1954. The natural regulation of animal numbers. Oxford, Clarendon Press.

**Lewis, J. R. and H. T. Powell.** 1960. Aspects of the intertidal ecology of rocky shores in Argyll, Scotland. I. General description of the area. II. The distribution of *Chthamalus stellatus* and *Balanus balanoides* in Kintyre. Trans. Roy. Soc. Edin. **64:** 45-100. •

**MacArthur, R. H.** 1958. Population ecology of some warblers of northeastern coniferous forests. Ecology **39:** 599-619.

**Moore, H. B.** 1935. The biology of *Balnus balanoides.* III. The soft parts. J. Mar. Biol. Ass. U. K. **20:** 263-277.

————. 1936. The biology of *Balanus balanoides.* V. Distribution in the Plymouth area. J. Mar. Biol. Ass. U. K. **20:** 701-716.

**Siegel, S.** 1956. Nonparametric statistics. New York, McGraw Hill.

**Southward, A. J.** 1955. On the behavior of barnacles. I. The relation of cirral and other activities to temperature. J. Mar. Biol. Ass. U. K. **34:** 403-422.

———— **and D. J. Crisp.** 1954. Recent changes in the distribution of the intertidal barnacles *Chthamalus stellatus* Poli and *Balanus balanoides* L. in the British Isles. J. Anim. Ecol. **23:** 163-177.

————. 1956. Fluctuations in the distribution and abundance of intertidal barnacles. J. Mar. Biol. Ass. U. K. **35:** 211-229.

Reprinted from Science, January 31, 1964,
Vol. 143, No. 3605, pages 471-473

# Volatile Growth Inhibitors Produced by Aromatic Shrubs

Abstract. *Root growth of* Cucumis *and* Avena *seedlings is inhibited by volatile materials produced by leaves of* Salvia leucophylla, S. apiana, *and* Artemisia californica. *The toxic substance may be deposited when dew condenses on affected seedlings in the field.*

The role of metabolic products in various forms of growth inhibition has been reviewed extensively since 1950 (1). We have in progress an analysis of inhibition of annual herbs by *Salvia leucophylla, S. apiana, S. mellifera, Artemisia californica*, and other aromatic shrubs. The localization of the toxic principles is a first step in their identifications and in the determination of ecological relationships.

The spacing and patterning of annual grassland species in and about colonies of *Salvia leucophylla* and *Artemisia californica* in the Santa Inez Valley, Santa Barbara County, California, suggested this study. Numerous isolated patches of both shrubs occur surrounded by grassland. Annual grasses and forbs are usually absent from the interiors of such patches and there is frequently a zone of bare soil extending 60 to 90 cm beyond the canopy of the shrub branches. Beyond this, a zone of differential inhibition may extend 2 to 6 or even 9 m. In the proximal part of this differential zone an almost pure stand of stunted *Erodium cicutarium, Festuca megalura*, and *Bromus mollis*

may occur from which the annual grasses of adjacent unaffected areas are almost totally excluded. Perennial plants such as *Stipa lepida* and *Poa scabrella* seem not to be affected, but seedlings of these are not observed in the zones of inhibition. The inhibition therefore appears to be effective at the time and place of seedling growth and establishment (2).

Preliminary assays showed *Avena fatua* and *Stipa pulchra* seeds and seedlings to be highly susceptible to inhibition by *Salvia leucophylla*. Exploratory assays were performed with *Cucumis sativus* pending the harvest of sufficient native seed supplies.

Whole and macerated young and mature roots of *Salvia leucophylla* failed to inhibit the growth of cucumber seedlings on filter paper in direct contact with the root materials. Similarly, leachate from pots of *Salvia* in native soil failed to inhibit cucumber when used to moisten seeds in germination chambers.

Crushed leaves of *Salvia leucophylla* and leafy twigs of *Artemisia californica* proved strongly inhibitory to both seed germination and seedling growth when assayed in contact. This suggested that toxic materials are localized in the leaves of these plants. Since both shrubs are highly aromatic and inhibition is recognizable 4 to 6 m beyond the reach of their branches, it seemed likely that the toxic principles might be volatile. Several experiments were designed to test this hypothesis and to serve as methods of quick assay for more extensive studies.

Crushed leaves of three shrub species were individually placed in the

Table 1. Growth of *Cucumis* and *Avena* seedling roots in an atmosphere containing volatile materials derived from various amounts of sliced shrub leaves (*Salvia* and *Artemisia*). Growth is expressed as average total length (in millimeters) of roots produced.

| Shrub | Grams of leaf | | | | |
|---|---|---|---|---|---|
| | 0 | 0.25 | 0.5 | 1.0 | 2.0 |
| *Cucumis sativus* | | | | | |
| S. leucophylla | 34.4* | 37.0 | 23.0 | 17.9 | 10.2 |
| S. apiana | 34.4* | 26.9 | 21.2 | 16.0 | 5.3 |
| A. californica | 34.4* | 18.3 | 10.5 | 6.4 | 3.9 |
| *Avena fatua* | | | | | |
| S. leucophylla | 57.5* | 51.5 | 21.2 | 27.3 | 15.9 |
| S. apiana | 57.5* | 20.9 | 38.4 | 24.5 | 11.0 |
| A. californica | 57.5* | 4.9 | 28.5 | 1.6 | 1.6 |

* Average of 60 seedlings.

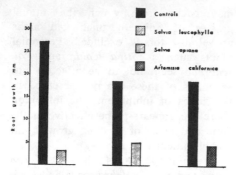

Fig. 1. Growth of *Cucumis* seedling roots suspended above crushed shrub leaves for 48 hours, expressed as average lengths of radicles for 20 seedlings.

bottoms of storage dishes. Filter papers bearing cucumber seeds and irrigated with distilled water were supported 4 cm above the leaves on a shelf of wire mesh coated with paraffin so that no aqueous film contact was possible. In the control moist towelling was substituted for crushed leaves. All dishes were then covered and sealed with petrolatum. Results are·expressed in terms of average radicle length produced in 48 hours by 20 seedlings (Fig. 1). In every instance volatile materials emanating from the crushed leaves radically inhibited seedling root growth.

Finely sliced leaves of *Salvia leucophylla*, *S. apiana*, and *Artemisia californica* in varying quantities were placed in 10-ml beakers standing in storage dishes. A uniform pad of cellulose sponge 4 mm thick, soaked in distilled water, was placed beside the beaker on the floor of each dish. Seeds of *Cucumis sativus* and *Avena fatua*, soaked for 2 hours in distilled water, were sown between layers of moist filter paper on the sponge, and the dish was then sealed with petrolatum. *Cucumis* seeds were germinated at a constant temperature of 28°C while *Avena* seeds were subjected to alternating 12-hour periods of 25°C and 17°C, respectively, ˙preliminary tests having proved these thermoperiods effective.

Results were recorded as total root length (including branches) produced in 48 hours by *Cucumis* and in 120 hours by *Avena*. The record of the root growth, expressed as averages of those seeds which germinated of the 20 sown in each treatment, appears in Table 1. Germination of *Cucumis* seed

approached 100 percent while *Avena* varied from 50 to 75 percent. As the amount of leaf material was increased, there was an increased inhibition of root growth. In the case of *A. californica*, 1.0 g resulted in almost complete inhibition, and additional leaf material proved superfluous.

The lack of any conditions in the field comparable to those in the preceding experiments suggested that the volatile inhibitors must be evaporated from uninjured leaves and deposited, perhaps trapped in dew, upon the inhibited seedlings. In an effort to test this hypothesis, artificial dew condensed on cooling coils was produced from the atmosphere in several places, some where plants of *Salvia leucophylla* were growing and some free of all plants suspected of inhibitory capacity. The dew thus produced was used to soak seeds of *Cucumis* and to irrigate filter paper germination beds sealed in petri dishes.

Several trials proved the "artificial-dew" technique to be very erratic. However, a trial performed on a dry day in early spring when the plants appeared to be at the height of their seasonal growth yielded the results here reported. Tests were made from the atmosphere surrounding (i) ten potted plants of *Salvia leucophylla* grouped on a greenhouse bench in front of the condenser coils, (ii) an empty bench in a neighboring greenhouse containing miscellaneous plants but no *Salvia*, and (iii) distilled water. The results of seedling growth were recorded by measuring the length of the radicle and of each lateral root and then summing these lengths for each seedling. The average lengths for 20 seedlings, respectively, were (i) 57.5 mm, (ii) 176.9 mm, and (iii) 140.6 mm. It is tempting to speculate about the reduction in root growth of more than 50 percent. However, this technique does fail in that a single collection in less than an hour cannot equal nightly depositions over a period of weeks. Although field experimentation is still to be performed, it appears that whole plants of *Salvia leucophylla* release a volatile substance that condenses in dew and that significantly inhibits the growth of cucumber roots.

Although the production of growth inhibitors has been demonstrated for a variety of plants, we believe this to be the first demonstration that a volatile inhibitor may be effective in the field. Its suggested deposition in dew would constitute a novel mechanism of ecological interaction.

CORNELIUS H. MULLER
WALTER H. MULLER
BRUCE L. HAINES

*Department of Biological Sciences,
University of California, Santa Barbara*

**References and Notes**

1. H. Börner, *Botan. Rev.* **26**, 393 (1960); S. Garb, *ibid.* **27**, 422 (1961); R. Knapp, *Experimentelle Soziologie der Höheren Pflanzen* (Eugen Ulmer, Stuttgart, 1954), vol. 1; F. W. Woods, *Botan. Rev.* **26**, 546 (1960).
2. Detailed analysis in preparation.
3. Supported by contract GB-149, National Science Foundation.

23 October 1963

Reprinted from Science, October 4, 1963, Vol. 142, No. 3588, pages 15-23

# The Saguaro: A Population in Relation to Environment

Reproduction and survival are more affected by
man's intrusion than by environmental extremes.

W. A. Niering, R. H. Whittaker, C. H. Lowe

The saguaro (*Cereus giganteus*, *Carnegiea gigantea*) a giant cactus, is a conspicuous and important plant of the Sonoran Desert in southern Arizona and northern Mexico (Sonora). Since the turn of the century it has been known to be failing to reproduce in certain environments (*1*). This failure has stimulated considerable research on various aspects of its biology (*2*). Decline in reproduction dates from the rapid growth of the cattle industry in the 1880's, an influence which has left a lasting imprint on parts of the Southwest. The aim of this article is to combine the knowledge of saguaro biology with the authors' population data from the Santa Catalina Mountains and adjacent ranges in a discussion of saguaro as a natural population in relation to environment and disturbance. The influence of climate, soils, overgrazing, and heavy rodent populations is considered in relation to saguaro survival (*3*).

## Biology and Distribution

The saguaro (*Cereus giganteus*, *Carnegiea gigantea*) is often more than 9 meters tall, with a trunk more than 40 centimeters in diameter in larger individuals. A member of an essentially subtropical group (the subfamily Cerinae), it occurs mainly in the Sonoran Desert, where it grows primarily at elevations below 1400 meters (4500 ft). It flowers in May and June and produces large numbers of seeds; the larger plants produce as many as 200 fruits of 2000 seeds each (*4*, *5*). Any of various circumstances may prevent the seeds and seedlings from developing: because of environmental conditions they may not germinate; rodents may eat them; the roots of young plants may be washed out; and the plants may be killed by freezing temperatures (*4*, *6*, *7*). A very small fraction of the seedlings survive and maintain the population. Most of the seedlings that survive are in sheltered places, underneath paloverde (*Cercidium microphyllum*) and other plants, within shrubs and grass cushions, and on rocky slopes between rocks and in mats of *Selaginella*. Groups of several saguaros of different ages may often be seen beneath, and rising through, a single paloverde tree or other "nurse plant." Growth in the early years is slow; it probably takes a plant about 10 years to reach a height of 2 centimeters and 20 to 50 years to reach 1 meter (*4*). Later growth is at a rate of about 5 to 10 centimeters per year, varying with age and summer precipitation (*1*, *8*). The age-height relation makes it possible to estimate the ages of saguaros of different heights in a population.

Saguaros reach ages of probably 150 to 200 years (*9*). The mortality for mature individuals in an undisturbed stand is estimated as 0.7 percent per year (*10*, p. 344). Death may result from washing out of roots, from windthrow, from freezing, and from bac-

The authors are ecologists in, respectively, the department of botany, Connecticut College; the department of biology, Brooklyn College; and the department of zoology, University of Arizona.

terial necrosis. The bacterium *Erwinia carnegieana* is transmitted by a moth and its larva (*7, 11*). Although saguaros become infected from time to time, their ability to wall off larval tunnels, woodpecker holes, and other wounds with corky tissue (*12*) generally prevents spread of the infection. Death of the saguaro by freezing or other cause is accompanied by rapid multiplication of the bacteria and by tissue disintegration. While it is clear that bacteria multiply in dying tissue and moribund individuals, it has not been established to what extent bacteria are capable of becoming pathogenic in large, otherwise healthy individuals.

### Study Areas

The primary study area of our investigation is a transect along the Mt. Lemmon Highway in the Santa Catalina Mountains from an elevation of 1400 meters (4500 ft) to the base of the mountains at 900 meters (2900 ft), and down the valley slope or bajada to Tucson, 750 meters (2500 ft). North of the city, samples were taken also on the upper part of the bajada along Campbell Avenue. Other study areas are Tumamoc Hill, in the Tucson Mountains, and the two parts of Saguaro National Monument — the original monument in and below the Rincon Mountains east of Tucson and the new Tucson Mountain District west of Tucson, on the west slope of the Tucson Mountains.

The rocky slopes of the Catalinas and Rincons are composed primarily of granitic gneiss; the Tucson Mountains are primarily volcanic. On the rocky slopes, soil development is limited, occurring primarily in shallow pockets on the granite and, on Tumamoc Hill, within the interstices and beneath volcanic boulders. A deeper soil characterizes the basin or valley deposits of the bajadas, although the texture is variable. Soils of the bajadas below the Rincon Mountains and along the Mt. Lemmon Highway are primarily sandy gravels; those along Campbell Avenue are rocky, coarser soils. Those of the Tucson Mountains include both these textural types.

An ideal of physiological ecology is the establishment, by experiment, of the level of a critical factor which limits a population along an environmental gradient. The context in which populations occur in the field makes simple application of the factor-boundary concept impossible for several reasons. (i) Most natural populations along continuous environmental gradients show, instead of sharp boundaries, curves of population abundance that are apparently binomial in form (*13*). The population has its maximum density in an optimum environment and declines gradually and continuously away from this, with decreasing numbers of individuals as a result of decreases in the probabilities of reproduction and survival. (ii) The width of the environmental gradient occupied by the population is a function not merely of the physiological tolerance of an average individual but also of the range of genetic diversity in the population (*14*). The occurrence of different biotypes permits the population to survive at opposite extremes of its environment. (iii) The environmental gradient affecting the level of population is a "complex-gradient" of many environmental variables which change in parallel (*14*). More than one of these variables may affect the probability of survival of different biotypes; different factors differently affect different stages of the life history; and some factors may be effective mainly through averages affecting normal population processes, others through extreme fluctuations that result in catastrophe for a population. (iv) Effects of other organisms may be essential factors in the environmental gradient (*15*). Along a given gradient the population may decline in one direction primarily because the physical environment is increasingly unfavorable, whereas it may decline in the other direction primarily because of increasing competition of other species which flourish more than the species in question as the environment becomes more favorable. Consequently, in the presence of other organisms, the population center or optimum in the field may depart widely from the physiological optimum where the plant in question might grow best if there were no competition.

### Elevation and Temperature

The first three histograms of Fig. 1 show the relation of the saguaro population to elevation on rocky south-facing slopes of the Santa Catalina Mountains. The population declines with increase in elevation, from maximum levels on the hottest, lower slopes of the mountains to low levels above 1200 meters (4000 ft); only a few individuals occur up to 1400 meters. South-facing slopes below 1200 meters support the spinose-suffrutescent phase of the Sonoran desert scrub (major plants are *Cercidium microphyllum*, *Fouquieria splendens*, *Prosopis juliflora*, *Encelia farinosa*, *Janusia gracilis*, *Jatropha cardiophylla*, *Calliandra eriophylla*, and *Opuntia* spp.); southern slopes above 1200 meters support desert grasslands. Along this gradient, increase in elevation implies decreases in mean and extreme temperatures, increase in precipitation and decrease in evaporation (*16*), and change in plant competition with increasing grass cover.

It was suggested by Shreve (*17*) that distribution of saguaro is limited to the north, or with elevation, by the latitude or altitude at which infrequent winter freezing temperatures persist for more than 24 hours. Recent experimental work by Lowe (*6*), with analysis of weather-station records for areas inside and outside the distributional boundary for saguaro, strongly supports Shreve's thesis. Sensitivity to temperature is also manifested in the saguaro, as in some of its relatives (*18*), by an increase in diameter and a decrease in the number of flutings of the stem from the southern toward the northern part of its range, where a low surface-mass ratio is advantageous, increasing the plant's capacity to retain heat—a botanical Bergmann trend.

From 11 to 13 January 1962, the effects on saguaros of one of the winter freezes which, from time to time, kill or damage the plants in the northern part of their range were studied by Lowe in the Santa Catalina Mountains. He observed tissue temperatures, air temperatures, and saguaro mortality. Freezing temperatures continued after the first night through the next day and into the second night. During the first night some of the smaller saguaros were frozen; retention of heat by the massive stems of larger individuals delayed the fall of temperature in these plants, but many froze during the second night. In the morning the thawed tissues lost turgor; during the weeks that followed, the dead tissues decomposed through bacterial necrosis. Saguaro stands on the lower slopes of the Catalinas became scenes of devastation (Fig. 2). The most severe damage was to the larger saguaros some meters above ground level and on the southeast sides of the trunks, where freeze effects were aggravated by wind and rapid thawing of tissues struck by the morning sun.

Such environmental catastrophe may produce population pulsation—slow expansions terminated by abrupt contractions. The freeze of 1962, however, reduced the density rather than the spatial extent of the saguaro population. The average mortality of saguaros more than 3½ meters tall in the samples increased with elevation, from 10 percent at 900 to 1050 meters, through 22 percent at 1050 to 1200 meters, to 30 percent above 1200 meters (Fig. 1, *a–c*, solid bars). Even where mortality was highest (up to 70 percent on an exposed upper slope, Fig. 1, *g*; Fig. 2), some larger saguaros, perhaps of more resistant genotypes, survived. For smaller saguaros, sheltered under other plants and between rocks that reradiated heat during the night, the percentages of survival were higher. Some of the densest populations of small saguaros (5 to 30 cm tall), with mortality of less than 20 percent, were found in stands where mortality of the larger saguaros exceeded 50 percent (Fig. 1, *g*). Even so definite an environmental limitation as the occurrence of freezing temperatures for more than 24 hours acts (in this case, through differences in the percentages of mortality in different biotypes and

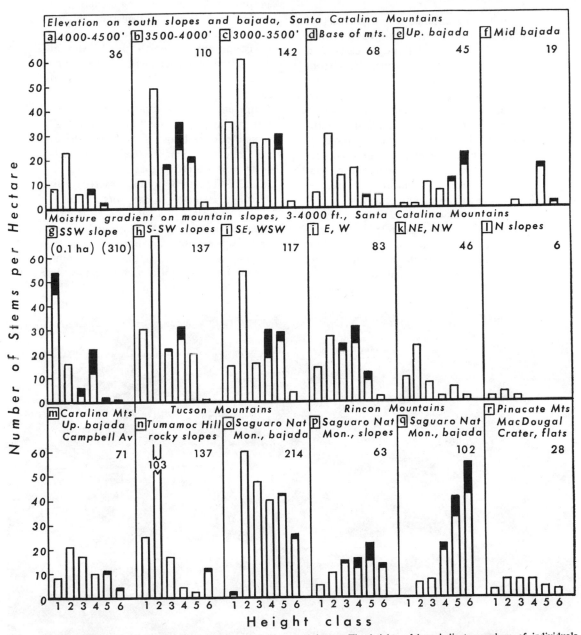

Fig. 1. Population histograms for saguaro in the area of Tucson, Arizona. The heights of bars indicate numbers of individuals per hectare (2.5 acres), as determined on the basis of ten 0.1-hectare samples in which the saguaros were counted, their heights and diameters were recorded, and the associated vegetation was analyzed (sample *g* is for a single 0.1-hectare area). "Height classes" are as follows: (1) up to 1 foot (0.3 m); (2) 2 to 6 feet (0.6 to 1.8 m); (3) 7 to 12 feet (2.1 to 3.6 m); (4) 13 to 18 feet (3.9 to 5.5 m); (5) 19 to 24 feet (5.7 to 7.3 m); (6) over 24 feet. Shaded portions of bars represent recently dead individuals, mostly killed in the freeze of January 1962. The number at upper right in each graph is the number of living individuals more than 0.3 meter tall per hectare. Age height relationships for the bajada at Saguaro National Monument (where growth is probably faster than it is in most of the populations illustrated) are as follows: 0.3 meter, 13 years; 1.8 meters, 30 years; 3.6 meters, 48 years; 5.5 meters, 74 years; 7.3 meters, 102 years (8). Sample *r* is for a stand in the Pinacate Mountains, Sonora. [Data courtesy of R. M. Turner and J. R. Hastings]

153

age groups) to produce the gradual decline in population density with increasing elevation.

### Moisture Gradient

In the mountains, an environmental gradient that leads from open southwest-facing slopes through east- and west- to north-facing slopes (and from these to sheltered lower slopes and canyon bottoms) is a topographic moisture gradient. Maximum exposure to the afternoon sun renders the southwestern slopes the dry-hot extreme of this gradient. Along the gradient toward northern slopes, evaporation decreases, available moisture increases, exposure to sunlight decreases, and temperatures decrease (16, 19). Figure 1, g to l, shows the response of the saguaro population to the gradient from southwestern to northern slopes.

Maximum populations occur in the most arid environments in the moun-

tains, the open southern and southwestern slopes at lowest elevations. Although the saguaro population is limited at the western edge of its geographic distribution by increasing aridity (17, 20), the driest conditions in the Tucson area are within the range of conditions at which the maximum population may occur. From the southern through the eastern and western slopes, all bearing the spinose-suffrutescent desert described, the population declines until the "more favorable" moisture conditions of northern slopes are reached, where the spinose-suffrutescent desert grades into a somewhat different Sonoran desert scrub with larger shrubs (*Simmondsia chinensis*, *Coursetia microphylla*, *Aloysia wrightii*, and so on). Although there are few saguaros on northern slopes, larger numbers are found in some shrub and mesquite communities in draws and canyons where, presumably,

Fig. 2. A saguaro stand in January 1963, on an upper southern slope of the Santa Catalina Mountains (925 m), showing severe damage caused by the freeze of January 1962 and by bacterial necrosis that followed. Paloverde and ocotillo (*Fouquieria splendens*) comprise the larger associated vegetation. Note the excellent ground cover, the result of 25 years of protection against grazing. Data for the stand are given in Fig. 1, g.

there is more moisture than there is on open northern slopes. Consequently, it seems possible that a decrease in exposure to light, as well as a decrease in temperature, limits the occurrence of plants such as these, with a photosynthetic surface that is small relative to their mass, on steep northern slopes. The fact that many of the largest saguaros occur in canyons and draws suggests that the environmental optimum for maximum population density on dry slopes, and the physiological optimum for best growth of individuals in moister conditions, are widely separated.

## Slope and Bajada

The saguaro population decreases abruptly from the mountain slopes down to the valley plains or bajada in the transect area (Fig. 1, c–f). As compared to densities on the slopes, the densities of larger individuals are about half as high on the upper edge of the bajada, on rock platform or pediment with spinose-suffrutescent desert (Fig. 1, d) and on coarse upper-bajada soils with paloverde-bursage (Cercidium microphyllum-Franseria deltoidea) desert (Fig. 1, m). From the upper edge of the bajada the population declines gradually down the valley slope through middle bajada (Fig. 1, d–f) to the lower-bajada creosote-bush (Larrea divaricata) desert near Tucson, in which the saguaros are few and widely scattered. The primary environmental change down the bajada is a change in soil characteristics (21), including a gradual shift from coarse soils in which saguaro reproduces effectively to the finer soils of the creosote-bush desert. Because of the thermal inversion of the valley (22), winter temperatures become lower and less favorable to the survival of saguaros as one goes down the bajada.

Some of the very finest stands, in which thousands of serried saguaros may be viewed across miles of desert plains (Fig. 3), occur on upper bajadas,

Fig. 3. A mature stand of saguaro on bajada in the Tucson Mountains section of Saguaro National Monument, in 1962. Paloverde is the conspicuous associate; cane cholla may be seen in the foreground. Data for the stand are given in Fig. 1, o. [Hiram L. Parent]

especially those that support less xerophytic desert communities and those that are transitional between desert and desert grassland. Such stands may have both high population densities and high proportions of large individuals (Fig. 1, *o* and *q*), but in most of these stands there are few young plants to replace older ones that die. Parallel occurrences of numerous young individuals on rocky slopes and poor reproduction on the bajadas may be seen for the three study areas represented in Fig. 1.

### Effects of Grazing

As we mentioned earlier, age-height relationships suggest that, in many stands, saguaro reproduction has declined since the 1880's (*1*). At that time, great numbers of cattle were brought into Arizona in a favorite get-rich-quick scheme (*23, 24*); by 1890 there were about 114,000 cattle in Pima County alone (*25*). With reduced productivity or destruction of valley grasslands by grazing and erosion, the herds spread widely into more arid areas, into remote valleys, and up mountain slopes. As a result of overgrazing and of drought from 1891 to 1893, great numbers of cattle died (*24–26*), and the cattle populations declined thereafter to more reasonable levels.

During this period, disturbance of plant cover, both in the centers of valleys and on slopes that drained into the valleys, produced increased runoff from storms, floods of new intensity, the gouging of deep new channels or arroyos in valleys, and destruction of valley forests and meadows by erosion and the lowering of water tables— processes that have been effectively described for the Tucson area by various

Fig. 4. A disturbed stand of saguaro (grazed until 1958) on upper bajada and lower slopes of the Rincon Mountains section of Saguaro National Monument in January 1963. Paloverde, ocotillo, and prickly pear are the conspicuous associated vegetation. The Santa Catalina Mountains appear in the background.

authors (*10, 24, 26–28*). Failure of the saguaro to reproduce may thus be a detail in the broader picture of the consequences of man's use of the Southwest—of the cutting of arroyos and channels and of changes in the character of desert grasslands that resulted from grazing and efforts to protect these lands against fire (*29*).

The data on saguaro reproduction suggest a pattern. The rock and shrub cover of steep mountain slopes offer young saguaros protection against cattle. Saguaro is reproducing on all such mountain slopes observed in our study, including slopes on which there was moderate grazing, but intensive grazing can prevent the reproduction of saguaro even on rocky slopes, as observed by Shreve (*1*) for Tumamoc Hill and for lower slopes of the Santa Catalina Mountains. The paloverde-bursage desert has never contained much grass and has been lightly grazed (*30*); in most such stands saguaro is reproducing (Fig. 1, *m*). Plant communities of the lower bajada and those transitional to desert-grassland have contained grass; they have been grazed, and in them saguaro has, in general, been reproducing poorly since the 1880's.

## Damage by Rodents

Rodents and rabbits have much to do with the difference in density of saguaro on the slopes and on the bajada, and with the effects of grazing. Some rodents eat young saguaros with apparent relish, presumably more for water than for food. In one test at Saguaro National Monument, all but 14 of 800 young saguaros planted in the desert were dead in 6 months; after 2 years these 14 and all but 30 of 800 plants in cages were dead. All but about 100 of the 1570 dead saguaros were killed by rodents; the wire cages merely delayed death until the rodents had tunneled under the wire (*7*). Consumption by rodents is probably the principal hazard to young saguaros, and this (together with microclimatic effects) explains why most young saguaros that survive under natural conditions are those that are hidden by shrubs, grasses, and rocks, where they are less apt to be discovered and eaten by rodents.

Rodent populations differ both quantitatively and qualitatively under the very different soil conditions of rocky slopes and bajada (Table 1). It has been observed in both field and laboratory that the ground squirrels and wood rats which predominate on the bajada eat young saguaros; species which predominate on rocky slopes do so less frequently (*Peromyscus eremicus*) or not at all (*Perognathus intermedius*).

The rodent populations may thus tend to keep saguaro populations at lower levels on the bajada than on rocky slopes. Grazing intensifies the difference. Vulnerable grasses and low shrubs on the bajada are easily destroyed by grazing, while other species, including cholla (*Opuntia fulgida*), prickly pear (*Opuntia phaeacantha, O. engelmannii,* and so on), burroweed (*Haplopappus tenuisectus*), and snakeweed (*Gutierrezia* spp.) increase. An abundance of these and other species characteristically indicates that the desert and desert grassland has been disturbed through grazing. As grass cover decreases and cacti increase, the density of wood rats increases. The wood rats, which use dead cholla and segments of dead prickly pear to build their nests and live prickly pear as a principal food (*31*), feed also on saguaro and other species and may become numerous enough to affect the survival of plant populations and the composition of the plant community. With grazing, the population of jackrabbits also increases, and these affect the plant community by browsing paloverde and other saguaro "nurse plants," as well as cacti (*32*). In such an overgrazed community the young saguaro faces a combination of adversities—the reduction or extinction of protecting grass and shrubs, an increase in the population of rodents that eat the unprotected plants, and trampling and consumption by cattle.

The role of rodents in the effects of overgrazing may be further aggravated by an increase in the rodent population

Table 1. Relative densities (individuals per 100 traps, per night of trapping) and species biomasses (live weights in grams per 100 traps, per night of trapping) of rodents and lagomorphs, for disturbed desert on bajada at Saguaro National Monument below the Rincon Mountains, and for rocky slopes of southern to western exposure protected from grazing, at altitudes of 975 to 1035 meters in the Santa Catalina Mountains. The data are based on 535 trap-night units (number of traps times nights of trapping) for the same period (from 16 to 19 May 1963) at both stations.

| Species | Density | | Biomass | |
|---|---|---|---|---|
| | Bajada | Rocky slope | Bajada | Rocky slope |
| Ground squirrel (*Citellus harrisi* and *C. tereticaudus*) | 10.8 | 0.6 | 879 | 56 |
| Wood rat (*Neotoma albigula*) | 4.3* | 2.4 | 460* | 406 |
| Cactus mouse (*Peromyscus eremicus*) | 0.4 | 7.1 | 14 | 144 |
| Grasshopper mouse (*Onychomys torridus*) | 0.2 | | 4 | |
| Kangaroo rat (*Dipodomys merriami*) | 4.7 | | 183 | |
| Pocket mouse (*Perognathus* spp.) | 8.4 | 15.9 | 147 | 208 |
| Cottontail (*Sylvilagus auduboni*) | 0.2 | | 137 | |
| Totals | 29.0 | 26.0 | 1824 | 814 |

* Data for *Neotoma* on bajada were obtained from 24 to 27 April 1963.

that results from programs of coyote control. The lack of saguaro less than 30 centimeters tall on the bajada in the Tucson Mountains section of Saguaro National Monument (Fig. 1, *o*) is believed to be a consequence of grazing prior to 1938 and of a program of coyote control in the 1930's. A high rodent population developed in the sandy soils and has kept saguaro reproduction at low levels from the 1930's to the present. The Rincon Mountains section of the National Monument has been severely affected by a combination of overgrazing and predator control. The area has been grazed since the grazing heyday of the 1880's; grazing continued in the lower elevations of the Monument from the time of its establishment to 1958, and

the upper slopes are still being grazed (*33*). There is some reproduction of saguaro on the rocky slopes (Fig. 1, *p*), but the growth on many of these slopes differs from that on slopes in the Catalina Mountains study area. The effects of continuous heavy grazing of the Rincon slopes are reflected in a pronounced reduction of saguaro reproduction and in cover of smaller perennial plants (Table 2), suggesting the condition of overgrazed lower slopes of the Catalinas, as shown in early photographs (*10*, plates 64, 65), and indicated by soil erosion.

The vegetation at low elevations in the Rincon Mountains section of Saguaro National Monument represents an advanced stage of the degradation process in a vulnerable community

Table 2. Coverage (in percentages) in protected and overgrazed desert in the Santa Catalina Mountains (protected from grazing for about 25 years) and in the Rincon Mountains region of Saguaro National Monument (grazed).

| Site | Catalina Mountains, protected | | Rincon Mountains, grazed | |
|---|---|---|---|---|
| | South slopes (915–1220 m) (spinose-suffrutescent) | Upper bajada (825–850 m) (paloverde bursage) | South slopes (945–1000 m) (spinose-suffrutescent) | Upper bajada (885 m) (disturbed desert) |
| Paloverde and mesquite | 9.8 | 12.6 | 4.3 | 9.9 |
| Spinose shrubs | 5.8 | 1.8 | 2.7 | 3.9 |
| Cacti | 2.5 | 2.7 | 2.7 | 7.2* |
| Suffrutescent (except for burroweed) | 9.4 | 22.6 | 4.0 | 0.92 |
| Grass | 2.5 | 0.4 | 0.9 | .02 |
| Other perennial herbs | 0.13 | .003 | .22 | |
| Burroweed | | | | 1.4 |
| Selaginella | 4.4 | | .2 | |

* The value for bajada in the transect area was determined separately.

(Fig. 4). On the lower flats and adjacent parts of the study area (Fig. 1, *q*) there is no reproduction of saguaro, while older saguaros are dying at a rate (about 2 percent per year) which implies that the last individuals will disappear from this part of the Monument between 1990 and 2000 (*34*). Undergrowth of the stand is strongly dominated by prickly pear (308 clumps per hectare), cholla, and burroweed (1048 plants per hectare); there are almost no grasses, and the

herb and semi-shrub cover, except for burroweed (Table 2), is the lowest that we found in our studies of vegetation in the area. Wood-rat nests are numerous (25 dens per hectare in the study area). Holes where tissues have been eaten by rodents are conspicuous in some older saguaros, especially where branches of paloverde nurse trees give wood rats access to the upper parts of saguaro stems. In some saguaros the rats have eaten circular staircases through the tissues surrounding the

Fig. 5. A group of saguaros which became established under a paloverde nurse tree, showing severe damage from rodents. There is a wood-rat den within the clump of cacti, and an internal spiral rodent runway may be seen in the second stem from the right. The group is on upper bajada of the Rincon Mountains section of Saguaro National Monument.

central column (Fig. 5). Soil erosion is evident, and though in the past dead, mature paloverdes were rarely seen (*35*), there are numerous such dead trees in this community. Intensive browsing on young paloverde by rabbits is reducing the rate of replacement of these nurse plants. Here the saguaro is a dying population in a stricken community. When the deterioration that results from grazing has proceeded to this point, the original community has been replaced by a new one, in which the wood rat and ground squirrels are a dominant influence, in which the saguaro cannot recover, and in which any change, even though grazing should be wholly eliminated, is likely to be very slow by the time-scale of human purpose.

## Grazing and Climate

Heavy grazing, drought, and the cutting of arroyos occurred simultaneously in much of the Southwest. A number of authors have discussed the possibility that drought was an important secondary, or even primary, cause of arroyo cutting (*10, 28, 36*). Both grazing and drought may produce arroyo cutting through reducing plant cover, and both climate and grazing must affect the probability of survival of saguaro seedlings. So pervasive was the influence of grazing, even on mountain slopes and in remoter areas, that it is difficult to find control areas where the effects of grazing and of drought may be separated.

Much evidence, in addition to that discussed, bears on the failure of saguaro to reproduce. (i) The reproduction of saguaro was reduced, on both bajadas and rocky slopes, during the period of most intense grazing. Since then, the rate of reproduction has increased both on rocky slopes and on some bajadas protected from grazing [for example, Tumamoc Hill, fenced in 1907 (Fig. 1, *n*), and Campbell Avenue (Fig. 1, *m*), protected for 25 years]. (ii) In those locations, reproduction, which had declined sharply under the earlier grazing-plus-drought conditions,

was adequate during the post-1942 drought, which was considered more severe (*37*). (iii) During peak periods of grazing, reproduction of saguaro continued in some very inaccessible situations. Many young saguaros may be seen in photographs of very steep slopes in Sabino Canyon (for example, in Arizona Pioneers' Historical Society Museum photographs Nos. 7-4092 and 7-4069), taken about 1900. No sharp decrease in reproduction accompanied drought in MacDougal Crater (Fig. 1, *r*), where steep rock walls exclude cattle, even though the crater floor is of level, sandy soils of the type which elsewhere are most vulnerable to grazing damage and favorable to the development of high rodent populations, and despite the apparent effects of the post-1942 drought in killing paloverde and creosote bush in the same community (*10*, p. 357). (iv) The heaviest reproduction of saguaro at present in the Tucson area is on some of the driest slopes, and populations are reproducing well in more arid climates west of Tucson, for example in the Pinacate Mountains (Fig. 1, *r*) (*10*). (v) The same decrease in the reproduction of saguaro during peak periods of grazing is reflected in the histograms for different slopes in Fig. 1 (the 2.1- to 3.6-m class in histograms *a*–*d* and *g*–*j*, when allowance is made for slower growth than at Saguaro National Monument; the 3.9- to 5.5-m class in the less arid slope of histogram *k*) and for different bajadas. Thus, the availability of more moisture did not compensate in some of these situations for climatic drought; in all situations the populations were affected by grazing. Our data are consistent with the view that the failure of saguaro to reproduce depends on two factors in combination—the amount of grazing and the relative vulnerability of the community to harmful effects of grazing, as determined by the soil.

It should not be assumed that all arroyo cutting is a consequence of grazing, but for the Santa Cruz Valley one may make several observations. (i) The time sequence strongly suggests that, here, arroyo cutting was a consequence of grazing; the valley and the slopes were heavily grazed for years before the drought of 1891–93 intensified the effects of grazing on plant cover and runoff and thus initiated channel cutting. (ii) The numbers of cattle and the intensity of grazing seem clearly to have been sufficient to produce increased runoff, floods, and channel cutting. It is doubtful that the drought of 1891–93 was of such extraordinary intensity, by comparison with previous droughts, as to have caused the channel cutting. (iii) Photographs taken at the turn of the century show these mountain slopes denuded of grass cover, through grazing (*10*, especially pp. 212–222). In Arizona, such slopes have recovered their grass cover where they were not overgrazed, despite the post-1942 drought, but in Sonora similar denudation may be seen at present in comparable overgrazed desert grasslands and oak woodlands. Known changes in vegetation that occurred between 1880 and 1910, which both increased runoff and made the valley floor vulnerable to cutting, may be regarded as direct consequences of grazing. Primary responsibility for arroyo cutting may lie with man himself (*26, 38*), and it is likely that in the Santa Cruz Valley the drought did little more than (to reverse Bryan's metaphor) pull the trigger of a gun loaded by years of overgrazing.

As for the future of the saguaro, it is evident that this is a highly successful species, well adapted to growth in a dry and unstable climate, maintaining itself well where it is not disturbed by man and grazing animals. The saguaro is in no danger of disappearing on ungrazed slopes of desert mountains or in undisturbed paloverde-bursage desert on bajadas. In many other bajada communities the saguaro is likely to disappear if there is no protection from grazing, or if the effects of grazing are already too far advanced for the saguaro population to recover even if it is now protected. The population on the rocky slopes of Saguaro National Monument in the Rincon Mountains may be expected to recover from the effects of grazing when the cattle are removed; the bajada stand that extends westward from these mountains is in such a state of deterioration that it can probably be salvaged only through extraordinary effort. It may now be of value principally as a demonstration of the ruinous effects of long-continued grazing on a once-splendid saguaro forest of the upper bajada—a forest which the Monument was created to preserve.

## Summary

The saguaro is a major plant of the Sonoran Desert, occurring in a number of types of desert and extending into some desert grassland. The center of maximum population density in the Tucson area is on the driest slopes of mountains, at low elevations; the finest stands of large individuals occur on some of the upper parts of valley plains or bajadas. Toward higher elevations in the mountains the population is limited by low winter temperatures, which periodically kill large proportions of the population by freezing. Down the bajada slopes the population is limited by the occurrence of finer soils and by other factors. The population is reproducing well on rocky slopes and in some bajada communities but is failing to reproduce on the finer soils of bajadas affected by grazing. The kill by freezing is a temporary catastrophe, for many younger individuals survive the freeze. Grazing subjects the population to a gradual disaster, with slow decline to disappearance resulting from failure of the saguaro to reproduce. When the effects of grazing are far advanced and rodent populations are high, as in parts of Saguaro National Monument, these effects are largely irreversible.

### References and Notes

1. F. Shreve, *Plant World* **13**, 235 (1910).
2. ——, *J. Ecol* **5**, 210 (1917); J. Wilder, *Desert Plant Life* **12**, 65 (1940); P. C. Lightle, E. T. Standring, J. G. Brown, *Phytopathol.* **32**, 303 (1942); S. M. Alcorn and E. B. Kurtz, Jr., *Am. J. Botany* **46**, 526 (1959); S. M. Alcorn, S. E. McGregor, G. D. Butler, Jr., E. B. Kurtz, Jr., *Cactus and Succulent J.* **31**, 39 (1959); S. M. Alcorn, S. E. McGregor, G. Olin, *Science* **133**, 1954 (1961); E. B. Kurtz, Jr., and S.

M. Alcorn, *Cactus and Succulent J.* **32**, 72 (1960); R. M. Turner and J. R. Hastings, *Bull. Ecol. Soc. Am.* **43**, 97 (1962). See also S. E. McGregor, S. M. Alcorn, G. Olin, *Ecology* **43**, 259 (1962); C. H. Lowe, in *Arid Lands Colloq.* **1**, 54 (1959); S. M. Alcorn, *ibid.* **2**, 30 (1961); J. R. Hastings, *ibid.*, p. 30; —— and S. M. Alcorn, *J. Ariz. Acad. Sci.* **2**, 32 (1961); F. Shreve, *Cactus and Succulent J.* **7**, 66 (1935); A. M. Boyle, *Phytopathol.* **39**, 1029 (1949); A. F. Hemenway, *Am. J. Botany* **21**, 513 (1934); S. M. Alcorn and C. May, *Plant Disease Reptr.* **46**, 156 (1962).

3. In this article we discuss a project ("A study of southwestern mountain vegetation") supported by the National Science Foundation and an Arid Lands project supported by the Rockefeller Foundation. We thank S. M. Alcorn, R. R. Humphrey, E. B. Kurtz, Jr., H. J. Lutz, and R. M. Turner for comments on the manuscript.
4. F. Shreve, "Vegetation of the Sonoran Desert," *Carnegie Inst. Wash. Publ.* **591** (1951) (1951).
5. S. E. McGregor, S. M. Alcorn, G. Olin, *Ecology* **43**, 259 (1962).
6. C. H. Lowe, *Arid Lands Colloq.* **1**, 54 (1959).
7. S. M. Alcorn, *ibid.* **2**, 30 (1961).
8. J. R. Hastings, *ibid.*, p. 30; —— and S. M. Alcorn, *J. Ariz. Acad. Sci.* **2**, 32 (1961).
9. F. Shreve, *Cactus and Succulent J.* **7**, 66 (1935).
10. J. R. Hastings, thesis, University of Arizona (1963).
11. A. M. Boyle, *Phytopathol.* **39**, 1029 (1949).
12. A. F. Hemenway, *Am. J. Botany* **21**, 513 (1934).
13. R. H. Whittaker, *Northwest Sci.* **25**, 17 (1951); R. T. Brown and J. T. Curtis, *Ecol. Monographs* **22**, 217 (1952).
14. R. H. Whittaker, *ibid.* **26**, 1 (1956).
15. R. Knapp, *Experimentalle Soziologie der höheren Pflanzen* (Ulmer, Stuttgart, 1954).
16. F. Shreve, "The vegetation of a desert mountain range as conditioned by climatic factors," *Carnegie Inst. Wash. Publ.* **217** (1915) (1915).
17. ——, *Plant World* **14**, 136 (1911).
18. R. S. Felger, thesis, University of Arizona (1959).
19. G. A. Pearson, *Ecology* **1**, 139, 289 (1920).
20. L. Benson, *The Cacti of Arizona* (Univ. of Arizona Press, Tucson, ed. 2, 1950).
21. T. W. Yang, thesis, University of Arizona (1957); —— and C. H. Lowe, Jr., *Science* **123**, 542 (1956).
22. W. V. Turnage and A. L. Hinckley, *Ecol. Monographs* **8**, 529 (1938).
23. P. Hamilton, *The Resources of Arizona*
(Bancroft, San Francisco, ed. 3, 1884).
24. J. J. Thornber, *Univ. of Arizona Agricultural Experiment Station Bull.* **65** (1910), p. 245.
25. J. J. Wagoner, *Univ. of Arizona Social Sciences Bull.* **20** (1952), p. 1.
26. C. W. Thornthwaite, C. F. S. Sharpe, E. F. Dosch, *U.S. Department of Agriculture Tech. Bull.* **808** (1942), p. 1.
27. D. Griffiths, *U.S. Department of Agriculture Bureau of Plant Industries Bull.* **4** (1901), p. 1; G. E. P. Smith, *Univ. of Arizona Agricultural Experiment Station Bull.* **64** (1910), p. 81; ——, *Univ. of Arizona Agricultural Experiment Station Tech. Bull.* **77** (1938), p. 45.
28. J. R. Hastings, *Arid Lands Colloq.* **1**, 24 (1959); *J. Ariz. Acad. Sci.* **1**, 60 (1959).
29. R. R. Humphrey, *Botan. Rev.* **24**, 193 (1958); *Univ. of Arizona Agricultural Experiment Station Bull.* **299** (1958), p. 1.
30. ——, *ibid.* **302** (1960), p. 1.
31. C. T. Vorhies and W. P. Taylor, *Univ. of Arizona Agricultural Experiment Station Tech. Bull.* **86** (1940), p. 455; D. A. Spencer and A. L. Spencer, *J. Mammal.* **22**, 280 (1941).
32. C. T. Vorhies and W. P. Taylor, *Univ. of Arizona Agricultural Experiment Station Tech. Bull.* **49** (1933), p. 1; W. P. Taylor, C. T. Vorhies, P. B. Lister, *J. Forestry* **33**, 490 (1935).
33. The grazing allotment in 1957 was 353 cattle for a total Monument area of 9280 hectares (22,940 acres). After a fence had been constructed in 1958 to exclude cattle from the bajada, the grazing allotment was 262 in 1958 and 331 in 1962, on a grazed area of 7060 hectares (17,438 acres).
34. S. M. Alcorn and C. May, *Plant Disease Reptr.* **46**, 156 (1962).
35. F. Shreve, *Plant World* **14**, 289 (1911).
36. K. Bryan, *Science* **62**, 338 (1925); ——, *Ecology* **9**, 474 (1928); ——, *New Mexico Quart.* **10**, 227 (1940); H. V. Peterson, in *Applied Sedimentation*, P. D. Trask, Ed. (Wiley, New York, 1950), pp. 407–434; L. B. Leopold, *Trans. Am. Geophys. Union* **32**, 347 (1951); S. A. Schumm and R. F. Hadley, *Am. J. Sci.* **255**, 161 (1957).
37. J. E. McDonald, *Univ. of Arizona Institute of Atmospheric Physics Tech. Rept.* **1** (1956), p. 1.
38. J. L. Rich, *Am. J. Sci.* **32**, 237 (1911); R. W. Bailey, *J. Geol.* **43**, 337 (1935); C. K. Cooperrider and B. A. Hendricks, *U.S. Department of Agriculture Tech. Bull.* **567** (1937), p. 1; W. P. Cottam and G. Stewart, *J. Forestry* **38**, 613 (1940); E. Antevs, *J. Geol.* **60**, 375 (1952).

*Reprinted from*

THE CANADIAN ENTOMOLOGIST

Volume 96, Numbers 1-2, Jan.-Feb. 1964

# Qualitative Changes in Populations in Unstable Environments[1]

*By* W. G. WELLINGTON

Forest Entomology and Pathology Laboratory, Victoria, B.C.

**Abstract**                                          *Canad. Ent.* 96: 436-451 (1964)

Inactive moths of *Malacosoma pluviale* (Dyar) oviposit near their birthplaces, and most of their offspring also are inactive. More active moths can travel farther before they oviposit, and always have a higher proportion of vigorous individuals among their progeny.

Such polymorphism allows the insect to cope with environmental diversity; e.g., inactive residents exploit favourable habitats, and active migrants colonize more severe habitats, or replenish the vigour of other populations.

Because the most active moths usually export the most vigorous progeny, the population left behind becomes less vigorous during successive generations. This steadily decreasing vitality eliminates local populations that are not replenished by vigorous immigrants.

Qualitative changes in *Malacosoma* populations follow this basic pattern, but the rate of deterioration is affected by the habitat. Departing migrants fly too high to be stopped by small trees in farmland, but many are stopped near their source by tall trees in forests. Deterioration therefore is slower in forests. Forests also delay return migration to nearby farmlands, and thus allow some farmland populations to deteriorate unchecked.

In a fluctuating climate, the size of the area tolerable for the species varies annually. When it begins to expand, the vigorous progeny of active moths can take immediate advantage of slight local improvements. Consequently, they are the first to exploit each marginal habitat that becomes tolerable. But while better climate persists, some less active descendants of these pioneers appear in all occupied habitats.

When the regional climate deteriorates, the tolerable area contracts, and *most* marginal populations are *totally* destroyed. Moreover, even within the contracted tolerable area, the harsher climate becomes intolerable for any deteriorated stock. In the next generation, therefore, the only regional survivors are vigorous colonies deposited in the tolerable area by some of the few migrants that escaped the widespread destruction of the preceding generation in the margins. Their descendants recolonize depopulated sections of the refuge, and so preserve the species in the region while the climate remains severe.

[1]Contribution No. 977, Forest Entomology and Pathology Branch, Department of Forestry, Ottawa, Canada. A paper presented during the Centennial of Entomology in Canada, Ottawa, September 1963.

## Introduction

Although natural control of populations may depend to a large extent on changes in their physical and biotic environments, our attempts to explain the regulation of animal numbers solely in terms of these changes are not always convincing. Perhaps they might be improved if we also considered some inherent properties of the animals concerned.

The literature of population genetics contains ample evidence that qualitative differences exist between the victims and the survivors of changing stresses: and studies of sensory physiology have shown that these differences also may be expressed in behavioural terms. This is not surprising, because what an animal does — and how it does it — may determine whether or not it survives. And whenever survival is a matter of having the proper attributes, the structure of later generations is inevitably affected. It seems unwise to neglect such effects in our studies of population dynamics.

I have presented evidence before to show why I believe that ecologists should study the qualitative structure of populations if they hope to build a more effective population theory. Earlier reports were concerned with descriptions of qualitative differences observed in populations of the western tent caterpillar, *Malacosoma pluviale* (Dyar), near Victoria, B.C., and with some of the changes in quality noticeable between generations (Wellington 1957b, 1959, 1960, 1962). The first part of this paper describes self-regulatory mechanisms that may produce these changes wherever the insect lives. The remaining parts show how different habitats or changing climates often modify the effects of these mechanisms.

## Expressions of the Qualitative Differences

Each western tent caterpillar female deposits its full complement of eggs in a single mass. The larvae that emerge display different amounts of activity, and they also differ in their ability to perform directed movements in response to environmental stimuli. Some are agile and capable of independent, directed movements while they are separated from their fellows. These we call Type I larvae (Wellington 1957b). The rest (Type II) cannot respond effectively to sources of stimulation while they are isolated.

But different kinds of Type II larvae display different amounts of activity (Wellington 1957b, 1960). Type IIa larvae are nearly as active as Type I individuals: they are simply too disorientated to travel far alone. Type IIb larvae are less active, and IIc larvae are so sluggish that they seldom move. In fact, some cannot free themselves from their eggs.

These differences in activity and behaviour affect rates of development and survival after eclosion (Wellington 1957b, 1960). They persist in modified form into the adult stage, when they appear as differences in responsiveness and in flight capacity. For example, a Type I larva gives rise to a very active adult, whereas a Type IIb larva transforms to a rather sluggish moth. The level of adult activity in turn provides a clear indication of the kind of progeny a female may produce (Table I).

The progeny of any female display a wide range of activity, but the proportions of active and less active individuals that emerge from her eggs vary with her own position on the activity scale (Table I). An active female that is capable of lengthy pre-oviposition flights has a good complement of the active types of larvae (I and IIa) among her progeny, but very few of the most sluggish type. The progeny of less active females include fewer Type I larvae, and correspondingly larger proportions of Types IIb and IIc. These mixtures affect the level of group activity in the colonies that form soon after eclosion. The most active groups have the largest proportion of agile larvae (Wellington 1957b, 1960).

TABLE I

Types of progeny produced by *M. pluviale* females differing in activity and flight capacity

| Type of moth: | Longest single flight (min.) | Types of progeny | | | | | | |
|---|---|---|---|---|---|---|---|---|
| | | I | IIa | IIb | IIc | Unhatched larvae | Partly developed embryos | Totals |
| Active (I) | 15.0 | 47 | 59 | 109 | 8 | 3 | 5 | 231 |
| Inactive (IIb) | 0.5 | 4 | 17 | 77 | 27 | 15 | 30 | 170 |

The level of colonial activity is expressed in several ways (Wellington 1957b, 1960, 1962). The more active colonies forage farther from their tents, and usually develop faster than less active groups. But the size, shape, and number of tents per colony reflect the group's past and present behaviour and activity very accurately. Consequently, a large amount of information concerning the structure of any local population can be gathered by counting and classifying all its tents. Fig. 1 shows examples of the different kinds that should be distinguished during surveys of local populations (see also Wellington 1957b, 1962).

The tents shown in Fig. 1 are products of fourth-instar larvae; i.e., they are the largest their respective colonies could construct. With certain exceptions

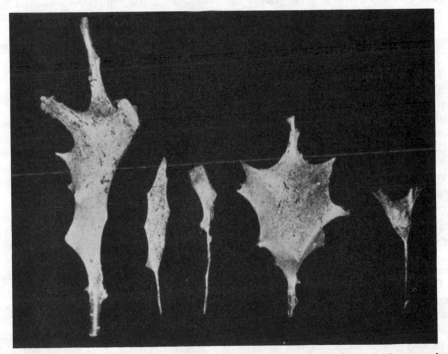

Fig. 1. Five kinds of fourth-instar tents that should be distinguished during population surveys. The arrangement from left to right shows the decreasing amounts of activity displayed by the colonies in the fourth instar, but the colony that formed the large compact tent had been more active earlier. Until it lost agile larvae during the third instar, it made elongate tents: thereafter, its activity declined, and the tent shape changed. Size ranges for each type: *Elongate*— large, > 8 inches; medium > 5 < 8 inches; small, < 5 inches. *Compact*— large, > 4 inches; small, < 1 inches. Specimen dimensions: *Elongate*— large, 14 x 4.75 inches (35.6 x 12.1 cm.); medium, 7 x 1.5 inches (17.8 x 3.8 cm.); small, 4 x 1.25 inches (10.2 x 3.2 cm.). *Compact*— large, 8 x 6 inches (20.3 x 15.2 cm.); small, 3 x 2.25 inches (7.6 x 5.7 cm.).

165

(Wellington 1962), the size of a tent indicates the activity level of its builders: the smaller the tent, the less active the colony. Similarly, a change in tent shape from elongate to compact during the life of a colony indicates some loss of the agile members, with a corresponding reduction in group activity. The least active colonies — products of females that are just capable of successful oviposition—make very small tents. Most of these tents are compact and pyramidal, but some are elongate (i.e., clavate). The shape depends on the proportions of the different types of larvae that emerge and establish themselves successfully.

This knowledge helps us to understand what is happening in any local population. We can estimate the activity levels of the parents while we record the qualitative differences displayed by their progeny. And we can make annual comparisons, even while numbers are very small, because the tents are so easy to find. Thus we can search with some hope of success for the mechanisms that operate in a population at low density and during release.

## Qualitative Changes in Natural Populations

*Intrinsic Mechanisms*

The basic mechanism of qualitative change in a local population can be understood best by following the sequence of events depicted in Fig. 2. This shows the establishment of an infestation in a new locality. If such places are several miles from the nearest source of moths, only the vigorous females from this source can fly far enough to reach them. The colonies that develop from their eggs are all extremely active, with large clavate tents and lengthy foraging highways. Fig. 2 shows the progressive deterioration in quality that takes place during subsequent generations in the immediate vicinity of one such colony.

In a favourable environment, many of the active members of the pioneer colony reach the adult stage. The most active become vigorous moths, capable of initial flights of 15 min. or more, even while laden with eggs. Therefore, if nothing arrests them at their birthplace, they fly away before they oviposit. But the high level of group activity during the colonial period also ensures the survival of many of the less active members (Wellington 1960). These have reduced flight capacities (Table I). In fact, some are scarcely able to fly, and none can fly very far. Consequently, the second resident generation includes all their progeny, but only some of the progeny of stronger fliers.

The colonies these inactive moths produce are less active than the pioneer colony: i.e., they each have fewer active and more inactive members (Table I). Therefore, they contribute an even greater proportion of inactive colonies to the third resident generation. And so the process of deterioration accelerates. An increasing number of increasingly sluggish resident colonies each produce fewer and fewer active individuals. Eventually, the proportion of active members per colony becomes so small that whole colonies die. (They become too sluggish to leave their tents to feed (Wellington 1957b, 1960).) Local extinction due to increasing sluggishness is thus inevitable, unless better-quality immigrants arrive in the locality. But migrants do not always appear in areas as small as the one shown in Fig. 2. Consequently, restricted populations often collapse, especially when they are isolated in any way from other sources.

The very local type of deterioration described above takes place in any habitat. It is simply a product of the different flight capacities of active and inactive moths. But it requires at least four generations for its fullest expression. Therefore, favourable climate must persist that long to allow the deteriorating stock to exterminate itself. Sometimes, the period of favourable climate is sufficiently prolonged: sometimes it is not. Before we discuss the effects of change-

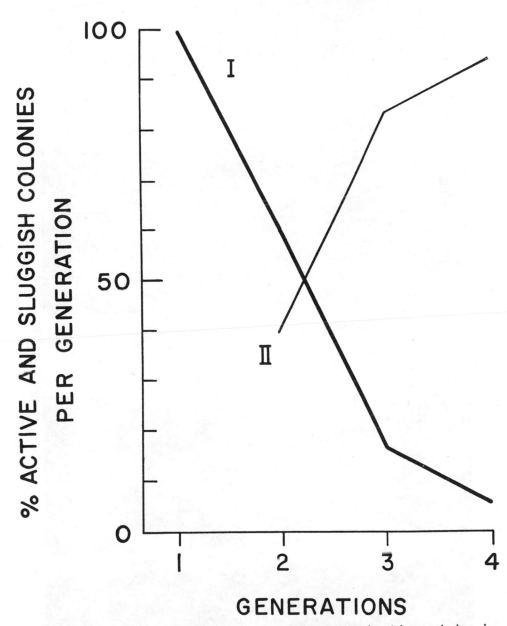

Fig 2. Progressive deterioration of a small population that developed from a single active colony. Curve I: annual changes in the percentage of active colonies that formed large or medium elongate tents. Curve II: percentages of inactive colonies that formed compact or small elongate tents. In four generations, numbers were: large— 1,0,0,0; medium— 0,3,2,1; small— 0,1,6,6; compact— 0,1,4,12. Distance occupied: 0.05 mile of roadside hedgerows.

Fig. 3.   Typical farmland habitat:   most of the trees are less than 15 ft. high.

Fig. 4.   Forest habitat:   some of the deciduous trees are taller than 80 ft.

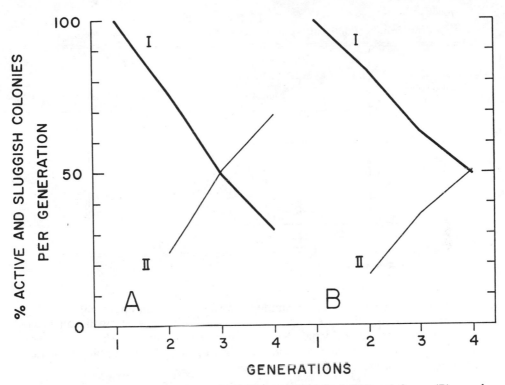

Fig. 5. Differences in the rate of deterioration of farmland (A) and forest (B) populations. In both diagrams, curves I and II show the annual changes in the percentages of active and inactive colonies, respectively. Numbers per generation in A were: 8, 25, 117, 208; in B: 4, 18, 80, 153. Distances occupied: 1.5 miles of roadside vegetation in each habitat.

able climate, however, we must examine the effects of different tree heights and densities in areas larger than that in Fig. 2.

*Modifications Imposed by Different Habitats*

In areas a square mile or more in extent, patterns of population change begin to show some dependence on the size and spacing of the trees within the habitat. In farmland that has only scattered clumps of small trees (Fig. 3), the pattern of population change in large areas still resembles that in Fig. 2. This is shown in Fig. 5a. But a modified pattern emerges in forests that have extensive areas of tall trees (Figs. 4 and 5b). The proportion of active colonies per generation does not decrease so rapidly in large forests as it does in open country, and so it remains higher than the percentage of inactive colonies for at least one more generation (Fig. 5b). (Moreover, intermediate types of country, less open than in Fig. 3, but more open than in Fig. 4, have intermediate types of population change, in which the gap between the two curves in the fourth generation is not so large as it is in Fig. 5a.)

The maximum height of trees in the vicinity of Fig. 3 was less than 30 ft. Many were less than 15 ft. high. In contrast, some of the deciduous trees in the vicinity of Fig. 4 were taller than 80 ft. Any type of colony may occur on the topmost branches of small trees, but colonies with small pyramidal tents do not occur above 30 ft., and the size and activity of the remaining types of colonies increase with height. This stratification is illustrated in Table II.

TABLE II

Stratification of different types of colonies on newly infested *Alnus* sp.

| Colony height (ft.) | Types of fourth-instar tents* | | | | |
| | Elongate | | | Compact | |
| | Large | Medium | Small | Large | Small |
|---|---|---|---|---|---|
| 50–60 | 9 | – | – | – | – |
| 40–50 | 9 | 4 | – | – | – |
| 30–40 | 2 | 6 | 4 | 1 | – |
| 20–30 | – | 3 | 3 | – | – |
| 10–20 | 2 | 3 | 2 | – | 1 |
| 0–10 | – | 1 | – | – | – |
| | 22 | 17 | 9 | 1 | 1 |

*See Fig. 1 legend for size ranges.

Table II was derived from a sudden invasion of a clump of 60-ft. alders approximately 0.1 sq. mile in extent. The height limitations of small and intermediate clavate tents are evident. Some very active colonies with large clavate tents also occurred at comparatively low levels, but many were higher than their less active counterparts.

Since colony activity reflects adult activity, stratification of colonies is a result of differences in the flight characteristics of active and less active females. Inactive females never oviposit high in the trees because they are too weak to fly upwards for long. On the other hand, vigorous females can fly sufficiently high to reach the tops of tall trees. Indeed, they often fly upwards (i.e., "tower") *before* they begin level flight (see also Southwood 1962).

Moths that tower fly far above most potential obstructions in open country. Unless they encounter obstructions, they continue to fly until fatigue forces them to stop. Table III, from an isolated 40-ft. alder in open farmland, shows that they sometimes encounter the upper parts of tall trees in otherwise low vegetation. But where such trees are rare, many vigorous adults may travel far before they settle. The curves of Fig. 5a show the consequences for the population they desert.

TABLE III

Stratification of elongate tents on an isolated 40-ft. tree in otherwise low vegetation

| Colony height (ft.) | Tent size | | |
| | Large | Medium | Small |
|---|---|---|---|
| 27–35 | 3 | 1 | – |
| 19–27 | – | 4 | – |
| 8–19 | – | 2 | 4 |
| | 3 | 7 | 4 |

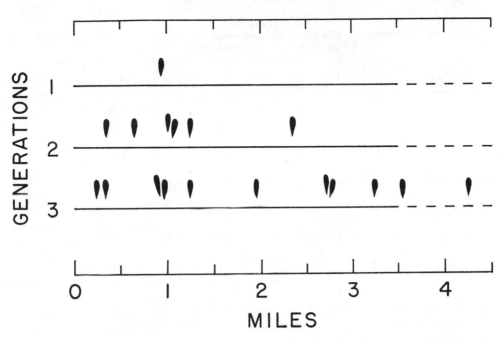

Fig. 6. The distribution of extremely active colonies along a forested roadside after the first colony was established in the area. Solid lines: virtually unbroken lines of tall trees along both sides of the road. Broken lines: a section of road in which there were occasional patches of lower vegetation.

In extensive tracts of forest, many active moths soon encounter tall trees. Although some females still manage to fly considerable distances before they oviposit, many stop sooner than they would in open country. Thus they still contribute to their own population, and so maintain a higher proportion of vigorous colonies within it for a time (Fig. 5b).

Fig. 6 shows the spread of active colonies along a forested roadside after the establishment of a single pioneer colony in the area. The country of the left-hand side of the diagram resembled that in Fig. 4, so that even towering moths were channeled along the road by the bordering stands of very tall conifers that backed the deciduous trees. Consequently, few active females were able to fly very far without encountering tall deciduous trees. Slightly longer flights were possible where occasional patches of lower vegetation broke the roadside fringes of tall trees. (This part of the road is indicated by broken lines in the diagram.)

Shorter flights not only delay deterioration of woodland populations; they also affect the interchange of vigorous individuals between open and forested areas. Drainage of vigorous moths from open to wooded country may go on for several generations before any appreciable reverse flow can develop. In the patchwork of forests and farmlands near Victoria, such delays in the return movement of vigorous moths from forests to farmland allow the farmland populations to deteriorate unchecked.

In one farmland population between 1956 and 1960, the percentages of adult females in three different activity categories varied as shown in Table IV. These data were obtained by drawing representative samples of 200 larvae from the population each year, classifying them according to their behaviour (Wellington 1957b, 1960), and rearing them to the adult stage in the laboratory. The adult females were placed in their respective activity categories by testing their flight

TABLE IV

Deterioration and resurgence of a farmland population: annual changes in the percentages of adult females in three different activity categories

| Female category: | 1956 | 1957 | 1958 | 1959 | 1960 |
|---|---|---|---|---|---|
| A. Active | 10.0 | 2.6 | 0.0 | 25.0 | 10.0 |
| B. Inactive | 30.0 | 20.5 | 63.6 | 42.9 | 53.3 |
| C. Extremely sluggish | 60.0 | 76.9 | 36.4 | 32.1 | 36.7 |

activity for two days after they emerged (Wellington 1957b, 1960). The categories shown in the table are: A—females vigorous enough to establish active colonies; B—other, less active females unable to produce active colonies; C—females too sluggish to oviposit.

There was a steady decline in the percentage of active females between 1956 and 1958 (Table IV), followed by a sudden increase in 1959. That increase was an expression of the rejuvenation of the population during the 1958 oviposition period. But by 1958, the farmland population had been reduced to 49 colonies, none of which was active, and none of which survived. Nevertheless, in 1959, 50 colonies were established in the area; 13 of these (26%) were extremely active, and none was sluggish.

In 1958, the proportion of active females in samples from the surrounding forests ranged between 11 and 21%. These records show that the forests eventually supplied population to the farmland, but they also show the lag in the replenishment process. Prior to 1958, there were even higher percentages of active adults in the forests; e.g., 36.4% in one infestation in 1956. But all the adults produced in the woodland were absorbed there until 1958, when some took flight sufficiently close to the forest border to return easily to open country.

## Some Climatic Effects

Severe climate in surrounding areas also may delay the replenishment of deteriorating populations. Many of the present forests near Victoria are located in rugged terrain where the average climate makes intensive agriculture unprofitable as a long-term venture. The climates of such forests often are severe, and sometimes they are intolerable for tent caterpillars.

The moths of each generation of *Malacosoma* disperse and oviposit during stable summer weather, when microclimatic differences between trees in hillside forests and in valley farmlands may be comparatively small. But their progeny emerge early in the following spring, when the weather is more variable, and differences among terrain climates — and so between tree climates — may be large or small. Whether or not the progeny survive depends on the local climate they encounter after eclosion.

The young larvae require frequent sunshine and occasional rainfall during their first instar (Wellington 1958). Sunshine warms their tent so that they can feed during periods of low air temperature. Occasional rainfall protects them from desiccation. But rainfall also makes them sluggish, and they may starve if it is too prolonged. During prolonged cloudiness, of course, they are too cold to feed. When the weather is variable, active colonies are able to resume feeding more quickly than their sluggish counterparts. Consequently, they can survive in wetter, cloudier areas. But even they succumb if clouds and rain prolong their first instar much beyond 30 days.

Between 1953 and 1956, the regional circulation was characterized by annual decreases in the amount of westerly airflow each spring. On Vancouver Island, westerly airflow increases rainfall and cloudiness, but terrain effects produce more cloud and rainfall over hills than over valleys (Wellington 1954, 1957a, 1958). As the frequency of westerly flow decreased, therefore, the climates of valley farmland became increasingly favourable for all types of tent caterpillars, but many of the hillside forests remained intolerable for the most vigorous tent caterpillars until 1956. Active moths entered such forests during each summer flight, but their progeny died regularly until the spring of 1956.

In the spring of 1956, there was minimal westerly flow, and long periods of cloudless weather occurred over the hillside forests as well as in valley farmlands. Thus the area favourable for tent caterpillars suddenly expanded, and peak abundance coincided with maximum distribution. But this delayed establishment of vigorous populations in marginal forests meant that many farmland populations had already begun to deteriorate before their potential sources of replenishment even existed. This delay also affected the population illustrated in Table IV. The effects of terrain climates during subsequent years may be seen in Fig. 7. This shows climatic differences observed between a hill and its adjacent valley during the periods of first-instar development, 1956-1962.

After 1956, spring weather deteriorated until 1958. But even in 1958, the mosaic of terrain climates provided some pockets that were tolerable for the most vigorous colonies (Fig. 7). Even the least severe climates were intolerable for weaker colonies, however. The species was eliminated, therefore, wherever weak colonies were its only representatives in 1958; e.g., in parts of the valley farmlands (Table IV). Whether this elimination was brief (Table IV), or more prolonged, depended on the fate of the marginal populations that surrounded these places (Fig. 7).

For example, the most severe hill climates of 1958 destroyed any marginal population exposed to them, irrespective of its quality. Farmlands adjacent to such hills were not immediately repopulated. But in some of the more gradual transition zones between hills and valleys, weather of intermediate severity killed only the weak, and left a small residue of vigorous stock. It was this stock that promptly re-entered some of the depopulated farmlands (Table IV). Since this happened in only a few places, however, the regional population remained much reduced in numbers and extent in the spring of 1959. In that year, the surviving population was virtually restricted to farmland refuges. The vigorous individuals that withstood 1958 left few offspring capable of surviving elsewhere.

Spring weather was more favourable between 1959 and 1962. But the tolerable area expanded more gradually than it contracted (Fig. 7), and the spring of 1962 was the first in which re-establishment could take place in the most severe terrain climates. In the intervening years, pioneers from occupied refuges slowly reoccupied others left empty in 1958. They also entered marginal habitats, but their progeny died wherever the climate remained severe. During this period, however, climates in the centres of farmland refuges improved sufficiently for less active colonies to survive (Fig. 7), so that qualitative deterioration began in the oldest populations (Figs. 2 and 5a).

The sequence of events prior to 1956 was thus repeated between 1958 and 1962. Severe climate at first prevented vigorous colonies from occupying marginal environments, and this delay contributed to the collapse of a few older populations in the farmland refuges while their environment actually was favourable (cf. Milne 1962). And as marginal forests became habitable, their extensive areas of tall trees imposed a further delay by hindering emigration of their vigorous populations to adjacent refuges. Redistribution of the regional population

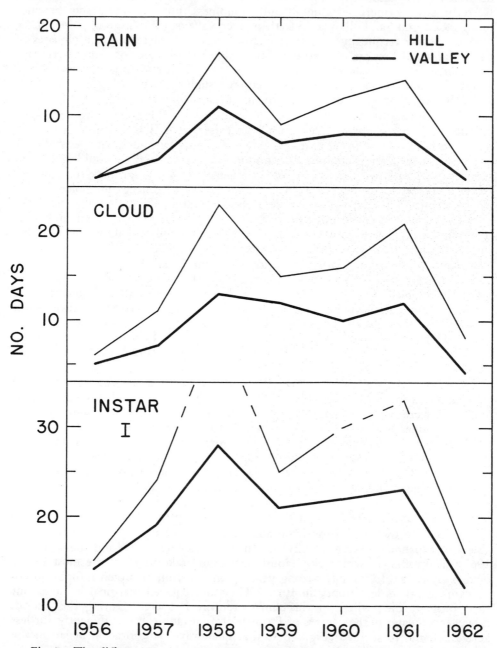

Fig. 7. The different numbers of cloudy and rainy days recorded in a valley and on an adjacent hill during the first emergence and subsequent development of first-instar larvae in the two localities. Broken lines: years in which there was virtually no survival of first-instar larvae that emerged on the hill during the periods illustrated. The period of first-instar development always included part of April, but occasionally began late in March or ended early in May.

after 1958 thus was delayed by the same environmental factors that operated before 1956.

Furthermore, these delays are bound to affect distribution and abundance when the tolerable area contracts again. Many refuges will be depopulated when more severe climate returns, because there will not have been sufficient time (Birch 1962) to replenish their weak populations with vigorous immigrants. And since most of the vigorous colonies in marginal areas also will die when their habitats become intolerable (Andrewartha 1961; Andrewartha and Birch 1954; Birch 1957), the few vigorous individuals that re-enter the refuges once again will be the only survivors in the region.

In this section, I have emphasized the adverse consequences of delayed migration between the different habitats of an unstable climatic mosaic. This emphasis was reasonable, because the consequences for many individuals are disastrous. But the delays imposed by severe climates on the establishment of vigorous populations in some habitats also ensure the survival of this species in its unstable environment. They counterbalance inevitable deterioration in all localities by providing a succession of new, and therefore extremely vigorous, populations in different localities during the years in which climate improves and distribution and abundance increase. Thus, while older populations deteriorate, there is always a nucleus of very vigorous, highly resistant stock on which the species can depend when the regional climate suddenly becomes more severe. This seems to be how qualitative differences operate in conjunction with climate to preserve the species in a heterogeneous, unstable environment. But it is preservation at the expense of most members of some generations!

### Discussion

The delays imposed on establishment and dispersal by physical and biotic aspects of habitats influence the distribution and population dynamics of the western tent caterpillar by affecting individuals that have varying abilities and requirements. But it is not difficult to see that the physiological differences involved also may have their own effects on population dynamics in any habitat. Not all forests have marginal climates. And wherever the environment remains favourable for a few generations, excessive deterioration of the local population may occur. Tall trees may slow the process by arresting some vigorous emigrants (Fig. 6): they do not stop it (Fig. 5).

Extreme deterioration of a local population, therefore, is first a product of differential dispersal, and then a product of time and climate. Increasing term of residence in a favourable locality is always accompanied by steady accumulation of more and more sluggish individuals. The deaths that follow, however, are not related to increasing density. Nor are they necessarily related to any further action of physical or biotic factors of the environment (see also Chitty 1960). Sluggish individuals (and colonies) die in sparse as well as in dense populations. They die in the absence of enemies, while exposed to a favourable climate, and surrounded by abundant food. They are simply too sluggish to leave their tents, and so they starve. One might argue that they become too weak to withstand the supposedly favourable climate, but this is not so. They survive in the laboratory in climates less favourable than the best they encounter in the field, as long as they are kept directly on their food (Wellington 1957b).

There is some conflict between the facts in the preceding paragraph and recent statements concerning the relative importance of population quality, intraspecific competition, and the total environment as population regulators (Milne 1962). Regulatory systems proposed by Milne (1962) and by others before him (Andrewartha and Birch 1954) for populations in general often seem applicable to

*M. pluviale* populations. But sometimes they are not. Climate is not always directly responsible for the collapse of these populations, and intraspecific competition never is. In some places, self-regulation through qualitative deterioration is the primary mechanism. Thus it forms an essential part of the explanation of the natural control of *M. pluviale* populations; a point which should be kept in mind during future discussions of general theory.

Annual surveys of the proportions of different types of individuals in different places provide several important clues during population studies. In the present work, the delaying effects of forests on dispersal could not have been established without some record of the heights at which different types of colonies were located on the trees: but such expressions of individual characteristics may have more general applications.

For example, the abundance of spring populations of the forest tent caterpillar (*M. disstria* Hbn.) may be predicted quite accurately during the preceding autumn by counting egg bands on the host trees. When numbers are declining, however, spring abundance will be consistently over-estimated if all the eggs on a tree are counted. The error arises because many eggs deposited low on the trees never hatch. Consequently, the estimates can be improved if one samples only the upper parts of tree crowns (G. T. Silver, personal communication, unpublished data).

This restriction of viable eggs to higher parts of trees is another expression of the flight characteristics of vigorous females. But it also is an example of the different approach to population studies that can be developed through consideration of qualitative differences. In population studies, there are various methods of measuring mortality within each generation, but no ordinary method can distinguish individuals that may survive from those that are bound to die. In populations of *M. pluviale*, however, we are now able to recognize a class of individuals that *cannot* survive in any environment. We can therefore neglect these individuals and concentrate on the potential survivors: the only individuals that can affect the next generation. It should be possible to do this with other species as well as with *Malacosoma*.

The method has interesting possibilities. For example, in order to eliminate *M. pluviale* from a large area when its numbers are small, it is only necessary to kill the few active colonies that can produce survivors. Sluggish colonies can be left to die of their own ineptitude. Of course, this method is feasible only because the insect builds conspicuous tents, but it shows how qualitative differences may affect control operations. (Species that do not display their differences so conspicuously might still be treated on an areal basis; e.g., control measures could be restricted to areas where the population was most vigorous. Such areas could be identified by testing the activity of representative groups drawn from their populations.)

Variations in behaviour or activity have received only limited attention in many investigations of population dynamics. This seems unrealistic, since there is much concern with variations in developmental rate, survival, and reproductive success, all of which are consequences of differences in behaviour or activity. Our understanding of population phenomena will be incomplete until we know how the actions of individuals contribute to their success or failure in different environments. Above all, we need more information on the qualities of the survivors of each generation, since these attributes determine the structure, if not the numbers and distribution, of the next. No one would deny the folly of severing population studies from their evolutionary roots by neglecting an important cause of natural selection (Orians 1962). But that is what we do when we neglect qualitative differences among the animals we study.

## Conclusions

*Malacosoma* copes with environmental instability by maintaining sufficiently wide ranges of behaviour and activity in all its stages of development to survive *temporarily* in a variety of temporary habitats. Adult emigration also helps to reduce the chances of extinction in these unstable environments. Persistent probing of the diversity of their surroundings by the moths of each generation ensures that potentially suitable territory will not be overlooked by pioneers that regularly leave source areas at every source density (see also Johnson 1960; Kennedy 1961; Southwood 1962). But the qualitative differences between the moths that leave and those that stay have important population consequences.

Differences in flight capacity divide the adults of each generation into obligatory residents and migrants (Southwood 1962). Increased tree heights in forests may decrease the flight range of active migrants; but even in dense forests, active moths are the only individuals capable of travelling appreciable distances from their birthplace. Therefore, they are most likely to colonize new habitats. They also are most likely to waste their progeny in unsuitable places.

Both colonization and wastage affect the structure of the populations these migrants desert, because both involve export of the most vigorous parents and progeny. In unstable environments, however, export of maximum vigour from refuge populations is necessary for successful colonization of the less hospitable places outside. It is convenient, to say the least, that the pioneers likely to penetrate farthest into marginal habitats also produce the most resistant progeny. Such individuals are able to take immediate advantage of a slight improvement in a marginal climate.

In many instances, occupation of marginal habitats by vigorous pioneers eventually leads to local increase and diversification, since climatic improvement, once begun, tends to continue for a time. The initial stages of diversification also are advantageous, since they provide some less active individuals for further exploitation of the immediate habitat as well as more pioneers for further extension of the range, and for ultimate replenishment of the original refugia. Local exploitation, range extension, and replenishment are all forms of insurance against environmental instability. But the qualitative deterioration these processes leave in their wake has adverse population consequences wherever maximum favourability of the local environment is maintained for three or four generations.

Some of these findings may have broader applications, because other animals with similar (Laux 1962; Laux and Franz 1962) or with very different (Campbell 1962; Chiang 1961) habits seem to have similar attributes. In addition, many species that fluctuate markedly in abundance also occupy habitats that are biologically or physically unstable. Such animals should be examined for traces of polymorphism similar to those recorded here; or for other physiological differences that could have comparable effects on their population dynamics.

### Acknowledgments

I am indebted to R. R. Lejeune, J. A. Chapman and G. T. Silver for their many helpful discussions of the problems that arose during this investigation; and G. T. Silver also is to be thanked for permitting inclusion of some unpublished observations in the paper. Dennis Chitty, of the University of British Columbia, deserves special thanks for some trenchant criticism and several stimulating ideas, all of which have been very helpful. Several students and technicians have helped during annual surveys, but in recent years, Mrs. T. McIlveen and Miss Sandra Lee have done the final compilations. Miss Lee also prepared the diagrams, and A. Craigmyle supplied the photographs.

## References

Andrewartha, H. G. 1961. Introduction to the study of animal populations. University of Chicago Press, Chicago.

Andrewartha, H. G., and L. C. Birch. 1954. The distribution and abundance of animals. University of Chicago Press, Chicago.

Birch, L. C. 1957. The role of weather in determining the distribution and abundance of animals. *Cold Spr. Harb. Symp. quant. Biol.* 22: 203-218.

Birch, L. C. 1962. Stability and instability in natural populations. *N.Z. Sci. Rev.* 20: 9-14.

Campbell, I. M. 1962. Reproductive capacity in the genus *Choristoneura* Led. (Lepidoptera: Tortricidae). I. Quantitative inheritance and genes as controllers of rates. *Canad. J. Genet. Cytol.* 4: 272-288.

Chiang, H. C. 1961. Fringe populations of the European corn borer, *Pyrausta nubilalis*: their characteristics and problems. *Ann. ent. Soc. Amer.* 54: 378-387.

Chitty, D. 1960. Population processes in the vole and their relevance to general theory. *Canad. J. Zool.* 38: 99-113.

Johnson, C. G. 1960. A basis for a general system of insect migration and dispersal by flight. *Nature, Lond.* 186: 348-350.

Kennedy, J. S. 1961. A turning point in the study of insect migration. *Nature, Lond.* 189: 785-791.

Laux, W. 1962. Individuelle Unterschiede in Verhalten und Leistung des Ringelspinners, *Malacosoma neustria* (L.). *Z. angew. Ent.* 49: 465-524.

Laux, W., and J. M. Franz. 1962. Über das Auftreten von Individualunterschieden beim Ringelspinner, *Malacosoma neustria* (L.). *Z. angew. Ent.* 50: 105-109.

Milne, A. 1962. On a theory of natural control of insect population. *J. theoret. Biol.* 3: 19-50.

Orians, G. H. 1962. Natural selection and ecological theory. *Amer. Nat.* 96: 257-263.

Southwood, T. R. E. 1962. Migration of terrestrial arthropods in relation to habitat. *Biol. Rev.* 37: 171-214.

Wellington, W. G. 1954. Atmospheric circulation processes and insect ecology. *Canad. Ent.* 86: 312-333.

Wellington, W. G. 1957a. The synoptic approach to studies of insects and climate. *Annu. Rev. Ent.* 2: 143-162.

Wellington, W. G. 1957b. Individual differences as a factor in population dynamics: the development of a problem. *Canad. J. Zool.* 35: 293-323.

Wellington, W. G. 1958. Meteorology in population dynamics. *Int. J. Bioclim. Biomet.* 2 (Pt. III, Sect. B).

Wellington, W. G. 1959. Individual differences in larvae and egg masses of the western tent caterpillar. *Can. Dep. Agric. For. Biol. Div. Bi-m. Prog. Rep.* 15: 3-4.

Wellington, W. G. 1960. Qualitative changes in natural populations during changes in abundance. *Canad. J. Zool.* 38: 289-314.

Wellington, W. G. 1962. Population quality and the maintenance of nuclear polyhedrosis between outbreaks of *Malacosoma pluviale* (Dyar). *J. Ins. Pathol.* 4: 285-305.

Reprinted from *J. Anim. Ecol.* **37**, 595–614, October 1968

# EXPERIMENTS ON POPULATION CONTROL BY TERRITORIAL BEHAVIOUR IN RED GROUSE

By ADAM WATSON and DAVID JENKINS*

*Nature Conservancy Unit of Grouse and Moorland Ecology,
Natural History Department, University of Aberdeen*

## INTRODUCTION

Male red grouse (*Lagopus lagopus scoticus* (Lath.)) contest for territory each autumn, and some males are successful while others fail to secure territories. This paper describes experiments undertaken to test whether males which were not occupying territories could become territorial if the established territory owners were removed; that is to say, whether the number of breeding males was being limited simply by the territorial accommodation available or by some deficiency in the unsuccessful birds.

Previous research consisted of counts of the grouse on 100–120 ha study areas on heather (*Calluna vulgaris* L. (Hull)) moorland in north-east Scotland, with more detailed studies of the behaviour of individually marked birds on smaller parts of these areas (Jenkins, Watson & Miller 1963, 1967). Territorial behaviour, courtship and pair formation are described by Watson & Jenkins (1964). The population studies showed that there were many more grouse in autumn, even after the grouse shooting was over, than in the following spring. The behaviour studies showed that grouse populations from October to May consisted of (a) cocks which courted hens and defended territories, plus hens paired with them (territorial birds), and (b) non-territorial birds which did not defend territories, show courtship, pair up, or breed. Classes (a) and (b) both included birds less than 1 year old (called 'young' in this paper) and older birds. On average, 52% of the August population later became non-territorial over the autumn and winter and died before the next April–May (Jenkins *et al.* 1967), whereas both young and old territorial grouse survived the winter well and bred next summer. Consequently we postulated (Jenkins *et al.* 1967) that possession of territory was essential for breeding, and that territorial behaviour in autumn greatly limited the size of the next spring's breeding stock.

These hypotheses were open to the criticism that although territorial behaviour was associated with the population changes, it might not really be preventing the non-territorial grouse from taking territories. The crux was to find if they would take territories and breed when vacant ground was made available. If they did not, the hypotheses would be refuted. One might then explain the presence of non-territorial birds simply by suggesting that they were immature individuals, as in many other species where some individuals do not breed till 2 years old or more.

## STUDY AREAS

Experiments before 1962 were done at Glen Esk in Angus, and subsequent experiments at Kerloch in Kincardineshire. The experimental areas at Glen Esk were on parts A1

* At Bureau of Animal Population 1952–56. This paper was offered as a tribute to Mr Charles Elton on his retirement from the Directorship of the B.A.P. but arrived too late to be included in the special issue of February 1968.

H    J.A.E.

and C (32 and 57 ha), separated by the 20 ha control area on part A2 and by a few fields (Fig. 1). All three areas were at about 230 m altitude. They were covered mainly by heather, which occurred in a patchwork of different ages due to fairly regular rotational burning in many small fires.

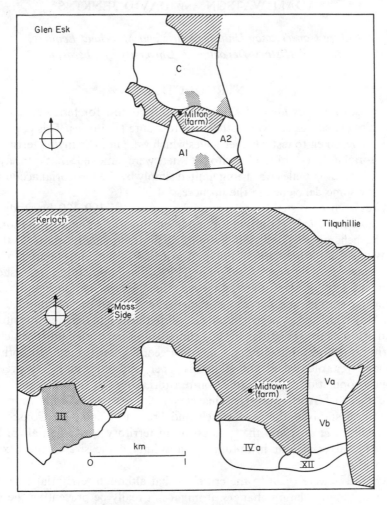

FIG. 1. Map of study areas at Glen Esk and Kerloch.

Notes: (a) The hatched areas show fields, scrub and woodland, and the rest is heather moorland, (b) the stippled areas indicate where removal experiments were done involving only part of a study area.

At Kerloch, the 40 ha experimental and the 32 ha control areas at parts V and IVa were on fairly uniform unburned heather at about 150–200 m altitude. Part IVa had a few boggy places, but was mostly dry and well drained like part V. Both areas were little grazed, except the south end of part V and the northern section of part IVa which were heavily grazed by cattle and sheep. The breeding stock of grouse on parts V and IVa remained fairly stable at twenty-three to twenty-seven and twenty-one to twenty-two birds in spring 1962 and 1963 before the experiments began, and was twenty-seven to thirty birds at part IVa during the 2 years of experiments, 1964–65.

Two other experimental areas at Kerloch were used less often. The 43 ha part III and the 12 ha part XII were mostly dry and well drained but with a few boggy places. They were covered mostly with heather that was fairly uniform and unburned, but heavily grazed by sheep and cattle.

## METHODS

A Land Rover was used as a mobile hide for making total counts (i.e. censuses) of all red grouse present (Jenkins *et al.* 1963) on the experimental and control areas, for studying their behaviour, and for shooting selected birds with a 0·22 in. rifle. The work began at Glen Esk, with three small experiments where grouse were caught in wire traps with funnel

Table 1. *Total numbers of individual territorial cocks removed and subsequently replaced, and of non-territorial cocks on nearby areas available for replacement*

| | No. of territorial cocks | | |
| Experiment | Removed (i.e. number at beginning) | Replaced (i.e. number at end)¶ | No. of non-territorial cocks† on nearby areas of 1 km² (excluding control areas) |
| --- | --- | --- | --- |
| 1 | 10§ | 10 | 23*‡ |
| 2 | 13 | 15 | 39* |
| 3 | 10 | 9 | 45* |
| 4 | 5 | 5 | 45* |
| 5 | 15 | 11 | 39 |
| 6 | 5 | 4 | 37 |
| 7 | 2 | 1 (temporary removal) | 26 |
| 8 | 3 | 0 (temporary removal) | 12 |
| 9 | 3 | 0 | 7 |
| 10 | 4 | 0 | 5 |
| 11 | 4 | 3 | 5 |
| 12 | 3 | 2 | 5 |
| 13 | 2 | 0 | 2 |

* In August–September (Experiments 1–4) the status of young birds was not yet known before removals were begun, and some would have become territorial in October in the absence of removals. These figures are therefore not exactly comparable with the rest. The young were not sexed, and the number of cocks in these cases is estimated by dividing the total number of young by two.

† The total number of individual non-territorial birds visiting or resident during counts over the two weeks before removals were begun was higher than the number seen on any one count. Many birds were not known individually, so these figures are minima, and the actual number available would be higher. The numbers of non-territorial cocks available on the experimental and control areas are in Appendix Table A.

‡ Unusually low figure because of poor breeding success.

§ See text, Experiment 1.

¶ Includes additional replacement in April–May, after earlier experiments up to March (see Fig. 2).

entrances, kept captive for a few days, and then released. This method was intended to answer two questions with each bird: was it replaced, and did it regain its territory after release? Subsequent experiments at Kerloch involved removing part or all of the population on certain areas by shooting. In some experiments we shot only the young cocks, and in others both young and old cocks. In later experiments all grouse of both sexes were shot, to avoid the possibility that newcomers might adjust their territory size to the areas used by hens left unshot.

The experiments were preceded by a study of the numbers and social status of all red grouse on the experimental and control areas, and on adjacent ground 150 m all around. The same work was also being done on nearby study areas of at least 1 km² and ranging up to 2 km²; this provided useful data on the number of birds available in nearby ground (Table 1). In different years 50–95% of the birds on these areas were individually marked with numbered plastic back tabs. Most unmarked birds were individually recognizable by variations in their plumage, using detailed field sketches of each bird. We knew which newcomers had formerly occupied neighbouring territories or had previously been without territories, which of them had previously been territorial and had later lost their territories before the shooting, and also which of them were previously unknown and with uncertain status because they had come from outside the areas being studied. Only one of these previously unknown birds was a cock but eleven were hens (Table 2); this was because more hens were unmarked and not recognized by plumage. At least 3 days of preliminary study were needed to discover the numbers and social status of all birds before each spring experiment and 1 week before each autumn one. In fact, all experiments except Experiment 1 were preceded by several weeks or months of work, during which the size of territories occupied by the birds was also measured. Shooting-out took at least 1 day but usually 2–3 days, and in Experiment 5, 2 weeks were needed. It was fairly easy to shoot most birds in the first few hours but increasingly difficult to shoot the remainder. Usually a whole day was needed to shoot the last one or two, and sometimes longer. As a result of this delay, replacement began before all the existing birds had been shot in Experiments 1, 2, 3 and 5, but any newcomers that appeared during this period were also shot. In Experiments 2, 3 and 5 it was impossible to shoot one particularly wary cock even during several days' attempts.

In spring, the breeding of hens was checked as a routine on experimental and control areas, by finding nests and young. In a few rare cases where neither were found, the characteristic large 'clocker' droppings of the incubating hen indicated that she was breeding.

## RESULTS

For ease in understanding the results, the experiments are described not in the order in which they were done, but grouped instead according to season. This is because it became clear after the experiments were done that the pattern of replacement varied seasonally (Fig. 2). Subsidiary details are given in the Appendix. Seasonal changes in behaviour are briefly described at the beginning of each seasonal section, to give some background to the experiments. Fuller details about the annual cycle of behaviour are given in Jenkins *et al.* (1963, 1967).

### A. *July–September*

During this period, old cocks (i.e. cocks that had bred that year and had been reared in some previous year) showed territorial behaviour only in the early morning, defending territories in the same place and of approximately the same size as in the previous winter and spring. They usually joined their families for the rest of the day. The families sometimes broke up as early as mid-August but usually in late September or early October,

Table 2. *The age and previous status of cocks taking territories and new hens paired with them, on experimental areas after shooting*

| Period of shooting | | August–early October | | | November–December | | | February–June | | |
|---|---|---|---|---|---|---|---|---|---|---|
| Previous status | | Juveniles* (non-territorial) | Moved from a former territory | Unknown | Non-territorial | Moved from a former territory | Unknown | Non-territorial | Moved from a former territory | Unknown |
| Cocks Number of new territorial cocks { | Young | 46 | 0 | 0 | 9 | 1 | 1 | 8 | 0 | 0 |
| | Old | – | 11 | 0 | 2† | 1 | 0 | 1† | 1 | 0 |
| | Total | 46 | 11 | 0 | 11 | 2 | 1 | 9 | 1 | 0 |
| Hens Number of new paired hens { | Young | 23 | 0 | 0 | 1 | 0 | 4 | 2 | 0 | 3 |
| | Old | – | 8 | 2 | 1† | 1 | 1 | 0 | 1 | 1 |
| | Total | 23 | 8 | 2 | 2 | 1 | 5 | 2 | 1 | 4 |

* Most young birds were in family parties in August–September, and if no old birds were shot they did not take territories till early October. Hence their social status could not usually be classified till October, but none of them had a territory prior to the shooting.

† Non-territorial old birds had been territorial in the previous year but had lost their old territories in October. Birds which had moved from a former territory had held a territory were now equivalent to non-territorial young which had failed to get territories in October. Birds which had moved from a former territory had held a territory elsewhere at the time of the shooting, but moved to colonize the vacant areas after a shooting. There are some replacement figures consequent on a removal experiment in an earlier period, e.g. the February–June data include April–May replacements long after Experiment 6 in November–December, and the August–October data include replacements long after Experiments 9, 10 and 13.

mainly as a result of aggressive encounters among the young birds (Watson & Jenkins 1964).

### Experiment 1—*early August* 1965—*complete removal*

This was done on part V at Kerloch where there was a breeding stock of seven cocks and seven hens in June. Most of their eggs and young were collected; and all the remaining adults and young were shot from 1 to 3 August. On 3 August an extra pair with their brood had appeared; and two young cocks and an old cock were already showing territorial behaviour before all the original resident birds had been shot. All the newcomers were shot, leaving the whole area vacant. Two days later, two pairs with broods,

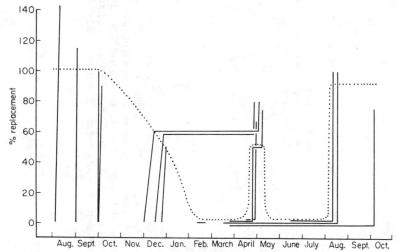

Fig. 2. Seasonal variation in the rate and extent of replacement of cock grouse taking territories following thirteen removal experiments; each solid line refers to one separate experiment.

Notes: (a) The percentage replacement is based on the final number of territorial cocks divided by the initial number. The data therefore exclude any replacement cocks which took territories and were themselves shot before an experimental shooting was completed. The results fall into five main sets—August–October, November–December, February–March, April–June and the next August–October. The dotted line indicates the approximate replacement for each set, adding up the percentage replacement for each experiment and taking a mean for each set. (b) The horizontal lines in spring and summer indicate no replacement, but are separated for clarity. (c) The second December experiment was run only for 3 days. (d) The first August result is probably artificially high because of the low breeding stock left after two earlier experiments. The replacement rate was only 100%, based on the breeding stock before the earlier experiments and this figure is used in calculating the mean for the dotted line. The April mean figure includes two experiments with nil replacement. (e) The steepness of the lines indicates the rate of replacement.

four single young cocks and a group of young (four cocks, six hens) were on part Va and none on Vb. Six cocks were showing territorial behaviour 4 days later and ten cocks occupied the whole of part V from 7 days later until October, pairing up with eight young and two old hens. This suggested an increase over the territorial stock of seven cocks in June, but the June figure was lower than usual following experiments 11 and 12 in March and April. In fact the number of territorial cocks before these spring experiments was ten—the same as in August–October 1965.

On the control area at part IVa, the territorial stock on 1 August consisted of sixteen cocks and fourteen hens paired up with them. The old cock that moved to the vacant ground on the experimental area was no longer on part IVa after 3 August, but all the remaining twenty-nine territorial birds stayed on IVa during the period of shooting and colonization (1–10 August) on the experimental area.

### Experiment 2—late August 1963—removal of old cocks only

In August 1963 the population on part V at Kerloch comprised fourteen territorial old cocks, thirteen old hens paired up with the old cocks, sixteen young cocks, twenty-three young hens and two other young which were probably cocks. None of the young cocks showed territorial behaviour in August, and all were submissive to the fourteen old cocks. On 30–31 August, thirteen of the old cocks were shot but the fourteenth escaped. By 2 September, fourteen of the young cocks and one additional old cock which had moved from a territory outside the area had taken territories. The thirteen old hens were all paired up, and one young hen also. The size and shape of the new territories were similar to the old, except on part Vb (Fig. 1) where two small extra territories were held by unmated cocks (all the others were paired up). The number of cocks taking territories on Va was similar to the number available. Seven old cocks were shot, and seven young cocks plus one surviving old cock were left. All seven young cocks took territories and the cock that escaped took an eighth territory. However on Vb where six old cocks were shot and eleven young cocks were left, only seven young cocks took territories plus one old cock from outside the area.

On the control area at part IVa there were no changes in the territorial stock of eleven adult pairs during the period of shooting and colonization (end of August–beginning of September) on the experimental area.

### Experiment 3—late September 1964—removal of all cocks and some hens

There were eleven old-established territories on part V at Kerloch, still remaining from the spring, and the population now consisted of eleven old cocks, ten young cocks, fourteen old hens and ten young hens. Ten old cocks and all ten young cocks were shot on 29–30 September. This was before the young showed any territorial behaviour. Six old hens and five young hens were also shot. On 1 October after the shooting there were one old cock, eight old hens, five young hens, and no young cocks (i.e. no immediate replacement occurred). Next day, two young cocks from elsewhere and two old cocks which had deserted their former territories elsewhere were already showing territorial behaviour, the latter two being already joined by two old hens of previously unknown status. These six birds were also shot.

Colonization continued rapidly, with five new territorial cocks at 3 days, seven at 4 days, and nine from 7 days onwards. Seven of these nine new cocks were young and the two old ones had left their former territories outside the area. Including the unshot original old cock, the territorial population of ten cocks and eleven hens was slightly lower than before shooting.

On the control area at part IVa there were no individual changes in the stock of fourteen territorial cocks and eleven hens paired up with them during the period of shooting and colonization on the experimental area (end of September–beginning of October).

### Experiment 4—late September 1964—complete removal

Five old cocks and four old hens living on the 12 ha part XII at Kerloch—the entire population there—were shot on 30 September, concurrent with experiment 3 on the adjacent part V. This was before any young birds showed territorial behaviour. No grouse were present on 2 October, but 3 days later the whole area was occupied by four new pairs of young birds and one pair of old birds. All neighbouring pairs were still present. The control for this experiment was the same as for the concurrent experiment 3.

### Conclusions

1. Young cocks showed territorial behaviour in early and late August (Experiments 1 and 2) on vacant ground, but not before mid-September (and not usually before early October) on the control area where territories were still occupied by old birds in August–September. Hence young birds were capable of territorial behaviour earlier than they usually showed it, but were presumably inhibited by the presence of the more dominant old birds.

2. The previous territorial density was reached within 2 days when all young cocks were left unshot (Experiment 2), but more slowly when both young and old cocks were shot (Experiments 1, 3 and 4).

3. Forty-six of the new territorial cocks were young birds (Table 2) but eleven old cocks left their former territories outside the area and moved to the vacant ground, in two cases accompanied by their hens and young (these figures include replacements in August–October long after Experiments 9, 10 and 13). There were similar results with the hens that colonized.

4. Newcomers settled to about the same territorial density as before shooting, whether all the formerly resident cocks and hens were shot or not.

5. A total of sixty-four vacancies for territorial birds was made during these experiments (including one natural disappearance, in Appendix, Experiment 3), and the total number of replacements was seventy-two. On the control area there was only one individual change out of an original total of seventy-nine territorial birds, during the periods of shooting and colonization on the experimental area. This single case involved a cock that moved to the experimental area. Table 2 shows ninety replacements, but this includes replacements in August–October long after Experiment 9, 10 and 13.

### B. *November–December*

Many young cocks first challenged the old cocks and took new territories in late September–early October and many young hens paired up at this time (Watson & Jenkins 1964). A new pattern of territories was then established. Old birds which lost their territories were then equivalent to those young birds that failed to pair up or get territories in the first place. Territorial behaviour occurred only in the morning, and non-territorial birds fed freely on these territorial areas in the afternoon (Jenkins *et al.* 1963).

### Experiment 5—*late November* 1963—*removal of all cocks*

Fifteen new cocks took territories on part V at Kerloch after experiment 2 and one of the previous old cocks escaped shooting. These fifteen colonizing birds were all shot on 15–29 November, leaving one old territorial cock. None of the fourteen hens paired up with them was shot.

The first immigrant cock showed territorial behaviour on 29–30 November, another after 3 days, four after 5 days, five after 6 days, seven after 10 days and nine after 14 days. Seven colonists were young cocks and two were old cocks which had been evicted from their territories outside the area in October. The shooting lasted 2 weeks, but ten of the previous territories were already vacant by 17 November. Since most of the vacant territories were filled only from 7 to 16 December, most of the new birds took 3–4 weeks to show territorial behaviour, although they had often been seen on the area earlier.

Including the single old cock that escaped shooting, there were ten territorial cocks from 12 December 1963 to April 1964, and sixteen hens paired with them from late December to March. One territorial old cock disappeared in early April, and in early May three non-territorial young cocks occupied new territories. The eventual summer stock was twelve cocks and fourteen hens, which all bred.

On the control area at part IVa, the only changes in the territorial stock of sixteen cocks and thirteen hens during the period of shooting and colonization on part V (mid-November–mid-December) were that two hens disappeared in late November and were replaced by two hens of previously unknown status.

### Experiment 6—mid-December 1964—complete removal

All five pairs (four of young birds and one of old) on part XII at Kerloch were shot on 16 December. Next day one previously non-territorial young cock showed territorial behaviour, but numbers built up more slowly than after Experiment 4 on this area in September 1964, with one territorial cock after 3 days, two after 7 days and three after 12–14 days. Four young hens of previously unknown status paired with these three cocks after 12–14 days. In late April a non-territorial young cock occupied an extra territory and was later joined by a young hen of unknown status, thus bringing the breeding stock of nine birds almost to the previous year's level of ten. On the control area at part IVa, there were no changes in the territorial stock of fifteen pairs during the period of experiment and colonization in late December.

### Experiment 7—late December 1960—temporary removal

At Glen Esk on 22 December, two young cocks A and B were trapped on the same afternoon and removed from territories 400 m apart on part C. Their hens were not removed. By next morning, a previously non-territorial young cock had occupied A's territory and paired up with hen A; and a neighbouring territorial cock N had enlarged its own territory to include B's territory and was courting hen B. Cocks A and B were released after $2\frac{1}{2}$ days, having lost only 3% of their weight. They were seen next morning fighting with and driving out the invaders, and they chased them away for 400–600 m, far beyond their territories. A and B courted and formed pairs with their former hens on the same morning.

On the control area at part A2, the size and individual membership of the territorial stock remained at the same five pairs during the period of experiment in late December.

### Conclusions

After the annual competition for territories in October, the pattern of replacement on experimental areas was different from that in August–September. Replacement was rapid when only two individuals were removed (Experiment 7), but when all the cocks were shot on a large area (Experiment 5), or all birds on a large area (Experiment 6), territorial occupation of the whole area by newcomers took 2–4 weeks instead of 2–7 days as in August–September, and the number of territories over winter was smaller than before shooting. However in two experiments extra non-territorial cocks took territories months later in late April–early May, bringing the eventual number of territories nearly to what it was before shooting. Table 2 shows that most newcomers taking territories after these experiments were previously non-territorial young birds, but two were old birds which moved from territories held elsewhere at the time of the shooting and three were non-territorial old birds which had lost their former territories earlier at the annual competition for territories.

To sum up, compared with an original total of twenty-eight territorial vacancies, twenty-two new birds took territories. By contrast, out of an original total of sixty-nine territorial birds on the control areas, only two died or disappeared during the periods of shooting and colonization, and both were replaced.

## C. *February–late March*

Territories were defended all day long during this period, and non-territorial grouse were evicted whenever they were discovered by the territory owners. The non-territorial birds were forced to spend most of their time on grassy undefended areas where heather was scarce and where many of these birds were found dead in poor condition subsequently during the spring (Jenkins *et al.* 1963). Fewer non-territorial birds were still alive from February to the spring than in the autumn and early winter (Table 1, Appendix Table A).

### Experiment 8—*late February* 1961—*temporary removal*

At Glen Esk, three young cocks, C, D and E with adjacent territories on part A1 were taken into captivity on 22 February. Next morning, all three territories were divided among their neighbours. In each case the captive bird's hen paired up bigamously with one of the neighbours. No new birds were able to occupy the old territories. The captive cocks were released after 7 days, when they had lost only 2, 7, and 6% of their weight. Two mornings later they had regained their hens and former territories.

On the control area at part A2, the same six territorial cocks and hens were present throughout the second half of February during the period of experiment.

### Experiment 9—*mid-March* 1961—*temporary removal*

At Glen Esk, three neighbouring young cocks with adjacent territories totalling 2·9 ha were captured on 16 March. Cocks F and G were put in $2 \times 1 \times 1$ m cages on their own territories, and cock H in a garden 8 km away. The vacant 2·9 ha were completely occupied next morning by three neighbouring territorial cocks. The now unattached hens G and H paired up bigamously with two of the neighbouring cocks and the third unattached hen F disappeared. The two neighbours now occupying the ground round the two cages spent much time on the cage roofs, dominating the former territory-owners inside even though these were still within their old territories. Cock H escaped after 7 days (Appendix), having lost only 4% of its weight, but did not return to its territory, presumably because it was too far away. Cocks F and G were released after 10 days. Cock F, which had lost only 4% of its weight in captivity, reoccupied most of its old territory next day. It also regained its previous hen, which had earlier disappeared. Cock G, which had lost 15% of its weight, showed no territorial behaviour after release and hid from the other cocks, even on its former territory. After 4 days it moved to grass fields 400 m away and died later, at the beginning of April. Territories G and H were retained by the two neighbouring territorial cocks that had earlier taken them over, and hens G and H paired up bigamously and bred with these two cocks. No new bird colonized before mid-August, when three young cocks took territories on this area in mid-August and paired up with three young hens.

On the control area at part A2, the territorial stock remained stable with the same six cocks and six hens throughout the period of experiment, i.e. the second half of March and early April.

### Experiment 10—26–28 March 1963—removal of all cocks

Four old territorial cocks with adjacent territories were shot on part III at Kerloch (Fig. 1), leaving 15 ha vacant and four unattached hens. All four hens disappeared and none paired up bigamously with territorial cocks in the surrounding 80 ha. The area remained vacant of new territorial birds till October, when three new pairs of young birds colonized it. On the control area at part IVa, there were no individual changes in the territorial stock of ten cocks and ten hens during the period of experiment between 20 March and 20 April.

### Experiment 11—late March 1965—removal of most birds

The breeding stock on part Va at Kerloch after experiment 5 was five territorial cocks and five hens. Two pairs, two paired territorial cocks and a non-territorial young cock were shot from 28 to 31 March; one of the paired cocks' hens disappeared, and the other paired bigamously with the sole remaining cock. This cock now expanded his territory to occupy about one third of the vacant ground. No new birds had taken territories by 20 April, although two non-territorial young cocks were seen on each visit. These two non-territorial cocks eventually took territories on the still vacant part of Va in the last week of April. Only one was joined by a hen, which was the same bird that disappeared after the shooting in late March. Up to 21 April when experiment 12 began, the five territorial cocks and five hens on the adjacent part Vb were present but did not occupy the vacant ground on Va. In addition, a third new cock took a territory on the vacant ground in early May, although it was an old bird that had lost its previous territory in October 7 months before.

On the control area at part IVa, the territorial stock remained stable with the same fifteen cocks and fifteen hens throughout the period of shooting and colonization between 28 March and 21 April.

### Conclusions

No replacement occurred within a month after four shooting experiments from February to late March, although a total of sixteen vacancies was made and non-territorial birds were available in each case. One pair moved from a former territory but this was on the experimental area (Appendix, Experiment 10). Partial recolonization eventually occurred after only one experiment (no. 11). Possible reasons for this are given in the Discussion. No changes occurred on the control areas out of an original total of sixty-four territorial birds. This was the only set of experiments where the status quo immediately after the shooting experiments was maintained for at least 3 weeks on both experimental and control areas.

### D. Mid-April–June

Territorial defence declined greatly just before and during the breeding season (most clutches were begun in late April), and after the end of April it occurred only early in the morning.

*Experiment* 12—21–24 *April 1965—removal of most birds*

Three pairs were shot out of a stock of five pairs on part Vb. Only one non-territorial bird had been seen on six counts in March and none during counts in April. A week later two new non-territorial young cocks took territories there and a young and an old hen of unknown status joined them and bred. A fourth hen was shot on the nest on 18 May and next day a previously non-territorial young hen from elsewhere had paired up with the mate of the hen that was shot. The new hen bred later. Replacement at such a late date was interesting, since most hens were far on in incubation by then, the mean hatching date in that year being 27 May (Jenkins *et al.* 1967).

As in Experiment 11, the territorial stock on the control area at part IVa remained stable during the period of shooting and colonization in late April and May.

*Experiment* 13—10 *June 1964—removal of all cocks*

One old and one young territorial cock were shot on part XII at Kerloch. There were no replacements until 1–5 August, when two young cocks showed territorial behaviour, and were joined by an old hen and a young hen from outside the area. The territorial stock on the control area at part IVa stayed at fourteen cocks and thirteen hens throughout June.

*Conclusions*

There was only partial replacement after Experiment 12 in late April, none after two natural disappearances in April (Appendix, Experiments 5 and 10) and none after Experiment 13 in June (five replacements in all for April–June out of an original total of eleven territorial vacancies). There was also partial replacement in April–May following the incomplete replacement after Experiments 5, 6 and 11 which were done earlier in the winter. The gap in replacement after these three experiments totalled sixteen, and there were ten new territorial birds in April–May. A few non-territorial birds were sometimes present during the breeding season, and in Experiment 12 one of them paired up with a territorial cock and bred. There were no changes in the control area, out of an original total of fifty-seven territorial birds.

## MAIN CONCLUSIONS

The null hypothesis being tested was (a) that areas partially or wholly depopulated by shooting would not be recolonized, and (b) that individuals which had previously been non-territorial would all remain so and would not breed; in other words that the status quo occurring immediately after each of the thirteen removal experiments would continue. In fact neither result was found on the experimental areas except in three experiments in February–March and one in June, yet the status quo was almost wholly maintained on control areas where no shooting was done. Including the pair that moved in Experiment 11 (see conclusions for that section), a total of 111 new birds colonized to take territories by mid-summer, compared with 119 vacancies made experimentally. Yet on the control areas, where 269 territorial birds were present before the experiments, there were only three individual changes during the period of removals and colonization on the experimental areas. One moved to colonize a vacancy on an experimental area, and the other two disappeared and were themselves replaced. Whatever their previous status, all hens that were paired up with territorial cocks in May were known to breed (see Methods, last paragraph) on experimental and control areas.

Three main conclusions from these results are:

1. The size of breeding stocks was determined by territorial behaviour. Only territory owners bred, and birds failing to get territories in autumn did not occupy territories and breed unless there were subsequent vacancies through the removal of territory owners. The ultimate fate of birds that were still non-territorial in winter was therefore irrelevant to the size or regulation of the spring breeding stock. In fact most of them died after being forced to live largely off the moor (Jenkins *et al.* 1963), but even if they survived to the summer, which was rare (Table 1, Appendix Table A), they did not breed and so were not part of the breeding population.

2. In most experiments the shooting of the required number of birds took at least several days to complete. During this period, surviving territorial cocks whose neighbours were removed enlarged their territories, sometimes to meet other territorial birds from beyond. This implies that some previous pressure prevented these birds from enlarging their territories earlier. Similarly, increases in the number of non-territorial grouse during the period of colonization following a removal experiment (Appendix Table A) also suggest a greater previous pressure against settling.

3. The number of territory owners in spring on each experimental area was usually about the same as before shooting, showing that this form of population regulation results in a stability suited to some local feature of each area.

## DISCUSSION

The main problem raised is why the final territorial or breeding density in the spring after most shooting experiments was similar to that before the experiments (Table 1). Newcomers took territories of a similar size to those held previously on the area, whether or not some or all the previous birds were shot. Hence the territory size of the newcomers could not have been adjusted to that of the previous owners. These results would not be surprising if population density in spring and the brood size of fledged young were similar all over the adjacent areas of moor, but in fact these varied greatly on different parts of the moor in the same year, and in different years on the same area (Jenkins *et al.* 1967). Presumably the newcomers' territory size related to some habitat feature which did not change during the experiment. It was certainly not limited by the number of birds available on nearby areas (Table 1) or on the experimental and control areas (Appendix Table A).

### Speed and level of replacement reached

There was some seasonal variation, illustrated in Fig. 2. After experiments in August–September, the number of territorial grouse rose to the same level as before shooting—i.e. replacement was complete. Replacement was less complete after experiments in November–December, and remained incomplete over the winter. Although the number of non-territorial grouse did fall off over the winter many were still present in November–December (Table 1, Appendix Table A). The reason for this incomplete replacement is uncertain, but may possibly be that colonization in November–December proceeded with a slow succession of birds, compared with simultaneous or more rapid succession in earlier experiments. (Van den Assem (1967) found by experiment that more male sticklebacks (*Gasterosteus aculeatus* L.) can be accommodated in simultaneous introductions than in successive ones.) Replacement was least complete after experiments in February, March, April and June. Most non-territorial birds had by then died but some were present and yet did not take territories. Perhaps their capability for showing territorial behaviour was also important, as discussed below.

In August–September young cocks quickly took territories, often on the same day as the previous owners were shot. These were the most dominant young cocks. After October, when birds separated into distinct social classes, only a few birds that had been non-territorial before the experiments showed territorial behaviour immediately after-wards, and most showed it very gradually over a few weeks during which they increasingly spent more time on the area. Only two out of twenty cocks previously known to be non-territorial showed territorial behaviour on the first day. By contrast all fourteen cocks which left their former territories to move into vacant ground showed vigorous territorial behaviour from the time they were first seen there.

Clearly after October most non-territorial birds were incapable of showing territorial behaviour at once, even on vacant areas where all competition had been removed by the shooting of all the more dominant established birds. Possibly they could re-adjust to the new situation only slowly because they were not aggressive enough. There is some evidence that the gonads of most non-territorial cocks were smaller than those of territorial cocks after October–November, and this aspect is being studied further.

Up to January, vacant territories were usually colonized by previously non-territorial cocks, but in February–March they were partitioned among neighbouring territorial cocks which enlarged their former territories. Non-territorial cocks did try to settle but were excluded. This was probably because the established cocks that had defended their territories only on fine early mornings up to January expelled newcomers at all times of day and in almost all weathers in February–March (Jenkins *et al.* 1963, 1967). It cannot be simply that the non-territorial intruders were weak, since individuals which had failed to occupy vacant territories in February–March sometimes managed to take territories in late April–May, when fewer non-territorial birds still survived (Table 1, Appendix Table A) and when their condition would if anything be poorer. Furthermore areas with a lower stock after Experiments 5 and 6 in November–December and after two of the four later experiments in February–April were colonized almost up to the pre-shooting level by non-territorial birds in late April–early May. Non-territorial birds only rarely took new territories in April–May in undisturbed populations. A likely reason for this partial replacement is that newcomers which would probably have been ejected in February–March had more chance of settling in late April–May when territorial behaviour was declining and was largely confined to the early morning.

*Reaction of hens*

Hens whose mates were removed usually associated with incoming cocks that were previously non-territorial, or joined up bigamously with neighbouring territorial cocks. They did not continue to live on an area if no cocks were present, even in cases where they had lived on certain territories for 6 months or more. After Experiment 5 when cocks were shot in late November and the hens were left unshot, some hens paired bigamously with the newcomers and the excess of hens over the winter was bigger than was recorded (Jenkins *et al.* 1963, 1967) in undisturbed populations. However after Experiments 10 and 11, some hens which had been paired up for 6 months disappeared after their mates were shot and did not associate with other cocks on the area or on adjacent ground nearby.

## Visits by birds living mainly elsewhere

Territorial hens did not stay on an area if all territorial cocks were shot, but some returned on the first day when their former mates or new territorial cocks appeared (Experiments 9, 10 and 11). This immediate return suggests that they had visited their old territories occasionally during the period since they disappeared, otherwise they would not have known that new cocks had arrived. Yet they were not seen when we visited their former territories during this period, and so must have been spending most of their time elsewhere. By contrast, hens that were paired up were consistently seen on territories in spring. Non-territorial birds must also have paid occasional visits like this. The Appendix Table A shows that few or no non-territorial birds were on the experimental areas during counts before some of the experiments, yet larger numbers usually appeared as soon as vacant ground was made available. Larger numbers did not appear on the control areas at these times. Furthermore, non-territorial birds which came to the experimental areas during the period of colonization did not stay there after the experiment, by which time the vacant ground was either occupied by newcomers or else divided up by previous territorial residents left unshot. Clearly they must have been moving about and visiting these areas occasionally, but started spending much time there—and thus being seen by us—only when the territory owners were removed. Even territorial cocks with territories elsewhere must have been moving and occasionally visiting other areas, or they could not so often have left their former territories and moved so quickly up to 1 km to colonize the new areas (see next paragraph). This must have happened even at times when territory owners were observed to be very sedentary and largely confined to their territories (e.g. early August, late March).

## Leaving old territories

Table 1 shows that some grouse which colonized vacant areas had been occupying territories elsewhere at the time of the shooting, but moved in to the new areas quickly. Most of these birds had bred successfully on their former territories, in two cases for 2 and 3 years running, and some moved 1 km to the new ground. None of these birds was seen being evicted from its former territory. Probably they all left spontaneously, since no evictions of old cocks and hens were ever observed till late September–early October. Movements of territorial grouse to new territories occurred at all times from August to April. This was not expected and if no birds had been marked we might erroneously have assumed that all newcomers were previously non-territorial. The reason for these desertions is unknown. Possibly any large vacant area is more attractive than a former territory, provided the vacant space is much larger than the old territory (which was invariably the case with these experiments).

## Management implications

The main implications for management are that established old territorial grouse which get shot in August–September will be quickly replaced by young birds. Any local areas (up to at least 52 ha) where the stock gets wholly wiped out will be quickly colonized, and presumably much larger areas where the stock is less heavily shot would also fill up quickly. Therefore local variations in density due to differences in shooting pressure would probably even out later on. Very heavy shooting in November–December is not advisable, since it would probably lead to lower breeding stocks in the next spring. Similarly the gamekeepers' habit of shooting single cock grouse in November–December, usually when they are on their territories, could lead to lower breeding stocks if it were done intensively. However at present these practices of late shooting are seldom important since organized large-scale shooting is rarely done after the end of September.

## ACKNOWLEDGMENTS

We are grateful to Professor V. C. Wynne-Edwards for comments on the manuscript. Grouse were shot out of season under licence from the Nature Conservancy.

## SUMMARY

1. Thirteen experiments over 6 years, involving the removal of red grouse from certain study areas at every season, showed that the size of breeding stocks was determined by territorial behaviour.

2. The numbers, location and social status of nearly all birds were known on and around the experimental and control areas. Most birds were marked, and with most newcomers it was known whether they were territory owners attracted from elsewhere or were previously part of the non-territorial population.

3. Non-territorial birds took territories and bred only after vacancies were provided by the experimental shooting or temporary removal of territory owners. Territorial cocks whose neighbours were shot invariably enlarged their territories, thus implying some previous pressure against this. The number of territories in the following spring on the experimental areas usually rose to about the same level as before the shooting, whether some or all the previous territorial birds were shot and irrespective of the number of non-territorial birds available. By contrast, hardly any changes occurred on the control areas.

4. Most newcomers were non-territorial young birds, but a few were non-territorial old birds that had previously lost their former territories. Some old birds which were occupying territories elsewhere at the time of the shooting left their old territories and moved up to 1 km to take new territories on the vacant ground.

5. As early as the beginning of August, young cocks took territories on vacant ground, but their territorial behaviour was delayed till October if old-established birds were still present. Replacement was rapid and complete after experimental shootings in August–September. It was slower and incomplete after experiments in November–December, but eventually became almost complete in April–May. It was slowest and incomplete after shooting in February–April and June. Non-territorial birds were still available after October, but only a few of them reacted by showing territorial behaviour on vacant ground immediately after a shooting.

## REFERENCES

Jenkins, D., Watson, A. & Miller, G. R. (1963). Population studies on red grouse, *Lagopus lagopus scoticus* (Lath.) in north-east Scotland. *J. Anim. Ecol.* **32,** 317–76.

Jenkins, D., Watson, A. & Miller, G. R. (1967). Population fluctuations in the red grouse *Lagopus lagopus scoticus. J. Anim. Ecol.* **36,** 97–122.

Van den Assem, J. (1967). Territory in the three-spined stickleback *Gasterosteus aculeatus* L. *Behaviour,* Suppl. xvi, 1–164.

Watson, A. & Jenkins, D. (1964). Notes on the behaviour of the red grouse. *Br. Birds,* **57,** 137–70.

(*Received* 15 *November* 1967)

# APPENDIX

This Appendix adds subsidiary details to the main text. Table A gives data on non-territorial birds before and after the experiments, showing particularly that their number increased during the period of colonization following the removal of territorial birds.

## Experiment 1

On 3 August the extra pair and their two young came from 100 m outside part V. The old cock that took a territory on 3 August moved 1 km from the control area, where it had had a territory at least since spring 1962. On 5 August, two new pairs with broods of three and four young moved at least 1 km from their former territories. On 10 August seven young and three old cocks had territories (including an old cock which moved 500 m from its former territory).

On the control area, thirty adults and twenty young stayed till late September, except for one old cock that moved to the experimental area and one old hen that disappeared in September. There was no change in territory ownership till early October, when the first young cocks showed territorial behaviour. The territorial stock over winter was fifteen cocks and thirteen hens.

## Experiment 2

The same fourteen adult cocks and thirteen hens were on part V from April to August 1963 when thirteen old cocks were shot. A young cock reared on the area showed territorial behaviour and courted a widowed hen 2 h after her previous mate was shot. Immediately after all the shooting, another old hen left to pair up with a cock 400 m outside the area, but returned 3 days later to pair up with the young cock which had taken her former mate's territory. An old cock moved from its former territory $\frac{1}{2}$ km outside and was joined next day by its mate. The twenty-six non-territorial young reared on the area associated as remnant family parties with the old hens, but these groups broke up between 11 and 18 September and by 1 October only seven non-territorial birds were left.

On the control area, there were eleven adult pairs in April and August 1963, with twenty-three young in August. In mid-September, one old hen disappeared, the families broke up, and many young went into flocks. The first young cocks took two extra territories from 14 September onwards (early October is usually the earliest for this) but there were no major changes till early October. The eventual territorial stock from early October to April 1964 was sixteen cocks and thirteen hens.

## Experiment 3

Before the experiment, a territorial old cock on part V disappeared in the summer and was replaced in mid-August by a young cock that took the same territory and paired up with the old cock's previous mate. This showed that, as in experiments 1 and 2, young cocks can show territorial behaviour in August if old cocks are removed.

The first two old cocks which took territories after the experiment moved from former territories 400 m outside the area, and were joined by two old hens of previously unknown status; and the second two old cocks moved with their hens from territories 1 km away. Three of the eleven paired hens were young birds from outside. The remaining five young hens became non-territorial.

I    J.A.E.

Table A. *Changes in total numbers of individual\* non-territorial grouse available during removal experiments*

| | Experimental areas | | | | | | Control areas | | | | | |
|---|---|---|---|---|---|---|---|---|---|---|---|---|
| | No. before the experiment | | Maximum change during period of territory colonization | | Nett change after the experiment | | No. before the experiment | | Maximum change coincident with colonization on experimental area | | Nett change after the experiment | |
| Experiment | Cocks | Hens | Cocks | Hens | Cocks | Hens | Cocks | Hens | Cocks | Hens | Cocks | Hens |
| 1 | 2† (0) | 2† (0) | +14 | +16 | +3 | +6 | 20† | | 0† | | 0† | 0 |
| 2 | 18† | 23† | +2 | +2 | −6 | −4 | 12† | 11† | 0† | | 0† | 0 |
| 3 | 10† (0) | 10† (5)† | +3 | +2 | +3 | 0 | 35† | | 0† | | −7† | 0 |
| 4 | 0 | 0 | +3 | +3 | +1 | 0 | 35† | | 0† | | −7† | 0 |
| 5 | 2 | 7 | +7 | +5 | 0 | −1 | 9 | 36 | −1 | −1 | −1 | 0 |
| 6 | 0 | 2 | +2 | +4 | 0 | 0 | 11 | 27 | −2 | −3 | −3 | −4 |
| 7 | 0 | 0 | +2 | +2 | 0 | 0 | 1 | 6 | +1 | −2 | +1 | 0 |
| 8 | 2 | 3 | +3 | +2 | +1 | +1 | 2 | 6 | +1 | −1 | 0 | 0 |
| 9 | 2 | 3 | +4 | +1 | 0 | −1 | 2 | 3 | 0 | +1 | 0 | −1 |
| 10 | 1 | 0 | +1 | 0 | 0 | 0 | 2 | 3 | 0 | +1 | +1 | 0 |
| 11 | 2 | 2 | +2 | +1 | 0 | 0 | 0 | 0 | +1 | +1 | 0 | 0 |
| 12 | 2 | 0 | +3 | +1 | 0 | 0 | 0 | 0 | 0 | 0 | 0 | 0 |
| 13 | 0 | | +1 | 0 | 0 | 0 | 2 | 0 | 0 | 0 | 0 | 0 |

\* See footnote symbol (†) in Table 1.

† In August–September (Experiments 1–4), the status of some young birds—and in some cases on the control areas their sex also—were not known before removals were begun. These figures are therefore not exactly comparable with the rest.

Notes. 1. Numbers before the experiment were checked during counts in the two weeks before shooting began. ( ) Shows number after last removal and before first replacement, if this number was different. Numbers during the period of colonization were checked up to the date of last replacement. If no replacement occurred, numbers were checked during the two weeks after the last removal. Numbers after the experiment were checked during the two weeks following the period of colonization.

2. In Experiments 7, 8, 9 and 13, when only a small part of an experimental area was made vacant, the figures show the number of birds on that part and not on the entire area.

Conclusions. (a) The number of non-territorial birds increased on experimental areas during the period of territory colonization following the removal of territorial birds, while there was no change on control areas.

(b) On experimental areas, the nett change was usually less than the maximum change, suggesting that some limit was placed on the number of non-territorial grouse able to settle.

On the control area, fourteen territorial cocks and thirteen hens had thirty-five young on 1 August, and in mid-August one old hen died and another disappeared. Up to 8 October the remaining fifty grouse were present, although the families broke up after late September. By 16 October there were many changes in territory ownership and the territorial stock increased slightly to sixteen pairs, but the total number of grouse did not change.

### Experiment 5

An additional non-territorial young cock occupied a vacant territory on the same morning as the owner was shot, and was itself shot later. No others took territories in the 2 weeks of shooting, although up to nine non-territorial cocks were seen at a time. Two of these cocks took territories 1 and 2 weeks after the shooting was over. Two more colonists were old cocks which had been evicted from their former territories outside the area in October and had since been living as non-territorial birds on the control area. The young cock which colonized 3 days after the experiment moved from a territory ½ km away, but all the other young cocks were previously non-territorial.

Of the sixteen hens that were paired up over winter, twelve were from the original territorial stock of fourteen hens. Another two were an old hen and a young hen which had previously been non-territorial about 1 km away, one was an old hen which moved from a former territory 500 m away and one was an old hen of unknown status. Four of these sixteen hens disappeared in early March.

One territorial old cock disappeared from the experimental area in early April, and its mate paired with a non-territorial young cock which had moved in from the control area 1 km away by 7 April. On 9 April this new cock was driven away by a neighbouring territory owner which then occupied the vacant territory and paired up bigamously with the extra hen. This new young cock was again left without a territory but it continued to live on the experimental area, and when territorial behaviour declined in early May before breeding, it occupied a territory there and was joined by a young hen whose previous status was unknown. In early May, two other non-territorial young cocks from the control area also occupied territories on part V (experimental area). One of them paired with a previously non-territorial young hen, raising the breeding stock from ten cocks and twelve hens, to twelve cocks and fourteen hens. These all bred and except for one hen all survived the summer.

On the control area, the same sixteen territorial cocks, plus thirteen hens paired up with them, were present from early October 1963 to April 1964. Up to four non-territorial cocks and two hens visited part IVa until April–May, when some of them managed to take territories on the experimental area at part V. In early April, one territorial old cock disappeared and was replaced by another previously non-territorial old cock, and an old and a young territorial cock disappeared in early May.

### Experiment 6

The second colonist was an old cock which moved from its original territory 200 m outside the area. The other two colonizing cocks were young birds—one previously non-territorial and the other of previously unknown status.

On the control area, the territorial stock in early December was sixteen pairs. Two territorial cocks and one hen which had entered our traps were killed by stoats (*Mustela erminea* L.) there on 13 and 15 December. In one case the territory was annexed by two neighbouring cocks, in the other by a previously non-territorial cock which paired up with the single unattached hen. The territorial stock stayed at fifteen pairs from December to April.

## Experiment 8

When released at noon, the captive cocks flew out of sight and had not returned by evening, but next morning they were all back. Only cock C, which had lost least weight, regained its hen, and none fully regained its original territory. Two mornings later, all three had regained their hens and former territories. In early February before the experiment, one territorial hen disappeared on the control area and was replaced by a previously non-territorial hen.

## Experiment 9

Cock H, which escaped in good condition after 1 week in captivity in a garden, did not return to its former territory 8 km away. It showed territorial behaviour 2 days running on the nearest moorland 400 m away, but was driven out by local territorial cocks. On the third day it was seen at the garden and in nearby fields, and next day appeared among poultry at a farmyard, where it was found dead in poor condition 4 days later.

A total of eight different non-territorial cocks and four hens visited the experimental area in March and early April, three cocks in late April and two cocks up to August, but none occupied the ground made vacant. At the beginning of March, before the experiment, a territorial cock on the control area gave up its territory which was divided up by three neighbouring territorial cocks.

## Experiment 10

Two hours after cock I was shot, his hen had paired up bigamously with a neighbouring territorial cock J. By next morning cock J and another neighbour K had annexed about half the vacant ground and all of it by 6 days later. These two cocks and a third neighbour L were then shot, leaving four unattached hens.

Next morning the nearest territorial cock M and its mate deserted their territory and moved 300 m to cock I's territory. Cock M was then shot but flew off wounded in one foot and its hen disappeared within 1 h. This left 15 ha vacant and four unattached hens. All of these hens disappeared, none pairing with other territorial cocks in the surrounding 80 ha. A fifth previously unmated territorial cock disappeared in late March.

In the next week, cock M was seen twice in a nearby undefended bog, where it hid, did not call and flew weakly with a trailing leg; but by the eighth day it had recovered and flew around the first vacant territory giving many loud calls. Next morning it was associating with its original hen, although she had not been seen there since the shooting. It had about 30% more ground than on its former territory and about 10% more than the original owner I.

On the control area, one unmated young territorial cock gave up its territory in early March and was not replaced. This was before shooting began on the experimental area.

## Experiment 13

One of the old territorial cocks that enlarged its territory after the June experiment was killed by a bird of prey about 19–20 September, and by 24 September a young cock had occupied the vacant ground and next day paired up with a young hen.

Vol. XCIV, No. 878     The American Naturalist     September–October, 1960

# PREDICTION OF POPULATION GROWTH FORM IN
## *DAPHNIA PULEX* CULTURES*

PETER W. FRANK

Department of Biology, University of Oregon, Eugene, Oregon

A variety of theoretical models forecasting population numbers have recently been suggested (Leslie, 1945, 1948; Slobodkin, 1953; Ricker, 1954; Nicholson, 1954; Wangersky and Cunningham, 1956, 1957). All include cases in which fluctuations in numbers occur in single species populations existing in an environment that may be constant, except for effects produced by the members of the population. Numerous observations on a variety of animals, which do not yield stability where this would be expected from a logistic model, have stimulated interest in schemes that provide for numerical fluctuations. Typical examples of such observed populations are flour-inhabiting insects (Park, Gregg and Lutherman, 1941) and Daphnia (Pratt, 1943; Frank, 1952; Slobodkin, 1954). For these, the logistic curve is clearly inappropriate (Smith, 1952).

Hutchinson (1948), Slobodkin (1954) and Wangersky and Cunningham (1956, 1957) have emphasized particularly the role of various lags in producing instability. Lotka (1925), in his derivation of the logistic, treated this curve as a special case of growth of a homogeneous population. He did not develop other cases, where the members of the population differ in mass, in any detail. Since animals grow after birth, their effect on and response to the environment will vary, often significantly, with age and size. Many of the newer models recognize this property of organisms. These models are demographic in that they take into account structural features of a population.

An ideal demographic model requires information answering these questions: (1) What are the significant classes in the population? (2) What are initial numbers in each class? (3) What are the birth, death, immigration and emigration rates for every population class in each environment to which it is subjected? (4) If the model is to predict energetics, what is the biomass and rate of production of members in each class? (5) What happens when the environment changes? This environmental effect can not necessarily be predicted by interpolation between constant, but more extreme conditions. If a time lag exists because of a change, either in population composition or in external environment, how long is the lag, and what parameters does it affect? At what rate and to what extent does each class adjust?

In natural populations the effects of numerous extrinsic variables, mainly associated with weather and other species of organisms, must be known in detail. We must know how to predict changes in these extrinsic factors. In

*This investigation was supported by grants from the National Science Foundation (G-1054 and G-4894), and by the Graduate School of the University of Oregon.

some cases they will themselves be functions of the population whose numbers are to be predicted. There is no hope that we shall ever be able to make predictions at the level of this ideal demographic model for any but a few special situations. However, it is often possible to make reasonable estimates of population size, and short time projections based on these estimates and on natural history features are often of practical value. Improvements in these predictions will result from increased knowledge of what information will be most essential for success in such a venture, and which of the ideally desirable data are of less import, so that they may be ignored in a first approximation. A laboratory model can not provide the solutions to the general problem of prediction. It may, however, have considerable value in clarifying the role of factors that might otherwise be overlooked.

Population growth form has been characterized in the laboratory for three species of Daphnia, cultured under somewhat different conditions (Pratt, 1943; Frank, 1952; Slobodkin, 1954). The performance of these populations is at least grossly similar. Many of the vital statistics appropriate for testing models have been determined (Frank, Boll and Kelly, 1957). Thus one can delineate alternative predictive schemes, and contrast these with observed population growth. Even here, compromises between the desirable information and the practical difficulties involved in gathering it must be made. Every compromise damages the models somewhat. At best the empirical information permits one to make a slightly distorted prediction. The various departures are cumulative, so that a particular representation of a mathematical model does less and less justice to it the longer the period of prediction.

Study of the correspondence between models and observed population growth helps to define limits to the information that is critical. Inappropriate models are thus useful in providing clues to the effect of ignoring known variables. By making simplifications, it may be possible to indicate where, in future work, observations need to be made with care, and where cruder estimates will suffice. The contrasts between alternative theories, in this investigation, lead to rather unexpected information about the relative importance of the parameters that enter into our estimates. To what extent such information can be generalized is not known. Ultimately we hope to extend theoretical aspects of this study by determining minimal criteria for adequate representation of various features of growth form.

I should like to acknowledge the help of E. Novitski, who, in a number of discussions, helped in my formulation of the various models. I am also indebted to L. B. Slobodkin and F. E. Smith, who made useful comments on this manuscript.

## DATA FOR PREDICTION

The fundamental data specify size, growth, birth and death rates for all ages of Daphnia over a variety of constant densities that encompass what is expected in a growing population. This information, as well as the husbandry methods used in the present investigation, have been published (Frank *et al.*, 1957). To supplement the constant density data, a number of cohorts were observed throughout life as in previous work, except that density was varied systematically once during the life span. Shifts over a wide density range from four to 24 animals per cu. cm. and vice versa represent the most extreme conditions. In more meaningful shifts over smaller ranges, animals at initial densities of 16 and 32 per cu. cm. were changed to half these densities, and animals kept at eight and 16 per cu. cm. were shifted to twice these densities. Duplicate sets of six cohorts were observed in all cases, and changes were made at one of two ages, 12 or 24 days. It would have been desirable to discover the effect of changes in degree of crowding on younger animals. However, it has become evident that the density conditions under which very young animals live are not comparable to those for older and larger ones, so that such an experiment would require crowding young animals with older ones. This is not feasible because fertility of the adults is too high.

Except for exaggerating the effects of change, data for the wide-range density shifts do not differ from the rest. Because these shifts are much more abrupt than changes that occur in the population, their significance is small, and the data will not be presented in detail. The results for the smaller range shifts do not vary appreciably with age of the cohort. When the animals are older, changes yield less reliable data because of the greater number of deaths that have occurred.

Figure 1 summarizes information from animals that have undergone a density change when 12 days old. Values for age specific survival ($l_x$), natality ($m_x$) and individual size ($v_x$) at each of three constant densities are indicated by dotted lines for purposes of comparison. Curves for cohorts in which density is increased are shown by interrupted lines; decreased density cohorts by solid lines. Arrows mark the time at which density was changed. The $v_x$ curves have been fitted by eye.

Increased density provokes an immediate response of decreased survival. The higher mortality rate declines to normal after four days; subsequently, death rates do not differ materially from those of equally old animals that have lived at the new density all their lives. When degree of crowding is reduced, death rates at once become indistinguishable from those at the lower constant density. Since variances of mortality rates are relatively large, particularly at ages greater than 20 days, one is unlikely to find significant differences. Changes in density do not affect natality so quickly. After a shift, no change in reproductive performance is detectable for two to four days. Thereafter the rate adjusts and becomes that characteristic of the new density once a minimum of six and a maximum of eight days have passed. Growth shows yet a different response. Not only is compensation to density change immediate, but overcompensation occurs. When density is lowered animals grow faster, and when it is increased they grow more slowly than would be expected of Daphnia of that age at the new density. These results are similar, in general, to those of Anderson, Lumer and

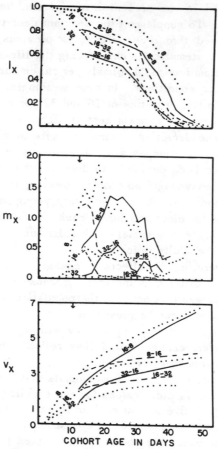

FIGURE 1. Effect of changing density on survival ($l_x$), natality per female day ($m_x$) and individual size ($v_x$). Density was changed at a cohort age of 12 days.
——————— Density has been decreased by 50 per cent.
— — — — Density has been doubled.
·········· Constant density controls.

Zupancic (1937) and of Frank (1952). Accordingly, animals of a given age and density need not have the same birth, death and growth rates unless they have had the same prior density experience. Whether animals of the same age and size will have constant vital statistics, as postulated in the model of Slobodkin (1953), is not certain from our data, but it seems improbable.

Each of the three variables thus reacts somewhat differently to changes in crowding. With some exceptions, which are immediate aftereffects of the density change, mortality rates compensate well. Natality adjusts rather precisely, but only after an initial period of lag. Growth rates overcompensate, particularly shortly after density changes. Even the variations called "small range" here are more abrupt than the changes in degree of crowding occurring in experimental populations. Large range shifts, that is, abrupt changes from four to 24 animals per cu. cm., produce some results that are absurd. For example, under these conditions mortality rate during the first two days following the density change increases to 0.75. In populations where mortality rates have been observed under conditions similar to ours, there is no indication that death rates ever reach such levels (Slobodkin, 1954). This is therefore certainly a spurious effect so far as growing populations are concerned. Although all our density shifts probably exaggerate the effects of such changes, they are probably not negligible in the populations to be predicted. However, a model accounting for the responses with precision would be exceedingly complex. The mortality effects are relatively minor and have been ignored in all our models. The natality lag could be incorporated into certain predictions in simplified fashion. The growth overcompensation proved troublesome, and the compromise made is not altogether satisfying, although it has the merit of being tractable.

## PREDICTIVE PROCEDURES

Predictive estimates have been made using six different models. Only one (Model C') of these was expected *a priori* to be suited to the populations studied. All others ignore known variables. However, the rest of the models were applied in an effort to discover precisely what the effects of such simplifications are. The models may be subdivided into one group (A–D), in which particular values of the age and density specific vital statistics are determined by numerical density, that is, the numbers in a population in a constant volume (25 cu. cm.) of medium; and another (B', C') in which the total volume of the animals specifies the magnitude of the density effect. The first category disregards differences other than age between the members of the population at any one time. In the second, density becomes indirectly dependent on the age structure of the population.

A. The logistic curve. Constants needed for this model were derived from values for the intrinsic rate of natural increase (r) at various densities, as previously described. Values for the predicted population numbers, $N_t$, were obtained from the density units given in the earlier paper by multiplying by 25, the volume of the experimental habitats in cu. cm.

In this connection, it is necessary to point out that the values for "instantaneous birth rate" (*b*) in the earlier report are incorrect, as noted by Smith (1958). The data for *b* are, in fact, values of $\beta$ (see Andrewartha and Birch, 1954, pages 44 and 47 for notation and the relation between these statistics). As a result of this error the death rates *d* are also incorrect (figure 3, table 4, Frank *et al.*, 1957). The logistic estimate is, however, unaffected, since *r* is correctly presented.

For the remaining models certain terms, some of which have been discussed more fully in the earlier report, are essential:

1. Variables in the predicted population
   - N  Total numbers
   - n  Numbers in one age class
   - V  Total volume of animals
   - w  volume of one individual Daphnia

2. Subscripts, *etc.*

   x  Age interval from x to x + 2 days

   t  Population age in days

   $a$  Age at beginning of reproductive period

   $\omega$  Age at end of life span (arbitrarily set at 52 days)

3. Vital statistics at constant density (from Frank *et al.*, 1957)

   v  Individual volume in cu. mm.

   s  Growth rate of an individual: $\dfrac{v_x}{v_{x-2}}$

   p  Survival rate: probability that an animal will survive during a given two day interval

   m  Birth rate: young produced per female in two days.

The data for predictive estimates consist of:

1. Initial values of the numbers and volumes of the members of the population for every age class.
2. Information about the time lag in vital statistics after changes in density.
3. Tables of v, s, p, and m at seven constant densities (1–32 per cu. cm.) and at all ages (Frank *et al.*, 1957).

Values for densities not given in the tables were estimated by linear interpolation. Extrapolation beyond the highest numerical density (32 per cu. cm.) was required in certain predictions at the population peaks. The assumptions were made that at a numerical density of 64 per cu. cm. birth rates were half, and death rates twice those at the highest observed density; growth rate was assumed to undergo no change. These assumptions are undoubtedly incorrect; however, large departures from them would be required to affect the predictions significantly.

Model B is similar to that of Leslie (1945). The population is defined by the relations:

$$n_{x+2,\,t+2} = n_{x,\,t}P_x(N_t)$$

$$n_{0,\,t+2} = \sum_{x=a}^{\omega} n_{x,\,t}m_x(N_t)$$

$$N_{t+2} = \sum_{x=a}^{\omega} n_{x+2,\,t+2} + n_{0,\,t+2}$$

Parentheses are used to characterize functions, and do not denote multiplication.

As in the remaining predictions, successive estimates of population numbers are got by tedious evaluation for each time interval in turn. The values at a population age of t + 2 days are calculated from known values at t days by considering the death rates that apply to each age class at that numerical density $N_t$, and by summing the births contributed by each age class. Prediction B differs from the logistic because (1) it uses discrete population growth intervals, and (2) it considers the effect of different initial age distributions. It ignores lags at the level of the individual. Model B' differs from B only in its criterion of density, which is volume. The equations for B can be readily modified by substituting $(V_t)$ for $(N_t)$ on the right side of the equations for Model B. However, the vital statistics data now apply to volume densities, and V must be calculated for the population in addition to N. Volume of an animal was assumed to follow the growth rate appropriate to that age and volume density, with one exception: if an individual had already attained the absolute size characteristic of a given age at a certain density, the assumption was made that the animal would remain the same size.

$$w_{x+2,\,t+2} = w_{x,\,t}s_x(V_t), \text{ except if } w_{x,\,t}s_x(V_t) \geqq v_{x+2}(V_t), \text{ in which case}$$
$$w_{x+2,\,t+2} = w_{x,\,t}.$$

$$w_{0,\,t+2} = 0.15$$

$$V_{t+2} = \sum_{x=0}^{\omega} w_{x+2,\,t+2}n_{x+2,\,t+2} + w_{0,\,t+2}n_{0,\,t+2}$$

Thus the increased growth rate that occurs when crowding is reduced is not accounted for; the decrease in growth rate at increased density is rather crudely approximated. Model B′ can be considered more realistic than B, since it takes into account the different crowding effects that animals of different sizes can be expected to have. However, because it treats birth rates as if they adjusted immediately to the population's density, it also ignores known information.

Predictions C and C′ correspond to B and B′ respectively, but include the observed natality lag in their formulation. This lag was estimated to average five days. Therefore in C and C′ the effect of density on birth rate was assumed to be that of the population that existed five days prior to a given population age. A simple modification in the formulas is all that is required: wherever $(N_t)$ or $(V_t)$ occur in B or B′, $(N_{t-5})$ or $(V_{t-5})$ must be substituted. This device is equivalent to assuming that birth rates are those characteristic of a certain density that existed five days previously, and then shift abruptly to a subsequent density. Actually there is a certain rate of accommodation during the lag interval. This has been ignored.

Model D, developed by Ricker (1954), was applied by him with surprising success to Pratt's (1943) data. It assumes that there is no further adjustment to density change once an animal has reached maturity. This prediction and the logistic may therefore be interpreted as opposite limiting cases of populations regulated by numerical density. The logistic presupposes instantaneous reaction of the population to density change; Ricker's formulation assumes maximal lag. This model requires values of adult numbers in successive generations at any one initial density. These values may be calculated, in our example, from existing vital statistics data (table 1). The table presents calculated generation length at each density as well as values for the net reproduction rate $R_0$ (Andrewartha and Birch, 1954), and population numbers expected in successive generations. Ricker's model makes no allowance for the existing differences in generation length, although it could, of course, be modified to include them. For details regarding the features of this model, the original paper (Ricker, 1954) should be consulted. We used six day intervals for successive estimates of the

TABLE 1

Statistics for Ricker's model (D)

| Density No./cc. | Net reproduction rate per generation $R_o$ | Numbers in generation | | Generation length, days T |
|---|---|---|---|---|
| | | i | i + 1 | |
| 1 | 39.3 | 25 | 983 | 13.2 |
| 2 | 41.0 | 50 | 2050 | 13.6 |
| 4 | 42.8 | 100 | 4278 | 13.8 |
| 8 | 26.4 | 200 | 5286 | 17.1 |
| 16 | 5.9 | 400 | 2365 | 19.2 |
| 24 | 0.48 | 600 | 288 | 18.2 |
| 32 | 0.13 | 800 | 101 | 27.7 |

Column 2 is derived from age specific birth and death rates in Frank *et al.* (1957). Column 3 gives the numbers per cohort, and equals column 1 times 25. Column 4 is the product of columns 2 and 3. The last column may be estimated from known data, as in column 2.

population, as did Ricker for Pratt's data on *D. magna*, since the refinement of finer intervals did not seem merited.

### COMPARISON OF PREDICTION AND OBSERVATION

The populations against which various models are tested include 12 replicates started with 25 animals in 25 cu. cm. of medium. In these, the stable age distribution for this density was approximated as closely as was possible. Six other populations initially had 400 Daphnia (200, 3–5 days; 100, 9–11 days; 50, 15–17 days; and 50, 21–23 days old). The days on which different replicates were observed were staggered by groups of three replicates, so that extrinsic factors that might have escaped control could be evaluated. All populations were censused at two-day intervals for 120–130 days.

When the models are applied to the populations with an initial 25 Daphnia, the curves of figure 2 result   At first glance, the large differences between the several predictions, although based on the same vital statistics, stand out. The most cursory examination reveals that certain models must be inadequate because of the discrepancies that exist between the predictions. It is profitable, for the moment, to compare the models further without having recourse to what is revealed by the observed populations.

The logistic model (A) and Prediction B are very similar, except that the asymptote is attained significantly faster in the logistic. With greater deviation of the initial population from the stable age distribution, somewhat larger differences between these models would result. Both theoretical populations level off when the numbers of animals reach 582, although there are, in Model B, minor fluctuations about this value. When Prediction B is contrasted with B′, the major possible role of size differences is emphasized. Although the two models differ only in their criterion of density, numbers as compared with volume, maximum population size in B′ is more than twice that of B, and major fluctuations are introduced by changes of size with age. This type of lag has been termed "populational" by Slobodkin (1954), as contrasted with "individual" lags, such as that in birth rate.

The natality lag produces similar, but smaller fluctuations with shorter period (Model C). Prediction C′ may be thought of as possessing the joint properties of B′ and C. Both populational and individual lags are considered. The two lags enforce each other, so that maximum population numbers are almost twice those of B′, and four times the asymptotic value of the logistic curve. Ricker's model yields a predictive curve that most resembles C′. Here a long individual lag, but no populational lag has been assumed.

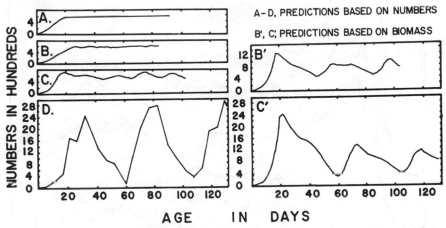

FIGURE 2. Predictive estimates of numerical population growth from an initial population of 25 Daphnia. Further explanation of the models in text.

Of the six models, only C′ makes use of all the known demographic information for Daphnia; it also contains some admitted distortions. It is gratifying that the growth form predicted by this model agrees rather well with that of observed populations. The six replicates of figure 3 provide a sample of the empirical observations. They have been successively displaced along the ordinate (by 400 animals) so that the individual curves will not obscure each other. Replicates 1, 2 and 3 were observed on the same days and received the same lots of food algae. The other populations were counted on alternate days. Some consistent differences are observable between these two subsets. However, in their general features the curves exhibit reasonable conformity. All empirical populations exhibit a peak of 2200–2550 animals between days 22 and 26. This is also true in the six replicates whose curves are not presented here. The timing and height of this peak agree well with Prediction C′. Observation and prediction are in general accord during the period of decline, roughly from day 22 to day 60. The second predicted peak is not realized fully in the observed populations. By this time the individual replicates are somewhat out of synchrony. However, even the third peak, predicted at 120 days, is roughly approximated in all twelve replicates. This is surprising, since the model must be expected to predict more poorly over long than over short periods. Ricker's model (D) predicts the times of successive peaks as well as does C′, but the amplitudes of the later fluctuations are much too high. Since his model is known to depart in major respects from what is known about the nature of lags in our animals, the existing correspondences between D and the observed populations must be considered fortuitous.

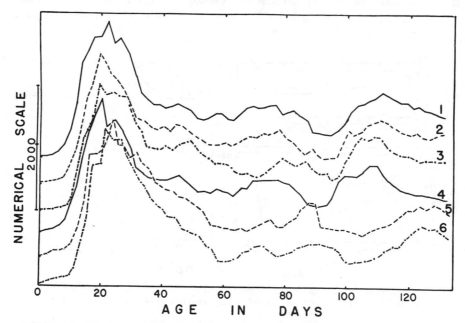

FIGURE 3. Numbers observed in six replicate populations with initial population of 25 Daphnia approximating the stable age distribution at that density. (The ordinate has been successively shifted by 400 for different replicates.)

Additional evidence that Model C′ yields a fairly good predictive estimate is provided by applying it to populations with an initial 400 animals. Comparisons between a single representative curve, Prediction C′, and that of Ricker (figure 4) indicate that C′ is fairly but not completely satisfactory. The initial peak is reached significantly faster in the predicted curve, but the agreement between prediction and observation is as good as may reasonably be expected, considering the liberties that were taken with the data. Ricker's model does not provide a good fit, although again the departures are primarily in amplitude.

Another test of Model C′ involves the dynamics of population change. The model actually predicts population size, total birth and death rates, and population volume. Unfortunately our observations provide no information on biomass, and yield only semiquantitative evaluations of birth and death rates in the populations. These have been estimated from changes in total population size, and the number of small animals noted at time of

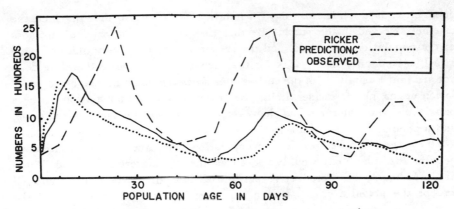

FIGURE 4. Comparison between the prediction of Model C′, D, and an observed population started with 400 Daphnia.

census. What happens in the model is in general agreement with our own observations, and those of Pratt (1943) and Slobodkin (1954). At the beginning, total birth rate is high and death rate is low. As the population increases in numbers, and as the individuals become older, birth rate declines as the result of the increased density, and because of the changes in age structure. At the population peak, births essentially cease. This prediction of the model holds for our populations. Death rate subsequently increases, but has once again declined at a population age of 30 to 40 days. This is purely the result of age structure: at this time the great majority of animals belong to intermediate age classes whose age-specific death rates are low even at high densities. After day 40, the predicted population once again decreases more rapidly, since now the animals are so old that their death rates are high. Up to this point, no renewed spurt of natality has occurred. This can be explained when one notes the predicted biomass. It does not reach its peak until about day 40, despite the considerable decline in numbers that has occurred by then. The decline is more than compensated by additional growth of the animals that remain. Only after day 40

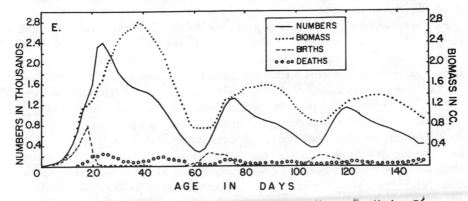

FIGURE 5. Population dynamics of Daphnia according to Prediction C′.

does biomass decline. By day 54 natality has risen so that the increase can be observed in the graph. By this time, most of the original members of the population have died, and the remainder are relatively old, and have small age-specific birth rates for that density. The cycle therefore does not attain the amplitude of the earlier one. Whenever new increases in population occur, numbers rise slightly before biomass. As population numbers pass their peak, biomass has, however, by no means reached its maximum, and a populational lag of about 18 days results from growth of the animals as they age. As net result, the population does not exhibit continuous generations, which one would expect from the life history features of Daphnia. Although the reproductive portion of their life span can include all except the juvenile stages that occupy approximately 15 per cent of the total life span, this reproductive capacity is not realized under our conditions of culture. Since natality varies so widely with changes in density, and individual growth continues when density is so high that reproduction is effectively nil, successive generations become almost discontinuous.

## DISCUSSION

This picture of population dynamics differs only in minor regards from earlier analyses of this and other species of Daphnia. Likewise the most satisfactory model is closely related to that of Slobodkin (1953), which was intended to be applicable to his populations of *Daphnia obtusa*. Appropriate data to test this model are not available. However, the relationships between the two models are sufficiently close that there is no reason to question that it would be suitable, given the proper limiting factors and sufficient empirical information. Both formulations are iterative, and can therefore be readily modified to accommodate additional information, such as the observed birth lag. Mathematically, they are rather inelegant. In Slobodkin's prediction, given a known energy input, age and size classes define values for birth, death and growth rates. In mine, time and volume density, acting on a population of specified age and size distribution, cause the vital statistics to take on certain values that determine the population. Were we to assume that energy input is limiting for our animals, the models could be made identical.

Attempts to identify the limiting factors in our Daphnia have not been completed. We are hoping to be able to correlate information from these animals with that of others. Richman (1957) and Slobodkin (1959) have obtained valuable information on the energetics of *Daphnia pulex*. Their data are for animals with a food régime of a different order of magnitude, and can not readily be integrated with ours at present.

Certain indications concerning the limiting factors operating in our system were derived from vital statistics information (Frank, *et al.*, 1957). At low densities a different density effect from that at higher levels of crowding obtains. The correspondence between our model and the observed populations provides another clue. It is not immediately evident why volume should provide a proper measure of whatever density means in a physiological sense. Yet there is virtually no doubt that the volume density model provides more than an accidental fit to our populational data, since there are so many independent areas of correspondence between them. We can therefore assume that volume density provides a suitable substitute for some variable that has the observed effects on vital statistics here attributed to density. Slobodkin (1954) has generalized about the role of crowding in Daphnia. He states that, in all known cases, density effects are indirect: results of interactions between animals and their external environment, rather than directly between animals. It is instructive to note that Richman's data for respiratory rates of small and large animals show about the same range of variation—about 15 fold—as does volume among our relatively crowded animals. This is not true of his dry weight measurements, which vary much less. Requirements used or metabolites produced by Daphnia are probably simple functions of respiratory rate. Thus it is likely that the limiting factor under population conditions is an indirect density effect. By chance, volume is sufficiently closely correlated with whatever causes the results attributed to density that it functions well enough in our predictions.

Comparisons between the models permit some evaluations of the relative contribution of different variables on the fluctuating growth form. The two relations that play the most important roles are those between births and density, and between age and size. None of the predictions that ignore size differences are at all indicative. This variable interacts with the rest, since it determines density. The effect of density on birth rate is characteristic of all models, and is the main reason for the attainment in them of an upper limit. Since such a labile birth rate is unusual, its general significance is small. Other density dependent variables could produce similar results. The effect of density change, particularly on natality, is far from negligible. However, the interaction between the population lag produced by size changes and the individual lag in birth rate is particularly noteworthy, and was unexpected. These two lags cause fluctuations that resemble those exhibited by Ricker's model, and could be represented by a model in which one lag is ignored and the other is exaggerated. A more general treatment of lags may perhaps be possible, since it is apparent that lags from several causes may be combined by a suitable function. The relation between growth and density has only minor effects on the shape of the population curve. Since Daphnia are able to adjust, not only are population peaks numerically higher than they would be without stunting, but the valleys are not so deep. As numbers decrease, additional growth of stunted animals occurs, and results in increased reproductive ability. Thus stunting may have a significant adaptive effect when it no longer is observable in the population.

The fluctuations in both models and populations are quite regular. Control of environmental variables is in part responsible. However, this regularity must be attributed in part to the short pre-reproductive period in the life span of Daphnia, since Ricker (1954) has demonstrated that, as this period increases in populations with overlapping generations, increasing irregularities develop.

The demonstration that a demographic model provides a successful approximation of an observed population in a relatively constant laboratory environment leads logically to the question of the general utility of predictions of this sort. Iterative models can be constructed that allow for virtually all contingencies one may expect to arise in various populations. The mathematics present little difficulty, and solutions for specified initial conditions are tedious only so long as they are not assigned to an electronic computer.

Despite this, such models are unlikely to solve the practical problems of forecasting specific natural populations because they require enormous amounts of information. The data available for making our predictions could have been restricted in several ways without doing gross damage to the model. The age intervals for which death and individual growth rates were estimated are much finer than necessary. However, this is not true to the same extent for birth rate, since the exact age when reproduction begins is rather critical. The density intervals for birth and growth rates are finer than was required. This does not hold for survival, which varies with density in more complex fashion. However, the total role of variations in death rate with density is relatively small, and even had density effects on mortality been ignored altogether, this would have been serious only among the young animals, where death rate soars at high density. Effects of density change need have been estimated only for one age group and one set of two densities.

It is evident that these simplifications could be applied only in retrospect, and only to this particular model. One generalization can, however, be made. The significance of the vital statistics information declines greatly with individual age, so that once the peak of the reproductive period is reached, virtually any approximation will be adequate. Conversely, what happens to the young stages is of extreme importance, and estimates at these ages must be precise. This conclusion is also implicit in Cole's (1954) treatment of natural history features of populations, and certainly has wide validity. It is unfortunate, therefore, although not surprising from an evolutionary point of view, that vital statistics information is most difficult to gather precisely for those age classes that are most important.

This unoptimistic analysis is not meant to imply that demographic models are useless, but rather that their function lies in a different direction. Our understanding of the behavior of populations has advanced considerably during recent years, largely as the result of increased attention to structural features. Bodenheimer's observation (1938) that the study of age distribution represented one of the most neglected areas in ecology is no longer so applicable today, although there is still a dearth of empirical information along these lines. Models simulating what is known qualitatively about various single species populations and about interactions of different types are likely to provide significant insights into the range of possible events in these systems. They may indicate observable entities that characterize some particular process. Thus they function partly to clarify what might otherwise be vague and seemingly intuitive ideas. They gain additional value whenever they can predict populational features that can be verified empirically. These predictions are unlikely to be specific and quantitative, since we rarely have enough information to estimate precisely the constants that enter into particular formulations. One may reasonably hope that demographic models can furnish useful generalizations. Most likely, however, theory and empirical observation will continue to advance concurrently rather than sequentially.

### SUMMARY

Available data on age- and density-specific birth, death and individual growth rates, combined with new information on lags in these statistics following density change, can be applied to models of population growth of Daphnia in a constant environment. Six alternative models have been tested. They range in complexity from the logistic curve to an iterative model that takes into account the initial age distribution, and effects of age, density and density change on natality, mortality and size. This complex model is the only one that provides a fair representation of observed events in experimental Daphnia populations. Several independent areas of agreement between observations and model provide assurance that the observed fit is not merely fortuitous.

The most important relations determining population growth form in this system are those between (1) natality and age, density and density change and between (2) size and individual age. Comparisons between the models emphasize that, in most organisms, the populational effects of different age and size classes can not be considered negligible in assessing population dynamics. Knowledge of the vital statistics of the younger members of a population is of paramount importance for demographic prediction.

### LITERATURE CITED

Anderson, B. G., H. Lumer and L. J. Zupancic, Jr., 1937, Growth and variability in Daphnia pulex. Biol. Bull. 68: 444–463.

Andrewartha, H. G., and L. C. Birch, 1954, The distribution and abundance of animals. University of Chicago Press, Chicago, Ill.

Bodenheimer, F. S., 1938, Problems of animal ecology. Oxford University Press, London, England.

Cole, L. C., 1954, The population consequences of life history phenomena. Quart. Rev. Biol. 29: 103–137.

Frank, P. W., 1952, A laboratory study of intraspecies and interspecies competition in Daphnia pulicaria (Forbes) and Simocephalus vetulus O. F. Müller. Physiol. Zool. 25: 178–204.

Frank, P. W., C. D. Boll and R. W. Kelly, 1957, Vital statistics of laboratory cultures of Daphnia pulex DeGeer as related to density. Physiol. Zool. 30: 287–305.

Hutchinson, G. E., 1948, Circular causal systems in ecology. Ann. N. Y. Acad. Sci. 50: 221–246.

Leslie, P. H., 1945, On the use of matrices in certain population mathematics. Biometrika 33: 183–212.

    1948, Some further notes on the use of matrices in population mathematics. Biometrika 35: 214–245.

Lotka, A. J., 1925, Elements of physical biology. Williams and Wilkins, Baltimore, Md.

Nicholson, A. J., 1954, An outline of the dynamics of animal populations. Austr. J. Zool. 2: 9–65.

Park, T., E. V. Gregg and C. Z. Lutherman, 1941, Studies in population physiology. X. Inter-specific competition in populations of granary beetles. Physiol. Zool. 14: 395–430.

Pratt, D. M., 1943, Analysis of population development in Daphnia at different temperatures. Biol. Bull. 85: 116–140.

Richman, S., 1958, The transformation of energy by *Daphnia pulex*. Ecol. Monogr. 28: 273–291.

Ricker, W. E., 1954, Stock and recruitment. J. Fish. Res. Bd. Canada 11: 559–623.

Slobodkin, L. B., 1953, An algebra of population growth. Ecology 34: 513–519.

    1954, Population dynamics in *Daphnia obtusa* Kurz. Ecol. Monogr. 24: 69–88.

    1959, Energetics in *Daphnia pulex* populations. Ecology 40: 232–243.

Smith, F. E., 1952, Experimental methods in population dynamics: a critique. Ecology 33: 441–450.

    1958, Letter to P. Frank, dated Oct. 31, 1958.

Wangersky, P. J., and W. J. Cunningham, 1956, On time lags in equations of growth. Proc. Nat. Acad. Sci. 42: 699–702.

    1957, Time lag in population models. Cold Spring Harbor Symp. Quant. Biol. 22: 329–338.

Reprinted from J. Fish. Res. Bd. Canada, 15(1), pp. 27–45, 1958.

# The Rôle of Competition in the Mortality of Hatchery Trout[1]

By Richard B. Miller

*University of Alberta, Edmonton, Alta.*

## ABSTRACT

The literature on the survival of hatchery-reared trout after release in streams is reviewed and the conclusion is reached that survival is poor in lakes and streams where a resident trout population already exists. In streams the deaths of planted trout occur very soon after their release and have been referred to as "delayed mortality". However, a comparison of survivals after planting in occupied and non-occupied streams shows that many of the deaths are not attributable to hatchery-background or transportation methods, but largely to some aspect of competition with resident trout. Some investigations which have sought to measure the relative survivability of wild and hatchery trout have not used *resident* wild trout and thus a crucial aspect of the competition has been omitted. Investigations at the Alberta Biological Station test stream, Gorge Creek, are described; in these a significant difference in blood lactic acid levels was found between hatchery trout with and without competition from resident trout. A tentative role is assigned competition as follows: introduced trout must compete for niches and for food. In the early stages of this competition they are continuously exercising; they exhaust stores of some metabolite and die either of acidosis or starvation.

## CONTENTS

## I. INTRODUCTION

A problem of major importance to fishery managers is the high mortality that occurs among hatchery-reared trout after they have been released in a stream or lake. It is the purpose of this paper to present the evidence that has been gathered concerning this mortality, to review briefly the investigations and

[1]Received for publication June 7, 1957.

speculations concerning its cause, and to offer a concept of the manner in which competition may play a major rôle.

At the present time the theory that competition may be important in the survival of hatchery fish is somewhat in disrepute among fishery biologists. This is partly, if not entirely, due to a failure to appreciate precisely what is implied by the term "competition". An excellent example of this lack of understanding is provided by an anonymous footnote on page 14 of the Progressive Fish-Culturist, No. 18, 1956, which cites a starvation experiment on rainbow and brown trout. Many of the trout were able to survive 248 days without food. From this fact the footnote concludes that it is doubtful if competition between wild and hatchery trout is important. Evidently, the author of the footnote thinks of competition as being competition for food. Much of the recent and current work on survival of hatchery trout in the presence of wild trout has been planned with the obvious, but not explicit, assumption that competition is solely *competition for food*. Before proceeding to the main purpose of this paper, therefore, it seems worthwhile to examine the concepts of competition that have been expressed by its serious students.

Charles Darwin (1859) first emphasized the importance of competition when he explained the part it played in natural selection. Darwin's idea of competition was the demand of more than one organism for the same resource of the environment in excess of immediate supply. It is quite clear that "resource" includes food supply but is not restricted to it. Implicit in Darwin's concept of competition is the factor of elimination. Any two species could not indefinitely occupy *identical* niches—one would disappear. Support for the "elimination" hypothesis was provided by Elton (1946). In a survey of the literature on ecological communities he pointed out that 85 per cent or more of the species in any one community are sole representatives of their genera; apparently interspecific competition had eliminated all but one species of each genus in each ecological community. Crombie (1947) reached similar conclusions, and in a survey of the literature on interspecific competition, concludes that Darwin's original thesis is adequately supported by facts from both field and laboratory.

Park (1954), reporting on his beautifully designed laboratory studies of competition between two beetle species, suggested interspecific competition to be . . . "those new events that emerge when two species populations coassociate and which lead in time to the persistence of one species and the selective elimination of the other". In Dr. Park's experiments two species of flour beetle were cultured together in vials of flour under a variety of conditions. In every case, one or the other species was eliminated. The definition amounts to expressing what competition is in terms of its result. What was implicit in Darwin's concept becomes explicit in Park's, and *vice versa*. Since it is not established by what mechanism competition caused one species of beetle to die out, the concept of demand for some resource in excess of supply is omitted from the definition.

For the student of competition in the field, Dr. Park's definition is not satisfactory. Field studies may demonstrate that some kind of interaction between two species is producing measurable effects on one or both species, but that these effects are not necessarily mortal. A good example is the careful study by Larkin and Smith (1954) on the effects on Kamloops trout produced by the invasion of their habitat by redsided shiners. The shiners depressed the growth rate of the trout by a full year. This result appears to have been achieved by competition for bottom organisms and by mutual predation, the shiners on trout fry and the adult trout on shiners. In a recent review of competition in freshwater fishes, Larkin (1956) accepts the Darwinian definition.

To Darwin's definition of demand in excess of supply, Solomon (1949) added two more points: (1) direct, active struggle between individuals or groups; and (2), the occupation or consumption by earlier arriving individual of something in limited supply, so that late-comers are automatically excluded or deprived. It may be argued that these two points are really contained in Darwin's broader statement; however, both points are useful in directing attention toward the mechanism by which competition may operate. They are particularly pertinent in the study of competition between wild and hatchery-reared trout, which, as will be argued, seems to consist of competition for *Lebensraum* that involves both active inter-individual struggle and struggle against environmental forces.

The nature of the data to be discussed is such that it is not profitable to distinguish between interspecific and intraspecific competition; the situations created by stocking hatchery trout are much the same whether the species stocked is the same or not the same as the wild resident species. In this paper, competition is used in the Darwinian sense as applied to mutual interactions between two species.

## II. DIFFERENTIAL SURVIVAL OF HATCHERY-REARED AND WILD TROUT

In the past twenty years a great deal of effort has been expended in measuring the catches of hatchery-reared trout after planting in streams and lakes. This work has been thoroughly reviewed by several authors (Miller, 1949; Smith, 1948; Schuck, 1948); since these reviews appeared, recent papers by Mullan (1955), Burdick and Cooper (1956) and Hale and Smith (1955) have provided further evidence. Broadly, it has been found that trout fry planted in lakes or streams containing breeding resident trout populations are taken in insignificant numbers by anglers. Such plantings have been largely abandoned. Instead, much larger trout were planted, at first in the fall. Again, returns were too low to justify the costs of the operations. The best returns (in lakes and streams with breeding residents) were obtained from legal-sized trout planted immediately prior to and during the angling season. The success of these plants varied somewhat from place to place, but a reasonable average return would be about 35% of the numbers planted. Detailed creel censuses in streams revealed that three-quarters of the returns were made in the first week or two after the release of the trout. Negligible numbers were creeled in the second summer, i.e., few or no planted trout seemed to have survived their first winter. Returns from lakes have been better, particularly in lakes where no resident population existed prior to planting. However, it has been frequently observed that these lakes do not continue to provide good fishing but deteriorate markedly in three to five years.

The studies referred to in the preceding paragraph do not, of course, demonstrate any differential mortality. In fact, the failure to catch more than, say, 35% of a planting does not necessarily mean that the other 65% died. However, the inference is strong that most of the uncaught fish did die; and if they did, the mortality rate exceeds that observed for wild trout. The studies of Nielsen *et al.* (1957) and of Miller (1952, 1954b, 1955) provide less inferential evidence. The former authors released trout in screened-off sections of Convict Creek. These sections could be deprived of their water, the pools pumped dry, and the fish recovered and counted. This work will be discussed in detail in a later section. For the present, let us examine Miller's experiments.

## THE GORGE CREEK EXPERIMENTS

Gorge Creek is one of the test streams of the Alberta Biological Station. It is located on the Eastern Slopes of the Rocky Mountains in Alberta, at an elevation, at its mouth, of 4,800 feet (1,460 m.). The stream and the experimental design have been previously described (Miller, *opera citata*). Briefly, Gorge Creek is a small, tributary stream, 6 miles (10 km.) long and 15 to 30 feet (4.5–9 m.) wide, flowing through steep shale banks into the Sheep River. It forms a series of gentle runs and rocky pools providing homes for about 1,000 small adult cutthroat trout per mile. There are no other fish species. Fish-proof sections were formed by building removable wood and wire fences across the stream at intervals of ¼-mile. Into one or more such sections, tagged, individually weighed, hatchery-reared cutthroat were released. Daily patrols of the sections were made, dead fish weighed and recorded, and living fish caught, weighed and released.

The results of many of these experiments have been reported in the papers already cited. When planted in sections containing resident trout, ⅓ of 3-year-old hatchery fish and 50% to 60% of 2-year-old hatchery fish died during the first two weeks of the experiment. The experiments usually lasted from June through September. During this time few or no wild trout died. Thus, there was demonstrated a very pronounced differential survival.

## III. CAUSES OF DIFFERENTIAL SURVIVAL

The greater mortalities of hatchery-reared trout have been generally ascribed to some failure in the hatchery technique. Schuck (1948) reviewed the literature dealing with returns of planted trout to anglers, concluded that these returns were too low, and suggested a number of features of the hatchery background that might account for the situation. Schuck's list included food, constant water temperatures and various water conditions. Some support for these ideas is provided by experiments in which survival of trout from different hatcheries exposed to similar conditions is compared. It was found that certain hatcheries produced a more viable trout (see Nielsen *et al.*, 1957).

Wales (1954) and Miller (1954b) both suggested that the absence of natural selection in the hatchery could account for the poor showing in the streams. Under natural conditions only about 1% of the fingerlings produced in the stream will survive. In the hatchery 40% or more are normally reared to legal-sized trout for planting.

The rôle of competition in differential survival has received considerable attention. Field experiments have been conducted by Miller (1955, and others to be described in this paper), Adelman and Bingham (1955) and Nielsen *et al.* (1957). The work of Black (1955, 1956, 1957) on the rise of blood lactate in exercised trout has an important bearing on the competition problem, particularly as his results suggest a possible mechanism by which competition could act.

In this section a series of experiments which have a bearing on the differential survival problem will be reviewed and some previously unpublished work will be described. The material has been grouped under two headings: Rôle of natural selection; and Effects of resident populations.

RÔLE OF NATURAL SELECTION

As previously mentioned, the small degree of natural selection in the hatchery has been suggested as a cause of the lower survival of hatchery trout. Fish reared in the quiet waters of a pond and fed regularly have been subjected to very little environmental pressure. When such fish are placed in a stream they are immediately exposed to much harsher conditions; perhaps those that would have died as fry or fingerlings, had they hatched in the stream, now succumb to environmental forces. A series of experiments done at Gorge Creek serve to substantiate this supposition. Portions of this work have been published (Miller, 1955); for the sake of completeness these portions and the unpublished data will be presented here together.

When it was established by several summers' experiments that 50% to 60% of the hatchery 2-year-olds died after release in a populated enclosure of Gorge Creek, the next step was to determine the survival of two other groups: these were first, wild fish, taken from Gorge Creek above the experimental enclosures and transferred to an enclosure; and second, trout which had been hatched in the hatchery but reared under natural stream conditions.

SURVIVAL OF WILD CUTTHROAT TROUT. In a first experiment, 152 trout were caught by angling in the upper portions of Gorge Creek; these were given numbered Petersen-type tags, weighed and carried in pails of water to an enclosure lower down the creek. Here they were released to find a living in competition with approximately three hundred resident wild trout. Only 2.4% of these trout succumbed to natural causes during the summer (Some were killed attempting to get through the upper screen of the enclosure; these have been considered "unnatural" mortalities.) The weight record is interesting: during their first 30 days in the enclosure the transplanted trout lost weight; the lowest average value was reached on the tenth day, when they weighed 90.5% of weight at transfer. By the fortieth day the fish had regained all lost weight and, from then on, made small gains.

A similar experiment was performed two years later (1953). In this, 209 wild trout were caught outside the enclosure area, tagged, weighed and transferred to the enclosure. During the summer 4.3% died. A maximum weight loss of 14.7% was observed; this was regained after 50 days.

Recoveries of fish from the first experiment were made in the two years following transfer and showed that 46% survived the first winter and 29% the second winter; these are the usual survival percentages for wild trout in Gorge Creek.

SURVIVAL OF STREAM-REARED HATCHERY TROUT. Two experiments have been carried out using trout which were hatched in the hatchery and then transferred to Bighill Creek. Bighill Creek contained no resident trout but offered typical trout stream habitat. The hatchery fish were retained by screens and left to fend for themselves, i.e., unfed.

In the first experiment several hundred trout that had spent one summer in the hatchery rearing pond were transferred to Bighill Creek and left there for 18 months. Then 58 of them were moved to an enclosure in Gorge Creek. Shortly afterward a flood washed out the screens and an unknown number of fish escaped. However, 27 were recovered by angling the same summer and 10 in the next summer. Thus at least 17.2% survived the winter. Weight records show that these trout lost 8.8% of their weight in 40 days, and that this was regained by 50 days.

A second experiment in 1954 used trout that had spent one summer in a rearing pond and 10 months in Bighill Creek. Seventy-six were transferred to an enclosure in Gorge Creek where 18.4% died during the summer. These fish lost 11.7% of their weight in 10 days but thereafter rapidly regained and were in excess of planted weight by the twentieth day.

These experiments demonstrate that under similar stream conditions, and in competition with a resident population, three grades of survival exist. The best survival of more than 90% is shown by transplanted wild trout; a middle grade of approximately 80% is shown by fish exposed to natural selection in a stream before planting; and the poorest survival is exhibited by pond-reared fish—40 to 50%. These findings certainly suggest that the low degree of natural selection in the hatchery may account for at least some of the poor survival of hatchery trout.

## EFFECTS OF RESIDENT POPULATIONS

The experiments reported above were all carried out by superimposing the experimental fish on a resident population. A number of experiments have been reported in which an effort has been made to assess the effects of these resident trout on the survival of the introduced trout.

THE GORGE CREEK EXPERIMENTS. The first experiment at Gorge Creek designed to test the effects of the resident trout on the survival of the hatchery trout was done in 1954 and has been reported (Miller, 1955). In this study two similar sections were screened off; in one, all the resident trout were killed with a rotenone poison; in the other the resident population of 340 catchable-size trout was left undisturbed. Into each section approximately 200 tagged, weighed, hatchery cutthroat trout were released. Two such releases were made in the no-competition enclosure.

A similar experiment, using the same two enclosures, was done in 1955 (unpublished) using brown trout and brook trout. The results of the two years' experiments are summarized in Table I.

TABLE I. Mortality and weight changes during the summer of release of brook, brown and cutthroat trout with and without competition from resident cutthroat trout. CT = cutthroat trout; BT = brown trout; EB = brook trout.

|  | No Competition | | | Competition | | |
|---|---|---|---|---|---|---|
|  | 1954 | | 1955 | 1954 | 1955 | |
|  | Lot I CT | Lot II CT | CT | CT | BT | EB |
| Mortality (%) | 16.0 | 12.4 | 10.5 | 54.5 | 59.2 | 49.5 |
| Percentage of planted wt. after 50 days | 127.3 | 110.5 | 218.0 | 98.2 | 93.0 | 100.0 |
| Av. wt. at planting (*ounces*) | 1.03 | 1.6 | 1.4 | 1.5 | 5.4 | 2.2 |
| Wt. range (*ounces*) | 0.5–3.0 | 1–4.5 | 1–3.5 | 0.5–5.0 | 1–11 | 1–4.75 |
| No. planted | 200 | 121 | 200 | 200 | 86 | 113 |

The mortality figures in Table I were obtained by actual counts of dead fish. The two stream sections were patrolled at least once each day, usually twice; the dead fish were picked out of the water, weighed and their tag numbers recorded. During the two summers no resident trout were found dead. The mortalities recorded in this way represent minimal values; dead fish not found or fish taken by predators are not included. However, predators are very rare in the area, and their effect is probably negligible; also, in the clear water, dead fish are very conspicuous and not likely to be overlooked. It is believed that the mortality figures are very close to the true values. Table I shows remarkably consistent results: hatchery trout in competition with resident wild trout suffered a mortality of 49.5–59.2%. Differences between mortality of brook, brown and cutthroat trout lie within the probable experimental error, although the brook trout appear to be slightly more resistant. The resident trout with which the hatchery fish were in competition ranged from 1 to 5 ounces (30–140 g.) in weight, average 2.6 ounces (74 g.); they had, then, no advantage in size over the brown trout, and only a slight advantage over the other two species.

All the competing species lost weight; after 50 days the survivors had completely (brook) or nearly (other species) regained their weights at planting time.

In sharp contrast, the hatchery trout planted in the enclosure from which the resident trout had been removed, suffered mortalities of only 10.5 to 16.0%. This is approximately one-quarter of the mortality of the fish faced with competition. It is well to remember that these fish (competition and no-competition groups) were in the *same* stream at the *same* time, separated only by a wire fence.

The weight changes in the two groups also show a sharp difference. The trout without competition show substantial increases; the average weight of those of one group more than doubled in 50 days. The detailed field records show that the weight gain began as soon as the fish were released in the experimental enclosure.

Survival over the first winter cannot be absolutely determined in Gorge Creek. The screens forming the enclosures are removed in the late fall and the fish are free to move down into the Sheep River. A few recoveries in the Sheep River have been made by angling; thus it is known that some do move down. It is believed the majority remain in the same enclosure area, where they are recovered by seining or rotenone poisoning the next spring. Figures obtained in this way indicate over-winter survivals of 15 to 18% for hatchery trout without competition and 3.5 to 13.3% for trout with competition (though, of course, once the screens are removed, both groups are exposed to competition).

These figures on over-winter survival, because of the unknown degree of emigration, are not believed to be reliable. Weights obtained in the second summer, however, are not subject to error and indicate significant differences. Weights of fish that had one summer without competition range from 137 to 226% of planted weight; weights of fish that had continuous competition range from 60 to 147% of planted weight.

DATA FROM OTHER STREAMS. Mullan (1956a) has found that, in Massachusetts streams, the anglers catch a higher percentage of the larger than of the smaller stocked trout. This was true of brook, brown and rainbow hatchery trout. This implies that the larger trout survived in greater numbers, presumably because their size helped them in competition with the resident trout in the streams. The same author (Mullan, 1956b) has conducted some preliminary work on stream reclamation with fish toxicants. He finds evidence of better survival of stocked rainbow and brook trout after the resident population has been eliminated or thinned out, thus eliminating or reducing competition.

DATA FROM LAKES. The technique of sport fish management made a great advance with the discovery of lake reclamation. Reclamation is the fundamentally simple process of applying fish toxicant to lakes and killing all, or nearly all, the resident fish population. After the water has lost its toxicity, trout are planted, usually as fry or fingerlings. The growth and survival of trout in these reclaimed lakes has been spectacular, and the technique has become a well-established management practice in several western states. In the past few years this type of management has spread to the mid-west and, in experimental stages, to the eastern states.

A generally admitted drawback to this management technique is that only the first stocking of hatchery trout exhibits the remarkable growth and survival. Each year after the first stocking the growth and survival of the current year's stocking grows poorer; after four or five years, survival may be negligible. So far, this history of poorer growth has been sparsely reported. Curtis (1951) has described one California lake in which a great improvement in yield from fingerling plants followed the removal of a resident population of four species of salmonids. Burdick and Cooper (1956) have published the history of plantings of fingerling rainbow trout in Weber Lake, Wisconsin. They bring out one point pertinent to this discussion: the survival in terms of returns to anglers was markedly reduced following the good survival of a previous year's planting. Thus 10,000 two-inch rainbow fingerlings planted in 1951 yielded only five fish; at this time survival of the 1950 planting of 10,000 three-inch rainbows was good. Miller and Thomas (1957) found that in one Alberta lake that contained no resident fish, the rainbow trout reached 13 ounces (37 g.) during the summer in which they were planted; a similar plant in the following year reached only 10 ounces (28 g.) in the same time; and in the third year, a weight of only 5 ounces (14 g.) was achieved.

All of this suggests that a resident population in lakes has the same competitive advantage over introduced fish as it has in streams. The magnitude of the effect is not precisely known and it is difficult to design an experiment in a lake that would yield precise or absolute mortality figures.

## IV. THE RÔLE OF COMPETITION

In the preceding section it has been shown that hatchery trout suffer much heavier mortalities in the presence of a resident wild population. The mechanism by which the resident trout exert their deleterious effects on the hatchery fish has been largely a matter of speculation. Preoccupation with the idea that competition for food is the major factor has influenced the design of a number of experiments.

### COMPETITION FOR FOOD

The importance of competition for food in fresh water fish populations has been recognized for a long time. Intraspecific competition is believed to be the cause of stunting in crowded populations and there are many examples of increased growth rates in fishes following reductions in their numbers by winter kills, or by heavy exploitation. The technique of fish pond management is based to a large extent on the need of preventing overpopulation with resultant stunting. The demonstration of reduced growth rate in Kamloops trout caused by competition for food with shiners has already been mentioned (Larkin and Smith, 1954).

The feeling that competition for food is unimportant in the survival of hatchery trout has its origin in the short time it takes for hatchery trout to die after their release. Reimers (1957) has shown that trout can live through long periods without food. Trout kept at low temperatures in outside ponds suffered 17.7% mortality after 120 days of starvation; at the same temperature in indoor ponds the mortality was 9.3%. In another experiment lasting through 180 winter days, only 2.0% of starved hatchery rainbow trout died and 8.0% of wild brown trout.

Adelman and Bingham (1955) planted wild and hatchery-reared brook trout together in screened-off enclosures of two Michigan streams. In Hunt

Creek 102 wild brook trout *from another stream* and 100 hatchery trout were used; after six months 28% of the hatchery and 59% of the wild fish were still alive. In a footnote the authors state that other fish (resident?) were in the experimental section so that it carried six times its normal population. In Slagle Creek 35 trout from Slagle and 90 hatchery trout were enclosed; after six months 64% of the hatchery and 37% of the wild trout were alive. Slagle Creek, during the experiment, carried three times the normal population. The authors conclude that there is no difference in viability of wild and hatchery-reared brook trout. However, this conclusion is rendered somewhat dubious by the unusual situations which prevailed in the experimental enclosures, and the inconsistency of the results. The trout used in the experiments were not only competing with each other, but also with a large population of other trout, possibly resident. Of greater value would be the differential survival figures for the fish already in the enclosures and the fish added, both wild and hatchery-reared.

An intensive six-year study of the survival of hatchery-reared rainbow trout was carried out in sections of Convict Creek, California, by Nielsen *et al.* (1957). The authors used four equivalent sections of the stream, separated by screens, and so laid out that the water could be diverted and the sections rendered dry for a complete and accurate count of fish. At the beginning of an experiment *all* trout were removed; then hatchery-reared, catchable-size rainbow trout were stocked with wild brown trout in one section, alone in another, and wild brown trout alone in a third section. All the wild trout were secured by seining in other parts of the stream, i.e., they were *not resident trout*. In none of the experiments was an initial high mortality observed; there were no significant differences in survival in the different sections. Survivals over summer periods varied from 36.8 to 85.1%.

The results of these experiments led the authors to believe that there was no difference in survivability of hatchery-reared and wild trout. However, as in Adelman and Bingham's work, the experimental design was such that important aspects of competition were not measured. Both hatchery and wild stocks were released simultaneously into a strange locality. The effect of a *resident* population was missing and it is not surprising that the heavy mortalities which normally follow plants in *populated* waters did not occur. It is pertinent to note that in 1953, section 2 of Convict Creek contained a rainbow trout population left over from the previous year. The rainbow superimposed on this resident group showed the lowest survival of that year's lots—39.8% as compared to 48.1, 76.6 and 76.1% in Sections 1, 3 and 4 (Nielson *et al.*, Table 15). The whole investigation shows that, *under the conditions established by the experiment*, hatchery-reared rainbow trout and wild brown trout are evenly matched.

## DELAYED MORTALITY AND BLOOD LACTATE LEVELS

For some years it has been well known that the mortality following planting of hatchery trout occurred mainly during the first week. Recently Horton (1956) has described this initial mortality as it has been observed in Oregon waters. In Oregon it has been known as "delayed mortality". Horton writes that it begins 24 hours after release of the trout and reaches a peak on the third or fourth day. The average total mortality is 10% but it may reach 93% in any one planting. The mortality begins with apparent nervousness in the fish; they school and swim in circles, rising often to bite at the surface; later the fish act as if they were blind and had lost their equilibrium. They jump out of the water or plunge into the bottom. Following this stage, some of the fish die, mouth agape.

Horton conducted a series of experiments in a search for methods of reducing the mortality. He loaded a hatchery truck, took the fish on a six-hour run and returned to the hatchery of origin where the fish *were placed in ponds, by themselves*, for seven-day observation. The runs were made at different water temperatures, using different aerating systems and varied methods of loading and unloading. Anaesthesia with sodium amytol was also tried. Significant differences in delayed mortality were associated with temperature and aeration methods.

In these experiments Horton actually tested the effects of various transportation methods on subsequent survival. Since the trout were returned to ponds in which they were not faced with competition, true "delayed mortality" was excluded from the tests.

Black (1955) measured the lactic acid concentration in the blood of various fishes in an unexercised state and again after 15 minutes of vigorous exercise, induced by chasing the fish in troughs. He found that in Kamloops trout yearlings blood lactate varied from 14.7 to 17.1 mg. %, unexercised, and from 99.5 to 100.2 mg. % after exercise. In Kamloops trout 2-year-olds the corresponding figures were 8.0 and 82.2 mg. %.

J. H. Wales pointed out to Dr. Black the phenomenon of "delayed mortality"; Black suspected that the prolonged exercise associated with transportation to the planting site might increase blood lactate levels to the point where lactic acid was a significant factor in the mortality. Accordingly (Black, 1956) he carried out an experiment in which hatchery trout were given a 90 minute trip in a tank truck and returned to the hatchery troughs. In two-year-old Kamloops trout the blood lactate was 51.0 mg. % during the first four minutes after the trip was completed. The lactate remained at this level for 20 to 24 minutes. then declined erratically to resting levels after two hours. Similar trout after 15 minutes exercise showed blood lactate levels of 75.7 mg. %; lactate rose for two hours after exercise to a peak of 117.0 mg. %, then declined to 20.4 mg. % after eight hours. Black got essentially similar results with 1.5-year-old lake trout after runs in the hatchery truck, except that blood lactate increased for one hour following the trip, then declined to resting levels after two hours.

These experiments suggest that rise in blood lactate *during transportation* cannot be responsible for delayed mortality. This is not surprising in view of the author's findings, described earlier, in which delayed mortality did not occur in trout planted in a stretch of Gorge Creek from which the resident trout had been removed, but did occur in the same hatchery stock, planted in another section of Gorge Creek in which the native trout were still present. The possibility that the resident native trout create a situation which leads to continued high blood lactate levels in the introduced hatchery fish seemed worthy of investigation. Such an experiment was done at Gorge Creek in 1956.

## BLOOD LACTATE EXPERIMENTS AT GORGE CREEK

The same two sections of Gorge Creek that were used in earlier survival tests were used in the present experiments. Section I consisted of $\frac{3}{4}$-mile (1.2 km.) of Gorge Creek, screened at each end, from which all resident trout were removed by application of a rotenone poison. Section II, above section I, was the same length, but contained a resident population of approximately 300 native cutthroat trout which weighed from 0.75–5.75 ounces, average, 2.6 ounces (21–163 g., av. 74 g.). These sections will be called No-competition Enclosure and Competition Enclosure, respectively.

On July 13, 1956, 204 tagged hatchery-reared cutthroat trout, ranging from 1.5 to 5.75 ounces in weight, average 2.6 ounces (42–163 g., av. 74 g.) were released in the Competition Enclosure. Blood samples were taken from some of them just before they were poured into the stream. The technique used was that of Black, and we are greatly indebted to Dr. Black for detailed advice given in personal correspondence.

The fish were planted in the morning; that afternoon a flash flood followed a severe rain storm; the lower screens of the Competition Enclosure were washed out and an unknown number of the trout was lost. However, 73 were later recorded in the Enclosure, enought to carry on with the experiment.

On July 25, 1956, 12 days later, 181 tagged hatchery cutthroat trout weighing from 0.5 to 3.0 ounces, average 1.5 ounces (14–85 g., av. 42 g.) were released in the No-competition Enclosure. Blood samples from several were taken immediately before release. The later planting date was chosen to help eliminate variables introduced by fluctuating stream conditions; if the two plantings had been made on the same date observed changes in blood lactate, following planting, might be due to identical stream flow rates which would obscure any effects of presence or absence of resident trout.

In the 60 days following the plantings, blood samples were taken at more or less regular intervals from 60 fish in the Competition Enclosure and 43 fish in the No-competition Enclosure. In addition blood samples were taken from 12 wild trout in the Competition Enclosure. The fish were caught by seining and the blood samples taken immediately on the stream bank. At the same time the fish were weighed and a daily record of mortalities was kept.

An interesting observation during the early weeks of the experiment was that the Competition Enclosure fish appeared to be exhausted; they could be caught in many cases by simply bending over and picking them up in the hand. Conversely, the No-competition trout were, at all times, as difficult to catch as the wild trout.

The total mortality of fish in the No-competition Enclosure was 9.4% a figure in good agreement with previous findings of 10.5, 12.4 and 16.0% (Table I). Only 34 fish (16.7%) were found dead in the Competition Enclosure;

this figure has little meaning because of the loss of an unknown number when the screens washed out.

TABLE II. Weight changes in hatchery-reared cutthroat trout after release in enclosures in Gorge Creek.

| Days after planting | Competition Enclosure | | No-Competition Enclosure | |
|---|---|---|---|---|
| | No. fish | % planted wt. | No. fish | % planted wt. |
| 0–10 | 19 | 91 | 15 | 99 |
| 11–20 | 24 | 101 | 23 | 104 |
| 21–30 | 9 | 96 | 3 | 100 |
| 31–40 | 7 | 87.5 | 11 | 106 |
| 41–50 | 9 | 92 | 7 | 112 |
| 51–60 | 5 | 84.5 | 0 | — |

The Competition Enclosure fish were, on the average, an ounce heavier than the No-competition Enclosure trout at the start. Despite this advantage, the data show that they consistently lost weight during the summer (Table II). Conversely, the smaller trout in the No-competition Enclosure exhibited a general increase in weight. These results serve to confirm previous findings reported earlier.

The results of the analysis of the blood lactic acid are shown in Table III. The analyses were performed using the Barker-Summerson technique, also employed by Dr. Black. We wish to acknowledge our considerable indebtedness to Dr. H. B. Collier, who undertook most of the work in the analyses.

TABLE III. Blood lactic acid (mg.%) in hatchery-reared cutthroat trout with and without competition from resident wild trout.

| Days after planting | Competition | | | No Competition | | |
|---|---|---|---|---|---|---|
| | No. of samples | Mean lactic acid | $\sigma_M$ | No. of samples | Mean lactic acid | $\sigma_M$ |
| 0 | – | — | — | 5 | 53.1 | ±27.3 |
| 1 | 8 | 37.3 | ±5.1 | 4 | 19.3 | ±11.7 |
| 3 | 4 | 27.1 | ±6.9 | 3 | 16.9 | ±3.7 |
| 5 | 4 | 28.5 | ±10.1 | 2 | 16.5 | ±7.5 |
| 7 | – | — | — | 3 | 27.1 | ±11.4 |
| 8 | 4 | 29.4 | ±12.7 | – | — | — |
| 9 | – | — | — | 3 | 36.0 | ±7.0 |
| 10 | 4 | 42.9 | ±10.2 | – | — | — |
| 12 | – | — | — | 3 | 29.5 | ±9.5 |
| 13 | 6 | 24.8 | ±5.2 | 2 | 8.9 | ±0.5 |
| 15 | 2 | 29.6 | ±2.6 | – | — | — |
| 17 | 4 | 12.6 | ±4.2 | – | — | — |
| 19 | 3 | 19.1 | ±5.7 | – | — | — |
| 20 | – | — | — | 3 | 14.7 | ±10.7 |
| 21 | 3 | 19.5 | ±3.9 | – | — | — |
| 27 | – | — | — | 3 | 9.9 | ±0.05 |
| 28 | 3 | 10.7 | ±0.4 | – | — | — |
| 32 | 3 | 14.7 | ±4.7 | – | — | — |
| 34/5 | – | — | — | 3 | 12.1 | ±5.0 |
| 39 | 3 | 10.7 | ±5.4 | – | — | — |
| 42 | – | — | — | 3 | 4.5 | ±1.8 |
| 46 | 3 | 16.5 | ±5.4 | – | — | — |
| 48 | – | — | — | 3 | 8.3 | ±1.5 |
| 50 | – | — | — | 3 | 6.9 | ±3.5 |
| 54/5 | 3 | 8.2 | ±2.7 | – | — | — |
| 60 | 3 | 4.7 | ±1.2 | — | — | — |

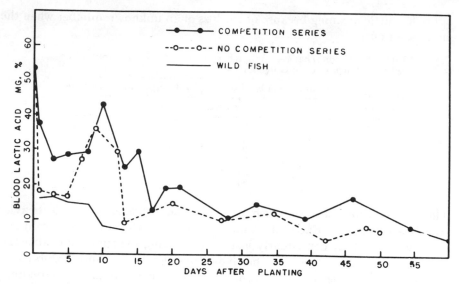

Lactic acid content of trout blood after release in Gorge Creek.

The data in Table III have been used to prepare the accompanying Figure, which shows the changes in blood lactic acid plotted against time. The highest lactic acid levels were found immediately after the 60-mile trip by non-aerated tank truck from the hatchery. After planting, both groups of trout showed a decline in blood lactate, followed by a rise on the ninth and tenth days. Thereafter, the levels fell gradually to the resting levels found by Black (1955) in two-year-old Kamloops trout of comparable size.

Also shown in the Figure are the 12 samples from wild trout in the Competition Enclosure. They are plotted on the same time scale as the Competition hatchery trout, i.e., zero time is July 13. The blood lactate level began at 16.0 mg. % and declined to 6.5 mg. % by day 13. This change could represent either the effects of decreasing rates of stream flow (after the flash flood on July 13) or a response, followed by adjustment, to the introduced hatchery trout. An experiment is being planned to investigate these alternative explanations.

A number of reasonably firm conclusions may be drawn from the results of this experiment:

(1) During the first 15 days there is a large difference (roughly 8 to 16 mg. %) in the blood lactic acid of the two groups of trout. The Competition group is higher.

(2) In this same period the lactic acid level in the Competition group is approximately three to five times the normal or wild level. In the No-competition group it varies from two to four times the wild level.

(3) The initial drop in both groups, followed by rises on the ninth and tenth days, is a real phenomenon, not associated with water conditions. This is known because zero time was July 13 in one group and July 25 in the other. This phenomenon suggests that some metabolite is very soon exhausted and that a period

of four or five days passes before the stock is replenished. This fits well with the observation that the trout begin feeding normally three or four days after release.

(4) The observed post-planting mortalities correspond in time with the observed period of high lactic acid levels. Table IV shows a summary of mortalities of various plantings of hatchery fish in sections of Gorge Creek occupied by wild trout.

TABLE IV. Post-planting mortality in four groups of 2-year-old hatchery-reared cutthroat trout superimposed on resident populations in Gorge Creek.

| Days after planting | 1950 200 trout | 1952 200 trout | 1954 200 trout | 1955 199 trout |
|---|---|---|---|---|
| 0 | 0 | 7 | 0 | 0 |
| 1 | 0 | 62 | 13 | 1 |
| 2 | 1 | 9 | 4 | 5 |
| 3 | 3 | 24 | 3 | 4 |
| 4 | 12 | 0 | 6 | 6 |
| 5 | 16 | 0 | 4 | 5 |
| 6 | 22 | 2 | 8 | 3 |
| 7 | 14 | 2 | 4 | 7 |
| 8 | 10 | 2 | 7 | 4 |
| 9 | 5 | 1 | 19 | 3 |
| 10 | 4 | 3 | 10 | 5 |
| 11 | 2 | 0 | 6 | 3 |
| 12 | 3 | 2 | 0 | 6 |
| 13 | 0 | 0 | 6 | 2 |
| 14 | 2 | 1 | 3 | 4 |
| 1–14 | 94 | 117 | 93 | 58 |
| Total for summer | 112 | 132 | 109 | 107 |
| Percentage within 14 days | 84 | 89 | 85 | 54 |

It is clear from Table IV that most of the trout die during the two weeks after planting—the period of high lactic acid levels. The lesser mortality of the 1955 plant may be because these trout were reared in circular wooden tanks with vigorously circulating water that kept them constatly swimming; all the others were reared in conventional rectangular ponds.

## V. DISCUSSION

It is a firmly established fact that hatchery-reared trout, when superimposed on a resident population, suffer very heavy mortalities; in streams a number of convincing investigations have demonstrated that the bulk of this mortality occurs in the first two weeks following plantings. The events in lakes are less well-documented but there is ample evidence that survival is poor when a resident population is present. It is also firmly established that survival is very good when there are no fish resident in the lake or stream into which the hatchery trout are released.

Experiments made to determine the cause of this so-called "delayed mortality" have failed to take proper account of the effects of the resident population. The effects of various feeding regimens in the hatchery, water temperatures, handling methods and transportation methods have been studied *but not in fish subjected to competition*. The experimental animals have been returned to hatchery ponds for observation. Thus these investigations measure only the portion of the mortality which may be due to events which take place before the trout are released in the stream or lake.

Other investigators have recognized that competition with wild trout may be a factor in mortality. However, there has been a general failure to recognize the importance of the wild trout being *resident*. Extensive studies have been conducted on the relative survival of wild and hatchery-reared trout in the same stream but, in every experiment, the wild fish were introduced to the study section *from some other place*; i.e., they were not residents. It is perhaps not surprising that no significant differential mortalities were observed under these conditions. Complementary studies established that trout could tolerate long periods of starvation. These two observations were interpreted, quite unjustifiably, as indicating that competition for food was not a factor in survival of hatchery trout.

There are a number of ways in which competition may exert effects that are not directly concerned with food supply. We are just beginning to learn something of the complexities of territorial behaviour and aggressiveness in fishes. Gerking (1953), Allen (1951) and Miller (1954a) have provided evidence that stream fishes have definite, rather limited territories that they inhabit throughout life. Newman (1956) has shown that these territories are defended; approaches of other fish of the same or different species are repelled. In fact a social order resembling the classic peck order in chickens exists in a population of stream trout.

With the information now available it is possible to construct a tentative *modus operandi* for competition in determining the survival of hatchery fish:

When a group of hatchery trout is released into a body of water already occupied with fish (trout, usually) of very similar habitat requirements, the classical Darwinian setting for competition is achieved. And this is true whether or not the introduced and resident fishes are of the same species. Solomon's (1949) concepts of active struggle and prior occupancy are also realized. The niches are mostly occupied and a fairly rigid social order is established among the resident trout. When hatchery fish are introduced to this society they must find a suitable niche as well as a food supply. This involves first filling any vacant niches; if there are not enough of these the losers in the game of "musical chairs" must seize a suitable niche by aggressive action. The experimental evidence indicates that this is no easy task. Thus wild Gorge Creek trout superimposed on resident trout lower down in the same stream suffered a loss of weight for about 30 days before they established themselves and began gaining. The rôle of natural selection is clear at this point: hatchery trout lost more weight and suffered high mortalities under these circumstances. Trout partly hatchery- and partly stream-reared were intermediate in weight loss and mortality.

The above interpretation is supported by the oft-repeated observation at Gorge Creek: superimposed trout remain out in the open, in schools, clearly visible to the observer for two to four weeks after release. Similar trout, in the same stream, but after removal of resident trout, entirely disappear within one hour of release.

In the stream then, the hatchery trout is faced with two problems, finding food and finding a home. It must compete for both with resident trout. During the early period of this competition the hatchery fish are forced to remain in the current. Here they suffer from accumulation of blood lactate due to the constant muscular effort in maintaining their position. A common observation is that plants of hatchery fish in populated streams drift, in a body, downstream. At this time the weaker fish succumb. What causes death is not yet established. It might be from general acidosis, or it might be the exhaustion of an essential metabolite faster than the fishes' powers of replacing it from the food supply. It is clear that, if this is the case, competition for food may become a crucial factor in survival.

The results of the lactic acid determinations on the Gorge Creek fish show what happened *only in those fish that survived*. Because the fish were tagged, they were individually recognizable and it so happened that only two of the fish used for blood samples subsequently died. Therefore the findings are biased in favour of the tougher fish. It is quite possible that the dying fish never managed to replace their metabolites and so actually died of starvation.

This explanation of the operation of competition is particularly fitted to stream dwelling fishes where the forces of the environment causing fatigue are much more potent than in lakes. However, it does not seem necessary to postulate a different mechanism in still water. The struggle for niches, the aggressive action of resident fish, would be the same. One would expect fewer planted fish to die, and the deaths should be spread over a longer period; and, indeed, these two differences are commonly observed in lake plantings.

From the practical point of view of the fishery manager, this theory of competition should offer some useful suggestions: good survival of hatchery stock should be obtained where heavy fishing pressure has materially reduced the resident trout; "rehabilitation" of lakes by poisoning resident populations should also include resident populations of desirable species (i.e., species normally stocked) when they are not providing satisfactory angling.

## VI. ACKNOWLEDGMENTS

The work of the Alberta Biological Station, both new and previously published, that I have described in this paper is supported jointly by the University of Alberta and the Department of Lands and Forests of the Province of Alberta. I particularly wish to thank three men belonging to the latter organization: Mr. E. S. Huestis, Fish and Game Commissioner, Mr. H. B. Watkins, Superintendent of Fisheries and Mr. W. H. Macdonald, Liaison Officer at Calgary. Mr. M. J. Paetz, Provincial Fishery Biologist, has given much assistance in the

44

actual field work, as have the following University of Alberta students: W. D. Wishart, D. A. Boag, R. G. Miller, D. Sheppard and R. Schlick.

I should like to again acknowledge my indebtedness and express my gratitude to Dr. E. C. Black, Department of Physiology, University of British Columbia and to Dr. H. B. Collier, Professor of Biochemistry, University of Alberta.

My best thanks are due Mr. A. Sinclair, Hatchery Superintendent, who has raised and tagged all the experimental fish.

## VII. LITERATURE CITED

ADELMAN, H. M., AND J. L. BINGHAM. 1955. Winter survival of hatchery-reared and native brook trout. *Prog. Fish-Culturist*, 17(4): 177–180.

ALLEN, K. RADWAY. 1951. The Horokiwi stream. A study of a trout population. *New Zealand Marine Dept., Fish. Bull.*, No. 10, pp. 1–231.

ANONYMOUS. 1956. *Prog. Fish-Cult.*, 18(1): 14.

BLACK, E. C. 1955. Blood levels of hemoglobin and lactic acid in some freshwater fishes following exercise. *J. Fish. Res. Bd. Canada*, 12(6): 917–929.

1956. Appearance of lactic acid in the blood of Kamloops and lake trout following live transportation. *Canadian Fish Culturist*, No. 18, pp. 20–27.

1957. Alterations in the blood level of lactic acid in certain salmonoid fishes following muscular activity. *J. Fish Res. Bd. Canada*, 14(2): 117–134.

BURDICK, M. E., AND E. L. COOPER. 1956. Growth rate, survival and harvest of fingerling rainbow trout planted in Weber Lake, Wisconsin. *J. Wildlife Management*, 20(3): 233–239.

CROMBIE, A. C. 1947. Interspecific competition. *J. Animal Ecol.*, 16: 44–73.

CURTIS, BRIAN. 1951. Yield of hatchery trout in California lakes. *California Fish and Game*, 37(2): 197–215.

DARWIN, CHARLES. 1859. The origin of species by means of natural selection or the preservation of favoured races in the struggle for life. London: Murray.

ELTON, CHARLES. 1946. Competition and the structure of ecological communities. *J. Animal Ecol.*, 15: 54–68.

GERKING, SHELBY. 1953. Evidence for the concepts of home range and territory in stream fishes. *Ecology*, 34(2): 347–365.

HALE, JOHN G., AND L. L. SMITH, Jr. 1955. Results of planting catchable-size brown trout, *Salmo trutta fario* L., in a stream with poor natural reproduction. *Progressive Fish-Culturist*, 17(1): 14–19.

HORTON, HOWARD F. 1956. An evaluation of some physical and mechanical factors important in reducing delayed mortality of hatchery-reared rainbow trout. *Progressive Fish-Culturist*, 18(1): 3–14.

LARKIN, P. A. 1956. Interspecific competition and population control in freshwater fish. *J. Fish. Res. Bd. Canada*, 13(3): 327–342.

LARKIN, P. A., AND S. B. SMITH. 1954. Some effects of introduction of the redside shiner on the Kamloops trout in Paul Lake, British Columbia. *Trans. Amer. Fish. Soc. for 1953*, 83: 161–175.

MILLER, R. B. 1949. The status of the hatchery. *Canadian Fish Culturist*, No. 4, pp. 19–24.

1952. Survival of hatchery-reared cutthroat trout in an Alberta stream. *Trans. Am. Fish. Soc. for 1951*, 81: 35–42.

1954a. Movements of cutthroat trout after different periods of retention upstream and downstream from their homes. *J. Fish Res. Bd. Canada*, 11(5): 550–558.

1954b. Comparative survival of wild and hatchery-reared cutthroat trout in a stream. *Trans. Am. Fish. Soc. for 1953*, 83: 120–130.

1955. Trout management research in Alberta. *Trans. 20th N. Amer. Wildlife Conf.*, pp. 242–252.

MILLER, R. B., AND R. C. THOMAS. 1957. Alberta's "pothole" trout fisheries. *Trans. Am. Fish Soc.* for 1956, **86**: 261-268.

MULLAN, JAMES, W., MS, 1955. An evaluation of Massachusetts' trout stream fishery. 11 pp., mimeo. (Paper presented to N.E. Division, Am. Fish. Soc., March 23, 1955).

 1956a. The comparative returns of various sizes of trout stocked in Massachusetts' streams. *Progressive Fish-Culturist,* **18**(1): 35–38.

 1956b. Some observations on the reclamation of a good, marginal, and a poor trout stream in Massachusetts. *Massachusetts Div. Fish and Game, Fish Bull.* No. 20, 19 pp. Mimeo.

NEWMAN, MURRAY A. 1956. Social behaviour and interspecific competition in two trout species. *Physiol. Zool.,* **29**(1): 64–81.

NIELSON, R. S., N. REIMERS AND H. D. KENNEDY. 1957. A six-year study of the survival and vitality of hatchery-reared rainbow trout of catchable size, in Convict Creek, California. *California Fish and Game,* **43**(1): 5–42.

PARK, THOMAS. 1954. Experimental studies of interspecies competition. II. Temperature, humidity, and competition in two species of *Tribolium. Physiol. Zool.,* **27**(3): 177–238.

REIMERS, N. 1957. Some aspects of the relation between stream foods and trout survival. *California Fish and Game,* **43**(1): 43–69.

SCHUCK, HOWARD A. 1948. Survival of hatchery trout in streams and possible methods of improving the quality of hatchery trout. *Progressive Fish-Culturist,* **10**: 3–14.

SMITH, L. L. 1948. Effectiveness of modern fish management practices: planting. *Proc. 38th Convention Inter. Assoc. Game, Fish and Conserv. Commissioners,* pp. 42–48.

SOLOMON, M. E. 1949. The natural control of animal populations. *J. Animal Ecol.,* **18**: 1–35.

WALES, J. H. 1954. Relative survival of hatchery and wild trout. *Progressive Fish-Culturist,* **16**(3): 125–127.

Reprinted from *The Canadian Entomologist*, Volume XCI, Number 5, May 1959.

# The Components of Predation as Revealed by a Study of Small-Mammal Predation of the European Pine Sawfly[1]

*By* C. S. HOLLING

Forest Insect Laboratory, Sault Ste. Marie, Ont.

## INTRODUCTION

The fluctuation of an animal's numbers between restricted limits is determined by a balance between that animal's capacity to increase and the environmental checks to this increase. Many authors have indulged in the whimsy of calculating the progressive increase of a population when no checks were operating. Thus Huxley calculated that the progeny of a single *Aphis* in the course of 10 generations, supposing all survived, would "contain more ponderable substance than five hundred millions of stout men; that is, more than the whole population of China", (in Thompson, 1929). Checks, however, do occur and it has been the subject of much controversy to determine how these checks operate. Certain general principles—the density-dependence concept of Smith (1955), the competition theory of Nicholson (1933)—have been proposed both verbally and mathematically, but because they have been based in part upon untested and restrictive assumptions they have been severely criticized (e.g. Andrewartha and Birch 1954). These problems could be considerably clarified if we knew the mode of operation of each process that affects numbers, if we knew its basic and subsidiary components. Predation, one such process, forms the subject of the present paper.

Many of the published studies of predation concentrate on discrete parts rather than the whole process. Thus some entomologists are particularly interested in the effect of selection of different kinds of prey by predators upon the evolution of colour patterns and mimicry; wildlife biologists are similarly interested in selection but emphasize the role predators play in improving the condition of the prey populations by removing weakened animals. While such specific problems should find a place in any scheme of predation, the main aim of the present study is to elucidate the components of predation in such a way that more meaning can be applied to considerations of population dynamics. This requires a broad study of the whole process and in particular its function in affecting the numbers of animals.

Such broad studies have generally been concerned with end results measured by the changes in the numbers of predator and prey. These studies are particularly useful when predators are experimentally excluded from the environment of their prey, in the manner adopted by DeBach and his colleagues in their investigations of the pests of orchard trees in California. This work, summarized recently (DeBach, 1958) in response to criticism by Milne (1957), clearly shows that in certain cases the sudden removal of predators results in a rapid increase of prey numbers from persistently low densities to the limits of the food supply. Inasmuch as these studies have shown that other factors have little regulatory function, the predators appear to be the principal ones responsible for regulation. Until the components of predation are revealed by an analysis of the processes leading to these end results, however, we will never know whether the conclusions from such studies apply to situations other than the specific predator—prey relationship investigated.

Errington's investigations of vertebrate predator—prey situations (1934, 1943, 1945 and 1956) suggest, in part, how some types of predation operate. He has

---

[1]Contribution from the Dept. of Zoology, University of British Columbia and No. 547, Forest Biology Division, Research Branch, Department of Agriculture, Ottawa, Canada. Delivered in part at the Tenth International Congress of Entomology, Montreal, 1956.

postulated that each habitat can support only a given number of animals and that predation becomes important only when the numbers of prey exceed this "carrying capacity". Hence predators merely remove surplus animals, ones that would succumb even in the absence of natural enemies. Errington exempts certain predator-prey relations from this scheme, however, and quotes the predation of wolves on deer as an example where predation probably is not related to the carrying capacity of the habitat. However logical these postulates are, they are only indirectly supported by the facts, and they do not explain the processes responsible.

In order to clarify these problems a comprehensive theory of predation is required that on the one hand is not so restrictive that it can only apply in certain cases and on the other not so broad that it becomes meaningless. Such a comprehensive answer requires a comprehensive approach, not necessarily in terms of the number of situations examined but certainly in terms of the variables involved, for it is the different reactions of predators to these variables that produce the many diverse predator-prey relations. Such a comprehensive approach is faced with a number of practical difficulties. It is apparent from the published studies of predation of vertebrate prey by vertebrate predators that not only is it difficult to obtain estimates of the density of predator, prey, and destroyed prey, but also that the presence of many interacting variables confuses interpretation.

The present study of predation of the European pine sawfly, *Neodiprion sertifer* (Geoff.) by small mammals was particularly suited for a general comprehensive analysis of predation. The practical difficulties concerning population measurement and interpretation of results were relatively unimportant, principally because of the unique properties of the environment and of the prey. The field work was conducted in the sand-plain area of southwestern Ontario where Scots and jack pine have been planted in blocks of up to 200 acres. The flat topography and the practice of planting trees of the same age and species at standard six-foot spacings has produced a remarkably uniform environment. In addition, since the work was concentrated in plantations 15 to 20 years of age, the closure of the crowns reduced ground vegetation to a trace, leaving only an even layer of pine needles covering the soil. The extreme simplicity and uniformity of this environment greatly facilitated the population sampling and eliminated complications resulting from changes in the quantity and kind of alternate foods of the predators.

The investigations were further simplified by the characteristics of the prey. Like most insects, the European pine sawfly offers a number of distinct life-history stages that might be susceptible to predation. The eggs, laid in pine needles the previous fall, hatch in early spring and the larvae emerge and feed upon the foliage. During the first two weeks of June the larvae drop from the trees and spin cocoons within the duff on the forest floor. These cocooned sawflies remain in the ground until the latter part of September, when most emerge as adults. A certain proportion, however, overwinter in cocoons, to emerge the following autumn. Observations in the field and laboratory showed that only one of these life-history stages, the cocoon, was attacked by the small-mammal predators, and that the remaining stages were inacessible and/or unpalatable and hence completely escaped attack. These data will form part of a later paper dealing specifically with the impact of small mammal predation upon the European pine sawfly.

Cocooned sawflies, as prey, have some very useful attributes for an investigation of this kind. Their concentration in the two-dimensional environment of the duff-soil interface and their lack of movement and reaction to predators considerably simplify sampling and interpretation. Moreover, the small mammals' habit of making a characteristically marked opening in the cocoon to permit removal of the insect leaves a relatively permanent record in the ground of the number of cocooned sawflies destroyed. Thus, the density of the destroyed prey can be measured at the same time as the density of the prey.

Attention was concentrated upon the three most numerous predators—the masked shrew, *Sorex cinereus cinereus* Kerr, the short-tail shrew, *Blarina brevicauda talpoides* Gapper, and deer mouse, *Peromyscus maniculatus bairdii* Hoy and Kennicott. It soon became apparent that these species were the only significant predators of the sawfly, for the remaining nine species trapped or observed in the plantations were either extremely rare or were completely herbivorous.

Here, then, was a simple predator-prey situation where three species of small mammals were preying on a simple prey—sawfly cocoons. The complicating variables present in most other situations were either constant or absent because of the simple characteristics of the environment and of the prey. The absence or constancy of these complicating variables facilitated analysis but at the expense of a complete and generally applicable scheme of predation. Fortunately, however, the small-mammal predators and the cocoons could easily be manipulated in laboratory experiments so that the effect of those variables absent in the field situation could be assessed. At the same time the laboratory experiments supported the field results. This blend of field and laboratory data provides a comprehensive scheme of predation which will be shown to modify present theories of population dynamics and to considerably clarify the role predators play in population regulation.

I wish to acknowledge the considerable assistance rendered by a number of people, through discussion and criticism of the manuscript: Dr. I. McT. Cowan, Dr. K. Graham and Dr. P. A. Larkin at the University of British Columbia and Dr. R. M. Belyea, Mr. A. W. Ghent and Dr. P. J. Pointing, at the Forest Biology Laboratory, Sault Ste. Marie, Ontario.

## FIELD TECHNIQUES

A study of the interaction of predator and prey should be based upon accurate population measurements, and in order to avoid superficial interpretations, populations should be expressed as numbers per unit area. Three populations must be measured—those of the predators, prey, and destroyed prey. Thus the aim of the field methods was to measure accurately each of the three populations in terms of their numbers per acre.

### Small-Mammal Populations

Since a complete description and evaluation of the methods used to estimate the density of the small-mammal predators forms the basis of another paper in preparation, a summary of the techniques will suffice for the present study.

Estimates of the number of small mammals per acre were obtained using standard live-trapping techniques adapted from Burt (1940) and Blair (1941). The data obtained by marking, releasing and subsequently recapturing animals were analysed using either the Lincoln index (Lincoln, 1930) or Hayne's method for estimating populations in removal trapping procedures (Hayne, 1949). The resulting estimates of the number of animals exposed to traps were converted to per acre figures by calculating, on the basis of measurements of the home range of the animals (Stickel, 1954), the actual area sampled by traps.

The accuracy of these estimates was evaluated by examining the assumptions underlying the proper use of the Lincoln index and Hayne's technique and by comparing the efficiency of different traps and trap arrangements. This analysis showed that an accurate estimate of the numbers of *Sorex* and *Blarina* could be obtained using Hayne's method of treating the data obtained from trapping with bucket traps.   These estimates, however, were accurate only when the populations had not been disturbed by previous trapping.   For *Peromyscus*, Lincoln-index estimates obtained from the results of trapping with Sherman traps provided an ideal way of estimating numbers that was both accurate and unaffected by previous trapping.

## N. sertifer Populations

Since small-mammal predation of *N. sertifer* was restricted to the cocoon stage, prey populations could be measured adequately by estimating the number of cocoons containing living insects present immediately after larval drop in June. This estimate was obtained using a method outlined and tested by Prebble (1943) for cocoon populations of the European spruce sawfly, *Gilpinia hercyniae* (Htg.), an insect with habits similar to those of *N. sertifer*.   Accurate estimates were obtained when cocoons were collected from sub-samples of litter and duff distributed within the restricted universe beneath the crowns of host trees.   This method was specially designed to provide an index of population rather than an estimate of numbers per acre.   But it is obvious from this work that any cocoon-sampling technique designed to yield a *direct* estimate of the number of cocoons per acre would require an unpractically large number of sample units.   It proved feasible in the present study, however, to convert such estimates from a square-foot to an acre basis, by stratifying the forest floor into three strata, one comprising circles with two-foot radii around tree trunks, one comprising intermediate rings with inner radii two feet and outer radii three feet, and one comprising the remaining area (three to five feet from the tree trunks).

At least 75 trees were selected and marked throughout each plantation, and one or usually two numbered wooden stakes were placed directly beneath the crown of each tree, on opposite sides of the trunk.   Stakes were never placed under overlapping tree crowns.   The four sides of each stake were lettered from A to D and the stake was placed so that the numbered sides bore no relation to the position of the trunk.   Samples were taken each year, by collecting cocoons from the area delimited by one-square-foot frames placed at one corner of each stake. In the first year's sample the frames were placed at the AB corner, in the second year's at the BC corner, etc.   Different-sized screens were used to separate the cocoons from the litter and duff.

Cocoons were collected in early September before adult sawflies emerged and those from each quadrat were placed in separate containers for later analysis. These cocoons were analysed by first segregating them into "new" and "old" categories.   Cocoons of the former category were a bright golden colour and were assumed to have been spun in the year of sampling, while those of the latter were dull brown in colour and supposedly had been spun before the sampling year.   These assumptions proved partly incorrect, however, for some of the cocoons retained their new colour for over one year.   Hence the "new" category contained enough cocoons that had been spun before the sampling year to prevent its use, without correction, as an estimate of the number of cocoons spun in the year of sampling.   A correction was devised, however, which reduced the error to negligible proportions.

This method provided the best available estimate of the number of healthy cocoons per acre present in any one year.   The population figures obtained ranged from 39,000 (Plot 1, 1954) to 1,080,000 (Plot 2, 1952) cocoons per acre.

## Predation

Small-mammal predation has a direct and indirect effect on *N. sertifer* populations.   The direct effect of predation is studied in detail in this paper.   The indirect effect, resulting from the mutual interaction of various control factors (parasites, disease, and predators) has been discussed in previous papers (Holling, 1955, 1958b).

The direct effect of predation was measured in a variety of ways. General information was obtained from studies of the consumption of insects by caged animals and from the analysis of stomach contents obtained from animals trapped in sawfly-infested plantations. More particular information was obtained from the analysis of cocoons collected in the regular quadrat samples and from laboratory experiments which studied the effect of cocoon density upon predation.

The actual numbers of *N. sertifer* cocoons destroyed were estimated from cocoons collected in the regular quadrat samples described previously. As shown in an earlier paper (Holling, 1955), cocoons opened by small mammals were easily recognized and moreover could be classified as to species of predator. These estimates of the number of new and old cocoons per square foot opened by each species of predator were corrected, as before, to provide an estimate of the number opened from the time larvae dropped to the time when cocoon samples were taken in early September.

It has proved difficult to obtain a predation and cocoon-population estimate of the desired precision and accuracy. The corrections and calculations that had to be applied to the raw sampling data cast some doubt upon the results and conclusions based upon them. It subsequently developed, however, that a considerable margin of error could be tolerated without changing the results and the conclusions that could be derived from them. In any case, all conclusions based upon cocoon-population estimates were supported and substantiated by results from controlled laboratory experiments.

## LABORATORY TECHNIQUES

Several experiments were conducted with caged animals in order to support and expand results obtained in the field. The most important of these measured the number of cocoons consumed by *Peromyscus* at different cocoon densities. These experiments were conducted at room temperature (ca. 20°C) in a screen-topped cage, 10' x 4' x 6". At the beginning of an experiment, cocoons were first buried in sand where the lines of a removable grid intersected, the grid was then removed, the sand was pressed flat, and a metal-edged levelling jig was finally scraped across the sand so that an even 12 mm. covered the cocoons. A single deer mouse was then placed in the cage together with nesting material, water, and an alternate food—dog biscuits. In each experiment the amount of this alternate food was kept approximately the same (i.e. 13 to 17 gms. dry weight). After the animal had been left undisturbed for 24 hours, the removable grid was replaced, and the number of holes dug over cocoons, the number of cocoons opened and the dry weight of dog biscuits eaten were recorded. Consumption by every animal was measured at either four or five different densities ranging from 2.25 to 36.00 cocoons per sq. ft. The specific densities were provided at random until all were used, the consumption at each density being measured for three to six consecutive days. Ideally the size of the cage should remain constant at all densities but since this would have required over 1,400 cocoons at the highest density, practical considerations necessitated a compromise whereby the cage was shortened at the higher densities. In these experiments the total number of cocoons provided ranged from 88 at the lowest density to 504 at the highest. At all densities, however, these numbers represented a surplus and no more than 40 per cent were ever consumed in a single experiment. Hence consumption was not limited by shortage of cocoons, even though the size of the cage changed.

The sources and characteristics of the cocoons and *Peromyscus* used in these experiments require some comment. Supplies of the prey were obtained by collecting cocoons in sawfly-infested plantations or by collecting late-instar larvae and allowing them to spin cocoons in boxes provided with foliage and litter. Sound cocoons from either source were then segregated into those containing healthy, parasitized, and diseased prepupae using a method of X-ray analysis (Holling, 1958a). The small male cocoons were separated from the larger female cocoons by size, since this criterion had previously proved adequate (Holling, 1958b). To simplify the experiments, only male and female cocoons containing healthy, living prepupae were used and in each experiment equal numbers of cocoons of each sex were provided, alternately, in the grid pattern already described.

Three mature non-breeding male deer mice were used in the experiments. Each animal had been born and raised in small rearing cages 12 x 8 x 6 in. and had been isolated from cocoons since birth. They therefore required a period to become familiar with the experimental cage and with cocoons. This experience was acquired during a preliminary three-week period. For the first two weeks the animal was placed in the experimental cage together with nesting material, water, dog biscuits and sand, and each day was disturbed just as it would be if an experiment were in progress. For the final week cocoons were buried in the sand at the first density chosen so that the animal could learn to find and consume the cocoon contents. It has been shown (Holling, 1955, 1958b) that a seven-day period is more than ample to permit complete learning.

## THE COMPONENTS OF PREDATION

A large number of variables could conceivably affect the mortality of a given species of prey as a result of predation by a given species of predator. These can conveniently be classified, as was done by Leopold (1933), into five groups:

(1) density of the prey population.
(2) density of the predator population.
(3) characteristics of the prey, e.g., reactions to predators, stimulus detected by predator, and other characteristics.
(4) density and quality of alternate foods available for the predator.
(5) characteristics of the predator, e.g., food preferences, efficiency of attack, and other characteristics.

Each of these variables may exert a considerable influence and the effect of any one may depend upon changes in another. For example, Errington (1946) has shown that the characteristics of many vertebrate prey species change when their density exceeds the number that the available cover can support. This change causes a sudden increase in predation. When such complex interactions are involved, it is difficult to understand clearly the principles involved in predation; to do so we must find a simplified situation where some of the variables are constant or are not operating. The problem studied here presents such a situation. First, the characteristics of cocoons do not change as the other factors vary and there are no reactions by the cocooned sawflies to the predators. We therefore can ignore, temporarily, the effect of the third factor, prey characteristics. Secondly, since the work was conducted in plantations noted for their uniformity as to species, age, and distribution of trees, there was a constant and small variety of possible alternate foods. In such a simple and somewhat sterile environment, the fourth factor, the density and quality of alternate foods, can therefore be initially ignored, as can the fifth factor, characteristics of the predator, which is really only another way of expressing factors three and four. There are thus only two basic variables affecting predation in this instance, i.e., prey density and predator density. Furthermore, these are the only essential ones, for the remainder, while possibly important in affecting the amount of predation, are not essential to describe its fundamental characteristics.

## The Basic Components

It is from the two essential variables that the basic components of predation will be derived. The first of these variables, prey density, might affect a number of processes and consumption of prey by individual predators might well be one of them.

The data which demonstrate the effect of changes of prey density upon consumption of cocooned sawflies by *Peromyscus* were obtained from the yearly cocoon quadrat samples in Plots 1 and 2. In 1951, Dr. F. T. Bird, Laboratory of Insect Pathology, Sault Ste. Marie, Ont., had sprayed each of these plots with a low concentration of a virus disease that attacked *N. sertifer* larvae, (Bird 1953). As a result, populations declined from 248,000 and 1,080,000 cocoons per acre, respectively, in 1952, to 39,000 and 256,000 in 1954. Thus predation values at six different cocoon densities were obtained. An additional sample in a neighbouring plantation in 1953 provided another value.

Predation values for *Sorex* and *Blarina* were obtained from one plantation, Plot 3, in one year, 1952. In the spring of that year, virus, sprayed from an aircraft flying along parallel lines 300 feet apart, was applied in three concentrations, with the lowest at one end of the plantation and the highest at the other. An area at one end, not sprayed, served as a control. When cocoon populations were sampled in the autumn, a line of 302 trees was selected at right angles to the lines of spray and the duff under each was sampled with one one-square-foot quadrat. The line, approximately 27 chains long, ran the complete length of the plantation. When the number of new cocoons per square foot was plotted against distance, discrete areas could be selected which had fairly constant populations that ranged from 44,000 to 571,000 cocoons per acre. The areas of low population corresponded to the areas sprayed with the highest concentration of virus. In effect, the plantation could be divided into rectangular strips, each with a particular density of cocoons. The width of these strips varied from 126 to 300 feet with an average of 193 feet. In addition to the 302 quadrats examined, the cocoons from another 100 quadrats were collected from the areas of lowest cocoon densities. Thus, in this one plantation in 1952, there was a sufficient number of different cocoon densities to show the response of consumption by *Sorex* and *Blarina* to changes of prey density.

The methods used to estimate predator densities in each study plot require some further comment. In Plots 1 and 2 this was done with grids of Sherman traps run throughout the summer. In Plot 3 both a grid of Sherman traps and a line of snap traps were used. This grid, measuring 18 chains by 4 chains, was placed so that approximately the same area sampled for cocoons was sampled for small mammals. The populations determined from these trapping procedures were plotted against time, and the number of "mammal-days" per acre, from the start of larval drop (June 14) to the time cocoon samples were made (Aug. 20-30), was determined for each plot each year. This could be done with *Peromyscus* and *Blarina* since the trapping technique was shown to provide an accurate estimate of their populations. But this was not true for *Sorex*. Instead, the number of *Sorex*-days per acre was approximated by dividing the number of cocoons opened at the highest density by the known number consumed by caged *Sorex* per day, i.e. 101. Since the number of cocoons opened at the highest cocoon density was

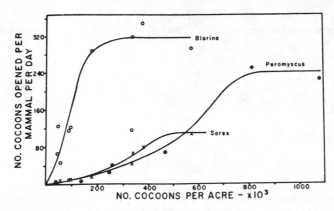

Fig. 1. Functional responses of *Blarina, Sorex* and *Peromyscus* in plots 1, 2, and 3.

151,000 per acre, then the number of *Sorex*-days per acre should be 151,000/101 = 1,490. This is approximately 10 times the estimate that was obtained from trapping with Sherman traps. When the various trapping methods were compared, estimates from Sherman trapping were shown to underestimate the numbers of *Sorex* by about the same amount, i.e. one-tenth.

With estimates of the numbers of predators, prey and destroyed prey available, the daily number of prey consumed per predator at different cocoon densities can be calculated. As seen in Fig. 1, the number of cocoons opened by each species increased with increasing cocoon density until a maximum daily consumption was reached that corresponded approximately to the maximum number that could be consumed in any one day by caged animals. For *Sorex* this of course follows from the method of calculation. The rates at which these curves rise differ for the different species, being greatest for *Blarina* and least for *Peromyscus*. Even if the plateaus are equated by multiplying points on each curve by a constant, the rates still decrease in the same order, reflecting a real difference in species behaviour.

The existence of such a response to cocoon density may also be demonstrated by data from the analysis of stomach contents. The per cent occurrence and per cent volume of the various food items in stomachs of *Peromyscus* captured immediately after larval drop and two months later is shown in Table I. When cocoon densities were high, immediately after larval drop, the per cent occurrence and per cent volume of *N. sertifer* material was high. Two months later when various cocoon mortality factors had taken their toll, cocoon densities were lower and

TABLE I

Stomach contents of *Peromyscus* trapped immediately before larval drop and two months later

| Time trapped | Approx. no. cocoons per acre | No. of stomachs | Analysis | Plant | *N. sertifer* | Other insects | All insects |
|---|---|---|---|---|---|---|---|
| June 16–21 | 600,000 | 19 | % occurrence | 37% | 95% | 53% | 100% |
| Aug. 17–19 | 300,000 | 14 | | 79% | 50% | 64% | 86% |
| June 16–21 | 600,000 | 19 | % volume | 5% | 71% | 24% | 95% |
| Aug. 17–19 | 300,000 | 14 | | 47% | 19% | 34% | 53% |

TABLE II

Occurrence of food items in stomachs of *Microtus* trapped before and after larval drop

| Time trapped | Plant | | N. sertifer | | All insects | |
|---|---|---|---|---|---|---|
| | No. of stomachs | % occurrence | No. of stomachs | % occurrence | No. of stomachs | % occurrence |
| before larval drop | 25 | 100% | 2 | 8% | 2 | 8% |
| after larval drop | 29 | 100% | 8 | 28% | 11 | 38% |

*N. sertifer* was a less important food item. The decrease in consumption of *N. sertifer* was accompanied by a considerable increase in the consumption of plant material and a slight increase in the consumption of other insect material. Plants and other insects acted as buffer or alternate foods. *Microtus*, even though they ate few non-plant foods in nature, also showed an increase in the per cent occurrence of *N. sertifer* material in stomachs as cocoon density increased (Table II). Before larval drop, when cocoon densities were low, the incidence of *N. sertifer* in *Microtus* stomachs was low. After larval drop, when cocoon densities were higher, the incidence increased by 3.5 times. Even at the higher cocoon densities, however, *N. sertifer* comprised less than one per cent of the volume of stomach contents so that this response to changes in prey density by *Microtus* is extremely low.

The graphs presented in Fig. I and the results of the analyses of stomach contents leave little doubt that the consumption of cocooned sawflies by animals in the field increases with increase in cocoon density. Similar responses have been demonstrated in laboratory experiments with three *Peromyscus*. As shown in Fig. 2, the number of cocoons consumed daily by each animal increased with increase in cocoon density, again reaching a plateau as did the previous curves. Whenever the number of prepupae consumed did not meet the caloric requirements, these were met by consumption of the dog biscuits, the alternate food provided. Only one of the animals (A) at the highest density fulfilled its caloric requirements by consuming prepupae; the remaining animals (B and C) consumed

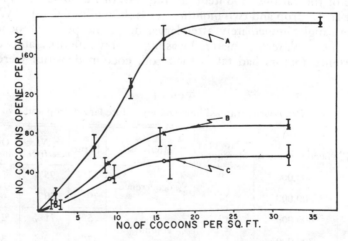

Fig. 2. Functional responses of three caged *Peromyscus* (means and ranges shown).

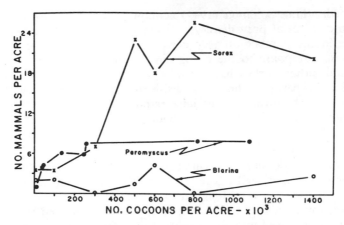

Fig. 3. Numerical responses of *Blarina, Sorex* and *Peromyscus*.

less than one-half the number of sawflies they would consume if no alternate foods were present. The cocoons used in experiments involving animals B and C, however, had been spun 12 months earlier than those involving animal A. When the characteristics of the functional response are examined in another paper, it will be shown that the strength of stimulus from older cocoons is less than that from younger cocoons, and that these differences are sufficient to explain the low consumption by animals B and C. The shape of the curves and the density at which they level is very similar for all animals, so similar that multiplying points along any one curve by the proper constant will equate all three. These curves are very similar to the ones based upon field data. All show the same form, the essential feature of which is an S-shaped rise to a plateau.

The effect of changes of prey density need not be restricted exclusively to consumption of prey by individual predators. The density of predators may also be affected and this can be shown by relating the number of predators per acre to the number of cocoons per acre. Conclusions can be derived from these relations but they are tentative. The data were collected over a relatively short period of time (four summers) and thus any relationship between predator numbers and prey density may have been fortuitous. Only those data obtained in plantations over 12 years old are included since small mammal populations were most stable in these areas. The data for the three most important species of predators are shown in the curves of Fig. 3, where each point represents the highest summer population observed either in different plantations or in the same plantation in different years.

The densities of *Blarina* were lowest while those of *Sorex* were highest. In this situation, *Blarina* populations apparently did not respond to prey density, for its numbers did not noticeably increase with increase in cocoon density. Some agent or agents other than food must limit their numbers. Populations of *Peromyscus* and *Sorex*, on the other hand, apparently did initially increase with increase in cocoon density, ultimately ceasing to increase as some agents other than food became limiting. The response of *Sorex* was most marked.

Thus two responses to changes of prey density have been demonstrated. The first is a change in the number of prey consumed per predator and the second is a change in the density of predators. Although few authors appear to recognize the existence and importance of *both* these responses to changes of prey density, they have been postulated and, in the case of the change of predator density, demonstrated. Thus Solomon (1949) acknowledged the two-fold nature of the response to changes of prey density, and applied the term *functional response* to the change in the number of prey consumed by individual predators, and the term *numerical response* to the change in the density of predators. These are apt terms and, although they have been largely ignored in the literature, they will be adopted in this paper. The data available to Solomon for review did not permit him to anticipate the form the functional response of predators might take, so that he could not assess its importance in population regulation. It will be shown, however, that the functional response is as important as the numerical.

It remains now to consider the effect of predator density, the variable that, together with prey density, is essential for an adequate description of predation. Predator density might well affect the number of prey consumed per predator. Laboratory experiments were designed to measure the number of cocoons opened by one, two, four, and eight animals in a large cage provided with cocoons at a density of 15 per square foot and a surplus of dog biscuits and water. The average number of cocoons opened per mouse in eight replicates was 159, 137, 141 and 159 respectively. In this experiment, therefore, predator density apparently did not greatly affect the consumption of prey by individual animals. This conclusion is again suggested when field and laboratory data are compared, for the functional response of *Peromyscus* obtained in the field, where its density varied, was very similar to the response of single animals obtained in the laboratory.

In such a simple situation, where predator density does not greatly affect the consumption by individuals, the total predation can be expressed by a simple, additive combination of the two responses. For example, if at a particular prey density the functional response is such that 100 cocoons are opened by a single predator in one day, and the numerical response is such that the predator density is 10, then the total daily consumption will be simply 100 x 10. In other situations, however, an increase in the density of predators might result in so much competition that the consumption of prey by individual predators might drop significantly. This effect can still be incorporated in the present scheme by adopting a more complex method of combining the functional and numerical responses.

This section was introduced with a list of the possible variables that could affect predation. Of these, only the two operating in the present study — prey and predator density — are essential variables, so that the basic features of predation can be ascribed to the effects of these two. It has been shown that there are two responses to prey density. The increase in the number of prey consumed per predator, as prey density rises, is termed the functional response, while the change in the density of predators is termed the numerical response. The total amount of predation occurring at any one density results from a combination of the two responses, and the method of combination will be determined by the way predator density affects consumption. This scheme, therefore, describes the effects of the basic variables, uncomplicated by the effects of subsidiary ones. Hence the two responses, the functional and numerical, can be considered the basic components of predation.

The total amount of predation caused by small mammals is shown in Fig. 4, where the functional and numerical responses are combined by multiplying the number of cocoons opened per predator at each density by the number of effective mammal-days observed. These figures were then expressed as percentages opened. This demonstrates the relation between per cent predation and prey density during the 100-day period between cocoon formation and adult emergence. Since the data obtained for the numerical responses are tentative, some reservations must be applied to the more particular conclusions derived

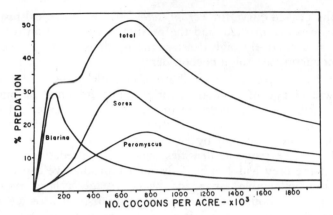

Fig. 4. Functional and numerical responses combined to show the relation between per cent predation and cocoon density.

from this figure. The general conclusion, that per cent predation by each species shows an initial rise and subsequent decline as cocoon density increases holds, however. For this conclusion to be invalid, the numerical responses would have to decrease in order to mask the initial rise in per cent predation caused by the S-shaped form of the functional responses. Thus from zero to some finite cocoon density, predation by small mammals shows a direct density-dependent action and thereafter shows an inverse density-dependent action. The initial rise in the proportion of prey destroyed can be attributed to both the functional and numerical responses. The functional response has a roughly sigmoid shape and hence the proportion of prey destroyed by an individual predator will increase with increase in cocoon density up to and beyond the point of inflection. Unfortunately the data for any one functional response curve are not complete enough to establish a sigmoid relation, but the six curves presented thus far and the several curves to be presented in the following section all suggest a point of inflection. The positive numerical responses shown by *Sorex* and *Peromyscus* also promote a direct density-dependent action up to the point at which predator densities remain constant. Thereafter, with individual consumption also constant, the per cent predation will decline as cocoon density increases. The late Dr. L. Tinbergen apparently postulated the same type of dome-shaped curves for the proportion of insects destroyed by birds. His data were only partly published (1949, 1955) before his death, but Klomp (1956) and Voûte (1958) have commented upon the existence of these "optimal curves". This term, however, is unsatisfactory and anthropocentric. From the viewpoint of the forest entomologist, the highest proportion of noxious insects destroyed may certainly be the optimum, but the term is meaningless for an animal that consumes individuals and not percentages. Progress can best be made by considering predation first as a behaviour before translating this behaviour in terms of the proportion of prey destroyed. The term "peaked curve" is perhaps more accurate.

Returning to Fig. 4, we see that the form of the peaked curve for *Blarina* is determined solely by the functional response since this species exhibited no numerical response. The abrupt peak occurs because the maximum consumption of prepupae was reached at a very low prey density before the predation was "diluted" by large numbers of cocoons. With *Sorex* both the numerical and functional responses are important. Predation by *Sorex* is greatest principally because of the marked numerical response. The two responses again determine the form of the peaked curve for *Peromyscus*, but the numerical response, unlike that of *Sorex*, was not marked, and the maximum consumption of cocoons was reached only at a relatively high density; the result is a low per cent predation with a peak occurring at a high cocoon density.

Predation by all species destroyed a considerable number of cocooned saw-flies over a wide range of cocoon densities. The presence of more than one species of predator not only increased predation but also extended the range of prey densities over which predation was high. This latter effect is particularly important, for if the predation by several species of predators peaked at the same prey density the range of densities over which predation was high would be slight and if the prey had a sufficiently high reproductive capacity its density might jump this vulnerable range and hence escape a large measure of the potential control that could be exerted by predators. Before we can proceed further in the discussion of the effect of predation upon prey numbers, the additional components that make up the behaviour of predation must be con-sidered.

### The Subsidiary Components

Additional factors such as prey characteristics, the density and quality of alternate foods, and predator characteristics have a considerable effect upon predation. It is necessary now to demonstrate the effect of these factors and how they operate.

There are four classes of prey characteristics: those that influence the caloric value of the prey; those that change the length of time prey are exposed; those that affect the "attractiveness" of the prey to the predator (e.g. palatability, defence mechanisms); and those that affect the strength of stimulus used by predators in locating prey (e.g. size, habits, and colours). Only those charac-teristics that affect the strength of stimulus were studied experimentally. Since small mammals detect cocoons by the odour emanating from them (Holling, 1958b), the strength of this odour perceived by a mammal can be easily changed in laboratory experiments by varying the depth of sand covering the cocoons.

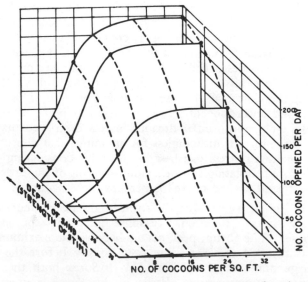

Fig. 5. Effect of strength of stimulus from cocoons upon the functional response of one caged *Peromyscus*. Each point represents the average of three to six replicates.

One *Peromyscus* was used in these experiments and its daily consumption of cocoons was measured at different cocoon densities and different depths of sand. These data are plotted in Fig. 5. Since the relation between depth of sand and strength of stimulus must be an inverse one, the depths of sand are reversed on the axis so that values of the strength of stimulus increase away from the origin. Each point represents the mean of three to six separate measurements. Decreasing the strength of the perceived stimulus by increasing the depth of sand causes a marked decrease in the functional response. A 27 mm. increase in depth (from nine to 36 mm.), for example, causes the peak consumption to drop from 196 to four cocoons per day. The daily number of calories consumed in all these experiments remained relatively constant since dog biscuits were always present as alternate food. The density at which each functional-response curve levels appear to increase somewhat as the strength of stimulus perceived by the animal decreases. We might expect that the increase in consumption is directly related to the increase in the proportion of cocoons in the amount of food available, at least up to the point where the caloric requirements are met solely by sawflies. The ascending portions of the curves, however, are S-shaped and the level portions are below the maximum consumption, approximately 220 cocoons for this animal. Therefore, the functional response cannot be explained by random searching for cocoons. For the moment, however, the important conclusion is that changes in prey characteristics can have a marked effect on predation but this effect is exerted through the functional response.

In the plantations studied, cocoons were not covered by sand but by a loose litter and duff formed from pine needles. Variations in the depth of this material apparently did not affect the strength of the perceived odour, for as many cocoons were opened in quadrats with shallow litter as with deep. This material must be so loose as to scarcely impede the passage of odour from cocoons.

The remaining subsidiary factors, the density and quality of alternate foods and predator characteristics, can also affect predation. The effect of alternate foods could not be studied in the undisturbed plantations because the amount of these "buffers" was constant and very low. The effect of quality of alternate foods on the functional response, however, was demonstrated experimentally using one *Peromyscus*. The experiments were identical to those already described except that at one series of densities an alternate food of low palatability (dog biscuits) was provided, and at the second series one of high palatability (sunflower seeds) was provided. When both foods are available, deer mice select sunflower seeds over dog biscuits. In every experiment a constant amount of alternate food was available: 13 to 17 gms. dry weight of dog biscuits, or 200 sunflower seeds.

Fig. 6 shows the changes in the number of cocoons opened per day and in the amount of alternate foods consumed. The functional response decreased with an increase in the palatability of the alternate food (Fig. 6A). Again the functional response curves showed an initial, roughly sigmoid rise to a constant level.

As cocoon consumption rose, the consumption of alternate foods decreased (Fig. 6B) at a rate related to the palatability of the alternate food. Each line indicating the change in the consumption of alternate food was drawn as a mirror image of the respective functional response and these lines closely follow the mean of the observed points. The variability in the consumption of sunflower seeds at any one cocoon density was considerable, probably as a result of the extreme variability in the size of seeds.

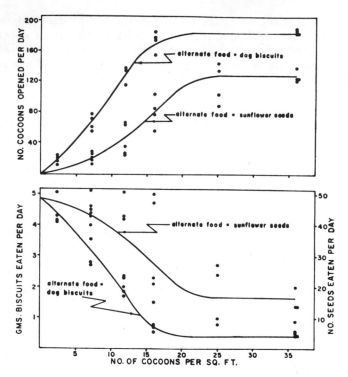

Fig. 6. Effect of different alternate foods upon the functional response of one *Peromyscus*. *A* (upper) shows the functional responses when either a low (dog biscuits) or a high (sunflower seeds) palatability alternate food was present in excess. *B* (lower) shows the amount of these alternate foods consumed.

Again we see that there is not a simple relation between the number of cocoons consumed and the proportion of cocoons in the total amount of food available. This is most obvious when the functional response curves level, for further increase in density is not followed by an increase in the consumption of sawflies. The plateaus persist because the animal continued consuming a certain fixed quantity of alternate foods. L. Tinbergen (1949) observed a similar phenomenon in a study of predation of pine-eating larvae by tits in Holland. He presented data for the consumption of larvae of the pine beauty moth, *Panolis griseovariegata*, and of the web-spinning sawfly *Acantholyda pinivora*, each at two different densities. In each case more larvae were eaten per nestling tit per day at the higher prey density. This, then, was part of a functional response, but it was that part above the point of inflection, since the proportion of prey eaten dropped at the higher density. It is not sufficient to explain these results as well as the ones presented in this paper by claiming, with Tinbergen, that the predators "have the tendency to make their menu as varied as possible and therefore guard against one particular species being strongly dominant in it". This is less an explanation than an anthropocentric description. The occurrence of this phenomenon depends upon the strength of stimulus from the prey, and the amount and quality of the alternate foods. Its proper explanation must await the collection of further data.

We now know that the palatability of alternate foods affects the functional response. Since the number of different kinds of alternate food could also have

TABLE III

The effect of alternate foods upon the number of cocoons consumed per day by one *Peromyscus*

| Alternate food | No. of exp'ts | No. of cocoons opened | |
|---|---|---|---|
| | | $\overline{X}$ | S.E.$\bar{x}$ |
| none | 7 | 165.9 | 11.4 |
| dog biscuits | 5 | 143.0 | 8.3 |
| sunflower seeds | 8 | 60.0 | 6.2 |
| sunflower seeds and dog biscuits | 8 | 21.5 | 4.2 |

an important effect, the consumption of cocoons by a caged *Peromyscus* was measured when no alternate foods, or one or two alternate foods, were present. Only female cocoons were used and these were provided at a density of 75 per sq. ft. to ensure that the level portion of the functional response would be measured. As in the previous experiments, the animal was familiarized with the experimental conditions and with cocoons for a preliminary two-week period. The average numbers of cocoons consumed each day with different numbers and kinds of alternate foods present are shown in Table III. This table again shows that fewer cocoons were consumed when sunflower seeds (high palatability) were present than when dog biscuits (low palatability) were present. In both cases, however, the consumption was lower than when no alternate foods were available. When two alternate foods were available, i.e., both sunflower seeds and dog biscuits, the consumption dropped even further. Thus, increase in both the palatability and in the number of different kinds of alternate foods decreases the functional response.

## DISCUSSION

### General

It has been argued that three of the variables affecting predation—characteristics of the prey, density and quality of alternate foods and characteristics of the predators — are subsidiary components of predation. The laboratory experiments showed that the functional response was lowered when the strength of stimulus, one prey characteristic, detected from cocoons was decreased or when the number of kinds and palatability of alternate foods was increased. Hence the effect of these subsidiary components is exerted through the functional response. Now the numerical response is closely related to the functional, since such an increase in predator density depends upon the amount of food consumed. It follows, therefore, that the subsidiary components will also affect the numerical response. Thus when the functional response is lowered by a decrease in the strength of stimulus detected from prey, the numerical response similarly must be decreased and predation will be less as a result of decrease of the two basic responses.

The density and quality of alternate foods could also affect the numerical response. Returning to the numerical responses shown in Fig. 3, if increase in the density or quality of alternate foods involved solely increase in food "per se", then the number of mammals would reach a maximum at a lower cocoon density, but the maximum itself would not change. If increase in alternate foods also involved changes in the agents limiting the numerical responses (e.g. increased cover and depth of humus), then the maximum density the small mammals could attain would increase. Thus increase in the amount of alternate foods could increase the density of predators.

Increase in alternate foods *decreases* predation by dilution of the functional response, but *increases* predation by promoting a favourable numerical response. The relative importance of each of these effects will depend upon the particular problem. Voûte (1946) has remarked that insect populations in cultivated woods show violent fluctuations, whereas in virgin forests or mixed woods, where the number of alternate foods is great, the populations are more stable. This stability might result from alternate foods promoting such a favourable numerical response that the decrease in the functional response is not great enough to lower predation.

The importance of alternate foods will be affected by that part of the third subsidiary component — characteristics of the predators — that concerns food preferences. Thus an increase in plants or animals other than the prey will most likely affect the responses of those predators, like the omnivore *Peromyscus*, that are not extreme food specialists. Predation by the more stenophagous shrews, would only be affected by some alternate, animal food.

Food preferences, however, are only one of the characteristics of predators. Others involve their ability to detect, capture, and kill prey. But again the effect of these predator characteristics will be exerted through the two basic responses, the functional and numerical. The differences observed between the functional responses of the three species shown earlier in Fig. 1 undoubtedly reflect differences in their abilities to detect, capture, and kill. The amount of predation will similarly be affected by the kind of sensory receptor, whether visual, olfactory, auditory, or tactile, that the predator uses in locating prey. An efficient nose, for example, is probably a less precise organ than an efficient eye. The source of an undisturbed olfactory stimulus can only be located by investigating a gradient in space, whereas a visual stimulus can be localized by an efficient eye from a single point in space — the telotaxis of Fraenkel and Gunn (1940). As N. Tinbergen (1951) remarked, localization of direction is developed to the highest degree in the eye. Thus the functional response of a predator which locates prey by sight will probably reach a maximum at a much lower prey density than the response of one that locates its prey by odour. In the data presented by Tothill (1922) and L. Tinbergen (1949), the per cent predation of insects by birds was highest at very low prey densities, suggesting that the functional responses of these "visual predators" did indeed reach a maximum at a low density.

### The Effect of Predation on Prey Populations

One of the most important characteristics of mortality factors is their ability to regulate the numbers of an animal — to promote a "steady density" (Nicholson, 1933; Nicholson and Bailey, 1935) such that a continued increase or decrease of numbers from this steady state becames progressively unlikely the greater the departure from it. Regulation in this sense therefore requires that the mortality factor change with change in the density of the animal attacked, i.e. it requires a direct density-dependent mortality (Smith, 1935, 1939). Density-independent factors can affect the numbers of an animal but alone they cannot *regulate* the numbers. There is abundant evidence that changes in climate, some aspects of which are presumed to have a density-independent action, can lower or raise the numbers of an animal. But this need not be regulation. Regulation will only result from an interaction with a density-dependent factor, an interaction

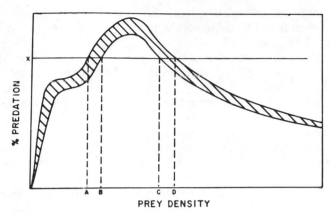

Fig. 7. Theoretical model showing regulation of prey by predators. (see text for explanation).

that might be the simplest, i.e. merely additive. Recently, the density-dependent concept has been severely criticized by Andrewartha and Birch (1954). They call it a dogma, but such a comment is only a criticism of an author's use of the concept. Its misuse as a dogma does not militate against its value as a hypothesis.

We have seen from this study that predation by small mammals does change with changes in prey density. As a result of the functional and numerical responses the proportion of prey destroyed increases from zero to some finite prey density and thereafter decreases. Thus predation over some ranges of prey density shows a direct density-dependent action. This is all that is required for a factor to regulate.

The way in which predation of the type shown in this study can regulate the numbers of a prey species can best be shown by a hypothetical example. To simplify this example we will assume that the prey has a constant rate of reproduction over all ranges of its density, and that only predators are affecting its numbers. Such a situation is, of course, unrealistic. The rate of reproduction of real animals probably is low at low densities when there is slight possibility for contact between individuals (e.g. between male and female). It would rise as contacts became more frequent and would decline again at higher densities when the environment became contaminated, when intraspecific stress symptoms appeared, or when cannibalism became common. Such changes in the rate of reproduction have been shown for experimental populations of *Tribolium confusum* (MacLagan, 1932) and *Drosophila* (Robertson and Sang, 1944). Introducing more complex assumptions, however, confuses interpretations without greatly changing the conclusions.

This hypothetical model is shown in Fig. 7. The curve that describes the changes in predation with changes in prey density is taken from the actual data shown earlier in Fig. 4. It is assumed that the birth-rate of the prey at any density can be balanced by a fixed per cent predation, and that the variation in the environment causes a variation in the predation at any one density. The per cent predation necessary to balance the birth-rate is represented by the horizontal line, x%, in the diagram and variation in predation is represented by the thickness of the mortality curve. The death-rate will equal the birth-rate at two density ranges, between A and B and between C and D. When the densities of the prey are below A, the mortality will be lower than that necessary to balance reproduction and the population will increase. When the densities of the animal are between B and C, death-rate will exceed birth-rate and the populations will decrease. Thus, the density of the prey will tend to fluctuate between densities A and B. If the density happens to exceed D, death-rate will be lower than birth-rate and the prey will increase in numbers, having "escaped" the control exerted by predators. This would occur when the prey had such a high rate of reproduction that its density could jump, in one generation, from a density lower than A to a density higher than D. If densities A and D were far apart, there would be less chance of this occurring. This spread is in part determined by the number of different species of predators that are present. Predation by each species peaks at a different density (see Fig. 4), so that increase in the number of species of predator will increase the spread of the total predation. This will produce a more stable situation where the prey will have less chance to escape control by predators.

Predation of the type shown will regulate the numbers of an animal whenever the predation rises high enough to equal the effective birth-rate. When the prey is an insect and predators are small mammals, as in this case, the reproductive rate of the prey will be too high for predation *alone* to regulate. But if other mortality occurs, density-independent or density-dependent, the total mortality could rise to the point where small mammals were contributing, completely or partially, to the regulation of the insect.

Predation of the type shown will produce stability if there are large numbers of different species of predators operating. Large numbers of such species would most likely occur in a varied environment, such as mixed woods. Perhaps this explains, in part, Voûte's (1946) observation that insect populations in mixed woods are less liable to show violent fluctuations.

I cannot agree with Voûte (1956 and 1958) that factors causing a peaked mortality curve are not sufficient for regulation. He states (1956) that "this is due to the fact that mortality only at low densities increases with the increase of the population. At higher densities, mortality decreases again. The growth of the population is at the utmost slowed down, never stopped". All that is necessary for regulation, however, is a rise in per cent predation over some range of prey densities and an *effective* birth-rate that can be matched at some density by mortality from predators.

Neither can I agree with Thompson (1930) when he ascribes a minor role to vertebrate predators of insects and states that "the number of individuals of any given species (i.e. of vertebrate predators) is . . . relatively small in comparison with those of insects and there is no reason to suppose that it varies primarily in function of the supply of insect food, which fluctuates so rapidly that it is impossible for vertebrates to profit by a temporary abundance of it excepting to a very limited extent". We know that they do respond by an increase in numbers and even if this is not great in comparison with the numerical response of parasitic flies, the number of prey killed per predator is so great and the increase in number killed with increase in prey density is so marked as to result in a heavy proportion of prey destroyed; a proportion that, furthermore, increases initially with increase of prey density. Thompson depreciates the importance of the numerical response of predators and ignores the functional response.

In entomological literature there are two contrasting mathematical theories of regulation. Each theory is based on different assumptions and the predicted results are quite different. Both theories were developed to predict the interaction between parasitic flies and their insect hosts but they can be applied equally well to predator-prey relations. Thompson (1939) assumes that a predator has a limited appetite and that it has no difficulty in finding its prey. Nicholson (1933) assumes that predators have insatiable appetites and that they have a specific capacity to find their prey. This searching capacity is assumed to remain constant at all prey densities and it is also assumed that the searching is random.

The validity of these mathematical models depends upon how closely their assumptions fit natural conditions. We have seen that the appetites of small mammal predators in this study are not insatiable. This fits one of Thompson's assumptions but not Nicholson's. When the functional response was described, it was obvious that predators did have difficulty in finding their prey and that their searching ability did not remain constant at all prey densities. Searching by small mammals was not random. Hence in the present study of predator-prey relations, the remaining assumptions of both Thompson and Nicholson do not hold.

Klomp (1956) considers the damping of oscillations of animal numbers to be as important as regulation. If the oscillations of the numbers of an animal affected by a delayed density-dependent factor (Varley, 1947) like a parasite, do increase in amplitude, as Nicholson's theory predicts (Nicholson and Bailey, 1935), then damping is certainly important. It is not at all certain, however, that this prediction is true. We have already seen that the assumptions underlying Nicholson's theory do not hold in at least some cases. In particular he ignores the important possibility of an S-shaped functional response of the type shown by small mammal predators. If the parasites did show an S-shaped functional response, there would be an *immediate* increase in per cent predation when host density increased, an increase that would modify the effects of the delayed numerical response of parasites emphasized by Nicholson and Varley. Under these conditions the amplitude of the oscillations would not increase as rapidly, and might well not increase at all. An S-shaped functional response therefore acts as an intrinsic damping mechanism in population fluctuations.

Oscillations undoubtedly do occur, however, and whether they increase in amplitude or not, any extrinsic damping is important. The factor that damps oscillations most effectively will be a concurrent density-dependent factor that reacts immediately to changes in the numbers of an animal. Predation by small mammals fulfils these requirements when the density of prey is low. The consumption of prey by individual predators responds immediately to increase in prey density (functional response). Similarly, the numerical response is not greatly delayed, probably because of the high reproductive capacity of small mammals. Thus if the density of a prey is low, chance increases in its numbers will immediately increase the per cent mortality caused by small mammal predation. When the numbers of the prey decrease, the effect of predation will be immediately relaxed. Thus, incipient oscillations can be damped by small-mammal predation.

We have seen that small mammals theoretically can regulate the numbers of prey and can damp their oscillations under certain conditions. Insufficient information was obtained to assess precisely the role of small mammals as predators of *N. sertifer* in the pine plantations of southwestern Ontario, however. Before the general introduction of a virus disease in 1952 (Bird, 1952, 1953), the sawfly was exhausting its food supplies and 70 to 100% defoliation of Scots, jack and red pines was observed in this area. Predators were obviously not regulating the numbers of the sawfly. After the virus was introduced, however, sawfly populations declined rapidly. In Plot 1, for example, their numbers declined from 248,000 cocoons per acre in 1952 to 39,000 per acre in 1954. The area was revisited in 1955 and larval and cocoon population had obviously increased in this plot, before the virus disease could cause much mortality. It happened, however, that *Peromyscus* was the only species of small mammal residing in Plot 1 and it is interesting that similar increases were not observed in other plantations where sawfly numbers had either not decreased so greatly, or where shrews, the most efficient predators, were present. These observations suggest that predation by shrews was effectively damping the oscillations resulting from the interaction of the virus disease with its host.

### Types of Predation

Many types of predation have been reported in the literature. Ricker (1954) believed that there were three major types of predator-prey relations, Leopold (1933) four, and Errington (1946, 1956) two. Many of these types are merely minor deviations, but the two types of predation Errington discusses are quite different from each other. He distinguishes between "compensatory" and "noncompensatory" predation. In the former type, predators take a heavy toll of individuals of the prey species when the density of prey exceeds a certain threshold. This "threshold of security" is determined largely by the number of secure habitable niches in the environment. When prey densities become too high some individuals are forced into exposed areas where they are readily captured by predators. In this type of predation, predators merely remove surplus animals, ones that would succumb even in the absence of enemies. Errington feels, however, that some predator-prey relations depart from this scheme, so that predation occurs not only *above* a specific threshold density of prey. These departures are ascribed largely to behaviour characteristics of the predators. For example, he does not believe that predation of ungulates by canids is compensatory and feels that this results from intelligent, selective searching by the predators.

If the scheme of predation presented here is to fulfill its purpose it must be able to explain these different types of predation. Non-compensatory predation is easily described by the normal functional and numerical responses, for predation of *N. sertifer* by small mammals is of this type. Compensatory predation can also be described using the basic responses and subsidiary factors previously demonstrated. The main characteristic of this predation is the "threshold of security". Prey are more vulnerable above and less vulnerable below this threshold. That is, the strength of stimulus perceived from prey increases markedly when the prey density exceeds the threshold. We have seen from the present study that an increase in the strength of stimulus from prey increases both the functional and numerical responses. Therefore, below the "threshold of security" the functional responses of predators will be very low and as a result there will probably be no numerical response. Above the threshold, the functional response will become marked and a positive numerical response could easily occur. The net effect will result from a combination of these functional and numerical responses so that per cent predation will remain low so long as there is sufficient cover and food available for the prey. As soon as these supply factors are approaching exhaustion the per cent predation will suddenly increase.

Compensatory predation will occur (1) when the prey has a specific density level near which it normally operates, and (2) when the strength of stimulus perceived by predators is so low below this level and so high above it that there is a marked change in the functional response. Most insect populations tolerate considerable crowding and the only threshold would be set by food limitations. In addition, their strength of stimulus is often high at all densities. For *N. sertifer* at least, the strength of stimulus from cocoons is great and the threshold occurs at such high densities that the functional responses of small mammals are at their maximum. Compensatory predation upon insects is probably uncommon.

Entomologists studying the biological control of insects have largely concentrated their attention on a special type of predator — parasitic insects. Although certain features of a true predator do differ from those of a parasite, both predation and parasitism are similar in that one animal is seeking out another. If insect parasitism can in fact be treated as a type of predation, the two basic responses to prey (or host) density and the subsidiary factors affecting these responses should describe parasitism. The functional response of a true predator is measured by the number of prey it destroys; of a parasite by the number of hosts in which eggs are laid. The differences observed between the functional responses of predators and parasites will depend upon the differences between the behaviour of eating and the behaviour of egg laying. The securing of food by an individual predator serves to maintain that individual's existence. The laying of eggs by a parasite serves to maintain its progenies' existence. It seems likely that the more a behaviour concerns the maintenance of an individual, the more demanding it is. Thus the restraints on egg laying could exert a greater and more prolonged effect than the restraints on eating. This must produce differences between the functional responses of predators and parasites. But the functional responses of both are similar in that there is an upper limit marked by the point at which the predator becomes satiated and the parasite has laid all its eggs. This maximum is reached at some finite prey or host density above zero. The form of the rising phase of the functional response would depend upon the characteristics of the individual parasite and we might expect some of the same forms that will be postulated for predators at the end of this section. To summarize, I do not wish to imply that the characteristics of the functional response of a parasite are identical with those of a predator. I merely wish to indicate that a parasite has a response to prey density — the laying of eggs — that can be identified as a functional response, the precise characteristics of which are unspecified.

The effects of host density upon the number of hosts parasitized have been studied experimentally by a number of workers (e.g., Ullyett, 1949a and b; Burnett, 1951 and 1954; De Bach and Smith, 1941). In each case the number of hosts attacked per parasite increased rapidly with initial increase in host density but tended to level with further increase. Hence these functional response curves showed a continually decreasing slope as host density increased and gave no indication of the S-shaped response shown by small mammals. Further information is necessary, however, before these differences can be ascribed solely to the difference between parasitism and predation. It might well reflect, for example, a difference between an instinctive response of an insect and a learned response of a mammal or between the absence of an alternate host and the presence of an alternate food.

The numerical response of both predators and parasites is measured by the way in which the number of adults increases with increase in prey or host density. At first thought, the numerical response of a parasite would seem to be so intimately connected with its functional response that they could not be separated. But the two responses of a predator are just as intimately connected.

The predator must consume food in order to produce progeny just as the parasite must lay eggs in order to produce progeny.

The agents limiting the numerical response of parasites will be similar to those limiting the response of predators. There is, however, some difference. During at least one stage of the parasites' life, the requirements for both food and niche are met by the same object. Thus increase in the amount of food means increase in the number of niches as well, so that niches are never limited unless food is. This should increase the chances for parasites to show pronounced numerical responses. The characteristics of the numerical responses of both predators and parasites, however, will be similar and will range from those in which there is no increase with increase in the density of hosts, to those in which there is a marked and prolonged increase.

A similar scheme has been mentioned by Ullyett (1949b) to describe parasitism. He believed that "the problem of parasite efficiency would appear to be divided into two main phases, viz.: (a) the efficiency of the parasite as a mortality factor in the host population, (b) its efficiency as related to the maintenance of its own population level within the given area". His first phase resembles the functional response and the second the numerical response. Both phases or responses will be affected, of course, by subsidiary components similar to those proposed for predation—characteristics of the hosts, density and quality of alternate hosts, and characteristics of the parasite. The combination of the two responses will determine the changes in per cent parasitism as the result of changes in host density. Since both the functional and numerical responses presumably level at some point, per cent parasitism curves might easily be peaked, as were the predation curves. If these responses levelled at a host density that would never occur in nature, however, the decline of per cent parasitism might never be observed.

The scheme of predation revealed in this study may well explain all types of predation as well as insect parasitism. The knowledge of the basic components and subsidiary factors underlying the behaviour permits us to imagine innumerable possible variations. In a hypothetical situation, for example, we could introduce and remove alternate food at a specific time in relation to the appearance of a prey, and predict the type of predation. But such variations are only minor deviations of a basic pattern. The major types of predation will result from major differences in the form of the functional and numerical responses.

If the functional responses of some predators are partly determined by their behaviour, we could expect a variety of responses differing in form, rate of rise, and final level reached. All functional responses, however, will ultimately level, for it is difficult to imagine an individual predator whose consumption rises indefinitely. Subsistence requirements will fix the ultimate level for most predators, but even those whose consumption is less rigidly determined by subsistence requirements (e.g., fish, Ricker 1941) must have an upper limit, even if it is only determined by the time required to kill.

The functional responses could conceivably have three basic forms. The mathematically simplest would be shown by a predator whose pattern of searching was random and whose rate of searching remained constant at all prey densities. The number of prey killed per predator would be directly proportional to prey density, so that the rising phase would be a straight line. Ricker (1941) postulated this type of response for certain fish preying on sockeye salmon, and De Bach and Smith (1941) observed that the parasitic fly, *Muscidifurax raptor*, parasitized puparia of *Musca domestica*, provided at different densities, in a similar fashion. So few prey were provided in the latter experiment, however, that the initial linear rise in the number of prey attacked with increase in prey density may have been an artifact of the method.

A more complex form of functional response has been demonstrated in laboratory experiments by De Bach and Smith (1941), Ullyett (1949a) and Burnett (1951, 1956) for a number of insect parasites. In each case the number of prey attacked per predator increased very rapidly with initial increase in prey density, and thereafter increased more slowly approaching a certain fixed level. The rates of searching therefore became progressively less as prey density increased.

The third and final form of functional response has been demonstrated for small mammals in this study. These functional responses are S-shaped so that the rates of searching at first increase with increase of prey density, and then decrease.

Numerical responses will also differ, depending upon the species of predator and the area in which it lives. Two types have been demonstrated in this study. *Peromyscus* and *Sorex* populations, for example, increased with increase of prey density to the point where some agent or agents other than food limited their numbers. These can be termed direct numerical responses. There are some cases, however, where predator numbers are not affected by changes of prey density and in the plantations studied *Blarina* presents such an example of no numerical response. A final response, in addition to ones shown here, might also occur. Morris *et al.* (1958) have pointed out that certain predators might decrease in numbers as prey density increases through competition with other predators. As an example of such inverse numerical responses, he shows that during a recent outbreak of spruce budworm in New Brunswick the magnolia, myrtle, and black-throated green warblers decreased in numbers. Thus we have three possible numerical responses — a direct response, no response, and an inverse response.

The different characteristics of these types of functional and numerical responses produce different types of predation. There are four major types conceivable; these are shown diagramatically in Fig. 8. Each type includes the three possible numerical responses — a direct response (a), no response (b), and an inverse response (c), and the types differ because of basic differences in the functional response. In type 1 the number of prey consumed per predator is assumed to be directly proportional to prey density, so that the rising phase of the functional response is a straight line. In type 2, the functional response is presumed to rise at a continually decreasing rate. In type 3, the form of the functional response is the same as that observed in this study. These three types of predation may be considered as the basic ones, for changes in the subsidiary components are not involved. Subsidiary components can, however, vary in response to changes of prey density and in such cases the basic types of predation are modified. The commonest modification seems to be Errington's compensatory predation which is presented as Type 4 in Fig. 8. In this figure the vertical dotted line represents the "threshold of security" below which the strength of stimulus from prey is low and above which it is high. The functional response curves at these two strengths of stimulus are given the form of the functional responses observed in this study. The forms of the responses shown in Types 1 and 2 could also be used, of course.

The combination of the two responses gives the total response shown in the

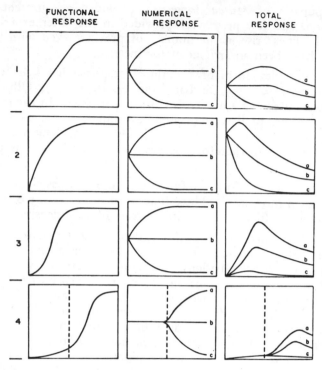

Fig. 8.  Major types of predation.

final column of graphs of Fig. 8.  Both peaked (curves 1a; 2a; 3a, b, c; 4a, b, c) and declining (1b, c; 2b, c) types of predation can occur, but in the absence of any other density-dependent factor, regulation is possible only in the former type.

This method of presenting the major types of predation is an over-simplification since predator density is portrayed as being directly related to prey density.  Animal populations, however, cannot respond *immediately* to changes in prey density, so that there must be a delay of the numerical response. Varley (1953) pointed this out when he contrasted "delayed density dependence" and "density dependence".  The degree of delay, however, will vary widely depending upon the rate of reproduction, immigration, and mortality.  Small mammals, with their high reproductive rate, responded so quickly to increased food that the delay was not apparent.  In such cases the numerical response graphs of Fig. 8 are sufficiently accurate, for the density of predators in any year is directly related to the density of prey in the same year.  The numerical response of other natural enemies can be considerably delayed, however.  Thus the density of those insect parasites that have one generation a year and a low rate of immigration results from the density of hosts in the preceding generation.

In these extreme cases of delay the total response obtained while prey or hosts are steadily increasing will be different than when they are steadily de-creasing.  The amount of difference will depend upon the magnitude and amount of delay of the numerical response, for the functional response has no element of delay.

## SUMMARY AND CONCLUSIONS

The simplest and most basic type of predation is affected by only two vari-ables — prey and predator density.  Predation of cocooned *N. sertifer* by small mammals is such a type, for prey characteristics, the number and variety of alternate foods, and predilections of the predators do not vary in the plantations where *N. sertifer* occurs. In this simple example of predation, the basic components of predation are responses to changes in prey density. The increase in the number of prey consumed per predator, as prey density rises, is termed the functional response. The change in the density of predators, as a result of increase in prey density, is termed the numerical response.

The three important species of small mammal predators (*Blarina*, *Sorex*, and *Peromyscus*) each showed a functional response, and each curve, whether it was derived from field or laboratory data, showed an initial S-shaped rise up to a constant, maximum consumption. The rate of increase of consumption decreased from *Blarina* to *Sorex* to *Peromyscus*, while the upper, constant level of consumption decreased from *Blarina* to *Peromyscus* to *Sorex*. The characteristics of these functional responses could not be explained by a simple relation between consumption and the proportion of prey in the total food available. The form of the functional response curves is such that the proportion of prey consumed per predator increases to a peak and then decreases.

This peaked curve was further emphasized by the direct numerical response of *Sorex* and *Peromyscus*, since their populations rose initially with increase in prey density up to a maximum that was maintained with further increase in cocoon density. *Blarina* did not show a numerical response. The increase in density of predators resulted from increased breeding, and because the reproductive rate of small mammals is so high, there was an almost immediate increase in density with increase in food.

The two basic components of predation — the functional and numerical responses — can be affected by a number of subsidiary components: prey characteristics, the density and quality of alternate foods, and characteristics of the predators. It was shown experimentally that these components affected the amount of predation by lowering or raising the functional and numerical responses. Decrease of the strength of stimulus from prey, one prey characteristic, lowered both the functional and numerical responses. On the other hand, the quality of alternate foods affected the two responses differently. Increase in the palatability or in the number of kinds of alternate foods lowered the functional response but promoted a more pronounced numerical response.

The peaked type of predation shown by small mammals can theoretically regulate the numbers of its prey if predation is high enough to match the effective reproduction by prey at some prey density. Even if this condition does not hold, however, oscillations of prey numbers are damped. Since the functional and numerical responses undoubtedly differ for different species of predator, predation by each is likely to peak at a different prey density. Hence, when a large number of different species of predators are present the declining phase of predation is displaced to a higher prey density, so that the prey have less chance to "escape" the regulation exerted by predators.

The scheme of predation presented here is sufficient to explain all types of predation as well as insect parasitism. It permits us to postulate four major types of predation differing in the characteristics of their basic and subsidiary components.

## REFERENCES

Andrewartha, H. G. and L. C. Birch. 1954. The distribution and abundance of animals. *The Univ. of Chicago Press*, Chicago.

Bird, F. T. 1952. On the artificial dissemination of the virus disease of the European saw-fly, *Neodiprion sertifer* (Geoff.). *Can. Dept. Agric., For. Biol. Div., Bi-Mon. Progr. Rept.* 8(3): 1-2

Bird, F. T. 1953. The use of a virus disease in the biological control of the European pine sawfly, *Neodiprion sertifer* (Geoff.). *Can. Ent.* 85: 437-446.

Bla'r, W. F. 1941. Techniques for the study of mammal populations. *J. Mamm.* 22: 148-157.

Buckner, C. H. 1957. Population studies on small mammals of southeastern Manitoba. *J. Mamm.* 38: 87-97.

Burnett, T. 1951. Effects of temperature and host density on the rate of increase of an insect parasite. *Amer. Nat.* 85: 337-352.

Burnett, T. 1954. Influences of natural temperatures and controlled host densities on oviposition of an insect parasite. *Physiol. Ecol.* 27: 239-248.

Burt, W. H. 1940. Territorial behaviour and populations of some small mammals in southern Michigan. *Misc. Publ. Univ. Mich. Mus. Zool.* no. 45: 1-52.

De Bach, P. 1958. The role of weather and entomophagous species in the natural control of insect populations. *J. Econ. Ent.* 51: 474-484.

De Bach, P., and H. S. Smith. 1941. The effect of host density on the rate of reproduction of entomophagous parasites. *J. Econ. Ent.* 34: 741-745.

De Bach, P., and H. S. Smith. 1947. Effects of parasite population density on rate of change of host and parasite populations. *Ecology* 28: 290-298.

Errington, P. L. 1934. Vulnerability of bob-white populations to predation. *Ecology* 15: 110-127.

Errington, P. L. 1943. An analysis of mink predation upon muskrats in North-Central United States. *Agric. Exp. Sta. Iowa State Coll. Res. Bull.* 320: 797-924.

Errington, P. L. 1945. Some contributions of a fifteen-year local study of the northern bob-white to a knowledge of population phenomena. *Ecol. Monog.* 15: 1-34.

Errington, P. L. 1946. Predation and vertebrate populations. *Quart. Rev. Biol.* 21: 144-177, 221-245.

Fraenkel, G., and D. L. Gunn. 1940. The orientation of animals. Oxford.

Hayne, D. W. 1949. Two methods for estimating population from trapping records. *J. Mamm.* 30: 339-411.

Holling, C. S. 1955. The selection by certain small mammals of dead, parasitized, and healthy prepupae of the European pine sawfly, *Neodiprion sertifer* (Goeff.). *Can. J. Zool.* 33: 404-419.

Holling, C. S. 1958a. A radiographic technique to identify healthy, parasitized, and diseased sawfly prepupae within cocoons. *Can. Ent.* 90: 59-61.

Holling, C. S. 1958b. Sensory stimuli involved in the location and selection of sawfly cocoons by small mammals. *Can. J. Zool.* 36: 633-653.

Klomp, H. 1956. On the theories on host-parasite interaction. *Int. Union of For. Res. Organizations, 12th Congress*, Oxford, 1956.

Leopold, A. 1933. Game management. Charles Scribner's Sons.

Lincoln, F. C. 1930. Calculating waterfowl abundance on the basis of banding returns. *U.S. Dept. Agric.* Circular 118.

MacLagan, D. S. 1932. The effect of population density upon rate of reproduction, with special reference to insects. *Proc. Roy. Soc. Lond.* 111: 437-454.

Milne, A. 1957. The natural control of insect populations. *Can. Ent.* 89: 193-213.

Morris, R. F., W. F. Chesire, C. A. Miller, and D. G. Mott. 1958. Numerical response of avian and mammalian predators during a gradation of the spruce budworm. *Ecology* 39(3): 487-494.

Nicholson, A. J. 1933. The balance of animal populations. *J. Anim. Ecol.* 2: 132-178.

Nicholson, A. J., and V. A. Bailey. 1935. The balance of animal populations. Part 1, *Proc. Zool. Soc. Lond.* 1935, p. 551-598.

Prebble, M. L. 1943. Sampling methods in population studies of the European spruce saw-fly, *Gilpinia hercyniae* (Hartig.) in eastern Canada. *Trans. Roy. Soc. Can., Third Series*, Sect. V. 37: 93-126.

Ricker, W. E. 1941. The consumption of young sockeye salmon by predaceous fish. *J. Fish. Res. Bd. Can.* 5: 293-313.

Ricker, W. E. 1954. Stock and recruitment. *J. Fish. Res. Bd. Can.* 11: 559-623.

Robertson, F. W., and J. H. Sang. 1944. The ecological determinants of population growth in a *Drosophila* culture. I. Fecundity of adult flies. *Proc. Roy. Soc. Lond.*, B., 132: 258-277.

Solomon, M. E. 1949. The natural control of animal populations. *J. Anim. Ecology* 18: 1-35.

Stickel, L. F. 1954. A comparison of certain methods of measuring ranges of small mammals. *J. Mamm.* 35: 1-15.

Thompson, W. R. 1929. On natural control. *Parasitology* 21: 269-281.

Thompson, W. R. 1930. The principles of biological control. *Ann. Appl. Biol.* 17: 306-338.

Thompson, W. R. 1939. Biological control and the theories of the interactions of populations. *Parasitology* 31: 299-388.

Tinbergen, L. 1949. Bosvogels en insecten. *Nederl. Boschbouue. Tijdschr.* 21: 91-105.

Tinbergen, L. 1955. The effect of predators on the numbers of their hosts. *Vakblad voor Biologen* 28: 217-228.

Tinbergen, N. 1951. The study of instinct. Oxford.

Tothill, J. D. 1922. The natural control of the fall webworm (*Hyphantria cunea* Drury) in Canada. *Can. Dept. Agr. Bull.* 3, new series (Ent. Bull. 19): 1-107.

Ullyett, G. C. 1949a. Distribution of progeny by *Cryptus inornatus* Pratt. (Hym. Ichneumonidae). *Can. Ent.* 81: 285-299, 82: 1-11.

Ullyett, G. C. 1949b. Distribution of progeny by *Chelonus texanus* Cress. (Hym. Braconidae). *Can. Ent.* 81: 25-44.

Varley, G. C. 1947. The natural control of population balance in the knapweed gall-fly (*Urophora jaceana*). *J. Anim. Ecol.* 16: 139-187.

Varley, G. C. 1953. Ecological aspects of population regulation. *Trans. IXth Int. Congr. Ent.* 2: 210-214.

Voûte, A. D. 1946. Regulation of the density of the insect populations in virgin forests and cultivated woods. *Archives Neerlandaises de Zoologie* 7: 435-470.

Voûte, A. D. 1956. Forest entomology and population dynamics. *Int. Union For. Res. Organizations*, Twelfth Congress, Oxford.

Voûte, A. D. 1958. On the regulation of insect populations. *Proc. Tenth Int. Congr. of Ent.* Montreal, 1956.

(Received April 16, 1959)

*Reprinted from* THE CANADIAN ENTOMOLOGIST, Volume 100, Number 6, June 1968

# EVOLUTION AND POPULATION ECOLOGY OF PARASITE–HOST SYSTEMS[1]

DAVID PIMENTEL and FREDERICK A. STONE

Department of Entomology and Limnology, New York State College of Agriculture, Cornell University, Ithaca, New York

## Abstract
                                                    *Can. Ent.* 100: 655–662 (1968)

The ecology and evolution of the parasite (*Nasonia vitripennis* Walker) and host (*Musca domestica* L.) were investigated in a specially designed multicelled population cage which provided ample space-time structure to the environment for free parasite–host interactions. The population characteristics exhibited by a control or newly associated parasite–host system were compared with an experimental parasite–host system which already had evolved a degree of ecological homeostasis. Population fluctuations in the experimental parasite population were dampened compared with the control parasite population which fluctuated with great intensity; and in addition, the mean number of parasites in the experimental systems was significantly lower (about ¼) than the mean number of parasites in the control system.

## Introduction

Interspecies evolution through genetic feedback in interacting parasite–host populations can result in the regulation of parasite numbers (Pimentel 1961). As both parasite and host species evolve toward greater ecological homeostasis, the result is greater population stability of both parasite and host species and a more uniform distribution of both species. Because of this, the parasite–host system has greater chances of survival in time and both species make increasingly more effective use of the environmental resources available to them.

Genetic feedback functioning as both a regulatory and stabilizing mechanism in population systems was tested under controlled laboratory conditions (Pimentel and Al Hafidh 1965). The premise of the experiment was that the numbers of parasitic feeding species (*Nasonia vitripennis* Walker) would be controlled as genetic resistance evolved in the host population (*Musca domestica* L.). Host

[1]This investigation was supported in part by a grant from the National Science Foundation (GB 4567) Environmental Biology.

density was held constant and parasite density was allowed to vary in response to genetic changes in the host.

During the study period of 1004 days, measurable evolution took place in both host and parasite populations. The experimental host population became more resistant to the parasite as evidenced by a drop in the average reproduction of 135 to 39 progeny per experimental female parasite and a decrease in average longevity from about 7 to 4 days. Selective pressure on the experimental host population lessened as the density of the parasite population declined to about one half that of the control. During the last 250 days of the 1004-day study period the control parasite population averaged about 3700 while the experimental averaged only 1900. In the experimental group the amplitude of the parasite population fluctuations was significantly damped indicating evolution toward greater population stability.

The purpose of this study was to determine how parasite–host systems, which already had evolved a degree of ecological homeostasis, would behave in an environment with ample space–time structure and where host numbers were allowed to fluctuate.

## Methods

The same wasp parasite (*Nasonia vitripennis*) and housefly host (*Musca domestica*) species were used. A comparison was made of the population characteristics exhibited by a control (wild stocks) which was a newly associated parasite–host population system and two experimental populations (designated A and E), both of which were parasite–host population systems in which some ecological homeostasis had already evolved. The three systems were started at different times and not replicated because manpower was not available. Stocks of the experimental populations were obtained from parasites and hosts that had evolved and interacted with one another for 2 years in the laboratory (Pimentel and Al Hafidh 1965).

Each parasite–host population was placed in a multi-cell population cage which consisted of 30 plastic boxes (3.7×5×7 in.) arranged in a 5 by 6 design and adjoined one to another by 0.25-in. inside diameter plastic tubes (Pimentel *et al.* 1963). The tube opening, extending 0.75 in. into each cell had a screen-covered disc (1 in. in diameter) attached at the end. The surface of the tube extending into the cage was covered with a light coating of vaseline to slow parasite dispersal. The disc had a hole through which parasite and host could move. Thus, to emigrate, parasites and hosts had to fly or jump on to the screen discs and enter the hole in the center of the disc. About 5% of the parasites were lost each week when they became lodged in the vaseline. This loss had no appreciable effect on the interaction of the parasite–host system (Pimentel *et al.* 1963). With this cage arrangement both parasite and host could disperse slowly from one cell to another and individual colonies could form within the cells. Each cell was ventilated with eight 1.25-in.-diameter openings covered with 120 mesh bronze screening. The laboratory was maintained at 80°±3°F and relative humidity of 40%±8. The population cages were continuously lighted from above with a 6-w bulb per cell.

The hosts were easily maintained since both larval and adult stages of the host used the same food medium; adults oviposited directly into the medium. In each cell of the population cage the food was placed in glass vials, 24×60 mm high. These were filled 75% full with the food medium (440 g dried skim milk, 365 g brewers yeast, 12 g agar, and 3950 ml of water). After the medium had cooled and formed a soft gel, about 1 g of liver was placed on the surface. One vial per day was added to each cell unit until a total of seven vials was present; thereafter, the oldest vial was removed and a fresh one introduced. The vials were held in a screen rack to keep them off the bottom of the cage and in this way the parasites were not hindered in their search for hosts which lay exposed on the cage bottom. Since the larval stage of the housefly is between 4 and 5 days under the experimental conditions, the host larvae had left the vials and pupated in the bottom of the cells by the time the oldest vial was removed 7 days later. Sometimes when larvae were extremely crowded, they crawled into the vial to be removed and they were discarded. Most larvae that were forced out of the vial prematurely, fell to the bottom of the cage and died.

Under the designed environmental conditions of the laboratory, the control parasite on its control host used in this study produced an average of 133±13.8 progeny per female, whereas the experimental parasite on its experimental host produced an average of only 46±7.8 progeny per female. All population systems were initiated with a mixed age distribution of parasites and hosts. The cells in the 30-cell population cages were numbered as follows:

|   |   |   |   |   |   |
|---|---|---|---|---|---|
| 1 | 6  | 11 | 16 | 21 | 26 |
| 2 | 7  | 12 | 17 | 22 | 27 |
| 3 | 8  | 13 | 18 | 23 | 28 |
| 4 | 9  | 14 | 19 | 24 | 29 |
| 5 | 10 | 15 | 20 | 25 | 30 |

Parasites and hosts were introduced in the following manner:

| Cell No. | Adults | Host larvae | Eggs | Parasite adults | Parasitized hosts | |
|---|---|---|---|---|---|---|
| | | | | | 1 day old | 10 days old |
| 8  | 4   | —   | —   | —   | —  | —  |
| 13 | 50  | 25  | 25  | —   | —  | —  |
| 18 | 100 | 50  | 50  | 50  | 10 | 10 |
| 23 | 200 | 100 | 100 | 100 | 40 | 40 |

Normally a weekly census was taken of the host pupae at the bottom of each cell. One- and two-week-old pupae were held in separate open plastic trays supported above the floor of each cell. Pupae were kept for 3 weeks to make certain all parasites had emerged. A record kept of the parasitized pupae for one control and one experimental system provided an indication of the rate of parasitism occurring in the host populations.

Parasite numbers were determined by counting living adults only. Male parasites lived for about 2 days and females for about 7 days. Thus, as with host pupae, the number of parasites recorded was generally a new lot produced during each week. Adult parasites and hosts were lightly anesthetized with carbon dioxide which had been bubbled through water to facilitate quick and accurate counting.

### Results

In the control the host population increased rapidly and within 6 weeks it had invaded all 30 cells in the population cage. In contrast, the parasite population lagged until about the 12th week when a rapid invasion of most cells in the cage occurred. Shortly after the 29th week, the host population crashed from the intense feeding pressure of the large parasite population (Fig. 1). Next the parasite population crashed because of the shortage of hosts. By the 35th week only an average of 0.1 host pupae per cell (a total of two pupae in one cell) remained in the control system. There were, of course, other life stages of the host population present in the system to continue the existence of the population system. Meanwhile the parasite population reached a low of 0.4 per cell at the 39th week with the adult parasites distributed in only three cells of the control system.

Then the host population increased again and host densities reached a high of 308 per cell at the 57th week (Fig. 1). The decline in host numbers following the second host increase was not as severe as the first, the low in this case was only 146 hosts per cell. Another peak occurred at the 83rd week.

The behavior of both experimental parasite–host population systems (E and A Figs. 2 and 3 respectively) differed significantly from the control system (Fig. 1). Within 6 to 7 weeks both experimental host populations had increased rapidly and reached peak densities; the population high in the A system was greater than the E system. Concurrently both parasite populations increased but neither increased in number above their host populations as the control parasite population did. In addition, neither parasite population caused its host population to crash. The lowest host density in the experimental systems was 131 per cell in the E system at the 17th week and was 330 per cell in the A system at the 43rd week. These densities were significantly greater than the lowest host density of the control system. The fewest number of cells occupied in the E system was 16 and in the A system 25. All of these statistics contrast significantly with those observed in the control population.

Parasite numbers in the experimental systems did not reach the high levels attained by the parasite population in the control system, but neither did they decrease to the low levels recorded for the control. Parasite density lows in the experimental systems were 1.3 per cell for the E system and 6.7 for the A system.

Population fluctuations in the control system were severe and differed significantly from the experimental systems (Figs. 1–3). The density of the control host population averaged 172.3 per cell for the study period and ranged from 0.1 to 416.1. The density of hosts in the E system averaged 171.6 per cell (similar to the control) but ranged only from 102.3 to 449.9 in the experimental E system. In the experimental A system the host populations had a density about double that of either the control or experimental E, with an average density of 462.6 (ranging from 329.6 to 652.6).

Parasite density in the control system averaged 117.7 and ranged from 0.6 to 437.7 (Fig. 1). Parasite densities in both experimental systems averaged about ¼ that of the control. In experimental system E the average number of parasites for the study period was 34.4 per cell (ranging from 1.3 to 204.6); in experimental system A the average number of parasites was 32.1 per cell (ranging from 6.7 to 71.1). Note that the mean densities of parasites in both experimental systems were quite similar but the average number of hosts in these two systems differed. We do not have an explanation for this.

The average number of cells occupied by hosts in the control system was less than that occupied by hosts in either experimental system. The number of cells

Figs. 1–3. Average number per cell of control hosts (      ) and parasites (----) (Fig. 1), of experimental E hosts and parasites (Fig. 2), and of experimental A hosts and parasites (Fig. 3) in a 30-cell population cage.

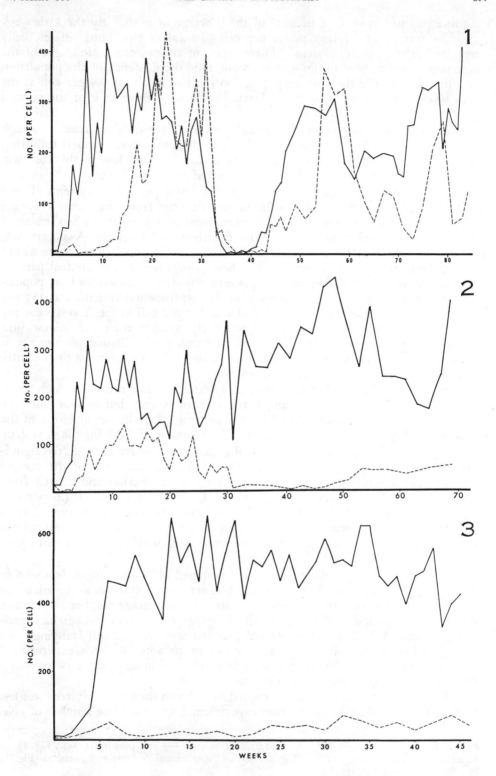

occupied by hosts in the control system averaged 24.0 and ranged from 1 to 30. The mean number of cells occupied by hosts for experimental E system averaged 28.7 (ranging from 16 to 30) and in experimental A system averaged 28.0 (ranging from 25 to 30).

The average number of cells occupied by the parasites in the control system was 16.7 and ranged from 1 to 30. In the experimental systems the average number of cells occupied by the parasites in experimental E system was 15.2 (ranging from 10 to 27) and in A system the average was 13.4 (ranging from 10 to 28). Although the average number of cells occupied by the parasites in the experimental systems was about the same, the minimum number of cells occupied by the parasites in the experimental was 10 compared with the minimum of 1 for the control.

Host parasitism rate in the control system averaged 64.4%, whereas in the experimental A system (no record for E) the parasitism rate averaged only 30.9% (Table I).

### Discussion

In this investigation the interactions of two experimental parasite–host systems which already evolved a degree of ecological homeostasis were compared with that of a control parasite–host system which had not evolved ecological homeostasis. In the control system there was an outbreak in parasite numbers shortly after the system was initiated and similar outbreaks occurred twice more during the life of the population system. These rapid increases in parasite numbers caused host numbers to decrease and in one instance to a low of only two host pupae. The total effect of these parasite outbreaks were fluctuations of great intensity in the parasite–host interactions of the control system. In both experimental systems, however, parasite numbers never exceeded host numbers and population fluctuations were dampened.

With both parasite and host numbers fluctuating most severely in the control system, marked differences also occurred in the average numbers of parasites and hosts. In general, parasite numbers of both experimental systems averaged only about ¼ those of the control system, but host numbers did not fit any clear pattern.

Parasite population trends of both experimental systems reflected the reduced reproductive potential of the experimental parasites on their resistant hosts. The experimental parasite on its host produced only 46 progeny per female, whereas the control parasite on its host produced about 133 progeny per female. Hence the rate of increase of parasites was directly affected by the quality of hosts which it fed upon. This influenced the dynamics of the parasite populations and also the survival and characteristics of the host populations.

Although no analysis was made of the reproductive potential of his parasite–host system, Utida (1957) reported that his wasp parasite (*Neocatolaccus mamezophagus* Ishil and Nagasawa) and the azuki bean-weevil host (*Callosobruchus chinensis* L.) apparently evolved toward some ecological homeostasis. In time, fluctuations of this system were damped and, associated with this change, there appeared a fall in the biotic potential of the parasite. Takahashi (1963) at the same laboratory reported that genetic evolution had taken place in his parasite (*Nemeritus canescens* Gavenhorst) and moth host (*Ephestia cautella* Walker) populations after long association, and this changed parasitism rates as well as other population characteristics.

TABLE I

Percentage parasitism of host pupae in the control and experimental A systems

| Week | Control | Exp. A | Week | Control | Exp. A |
|------|---------|--------|------|---------|--------|
| 1 | — | 86.2 | 43 | 60.1 | 67.5 |
| 2 | — | 77.8 | 44 | 53.9 | 47.4 |
| 3 | — | — | 45 | 37.4 | 50.9 |
| 4 | — | 34.0 | 46 | 50.6 | |
| 5 | — | — | | | Av. 30.9% |
| 6 | — | 24.6 | 47 | 43.6 | |
| 7 | — | — | 48 | — | |
| 8 | — | 11.5 | 49 | 44.2 | |
| 9 | — | 18.7 | 50 | — | |
| 10 | — | 15.0 | 51 | 49.6 | |
| 11 | — | — | 52 | — | |
| 12 | 16.4 | 14.6 | 53 | 36.9 | |
| 13 | 17.7 | 17.7 | 54 | — | |
| 14 | 27.2 | 17.4 | 55 | 67.7 | |
| 15 | 33.4 | 27.3 | 56 | — | |
| 16 | 41.8 | 19.7 | 57 | 71.0 | |
| 17 | 43.0 | 18.8 | 58 | — | |
| 18 | 45.3 | 21.8 | 59 | 85.5 | |
| 19 | 50.1 | 14.6 | 60 | — | |
| 20 | 56.2 | 16.6 | 61 | 79.7 | |
| 21 | 60.2 | 18.5 | 62 | — | |
| 22 | 70.1 | 19.9 | 63 | 72.3 | |
| 23 | 64.9 | 22.7 | 64 | — | |
| 24 | 75.6 | 24.5 | 65 | 67.1 | |
| 25 | 78.3 | 32.4 | 66 | — | |
| 26 | 77.7 | 25.3 | 67 | 78.6 | |
| 27 | 80.4 | 21.4 | 68 | — | |
| 28 | 89.7 | — | 69 | 74.2 | |
| 29 | 94.0 | 22.0 | 70 | 45.9 | |
| 30 | 96.8 | 26.1 | 71 | 53.4 | |
| 31 | 99.4 | 31.4 | 72 | 59.2 | |
| 32 | 100.0 | 22.4 | 73 | 60.9 | |
| 33 | 99.3 | 32.2 | 74 | 70.2 | |
| 34 | 82.2 | 32.3 | 75 | 79.4 | |
| 35 | 100.0 | 28.0 | 76 | 71.5 | |
| 36 | 68.0 | 29.3 | 77 | 82.3 | |
| 37 | 14.2 | 31.3 | 78 | 83.7 | |
| 38 | 56.0 | 42.8 | 79 | 92.6 | |
| 39 | 72.2 | 44.4 | 80 | 84.9 | |
| 40 | 55.5 | 35.4 | 81 | 77.8 | |
| 41 | 21.5 | 45.3 | 82 | 86.1 | |
| 42 | 44.8 | 47.8 | 83 | 76.8 | |
| | | | | Av. 64.4% | |

A comparison of the population trends exhibited by the parasite–host populations housed in the multi-cell cages to those exhibited by the populations housed in a single-cell cage system (in which host numbers were held constant), indicates general agreement between the studies. In both, the fluctuations were damped in the experimental parasite populations which had evolved a degree of ecological homeostasis with their host. Also in both studies the mean numbers of parasites in the experimental systems were significantly lower than the mean parasite numbers in the respective control systems. Thus during the last 250 days of the study period using the single-cell cage, the mean number of parasites in the experimental system was about ½ those in the control. Similarly in the multi-cell systems, mean experimental parasite numbers were about ¼ those of the control parasite numbers.

The distribution of hosts and parasites in the experimental systems typified what would be expected once parasites and hosts had evolved some balance in their supply–demand economy. That is, parasites were feeding primarily on "interest" (surplus energy of their host) but did not increase to a high enough level to feed on "capital" (energy necessary for the growth, maintenance, and reproduction of their host). In addition, hosts were uniformly distributed throughout the multi-cell cage and seldom were hosts eliminated from individual cells by the parasites. This resulted in a wide distribution of both hosts and parasites.

The space–time structure of the 30-cell cage while helpful to the survival of the experimental population systems was most important to the survival of the control population system. Spatial "gaps" between hosts were necessary to limit parasite numbers. It was the relative abundance and distribution of hosts that determined whether the parasite population increased or decreased. The experimental parasite–host systems with more integration and evolved balance in their supply–demand economy needed less space–time structure in their environment.

The wide distribution of parasites and hosts in space, plus the relative stability in population fluctuations of the experimental systems, contributed to the greater chances for their survival. Clearly a population which fluctuates severely and decreases to only a few individuals has less chances for survival. Stability in parasite–host populations, and a resulting wider distribution of parasites and hosts, would enable these systems to make the best use of the environmental resources available to them.

In the present study the number of cells occupied in the control parasite–host system was on the average less than the number occupied in the experimental parasite–host systems. This suggests there was probably less efficient use of the resources in the control system but more precise measurements would be necessary to document this in the population systems.

Interspecies evolution through genetic feedback in parasite–host, predator–prey, and herbivore–plant populations can result in the regulation of the numbers of the eating populations. As a regulatory mechanism, genetic feedback functions interdependently with competition, natural enemies, and environmental discontinuity. As indicated from this investigation, the functioning of the genetic feedback results in effective population control as evolution occurs, and a balance in the economy of the eating and eaten species is achieved. All of these factors contribute directly to a more uniform distribution of the eating and eaten species and generally enables the community system to make better use of the available environmental resources.

## References

Pimentel, D. 1961. Animal population regulation by the genetic feedback mechanism. *Am. Nat.* **95**: 65–79.

Pimentel, D., and Al Hafidh. 1965. Ecological control of a parasite population by genetic evolution in the parasite–host system. *Ann. ent. Soc. Am.* **58**: 1–6.

Pimentel, D., W. P. Nagel, and J. L. Madden. 1963. Space–time structure of the environment and the survival of parasite–host systems. *Am. Nat.* **97**: 141–167.

Takahashi, F. 1963. Changes in some ecological characters of the almond moth caused by the selective action of an ichneumon wasp in their interacting system. *Res. Popul. Ecol., Kyoto* **5**: 117–129.

Utida, S. 1957. Population fluctuation, an experimental and theoretical approach. *Cold Spring Harb. Symp. quant. Biol.* **22**: 139–151.

(Received 15 January 1968)

THOMAS PARK
University of Chicago

Chapter 13

# Competition: An Experimental
# and Statistical Study*

This paper constitutes a partial summary of a lecture given before the Bio-statistics Conference at Iowa State College on June 26, 1952. In order to meet limitations of space, the present version has been reduced by elimination of an introduction originally intended to define what is meant by competition and to discuss certain steps inherent in its study. This introduction will be published elsewhere along with more detailed presentation of the experimental data.

Thus, for the purposes of this paper only, I shall refer to interspecies competition merely as those new events which emerge when two species co-associate and which lead in time to the persistence of one species and the elimination of the other. This is not advanced as a general definition of competition.

The experimental material used in this study consisted of two species of flour beetles, *Tribolium confusum* Duval and *T. castaneum* Herbst. These forms have both conceptual and technical utility for the laboratory study of population phenomena: notably, the facts (1) that they utilize the same food (flour); (2) that their natality and mortality attributes are of the same order of magnitude; and (3) that by passing infested flour through bolting-cloth sieves a complete population census can be taken.

The research now to be reported is a laboratory study of single ("control") and mixed-species ("experimental") populations of flour beetles when cultured for many continuous generations under six combinations of temperature and humidity ("Treatments").

* This investigation was jointly supported by grants from the Rockefeller Foundation and the Dr. Wallace C. and Clara A. Abbott Memorial Fund of the University of Chicago.

## THE EXPERIMENTAL DESIGN

All populations regardless of treatment and species were started, counted, and maintained in precisely the same way. The experiment was initiated by introducing, in equal sex ratio, eight young adult beetles into a shell vial containing 8 gm. of medium (95 per cent sifted whole-wheat flour: 5 per cent brewers' yeast). These vials were placed in the appropriate incubators for 30 days, at which time the censuses were taken. A census consisted of counting the larvae, pupae, and adults, saving but not counting the eggs, and returning all living stages to 8 gm. of fresh medium for 30 days more. This procedure was repeated at 30-day intervals, and certain populations to date have been followed in this way for 1,440 days or forty-eight censuses—roughly the equivalent of 1,200 years in terms of human population history. The mixed-species cultures differed in handling from the above routine in that one operation was added, namely, the adult beetles were examined microscopically in order to permit their segregation into *T. confusum* and *T. castaneum* components.

An earlier study (Park, 1948) discussed competition when all cultures were maintained at one temperature and one humidity. Upon conclusion of this research it was decided to complicate the problem by introduction of three temperatures and two humidities. This adds ecological realism to the investigation in that it permits an evaluation of the role of the physical environment in terms of its influence on intraspecies and interspecies competition. The temperatures chosen were 34°, 29°, and 24° C.; the humidities, 70 per cent and 30 per cent. We shall refer to each combination of temperature and humidity as a "Treatment" and assign Roman numerals to specify the six combinations as follows:

> Treatment I:    34° C. and 70 per cent
> Treatment II:   34° C. and 30 per cent
> Treatment III:  29° C. and 70 per cent
> Treatment IV:   29° C. and 30 per cent
> Treatment V:    24° C. and 70 per cent
> Treatment VI:   24° C. and 30 per cent

It is mandatory that single-species populations be established in order to interpret the data derived from the mixed-species cultures. The single-species groups assess, relative to Treatments, the census performances of *T. confusum* and *T. castaneum* when only *intra*species competition is present. The mixed-species cultures, while also retaining an intraspecies and Treatment component, add to the system the qualitatively different phenomenon of *inter*species competition. It is quite valid to view the single-species cohorts as "controls" and the mixed-species as "experimentals."

The complete experimental design showing the factorial arrangement of the Treatments, the distribution of control and experimental populations, and the replication appears in Table 13.1. Several shorthand notations are used: *C* means control cultures; *E* means experimental cultures; lower-case *b* means *T. confusum;* and lower-case *c* means *T. castâneum.*

When embarking on a research program in laboratory population ecology, the investigator, in addition to all else, must be prepared to satisfy two requirements. First, the census history of each individual culture should be followed for a sufficient number of successive generations to assure that all possible time trends in the behavior of that culture are disclosed. Second, the

TABLE 13.1

THE EXPERIMENTAL DESIGN

| Treatment | Code | Population Category | Replication |
|---|---|---|---|
| I (34°:70%). . . . . . . | I-C-b | Single species, *T. confusum* | 20 |
| | I-C-c | Single species, *T. castaneum* | 20 |
| | I-E | Mixed species, *T. castaneum & T. confusum* | 30 |
| II (34°:30%). . . . . . | II-C-b | Single species, *T. confusum* | 20 |
| | II-C-c | Single species, *T. castaneum* | 20 |
| | II-E | Mixed species, *T. castaneum & T. confusum* | 30 |
| III (29°:70%). . . . . | III-C-b | Single species, *T. confusum* | 20 |
| | III-C-c | Single species, *T. castaneum* | 20 |
| | III-E | Mixed species, *T. castaneum & T. confusum* | 30 |
| IV (29°:30%). . . . . . | IV-C-b | Single species, *T. confusum* | 20 |
| | IV-C-c | Single species, *T. castaneum* | 20 |
| | IV-E | Mixed species, *T. castaneum & T. confusum* | 30 |
| V (24°:70%). . . . . . . | V-C-b | Single species, *T. confusum* | 20 |
| | V-C-c | Single species, *T. castaneum* | 20 |
| | V-E | Mixed species, *T. castaneum & T. confusum* | 30 |
| VI (24°:30%). . . . . . | VI-C-b | Single species, *T. confusum* | 15 |
| | VI-C-c | Single species, *T. castaneum* | 15 |
| | VI-E | Mixed species, *T. castaneum & T. confusum* | 20 |

replication should be adequate for each treatment introduced into the design. The first point explains itself. The second merits brief elaboration. Adequate replication is necessary for several important reasons. Taken by itself, each population is an individual unit. It may closely conform, in amplitude and/or magnitude, to the behavior of its fellows, or it may differ beyond the expectation of random error. The more the conformity, the more the average behavior of the array of replicates can be considered as the norm, and contrariwise. The point here is not so much that of assessing homogeneity or heterogeneity (obviously solvable by statistical methodology and obviously the standard reason for replication) but, rather, that of discovering the unusual case history or, even, the unique event. The latter can have great interpretative value and may lead into further investigation.

The amount of replication indicated in Table 13.1 has proved adequate for the present study. More experimental cultures were established than controls because, as we shall see, there is greater chance for an unusual event to occur when interspecies competition is operating, and the addition of ten cultures per Treatment increases the likelihood that such an event will be found. Treatment VI is less replicated than the others and was started at a later date. This, unfortunately, was necessitated solely by technical limitations. The numbers in the last column of the table are the numbers at the start. A few cultures over the course of time had to be dropped here and there either for reasons of inadvertent accident or because parasitic infection (*Adelina tribolii*) became evident (Park and Frank, 1950).

Finally, there is something to be said for giving the reader an inkling of the labor involved in studies such as these. This is advanced, not consciously in the spirit of rodomontade, but as a caution that population ecology, apart from its exciting theoretical aspects, contains much best described as unadulterated drudgery. The point can be driven home by reference only to the process of counting the beetles and neglecting all other necessary operations. Let us suppose that 400 populations are censused every 30 days and that, say, each vial yields 240 *Tribolium* of all stages but eggs. This means that some 96,000 individuals are counted per month. If the counts are continued for 990 days (thirty-three censuses), the data books would contain something in excess of 3,000,000 observations!

## THE SINGLE-SPECIES POPULATIONS

As stressed in the preface to this paper we are actually reporting here the substance of a lecture rather than publishing the details of an extensive investigation. This makes it necessary to omit numerous items many of which are highly important. Several of these omissions concern the control cultures, of which two are mentioned in the paragraph immediately following.

A population trend can be thought of as a time series describable by number of individuals (ordinate) against time (abscissa). To depict completely the control data in graphic form, we should be obliged to reproduce 115 such curves for *T. confusum* and 115 for *T. castaneum* distributed Treatment by Treatment. Such intensive representation clearly should not be done here, the enjoiner made earlier about the importance of replication notwithstanding. A further condensation could be achieved by graphing in similar fashion the replicate means for the two species in each of the six Treatments. These 12 curves were presented in the lecture as lantern slides but are excluded here in order to gain space for other matters. It should be stressed in passing, however, that different temporal trends are illustrated by the averaged data. For example, some curves depart relatively little over the course of time from a computed equilibrium density (e.g., I-*C-b;* VI-*C-c*); others exhibit an initial high peak around day 150 followed by essential equilibrium (III-*C-b;* V-*C-b*); still others are characterized by a sort of oscillation in that they describe an initial peak, a subsequent depression, and a secondary peak (III-*C-c;* V-*C-c*). The point to be established here is the significant one that the *pattern* of census history varies with the experimental design. That is to say, the data, considered as time series, show both between-species (within-Treatment) and within-species (between-Treatment) components.

From now on we shall discuss the control cultures in terms of the mean equilibrium density attained by each species in each Treatment over the entire period of observation. In some ways this is arbitrary and unrealistic, since, as just seen, census pattern does vary with time and since this variability, in itself, is a meaningful segment of the research. Even so, the method allows for an evaluation of the effect of temperature, humidity, and "interaction" (temperature $\times$ humidity) as these influence the averaged population densities of *T. confusum* and *T. castaneum*. As such, it permits the formulation of conclusions later to have interpretative value.

In order to understand fully the arithmetic of this method, let us work through a brief illustration. Suppose we select the record sheet for Replicate No. 1 of *T. confusum* in Treatment VI (i.e., VI-*C-b*-1). Here we find that total population per vial by 30-day intervals has the following values: 213 (30 days), 272 (60 days), 286 (90 days), 275, 263, and so on. These figures are converted to numbers per gram (dividing by 8), giving, respectively, 26.6, 34.0, 35.8, 34.4, and 32.9. If the population was not followed further (which of course was not the case), we would have a mean equilibrium density per gram for this replicate of 163.7/5, or 32.74. The last would be the datum used for this culture in all subsequent computations and representations. The other replicate means were found in the same way, and these array means constitute the data for the cohort. It is clear that the means are independent of each other in the statistical sense and thus can be utilized as needed in analysis.

The basic conclusion to be drawn from all the single-species cultures is the very simple one that, with one exception noted below, the populations successfully persist in all Treatments. In other words, although species and Treatment interact to affect both census pattern and equilibrium density, they do not result in population extinction (apart from certain vials of II-*C-c*). Since many of these populations from all conditions have now been maintained for over 1,470 days, it is completely valid to assume that they would never die out under obtaining procedures of husbandry unless new, deleterious influences developed or were introduced. As stressed earlier, this is a "control finding" necessary for interpretation of the interspecies data.

The one exception involves *T. castaneum* in Treatment VI (24°; 30 per cent) in which the entire group of fifteen replicates became extinct. The first population died at day 150; the last, at day 510. The mean extinction age was 350 ± 34.1 days with a standard deviation of ±132 days. It is thus obvious that these environmental conditions per se are inimical for population persistence of this species even though highly satisfactory for *T. confusum*. However, since reproduction and metamorphosis took place in all fifteen vials, the data for this series are included, and properly so, in the analysis of controls. More importantly, as later to be shown, we are prepared

TABLE 13.2

BIOMETRIC CONSTANTS FOR CONTROL POPULATIONS BY TREAT-
MENTS AND SPECIES, EXPRESSED AS TOTAL POPULATION PER
GRAM OF MEDIUM FOR THE PERIOD OF OBSERVATION

| Population | Mean±S.E. | Median | Mode | S.D. | C.V. | d.f. |
|---|---|---|---|---|---|---|
| | *(Tribolium confusum)* | | | | | |
| I-*C-b* . . . . . . . . . | 41.15±3.04 | 41.19 | 41.27 | 13.6 | 33.0 | 19 |
| II-*C-b* . . . . . . . . | 23.73±1.23 | 21.26 | 16.32 | 8.0 | 33.7 | 41 |
| III-*C-b* . . . . . . . . | 32.94±1.99 | 32.54 | 31.74 | 8.9 | 27.0 | 19 |
| IV-*C-b* . . . . . . . | 29.65±1.28 | 28.27 | 25.51 | 8.0 | 27.0 | 38 |
| V-*C-b* . . . . . . . . | 28.18±1.70 | 28.60 | 29.44 | 7.6 | 27.0 | 19 |
| VI-*C-b* . . . . . . . | 30.63±2.17 | 30.85 | 31.29 | 8.4 | 27.4 | 14 |
| | *(Tribolium castaneum)* | | | | | |
| I-*C-c* . . . . . . . . . | 38.25±1.53 | 37.91 | 37.23 | 9.7 | 25.4 | 39 |
| II-*C-c* . . . . . . . . | 9.52±0.85 | 8.58 | 6.70 | 3.3 | 34.7 | 14 |
| III-*C-c* . . . . . . . | 50.11±3.40 | 51.26 | 53.56 | 15.2 | 30.3 | 19 |
| IV-*C-c* . . . . . . . | 18.79±1.32 | 18.18 | 16.96 | 5.9 | 31.4 | 19 |
| V-*C-c* . . . . . . . . | 45.15±2.77 | 45.85 | 47.25 | 12.4 | 27.5 | 19 |
| VI-*C-c* . . . . . . . | 2.63±0.36 | 2.65 | 2.69 | 1.4 | 53.2 | 14 |

to make quite an instructive point when discussing the relation between Treatment VI and interspecies competition.

The data summarizing mean total population density computed in the fashion described earlier are set forth in Table 13.2. It will be noted from the right-hand column of the table that in three instances the numbers exceed the replication reported in Table 13.1. This was achieved wherever possible by adding experimental populations which became controls and were censused as such for long periods after one species had become eliminated.

Let us first examine the relation of Treatments to *T. confusum*. From

Table 13.2 it can be seen that the order of effect in terms of density is as follows:

$$I > III > VI > IV > V > II.$$

The equilibrium value achieved in Treatment I is significantly higher than those for any of the other conditions and that for II is significantly lower. All combinations of differences between Treatments III, VI, IV, and V could readily be accounted for by accidents of sampling, although this, of course, does not deny that some differences (e.g., III minus V) could be real and caused by different interactions within the vials. These definite conclusions seem permissible:

1. Relative to Treatments there are three levels of effect on population density.
2. Greatest density is sustained at 34° and 70 per cent (I).
3. By keeping temperature constant but lowering humidity by 50 per cent (in II; 34°, 30 per cent), the equilibrium value is significantly reduced from 41.15 to 23.73, or 42 per cent. In short, the extremes occur at the same temperature, this suggesting that moisture content of the medium is of prime significance at this temperature.
4. The intermediate density level ranges from 32.94 to 28.18 beetles per gram. This is displayed, irrespectively, by cohorts maintained at 29° and/or 24°; and at 70 per cent and/or 30 per cent.

The populational behavior of *T. castaneum* diverges from that of *T. confusum* in two distinct ways. First, this species reacts differently to the Treatments. And, second, it is capable of producing much higher, and much lower, densities. Arranging, again, the Treatments in order of descending effect, we see the following:

$$III > V > I > IV > II > VI.$$

Of the fifteen possible combinations of mean differences, all are significant except that between III and V (4.96 ± 4.38). The statistical tests are not, of course, independent. This is in sharp relief to the situation for *T. confusum*, where only nine of the fifteen couplets were significant and suggests immediately that *T. castaneum*, as a species population, is more responsive to the environmental conditions established in the laboratory.

From the above it follows that there are five, rather than three, levels of density described by the *T. castaneum* data and, further, that the decrements between levels are of greater magnitude. The principal ecological point which immediately strikes the eye, and which is quite at variance with the *T. confusum* findings, is the role played by humidity. It is evident that the three "high-producing Treatments" are those with 70 per cent r.h. (III, V, I); and contrariwise (IV, II, VI). Also, there is a large difference between the lowest of the high triplet and the highest of the low triplet as seen from the subtraction: I-*C-c* minus IV-*C-c* = 38.25 − ·18.79 = 19.46 ± 2.02. There are, as well, significant temperature effects, and their relations, in descending order, are

$$\begin{array}{ccccccc} 29° & > & 24° & > & \Big| 34° & > & \Big| 29° & > & \Big|, 34° & > & \Big| 24° \\ (70\%) & & (70\%) & & (70\%) & & (30\%) & & (30\%) & & (30\%) \end{array},$$

of which all differences but the first two have strong statistical validity. The homologous presentation for *T. confusum*, it will be remembered, was

$$\begin{array}{ccccccc} 34° & > & \Big| 29° & > & 24° & > & 29° & > & 24° & > & \Big| 34° \\ (70\%) & & (70\%) & & (30\%) & & (30\%) & & (70\%) & & (30\%) \end{array},$$

the significant levels being indicated by vertical lines.

TABLE 13.3

PERCENTAGE REDUCTION IN MEAN
DENSITY FOR EACH SPECIES
OWING TO TREATMENT*

| *Tribolium confusum* | | *Tribolium castaneum* | |
|---|---|---|---|
| Treatment | Per Cent Reduction | Treatment | Per Cent Reduction |
| I | 0% | III | 0% |
| III | $s$ <br> $-20\%$ | V | $ns$ <br> $-9.9\%$ |
| VI | $ns$ <br> $-25.6\%$ | I | $s$ <br> $-23.7\%$ |
| IV | $ns$ <br> $-28\%$ | IV | $s$ <br> $-62.5\%$ |
| V | $ns$ <br> $-31.5\%$ | II | $s$ <br> $-81.0\%$ |
| II | $s$ <br> $-42.3\%$ | VI | $s$ <br> $-94.8\%$ |

* $s$ = significant difference between couplets; $ns$ = nonsignificant difference.

It is also meaningful to examine the Treatments as they affect percentage decline in numbers rather than in terms of average densities. This appears as Table 13.3. Treatments result in less than 50 per cent reduction in density for *T. confusum*, while *T. castaneum* declines, stepwise, to $-95$ per cent. For the former species the first significant threshold (between I and III) is $-20$ per cent; for the latter, −24 per cent (between III and I); and both percentages are of similar magnitude. *T. confusum* shows one other significant break between V and II—this being accompanied by a decrease in density of −10.8 per cent. *T. castaneum*, on the other hand, shows four more such breaks, and these are, in order, −13.8 per cent (i.e., I minus V), −38.8 per cent, −18.5 per cent, and −13.8 per cent. The really large difference, that of −38.8 per cent, occurs between IV and I primarily in response to change in the humidity component.

Having examined the effect of Treatments on the two species considered independently, it is now relevant to set forth briefly the differences between species within each of the six Treatments. This information is summarized below along with the percentages that the smaller densities are of the larger densities.

Treatment I:    *T. confusum* > *T. castaneum* (92.9 per cent) (nonsignificant)
Treatment II:   *T. confusum* > *T. castaneum* (40.1 per cent) (significant)
Treatment III:  *T. castaneum* > *T. confusum* (65.7 per cent) (significant)
Treatment IV:   *T. confusum* > *T. castaneum* (63.4 per cent) (significant)
Treatment V:    *T. castaneum* > *T. confusum* (62.4 per cent) (significant)
Treatment VI:   *T. confusum* > *T. castaneum* (8.6 per cent) (significant)

To bring into greater relief the roles played by temperature and humidity, the same findings can be rearranged as follows:

| r.h. | Temperature | | |
|---|---|---|---|
| | 34° | 29° | 24° |
| 70 per cent....... | $b>c$ (*ns*) | $c>b$ (*s*) | $c>b$ (*s*) |
| 30 per cent....... | $b>c$ (*s*) | $b>c$ (*s*) | $b>c$ (*s*) |

With the exception of Treatment I, each of the physical environments significantly favors one species over the other when mean population density is used as the criterion. There are two instances for which *T. castaneum* is so favored and three for *T. confusum*. Relative to each other, *T. castaneum* fares better in high humidity and *T. confusum* in low humidity. The maximum percentage reduction between species occurs, as expected, in Treatment VI (−91.4); the next in Treatment II (−59.9). Treatments III, IV, and V reduce in each case the density of the less productive species by about one-third.

In summary, we can conclude that the physical environment, as specifically defined by these values of temperature and humidity, imposes, through the mediation of *intra*species competition, equilibria characteristic of both the species and the Treatment.

The foregoing review of the single-species populations establishes the relation between conditions and density and the levels at which these relations are statistically significant. One thing it does not do, however, is to assess that potential source of variability owing to *treatment interaction* as this term is understood by the statistician. Since this may be an important component of the total variation, some effort has been spent in its evaluation by application of analysis of variance to the control data.

It will be remembered (Table 13.1) that the replication of Treatment VI was 15 instead of 20. Before doing the analysis of variance, it was expedient to reduce the $N$ of other Treatments to 15—a reduction which achieves a total $N$ of 90 per species with equal numerical distribution among Treatments. This was accomplished by separately randomizing each group of populations and subsequently eliminating the requisite number of vials. Such procedure sacrifices replication, of course, but, as we shall see, the loss is negligible as it affects interpretation of the data.

To this date, 21 different analyses, out of a projected computation schedule of 38, have been worked through. Since we are arbitrarily limiting discussion in this paper to total population density for the period of observation and since the major reason for introducing the analysis of variance is to evaluate "interaction," our presentation will be limited to the following three components:

1. *T. confusum;* total population; total period.
2. *T. castaneum;* total population; total period.
3. *T. confusum + T. castaneum;* total population; total period.

The findings are summarized in Tables 13.4 and 13.5.

From Table 13.4 we note, happily, that the discrepancies among replicates are small for both species; in fact, they can be considered as identical to all intents and purposes. *T. castaneum* responds more vigorously to "Treatments" than does *T. confusum* as suggested by its much larger mean square. The interesting aspect, however, comes to light when the two species are compared relative to Treatment breakdown. This can be shown as follows:

|  | *T. confusum* | *T. castaneum* |
|---|---|---|
| (T) | No significant effect | Large effect |
| (H) | Large effect | Massive effect |
| (T×H) | Large effect | Slight (but real) effect |

The above tabulation adds a worth-while refinement to our earlier discussion. We then knew for *T. confusum* that humidity at certain temperatures significantly affected density (e.g., I; cf. II). This is now substantiated, but the point added is that this species, while not especially sensitive to temperature acting alone, is very responsive to the interaction of temperature and humidity. The summary for *T. castaneum* reinforces our prior knowledge about the outstanding role of humidity and the effect of temperature but adds the fact that, while interaction is real, its impact is relatively minor. In sum, the two species *considered as populations* respond rather differently to the Treatment components.

TABLE 13.4

ANALYSIS OF VARIANCE. TOTAL PERIOD: TOTAL
POPULATION: SPECIES SEPARATELY

| Source of Variation | d.f. | | Sum of Squares | Mean Square | P% |
|---|---|---|---|---|---|
| | | | *Tribolium confusum* | | |
| Total..................... | 89 | | 6699.72 | 75.28 | |
| Treatments.............. | 5 | | 3880.06 | 776.12 | |
| Temperatures........... | | 2 | 148.97 | 74.48 | >5% |
| Humidities.............. | | 1 | 1254.92 | 1254.92 | <1% |
| Temperature×Humidity.. | | 2 | 2476.17 | 1238.08 | <1% |
| Discrepance.............. | 84 | | 2819.66 | 33.57 | |
| | | | *Tribolium castaneum* | | |
| Total..................... | 89 | | 32652.71 | 366.88 | |
| Treatments.............. | 5 | | 29565.72 | 5913.14 | |
| Temperatures........... | | 2 | 2586.51 | 1293.25 | <1% |
| Humidities.............. | | 1 | 26298.09 | 26298.09 | <1% |
| Temperature×Humidity.. | | 2 | 681.12 | 340.56 | <1% |
| Discrepance.............. | 84 | | 3086.99 | 36.75 | |

Table 13.5 amalgamates the control data for the two species; doubles thereby the amount of replication ($N = 180$); and specifies further the breakdown of Treatments by adding a "between species" category, two first-order interactions ("species by temperature" and "species by humidity"), and one second-order interaction ("temperature by species by humidity").

The principal conclusion advanced in Table 13.5 is the important one that all sources of variation are significant. That is to say, every Treatment-component affects equilibrium density when the data are assembled in this way. In addition, the levels of significance are high. The largest $F$ value, of 551.21, is seen for humidity—a figure of prodigious size. The smallest $F$ value, that for T × H, is 6.29, well above the 1 per cent *P* value of 4.75. If the Treatment components are arranged in descending order of *F* values, the tabulation is as follows:

1. Humidity (555.21)
2. Species × humidity (228.44)
3. Temperature × species × humidity (38.61)
4. Temperature (24.25)
5. Species × temperature (14.64)
6. Between species (13.80)
7. Temperature × humidity (6.29)

TABLE 13.5

ANALYSIS OF VARIANCE. TOTAL PERIOD: TOTAL
POPULATION: SPECIES COMBINED

| Source of Variation | d.f. | Sum of Squares | Mean Square | P% |
|---|---|---|---|---|
| Total..................... | 179 | 39837.82 | 222.56 | |
| Treatments.............. | 11 | 33931.17 | 3084.65 | |
| Between species......... | 1 | 485.39 | 485.39 | <1% |
| Temperature............. | 2 | 1705.60 | 852.80 | <1% |
| Humidity............... | 1 | 19521.20 | 19521.20 | <1% |
| S×T.................... | 2 | 1029.88 | 514.94 | <1% |
| S×H.................... | 1 | 8031.81 | 8031.81 | <1% |
| T×H.................... | 2 | 442.55 | 221.28 | <1% |
| T×S×H............... | 2 | 2714.74 | 1357.37 | <1% |
| Discrepance............. | 168 | 5906.65 | 35.16 | |

## SUMMARY FOR CONTROL POPULATION

The following seven points are advanced in major summary of the preceding section devoted to single-species, control populations. It should be emphasized again that all these conclusions are derived exclusively from study of total-population "equilibria" as this was defined earlier.

1. Both species persist indefinitely in all Treatments with the exception of *T. castaneum* in Treatment VI (24°; 30 per cent).
2. The species respond differently to different Treatments:

   *a)* For *T. confusum* density is reduced by Treatments in descending order as follows:

   I | III  VI  IV  V | II ,

   the levels of significant difference being indicated by vertical lines.

   *b)* For *T. castaneum* the order is

   III  V | I | IV | II | VI .

3. *T. castaneum* is greatly affected by humidity. The lower humidity (30 per cent) invariably results in lowered population densities. It also responds to temperature but to a lesser degree.

4. *T. confusum* responds significantly to humidity but in less marked fashion. It is not as markedly affected by temperature per se but reacts strongly to the "interaction" of temperature with humidity.

5. In both absolute and relative terms, *T. castaneum* achieves larger, as well as smaller, populations than does *T. confusum*. This depends on the specific values of temperature and humidity.

6. Within each Treatment one species is significantly favored over the other with the exception of Treatment I (34°; 70 per cent), which is equally favorable for both.

7. Analysis of Variance discloses that *Tribolium* is sensitive to various first-order and second-order interactions among the Treatment components.

## THE MIXED-SPECIES POPULATIONS

Having examined certain of the relations between Treatments and control cultures, we now are prepared to extend the problem by considering *interspecies* competition. In passing from the level of the single-species to the mixed-species population, we obviously introduce an ecologically more complicated phenomenon. More specifically, we ask these two questions: Does such competition exist in fact, and, if so, what are its end-results as measured by the behavior of each of the competitor populations?

Before turning to the data, it seems advisable to set forth the issue in formal terms. We are confronted with two species living together in a spatially and temporally defined habitat from which is excluded all emigration and immigration. On purely logical grounds, the question arises as to what are the various possible consequences of continued competition in such a system. These are listed below, using *B* to refer to *T. confusum* and *C* for *T. castaneum*. In order to associate the possibilities with actualities, those propositions that find empirical realization in the present study are so designated by a statement contained within parentheses.

1. Species *B and C* co-exist indefinitely. (*Not realized*)
2. Species *B and C* become extinct. (*Not realized*)
3. Species *B or C* persist on an even chance basis among the replicates (i.e., survival of *B* only in 50 per cent of the cultures; and contrariwise). (*Not realized*)
4. Species *B* persists in *all* replicates; *C* becomes extinct. (*Realized in VI*)
5. Species *C* persists in *all* replicates; *B* becomes extinct. (*Realized in I*)
6. Species *B* persists in *most* replicates; *C* persists in *remaining* replicates. (*Realized in II, IV, and V*)
7. Species *C* persists in *most* replicates; *B* persists in *remaining* replicates. (*Realized in III*)

Of these seven possibilities, all but the first three find actual demonstration in the data of this study.

Successful persistence of both species (proposition 1) is not factually corroborated. This, a negative finding, is in harmony with usual reasoning about the assumed proportionality between degree of ecological similarity and intensity of competition. That is to say, it would not be expected that *T. confusum* and *T. castaneum* could share indefinitely the same habitat, since both are in stringent competition.

Extinction of both species (proposition 2) would be an unreasonable, though perhaps not impossible, event on the basis of knowledge derived from the controls. There, successful persistence of both forms living by themselves was the rule, with Treatments favoring one or the other. On such grounds it would be anticipated that competition would invariably permit one species to survive, not both to die.

Proposition 3 is included to suggest that chance alone could be the factor determining the outcome of competition. Under this idea the two species would be so evenly balanced that in one half of the replicates *T. confusum* would win and in the other half, *T. castaneum*. This situation also is not confirmed by the data.

There thus remain four propositions which do enjoy empirical substantiation. Propositions 4 and 6 share in common the fact that *T. confusum* is the "stronger" species. Propositions 5 and 7 disclose *T. castanoum* to be the stronger. Propositions 4 and 5 share in common the fact that the winning species is successful in *all* replicates. Propositions 6 and 7 disclose that one species wins more frequently but exceptions occur. To state it differently: Two categories of consequences are evident which may be termed "one-way" and "alternative." The former refers to 100 per cent persistence of one species among replicates within any one Treatment; the latter, to a greater persistence of one species but some persistence of the other. Finally, it is to be noted that the specific end-result of competition varies with the Treatment, but, irrespective of all else, extinction inexorably occurs in all 170 experimental populations!

In presenting the findings for the experimental cultures, it is again necessary drastically to limit discussion. The one aspect that seems best adapted to the objectives of this paper is the relation between Treatments and species elimination. This ignores the density relations of the two species during the interval prior to final elimination. Such relations are obviously involved in causation. But their elaboration necessarily would be detailed, and, while this will form the core of the definitive publication, it seems realistic essentially to exclude it here. In this report our interest lies, not in comprehensive documentation of a research program, but, rather, in broad illustration of an ecological problem by means of selected facts. The logic involved throughout runs as follows: control cultures persist; experimental cultures do not; experimental cultures differ only in that they add interspecies competition to the ecosystem; therefore, elimination is both the biological consequence and the index of interspecies competition. This reasoning demands modification for *T. castaneum* in Treatment VI—a modification later to be advanced.

If required, the reader may refresh his memory about the design of the mixed-species populations by reference to Table 13.1. In recollection, it can be said that these were maintained in all six relations of temperature and humidity; that no differences in husbandry, medium, or manipulation obtained; and that replication was greater than for controls. As mentioned earlier, when an experimental culture was censused, the adult beetles were

TABLE 13.6

CONSEQUENCES OF INTERSPECIES COMPETITION
IN TERMS OF EXTINCTION AND RELA-
TIVE TO TREATMENTS

| Treat-ment | Type of Effect | Species Favored | Per Cent of Replicates in Which Favored Species Wins | Per Cent of Replicates in Which Unfavored Species Wins |
|---|---|---|---|---|
| I...... | One-way | *T. castaneum* | 100 | 0 |
| II...... | Alternative | *T. confusum* | 90 | 10 |
| III..... | Alternative | *T. castaneum* | 86 | 14 |
| IV..... | Alternative | *T. confusum* | 87 | 13 |
| V...... | Alternative | *T. confusum* | 71 | 29 |
| VI..... | One-way | *T. confusum* | 100 | 0 |

examined microscopically in order to determine their species. This was continued as a precautionary measure for 90 days (three censuses) after each extinction to be certain the form presumed extinct did not reappear. A technical liability of *Tribolium* is that the immature stages cannot be differentiated relative to species. This means that, while counts of immatures were made just as for controls, the criterion of species numbers had to be restricted to the adult census, although it is possible arithmetically to estimate by species the larval and pupal components in experimental populations as Park (1948) has shown.

In setting forth the relation between Treatments, type of effect, and species extinction, Table 13.6 serves as a qualitative description of the entire group of mixed-species cultures. The table immediately documents the fact of competition and apportions its end-results among Treatments. It is to be seen that there are two one-way situations and four alternative situations.

The one-way effects are described by the complete persistence of *T. cas-*

*taneum* in high-temperature high-humidity and the complete persistence of *T. confusum* in low-temperature low-humidity. Thus, this change in these physical conditions totally reverses the outcome. One could claim with cogency that extinction in Treatment VI is not the result of the prevailing pressure of *T. confusum* on *T. castaneum*, since the latter is unsuccessful in this Treatment when living alone. This of course is true. But the interesting point to be made here is the suggestion that such competition apparently *hastens* the demise of *T. castaneum* in the twenty experimental populations when compared with the fifteen controls. The control replicates had a mean life-span of 350.0 ± 34.1 days. Co-living with *T. confusum*, however, *T. castaneum* persists only 271.5 ± 18.1 days, about three-fourths as long. The mean difference is 78.5 ± 38.6 days, and, since it is two times its standard error and in a reasonable direction, it strikes a note of reality. Owing to the "accident" that *T. castaneum* is unable to tolerate for many successive generations the environment of VI, we are in a position to hypothesize that interspecies competition adds a temporal effect in terms of extinction even when the habitat is physiologically unsuited for survival. An inference of this sort could not be derived from the other Treatments.

Several points about elimination pattern merit brief summary when alternative effects are in force. In the first place, all percentages listed in Table 13.6 depart significantly from an expectation of $\frac{1}{2}:\frac{1}{2}$ as tested by point-binomial. The closest conformity to this proportion is seen in Treatment V, but even here the difference is 2.3 × its standard error. Therefore, chance (proposition 3) may be excluded as the factor primarily determining whether one (or the other) species survives (or dies) among a particular group of replicates. In Treatments II, IV, and V *T. confusum* is the usual winner. Treatment III characteristically favors *T. castaneum*. For Treatments II, III, and IV, the favored, and unfavored, species persist to about the same frequencies (viz., 88 per cent : 12 per cent, approximately). As has been shown, the winning species type is not at such great advantage in V (71 per cent), although this advantage is obviously quite real.

The discussion of Treatment III can be strengthened by inclusion of findings taken from two other independent studies. Park (1948) competed these two flour beetles in 29° C., and 70 per cent r.h., and Kennington (1953) did likewise. The first report had *T. castaneum* the victor in 12 of 18 replicates (67 per cent); the second, in 19 of 20 replicates (95 per cent). Lumping the data of all three studies, and gaining thereby the impressive replication of 66, it is seen that in 55 instances *T. castaneum* survives (83 per cent) to be contrasted with 11 instances (17 per cent) for *T. confusum*. Thus, though the percentages differ somewhat, there is no doubt but that (*a*) the events are truly "alternative" in the sense defined and that (*b*) *T. castaneum* is the usual survivor.

## COMPARISON OF CONTROL AND EXPERIMENTAL POPULATIONS

This, the final section, is devoted to a contrast of control with experimental populations. The criteria used are population persistence and equilibrium densities for the controls and extinction-pattern and species-extinction-frequency for the experimentals. The findings are advanced, not only as a general summary, but also as a device to illustrate, at firsthand from the present data, certain hazards involved in extrapolation from one level of ecological organization (intraspecies population) to a distinctly more complex level (interspecies population). It should be made clear that the intent here is not to interject a note of mysticism. Most probably, if causation were better understood for the control cultures, the usual and exceptional events described by the experimentals could be more precisely anticipated. Also, it is quite possible that the criterion of control performance adopted (mean density) is not the best one to use in comparing the two population levels. After all, density is the end-expression of many interactions within the vials. If one selected certain meaningful interactions (e.g., fertility and egg-cannibalism) and utilized these in analysis, the predictability might be fulfilled in greater measure. Despite these admitted limitations, however, the notions now to be advanced do seem to have a certain theoretical interest.

The essential information, stripped to a bare minimum, is presented in Table 13.7. Before going ahead it seems desirable to explain the anatomy of the table in order that its content may be readily understood. The first column specifies the six Treatments. Then, the table is separated into two major parts pertaining respectively to controls and experimentals. Column 2 (for controls) shows which species, when living alone, maintained the higher density (above the horizontal line) and which the lower (below the horizontal line). Column 3 lists the percentage reductions exhibited by the lower-density species, taking for each Treatment the higher species as 100 per cent, and column 4 is concerned with the validity of such differences with $t > 2$ adopted as the level of significance. Column 5 (for experimentals) notes above the line that species which usually, or always, wins along with its percentage survival among replicates. The same information for the species which survived less frequently appears below the line. Explanation of column 6 (evaluation) is best deferred momentarily.

With the fact of competition and its consequences empirically established, it remains only to draw certain inferences about the behavior of experimental populations as this may be related to the behavior of controls. In approaching the problem, we ask of the data nine questions and then apportion the answers among the facts. In formulation of these questions the terms "expected" and "nonexpected" are used in this sense: If, say, one species is favored over the other when the two are not in competition but under identical Treatment, then the a priori expectation when competition exists is that the same species will remain at advantage in the same Treatment. This, by definition, constitutes an "expected" result; its obverse, a "nonexpected" result.

The nine questions, distributed among three categories, are as follows:

*Category 1:* Is the result expected (1), unexpected (1'), or not predictable (1'')?
*Category 2:* Is the result frequent (2), infrequent (2'), or unique (one-way) (2'')?
*Category 3:* Does the result enforce the control trend (3), contradict it (3'), or is it nondeterminable (3'')?

TABLE 13.7

COMPARISON OF CONTROL AND EXPERIMENTAL POPULATIONS
(For Discussion See Text)

| Treat-ment | Single-Species Populations | | | | Mixed-Species Populations | |
|---|---|---|---|---|---|---|
| | Higher Density _____ Lower Density | Per Cent Reduction of Smaller Density | *t*-Values between Species Densities | | Usual Winner (%) _____ Occasional Winner (%) | "Evaluation" (See Text) |
| I | *T. confusum* (41.15) _____ *T. castaneum* (38.28) | − 7.1 | 0.8 | | *T. castaneum* (100%) _____ None (0%) | 1'' 2'' 3'' ///////// |
| II | *T. confusum* (23.73) _____ *T. castaneum* (9.52) | −59.9 | 9.5 | | *T. confusum* (90%) _____ *T. castaneum* (10%) | 1  2  3 1' 2' 3' |
| III | *T. castaneum* (50.11) _____ *T. confusum* (32.94) | −34.3 | 4.4 | | *T. castaneum* (86%) _____ *T. confusum* (14%) | 1  2  3 1' 2' 3' |
| IV | *T. confusum* (29.65) _____ *T. castaneum* (18.79) | −36.6 | 5.9 | | *T. confusum* (87%) _____ *T. castaneum* (13%) | 1  2  3 1' 2' 3' |
| V | *T. castaneum* (45.15) _____ *T. confusum* (28.18) | −37.6 | 5.2 | | *T. confusum* (71%) _____ *T. castaneum* (29%) | 1'  2  3' 1  2' 3 |
| VI | *T. confusum* (30.63) _____ *T. castaneum* (2.63) | −91.4 | 12.7 | | *T. confusum* (100%) _____ None (0%) | 1  2'' 3 ///////// |

The notations in parentheses refer to the numerals in the evaluation column of Table 13.7.

If species relations are ignored, and attention focused exclusively on evaluation, certain trends are clearly discernible. Treatments II, III, and IV exhibit the identical pattern of 1, 2, 3/1', 2', 3'. This states that the species favored as a control usually wins when in competition, or, differently put, that competition characteristically enforces the trend to such a degree that one species survives while the other becomes extinct. But a complete reversal of this occurs about 12 per cent of the time. Here, competition contradicts the control trend, thereby causing the survival, and extinction, of opposite species.

The three remaining Treatments (I, V, VI) differ qualitatively from each other and from those just discussed. Take Treatment I (1″, 2″, 3″). *T. confusum* builds slightly larger densities in the controls, but the difference is negligible and without statistical validity. Perhaps the most logical forecast from this fact is that the two species would display 50:50 persistence among the experimental replicates. Yet, when the beetles are together, *T. castaneum invariably* wins. In this case, despite similarity of control performances, *T. castaneum* exerts upon its rival a pressure intense enough always to assure its own success.

In Treatment V (1′, 2, 3′/1, 2′, 3) the story is still different. As controls, *T. castaneum* maintains populations some one-third larger than does *T. confusum*. This leads to the expectation that the former species would be the winner in experimental cultures. This indeed happens, but it is the *unusual* rather than the frequent event. The *usual* finding is for the control trend to be contradicted by competition so that *T. confusum* emerges the winner. This is similar to occurrences in I except that there only one consequence was demonstrable.

Treatment VI (1, 2″, 3) affords the only instance for which prediction from the control to the experimental situation is completely realized. *T. confusum* controls are far superior to *T. castaneum* controls in terms of equilibrium densities. *T. castaneum* never persists in coassociation. However, this conclusion is obfuscated by the fact that *T. castaneum* is physiologically unable to tolerate the physical conditions of 24° C., and 30% r.h., for many successive generations. In other words, Treatment per se, in contradistinction to Treatment plus interspecies competition, induces extinction. But since, as was earlier noted, this species does persist significantly longer by itself than when with *T. confusum*, we are in a position to infer that interspecies competition enforces the control trend by accelerating the death of *T. castaneum*.

These various trends become more tangible if considered in conjunction with the kinds of factors which operate in a *Tribolium* ecosystem. Such factors fall into three general categories—physical environment, population processes, and survival responses—as follows:

I. Physical environment
  A. Temperature
  B. Humidity
  C. Interaction of temperature with humidity

II. Population processes
   A. Cannibalism
   B. "Behavior"
   C. Conditioning of medium
III. Survival responses
   A. Egg fecundity
   B. Egg fertility
   C. Rate and mortality of larval-pupal development
   D. Adult mortality

The factors listed under "physical environment" are self-explanatory. The "population processes" are those activities that emerge from the population's own activity. They achieve causal significance when they influence, in one direction or another, group survival. Thus cannibalism, constituted by the predation of eggs and pupae by large larvae and adults, is a source of mortality and can have real impact on the culture's census history. "Behavior" is important when interaction between beetles affects a response; e.g., crowding reducing fecundity. "Conditioning" refers to the extent to which the medium is altered by the population during the 30-day intercensus interval: an alteration involving nutritive depletion, contamination, and, perhaps, creation of a vial microclimate different from that of the incubator. If and when such conditioning consistently affects a response, it, too, is an item to be reckoned with.

The "survival responses" are those physiological attributes which, when expressed statistically for the group, influence shifts in numbers. They, in short, constitute birth rate and death rate, and all factors affecting the population must ultimately operate through these channels.

These matters are introduced, even though superficially, to suggest the complexity of the causation underlying the phenomena discussed in this paper. We have seen that the two species respond differentially to the physical environment as defined in terms of temperature and humidity. It is certain that for each Treatment this response has both a direct physiological component (autoecological) and a component derived from *intra*species competition (population processes). For example, temperatures affect fecundity of individual females. But superimposed upon this is an effect which varies with time, density, and age distribution. In general terms the rationale takes the form

This nexus permits population persistence at species-specific equilibria. When *inter*species competition is in force, the same rationale holds but is further

complicated by the impact of *T. confusum* on *T. castaneum*, and *T. castaneum* on *T. confusum*, as this is altered by Treatments. Such impact results in the *new* finding of invariable elimination of one species. However, the pattern of extinction (and survival) not only differs between Treatments but also may proceed to alternative consequences within Treatments. Analysis of causation, whether experimental and/or statistical, must proceed along these conceptual lines.

The above evaluation raises numerous questions of obvious intricacy. Study of causation constitutes an analytical extension of the research. The present paper, arbitrarily excluding so many of the basic data, has avoided this phase in order to place the problem in its biological framework and to advance evidence in its documentation. Although some progress has been made in the understanding of causation, I should be guilty of misrepresentation if the impression is left that the web of events in the treatment-control-experimental interaction is understood. This is an avenue for further research.

## ACKNOWLEDGMENT

My first debt is to Marian Burton Frank and Amelia Polnik, who, at successive times, took most efficient charge of the laboratory thus keeping the research continuously under way. I am grateful also to John Le Gay Brereton and Earl R. Rich of the University of Chicago for their critical reading of the manuscript. Others, who have helped in various ways and to whom it is a pleasure to acknowledge my appreciation, are L. C. Birch, T. Burnett, L. C. Cole, Charles Elton, F.R.S., A. E. Emerson, W. T. Federer, P. H. Leslie, Monte Lloyd, L. O. T. Mendes, R. S. Miller, Jerzy Neyman, and D. W. Strawbridge.

# Ecological Communities

Up to this point the papers in this book have dealt with interactions within a population or between populations of two species. As soon as an ecologist looks at more species he is beginning to study an ecological community or ecosystem. All field studies force one to study at least part of an ecosystem since species do not live alone or in two-species pairs.

The first task in this area has been to describe and classify communities. The early pioneers in this were Petersen (1918) and Warming (1909). The most intensive description published so far is that of Elton (1966). By recording the species and ecological events which occurred in habitats in a complex woodland, Elton provided the setting in which to study interactions within a community.

The first sort of community pattern recognized was probably the food chain or food web (Elton, 1927). Its description prompted questions such as what determines the number of trophic levels in a food web (Hutchinson, 1959), what is the amount and efficiency of transfer of energy from one trophic level to the next (Juday, 1940; Lindeman, 1942; Odum, 1957; Engelmann, 1961, 1966; Teal, Selection 30; Slobodkin, 1962; Phillipson, 1966), how is matter cycled through it (Kuenzler, Selection 29), and what proportion of the energy is channeled through the living grazers and carnivores versus through the decomposers (Macfadyen, 1963, 1964; Odum, 1962).

A second pattern which one can recognize is the spatial structure of communities.

Elton (1966) and MacArthur and MacArthur (Selection 26) have made divisions of communities into layers. Grazing of living plants takes place in the upper lighted layer of all communities: forests, grasslands, lakes, or oceans. Decomposer chains are usually in the substrate (Odum, 1962). Mineral nutrients are returned to the upper stratum by the plants on land and by water circulation in lakes and the seas. The regeneration of mineral nutrients by microorganisms in the substrate and medium has been studied by soil and aquatic ecologists (Brock, 1966).

If ecological communities have a spatial structure, how is it developed? When a community is destroyed, it rebuilds itself by a fairly orderly process called "ecological succession." This concept was first developed for terrestrial plant communities by Clements (1916), and has since been elaborated by Whittaker (1953), and extended in a somewhat different form to aquatic systems by Margalef (1963, 1968). Experimental studies of succession are few; in the laboratory there is the pioneering study of Woodruff (1912); in the field, Keever (Selection 22).

Not only is there a spatial structure developed in succession, but also the degree of variety or diversity changes. More different life-forms of plants and animals occur in a forest that in the herbaceous vegetation it succeeded. The number and relative abundance of species also change during succession. Much speculation but little evidence has been offered concerning questions such as does succession lead to a more "stable," complex community; is there a definite set of stages in succession and, if so, what mechanisms determine them; why are some communities more diverse than others; is there a relationship between stability and diversity; etc. Reviews and hypotheses concerning diversity are found in Margalef (1957), MacArthur (1965), Whittaker (1965), MacArthur and Wilson (1967), Pianka (1966) and Sanders (1968). There are difficult problems involved in treating the data bearing on this subject and readers are referred to Pielou (1966) and Lloyd, Inger, and King (1968) for information on diversity indices. Hairston (1959) deals with a variety of approaches to the subject. The kinds of distribution of relative abundances of different species in communities have been discussed by Preston (1962), Williams (1964), and Patrick (1967). Levins (1968), among others, discusses the problem of how species fit together into a community.

Interactions of organisms with the physical, "abiotic" parts of the ecosystem were once considered to be mainly one-way: the physical influencing the biological. However, the formation of soil or bottom ooze, the regeneration and cycling of mineral nutrients, and even the weather itself have been found to be profoundly influenced by the presence and activities of organisms. These effects, together with the concentration of certain chemical elements and compounds, have made it clear how interdependent are the parts of an ecosystem, and how important it is to understand these interrelationships as we modify our environments in our search for a higher standard of living. The type of approach, of seeing the ecosystem as a whole and analyzing it as such, has come to be known as systems ecology (Watt, 1966, 1968). Studies of the effects of pesticides illustrate how interrelated are the parts of the whole ecosystem (Rudd, 1964; Moore, 1967). In the past few years we have begun to realize that, like other species, humans may not be able to live only with a small set of domesticated species of plants, animals, and microbes. For physiological, epidemiological, and economic reasons, as well as for esthetic

ones, we may need to live within or near complex ecological communities.

J.H.C.
W.W.M.

### LITERATURE CITED

Brock, T. D. 1966. *Principles of Microbial Ecology.* Prentice-Hall, Englewood Cliffs, N.J. 306 pp.

Clements, F. E. 1916. Plant succession. Carnegie Institution of Washington Publication *242:* 1-512.

Elton, C. S. 1927. *Animal Ecology.* Sidgewick and Jackson, London.

Elton, C. S. 1966. *The Pattern of Animal Communities.* Wiley, New York. 432 pp.

Engelmann, M. D. 1961. The role of soil arthropods in the energetics of an old field community. Ecological Monographs *31:* 221-238.

Engelmann, M. D. 1966. Energetics, terrestrial field studies and animal productivity. Advances in Ecological Research *3:* 73-115.

Hairston, N. G. 1959. Species abundance and community organization. Ecology *40:* 404-416.

Hutchinson, G. E. 1959. Homage to Santa Rosalia or why are there so many different kinds of animals. American Naturalist *93:* 145-159.

Juday, C. 1940. The annual energy budget of an inland lake. Ecology *21:* 438-450.

Levins, Richard. 1968. *Evolution in Changing Environments.* Princeton Univ. Press, Princeton, N.J. 120 pp.

Lindeman, R. L. 1942. The trophic-dynamic aspect of ecology. Ecology *23:* 399-418.

Lloyd, M., R. F. Inger, and F. W. King. 1968. On the diversity of reptile and amphibian species in a Bornean rain forest. American Naturalist *102:* 497-515.

MacArthur, R. H. 1965. Patterns of species diversity. Biological Reviews *40:* 510-533.

MacArthur, R. H., and E. O. Wilson. 1967. *The Theory of Island Biogeography.* Princeton Univ. Press, Princeton, N.J. 203 pp.

MacFadyen, A. 1963. *Animal Ecology: Aims and Methods.* 2nd ed. Pitman, New York. 344 pp.

MacFadyen, A. 1964. Energy flow in ecosystems and its exploitation by grazing. In *Grazing in Terrestrial and Marine Environments.* D. J. Crisp, Ed. Blackwell, Oxford. pp. 3-20.

Margalef, R. 1957. La teoría de la información en ecología. Memorias de la real academia de ciencias y artes (Barcelona) *33:* 373-449. (English translation in General Systems Yearbook No. 3).

Margalef, R. 1963. On certain unifying principles in ecology. American Naturalist *97:* 357-374.

Margalef, R. 1968. *Perspectives in Ecological Theory.* Univ. of Chicago Press, Chicago. 111 pp.

MOORE, N. W. 1967. A synopsis of the pesticide problem. Advances in Ecological Research 4: 75-129.

ODUM, E. P. 1962. Relationships between structure and function in ecosystems. Japanese Journal of Ecology 12: 108-118.

ODUM, H. T. 1957. Trophic structure and productivity of Silver Springs, Florida. Ecological Monographs 27: 55-112.

PATRICK, R. 1967. The effect of invasion rate, species pool, and size of area on the structure of the diatom community. Proceedings of the National Academy of Science 58: 1335-1342.

PETERSEN, C. G. J. 1918. The sea bottom and its production of fish-food. Report of the Danish Biological Station 1918: 1-62.

PHILLIPSON, J. 1966. Ecological Energetics. St. Martin's Press, New York, 57 pp.

PIANKA, E. R. 1966. Latitudinal gradients in species diversity: A review of concepts. American Naturalist 100: 33-46.

PIELOU, E. C. 1966. The measurement of diversity in different types of biological collections. Journal of Theoretical Biology 13: 131-144.

PRESTON, F. W. 1962. The canonical distribution of commonness and rarity. Ecology 43: 185-215, 410-432.

RUDD, R. L. 1964. Pesticides and the Living Landscape. Univ. of Wisconsin Press, Madison. 320 pp.

SANDERS, H. L. 1968. Marine benthic diversity: A comparative study. American Naturalist 102: 243-282.

SLOBODKIN, L. B. 1962. Energy in animal ecology. Advances in Ecological Research 1: 69-101.

WARMING, E. 1909. Oecology of Plants, An Introduction to the Study of Plant Communities (Translated by P. Groom and I. Balfour). Clarendon Press, Oxford.

WATT, K. E. F. 1966. Systems Analysis in Ecology. Academic Press, New York. 276 pp.

WATT, K. E. F. 1968. Ecology and Resource Management: A Quantitative Approach. McGraw-Hill, New York. 450 pp.

WHITTAKER, R. H. 1953. A consideration of climax theory: the climax as a population and pattern. Ecological Monographs 23: 41-78.

WHITTAKER, R. H. 1965. Dominance and diversity in land plant communities. Science 147: 250-260.

WILLIAMS, C. B. 1964. Patterns in the Balance of Nature. Academic Press, New York. 324 pp.

WOODRUFF, L. L. 1912. Observations on the origin and sequence of the protozoan fauna of hay infusions. Journal of Experimental Zoology 12: 205-264.

[Reprinted from ECOLOGICAL MONOGRAPHS, **20**: 229-250. July, 1950]

# CAUSES OF SUCCESSION ON OLD FIELDS OF THE PIEDMONT, NORTH CAROLINA

## INTRODUCTION

### REVIEW OF LITERATURE ON OLD FIELD SUCCESSION IN THE PIEDMONT OF NORTH CAROLINA

#### SEQUENCE OF SUCCESSION

Several studies of the succession of plants following abandonment of farm land in the Piedmont of North Carolina have been made during the last fifteen years. Much of the emphasis in these studies has been placed on the arborescent stages involving pine as the original arborescent invader and its gradual replacement by climax oaks and hickories. Only two studies have dealt with details of the herbaceous stages of succession which almost always precede pine. Crafton & Wells (1934) discuss the early stages of succession based on general observations, quadrat studies of several communities on different types of soil, and on invasion of plants into spaded squares. Oosting (1942) gives quantitative data based on quadrat counts in fifteen fields of the first three years of abandonment, as well as extensive data on the arborescent stages of succession. There is general agreement, with only minor variations, on the sequence of dominating species in the early herbaceous stages of succession.

Crabgrass (*Digitaria sanguinalis* (L.) Scop.) usually is dominant in fields in the late summer and fall following cultivation. During the first year of abandonment of a field horseweed (*Leptilon canadense* L.) and crabgrass are almost always dominant; but horseweed, being a plant four to six feet tall, is the conspicuous species. Occasionally ragweed (*Ambrosia elatior* L.) is present in large enough numbers to share dominance with horseweed and crabgrass. On badly eroded fields *Diodia teres* Walt. and *Aristida dichotoma* Michx. are often the dominant plants, at least locally. During the second year following abandonment, crabgrass and horseweed are still present, but the horseweed plants are only about six inches tall and are hardly noticeable among the four- to six-foot asters (*Aster pilosus* Willd.) that are usually dominant in such fields. On eroded second-year fields, aster may be entirely absent, and some combination of ragweed, Diodia and *Plantago aristata* Michx. may be dominant. The third year following abandonment broomsedge (usually *Andropogon virginicus* L.) assumes dominance which it maintains until replaced by pine, the seedlings of which may appear among the broomsedge as early as the third year. Pines may be taller than the broomsedge by the fifth year, and form closed stands in ten to fifteen years.

Apparently the type of soil, if it is not eroded, has little influence on the sequence or duration of these early stages of succession, and most abandoned fields in the Piedmont of North Carolina are dominated in turn by crabgrass, horseweed, aster, broomsedge, and then the first arborescent plant, pine.

#### CAUSES OF SUCCESSION

Some work has been done dealing with the causes of old field succession in the Piedmont of North Carolina. Coile (1940) concluded that no changes in soil characteristics appear to be related in a causal manner to loblolly pine succession; the invasion of pine into abandoned land is related to the coincidence of a good seed year and climatic conditions favorable to early development of seedlings. He says that the decline of pine dominance at the end of one generation is caused by the failure of pine seedlings to compete with established forest vegetation for soil moisture and nutrients because of differences in habit of root growth between pines and hardwoods. Oosting and Kramer (1946) found the available water at the margins of forests, where several species of pines become established, to be as low as within the stands where pine seedlings make little growth. They concluded that light is probably more significantly controlling than soil moisture in the establishment of pines under forest stands.

Crafton & Wells (1943) suggest that one of the keys to the causes of early stages of old field succession lies in the water relations. They consider why crabgrass precedes broomsedge in succession, and conclude, from greenhouse experiments and field observations, that seedlings of crabgrass are more drought resistant than are those of broomsedge; consequently broomsedge does not become dominant until tall weeds form a protective covering for its seedlings. They also suggest that the exclusion of crabgrass and other species from the tall weed communities is caused by their intolerance of low light.

### OBJECTIVES OF PRESENT STUDY

#### THE PROBLEM IN GENERAL

Although these writers touch on causes of early old field succession there remain several questions which must be answered before the particular sequence can be explained adequately. If answers to these questions were available they might be applicable not only to early stages of secondary succession, but might also lead to a better understanding of the causes of succession in general. This study was initiated, therefore, with the broad objective of contributing to our knowledge of the causes of succession. The method was to attack the problem through old field succession as a particular example. Of the species involved, the major dominants of the first three years were given first consideration.

The problem resolved itself into several phases which are well represented by the following questions, then unanswered.

1. Why is horseweed, rather than some other plant, usually dominant in first year fields?
2. Why does horseweed fail to hold dominance more than one year?
3. Why is aster delayed in assuming dominance until the second year?
4. Why does aster fail to hold dominance after the second year?
5. Why is broomsedge delayed in assuming dominance until the third year?

It soon became apparent that progress would require consideration of certain puzzling questions involving minor variations from the normal sequence and duration of the successional stages. Here are the most pertinent ones:

1. Why are a few first-year fields clearly dominated by ragweed with almost complete absence of horseweed?
2. Why does aster occasionally share dominance with horseweed in first-year fields?
3. Why does second-year aster-dominance occasionally persist for an additional year or more?
4. What effect does erosion have on the general pattern of succession?

(The writer is indebted to Dr. H. J. Oosting for suggesting this study and for his advice and assistance.)

### SPECIFIC MATTERS FOR STUDY

To answer the foregoing questions, a number of specific points concerning the life histories of the dominant plants and the environmental factors influencing the survival and growth of these species needed clarification. Although taxonomic manuals indicate the approximate time of flowering of horseweed, aster, and broomsedge, it was not known with certainty when the seeds are fully mature and whether the seemingly mature seeds are capable of immediate germination or require a period of dormancy. Differences in time of maturity and differences in time of germination of seeds of the dominant species might influence the sequence of dominance.

No species can become established and hold its place in a community unless the seedlings can survive and grow to maturity. Species vary as to optimum environmental conditions for survival and growth, and often the conditions that are favorable for germination and early growth are not the most favorable for the later growth of the species. Little was known concerning the survival and growth of the dominant species of old fields. It became necessary, therefore, to determine when and where the seeds germinate under field conditions. A major

question to be answered concerned the dormancy of the seeds of the three dominants, and whether the failure of certain species to become established in old fields is caused by failure of seeds to germinate or by death of seedlings. Again it seemed necessary to learn what environmental conditions permit the seedlings to survive and grow and what conditions inhibit them.

Survival and growth of plants in natural communities are influenced by a number of factors working together in such a way that it is often difficult to determine what conditions separately or in combination cause the end results. Conditions of soil moisture in abandoned fields change with the increase of organic matter in the soil and the protection from evaporation by living plants and litter. A knowledge of the reaction of the particular species to variations in moisture conditions was needed to help answer the general problems of succession. A knowledge of the reaction of each species to the variations in light would help evaluate the effect of decreasing light in old fields on the trend of succession. Such information could best be gained by experimental methods in which all factors except the one being studied could be held as nearly constant as possible.

If horseweed produces some substance that inhibits growth of other horseweeds or stimulates the growth of asters, or if aster produces some substances that cause the decline of asters and stimulates the growth of broomsedge, this might prove to be one of the important causes of the sequence of succession. Such possibilities could best be checked by experiment.

The idea that one plant may produce some chemical compounds which are inhibitory or toxic to other plants was advanced by Pickering & Bedford (1914, 1917, 1919). Davis (1928) called attention to the injurious effects of black walnut on other species. Proebsting & Gilmore (1940) showed that neither exhaustion of plant nutrients or disease carried over from the last orchard could account for the failure of replanted peach orchards to make normal growth, but that peach roots added to virgin soil inhibited the growth of peach seedlings. Benedict (1941) showed that dried roots of bromegrass are inhibitory to bromegrass grown in sand cultures and suggested that an inhibitory substance in the roots may be responsible for the thinning of bromegrass stands after a few years. Bonner & Galston (1944) and Bonner (1946) found that water or nutrient solution in contact with roots of growing guayule plants accumulate substances which are toxic to the growth of guayule seedlings. Went (1942) in his study of annuals that grow near shrubs in the desert of the Southwest, suggested that the occurrence of one plant determines the presence of certain other plants through some unknown agent, presumably chemical. Went's observation that annuals grow near *Encelia farinosa* Gray led Gray & Bonner (1948) to consider the problem of whether or not growth inhibitors do arise from

Encelia plants, and they found that the leaves of Encelia, when placed on top of the sand culture in which tomatoes and other plants were growing, caused a striking inhibition of growth in these plants.

In most cultivated fields in this area harvest of a crop removes much of the aerial portion of the plants; consequently there is a minimum of organic matter in fields when they are abandoned. After a field is abandoned the plants that subsequently invade the area are left undisturbed to fall to the ground and eventually decay. This organic matter may influence the texture, water holding power, pH, and mineral content of the soil, and might contain some chemical substances that would be beneficial or harmful to plants growing in the soil containing it. Little was known concerning the effects of the dead plant parts of one species on the survival and growth of the same species or on other plants. The possibility that dead horseweed parts might inhibit the growth of other horseweed plants, either by producing some toxic substance or by causing an imbalance of minerals, needed to be considered. The effects of organic matter from aster or broomsedge upon other plants also needed to be known before the cause of old field succession could be determined.

Plants in a given community have mutual relationships, and all compete for water, light and available minerals in the soil. The effects of one species competing with individuals of the same species or of other species have been evaluated by a number of investigators. Brenchley (1919) planted mustard plants in pots with one, two, three, four, and five plants to a pot, and in comparing the final dry weights found the total weight of five plants in one pot to be about the same as that of the one plant in a pot. She found growth to be proportional to the amount of minerals in solution. Such knowledge of the effects of competition among dominant species in old field succession seemed necessary to answer some questions concerning the causes of old field succession.

## GENERAL PROCEDURE

### SEED MATURATION AND DORMANCY

A knowledge of as many details as possible of the life cycles of the three major dominants—horseweed, aster, and broomsedge—seemed necessary for an understanding of the causes of the particular sequence of early old field succession. Study of life cycles was begun with studies of seeds of the three species. Plants were observed in the field to determine time of seed maturity. Mature seeds were collected and tested for germination under a variety of conditions to find the elapsed time and environmental conditions affecting germination for each species.

### GERMINATION, SURVIVAL AND GROWTH UNDER FIELD CONDITIONS

Further studies of life cycles, as well as of survival and growth of plants under field conditions, were undertaken by means of a series of permanent quadrats in fields of different ages. List counts of species were made at intervals during a year to determine the number of seeds germinating, the season and environmental conditions of germination, and the number of seedlings living and growing to maturity. A knowledge of the number and kinds of plants growing in each community was gained from these permanent quadrats and this gave information concerning competition among the three dominants and among the dominants and other species.

Observations of permanent quadrats indicated the desirability of obtaining information from a large number of fields that had slightly varied histories. Therefore surveys were made of thirty fields. These surveys involved not only examination of the present vegetation, but talking to the owners or tenants about the last crop, its time of last cultivation, and the amount of erosion in such fields.

In connection with the permanent quadrats and field surveys, a number of individuals of the three species were measured to help evaluate the amount of growth made by the plants at different ages and under different field conditions.

### FACTORS INFLUENCING SURVIVAL AND GROWTH

Experiments were conducted in the greenhouse to determine the effects of variations of water and light on the survival and growth of the three dominants. Seedlings of each species were grown with three variations of light in combination with four variations of watering in such a way that the effect of each factor could be evaluated separately or in combination with the other.

Experiments were set up to see whether any one of the dominant plants produced some substance which, carried in soil water, would inhibit or stimulate its own growth or the growth of one of the other species. The three species were grown in separate pots, and all the water they received had percolated through the soil in which one of the species was growing. Size at various times and final dry weights were used to judge the effects of the different treatments.

Greenhouse experiments were carried out to check the effect of the dead plant parts of each of the old field dominants upon itself and upon each of the other species. Plants of each species were grown in soil containing chopped plant parts from each of the other species. This experiment gave information concerning the total effect of the specific organic matter on the growth of each species, but revealed little concerning the fundamental causes of the differences. A variation of this experiment using nutrient solution instead of distilled water was carried out to see whether the differences in growth between treatments was being caused by a mineral deficiency or by some other factor.

The effect of competition between broomsedge and aster was tested with a controlled field experiment in an attempt to solve the problem of why broomsedge replaces aster in old field succession. Young asters were transplanted to the vicinity of established broomsedge plants in the field, where other plants had been removed to eliminate their competition, and growth and survival of the asters in relation to distance from the broomsedge plant were studied.

# METHODS, RESULTS, AND CONCLUSIONS

## SEED MATURATION AND DORMANCY

METHODS. The three major dominants of old field succession, horseweed, aster, and broomsedge were observed in the field during two seasons to determine the time at which the seeds of each species matured. Mature seeds of the three species and also of ragweed were collected for testing germination under varying conditions. At weekly intervals during the months of November and December, 1947, seeds of each species were planted in two pots of soil, one pot being placed out of doors, and one in the germinating room of the greenhouse. If seeds of any species failed to germinate in the greenhouse, seeds were layered in damp sand in a cold room at a temperature of 10°C. and tested at intervals for germination. Seedlings grown in the greenhouse from the germinating seeds were compared from time to time with field specimens as an aid in recognizing seedlings in the quadrants being studied.

Three small plots in a first-year horseweed-dominated field were spaded on June 15, three others on July 15, and three on August 15. All plots were watched for seedlings of the species being studied to see when the seeds germinated in the field.

RESULTS. *Horseweed.* Horseweeds were observed blooming by the middle of July and some individuals were still blooming the last of October. The first mature seeds were collected early in August and germinated on damp filter paper about two weeks later. Horseweeds planted in soil at weekly intervals during November and December germinated outside through November, but did not germinate during the relatively cold month of December and many of the seedlings that had germinated during November died. Horseweed seeds that did not germinate outside when planted in December, germinated the following spring.

Horseweeds planted in the greenhouse germinated within two to five days regardless of the season. No seedlings of this species appeared in the spaded plots until the last week of August, at which time seedlings were found in abundance in the entire field.

*Aster.* A few scattered asters began to bloom in late September but most were in full bloom during late October and early November. The earliest mature seeds were collected the first of November from a few terminal heads of racemes. Aster did not germinate outside during November and December, but did show germination in the greenhouse seven to ten days after planting. Seeds planted outside germinated the following spring. No asters were seen at any time in the spaded plots.

*Broomsedge.* Soft immature seeds of broomsedge (*Andropogon virginicus* L.) were found the first of October, but firm seeds were not found until a month later. These seeds failed to germinate either in the greenhouse or outside during November or December. Seeds were layered in the cold room on December 8, and the first samples of these layered seeds germinated in the greenhouse on January 10. No seedlings of broomsedge were seen in the spaded plots.

*Ragweed.* Ragweed seeds collected in October failed to germinate in the greenhouse or outside unless layered. Seeds that were layered in the cold room on November 13 first germinated in the greenhouse on February 13.

CONCLUSIONS. Horseweed seeds mature as early as the first of August and are capable of germination soon after maturity. They may continue to germinate at relatively low temperatures during the late fall.

Aster seeds are not mature before the first of November. They may germinate soon after maturity in a warm environment, but not in the normally cool outdoor conditions that prevail around Durham in November.

Broomsedge seeds are not mature before the first of November and will not germinate under any conditions without a period of cold dormancy.

Ragweed seeds require a period of cold dormancy before they will germinate.

## GERMINATION, SURVIVAL AND GROWTH UNDER FIELD CONDITIONS

### PERMANENT QUADRATS

METHODS. In the late winter of 1947-1948 a search was made near Durham, North Carolina, for fields in which to locate permanent quadrats for the study of life cycles, survival, and growth. Fields that were not to be plowed that spring or summer were necessary and, since very little land was being abandoned deliberately because of the high price of farm products, such fields were difficult to locate. Such land as was being abandoned was usually badly eroded or otherwise unproductive. Nine fields were located, of which three had been last cultivated in 1945, three in 1946, and three in 1947.

Ten permanent quadrats one-fourth meter wide and one meter long were marked with stakes in each of the nine fields at intervals along a central line running the length of the field. In fields where furrows from the last cultivation were evident the arrangement was such that each plot included part of a ridge and a furrow. List counts of all species present were made in March, June, and September; the age of asters and broomsedge was estimated and each age group recorded separately. Counts of aster and broomsedge were made the following January in two fields of each age that had not been plowed by that time. When seedlings or young plants could not be recognized, samples were transplanted to pots in the greenhouse and later identified.

RESULTS. Species: Area curves made after each count indicated the one-fourth meter square quadrats were more than adequate for sampling at any season of the year.

*Horseweed.* Horseweed plants in the thirty quadrats in first-year fields showed an average density of

15.6 in March, 17.9 in June and 17.2 in September. In March these plants were rosettes ranging in diameter from one-half inch to six inches with many plants of the larger sizes. By June most of them had begun height growth, many being as much as one to two feet tall. In mid-July a large number were blooming, and although some were still only a few inches tall, the majority were between four and six feet tall. At the time of the last quadrat counts in late September, the plants that had bloomed first were nearly dead whereas some others were just beginning to bloom.

There were more than six times as many horseweeds per unit area in second-year fields as in first-year fields. The density in March was 97. In June the density had decreased to 78 and to 25 in September. In March most of the horseweed seedlings in second-year fields were less than a half inch in diameter, and none were seen that were more than one inch. Few finally grew to be more than a foot high, with the average being about six inches. These stunted plants began to bloom by the middle of July, and only a few remained alive until September.

Horseweed plants were found in only one third-year field. In this field there was an average of 123 seedlings per quadrat in March, 56 in June, and 18 in September. These plants in the third-year field were about the same size as those in the second-year fields.

*Aster.* There were only a few newly germinated asters (density 0.13) present in first-year fields in March, but by June the density had increased to 4.6, and in September it still averaged 4.6, but the decline in frequencies between June and September counts indicated that some of the seedlings had died and other seeds germinated.

The few asters beyond the seedling stage in the badly eroded second-year fields had a density of 0.07 in March and the same individuals lived through the season. Some aster seeds had germinated before March (density 4.9) in the second-year fields, and this number had increased by June to a density of 14.6. The survival of these plants could not be determined as the field containing the largest number of seedlings was plowed before September. The density of aster seedlings in the other two fields, however, was about the same in September as in June.

In the third-year fields aster plants with dead flowering stalks from the preceding year averaged 2.8 per plot. Most of these plants lived through the season and bloomed again in the fall (September density 2.4). Their height, however, was usually considerably less in their second year than in the first, as judged by the flower stalks still standing.

Some one-year old asters (density 8.0) were present in third-year fields. By June their density had dropped to 6.2, and the surviving plants were little larger than they were the year before.

The ground under the old asters in the third-year fields was almost completely covered with young aster seedlings, with a density in March of 321. Seedlings which survived to June (density 142) were scarcely larger than they were in March. September density had decreased to 45, including both young asters and seedlings of the current year which could not be distinguished from each other.

*Broomsedge.* There were no broomsedge seedlings in first-year fields in March, but in June their density was 2.2, and it increased to 4.6 by September. Of the two first-year fields checked for broomsedge in the following January, one showed the same number as in September and the other showed an increase from 4.4 in September to 5.8 in January. There was no way of knowing whether the same individuals were counted at the different times, or whether some died and other seeds germinated. Five one-year broomsedge plants were found in the ten quadrats of one of the first-year fields that had been abandoned late in June of the preceding year, and all five of these plants survived through the season.

No broomsedge seedlings were found in second-year fields in March. The June counts showed the low density of 0.8 and by September the value had increased to 1.4. Five one-year old plants that were found in the thirty quadrats in the second-year fields all lived throughout the period in which quadrat counts were made.

Broomsedge seedlings appeared earlier in third-year fields than in first- or second-year fields. The density in March was 1.0, and in June 19.8 and in September 61.7. In the two fields checked in January, the density in one remained the same as it was in September and in the other increased from 38.8 to 61.7. In third-year fields most of the broomsedge plants which were a year old survived, the density being 1.3 in March and 1.1 in September.

*Ragweed.* Young ragweed seedlings were found in all fields in March. In the first-year fields there was an increase in density from 1.4 in March to 3.5 in June, and nearly as high a count in September. The highest counts of ragweed were made in third-year fields, with densities of 6.3 in March, 3.5 in June, and 1.5 in September. Ragweeds in first-year fields, especially in one where the density of horseweeds and other plants was relatively low, usually grew to be branching plants three or four feet high. In second- and third-year fields the ragweeds were usually unbranched plants, less than a foot high except where they were growing in spaces unoccupied by many other plants.

*Other Plants.* There were 22 species of plants present in at least two of the three first-year fields studied. Aster, broomsedge, and pines, which later become dominants, are still in the seedling stages at this time. Horseweed, ragweed and crabgrass are the only ones of the 22 species that attain sufficient size or density to become dominants in the first year. A number of other plants that show relatively high densities and frequencies at some period of the year are small plants, no one of which alone covers enough area to be considered a dominant. Some of these species are *Sagina decumbens* (Ell.) Torr. and Gray, *Oenothera laciniata* Hill, *Plantago virginica* L., *Diodia teres* Walt., *Krigia virginica* (L.) Willd., *Polypremum procumbens* L., *Specularia perfoliata*

(L.) A. DC., *Draba verna* L., *Allium vineale* L., *Arabidopsis thaliana* (L.) Heynh.

Of the 25 species found in at least two of the three second-year fields, all but one, *Lespedeza striata* (Thunb.) H. & A., had been found in at least one of the first-year fields although sometimes with low densities. There were 23 species found in at least two of the third-year fields. Four of these, *Tecoma radicans* (L.) Juss., *Triodia flava* (L.) Smyth, *Solidago* spp., and *Erigeron racemosus* (Walt.) BSP. had not appeared in a field of a younger stage.

CONCLUSIONS. Horseweed is a winter annual, germinating in the fall, living as a rosette over winter, and blooming by mid-summer. Although the density is much lower in first-year fields than in second- or third-year fields, the percentage of survival and growth of horseweed plants is much greater in first-year fields than in the other two ages of fields.

Aster seeds germinate in the spring and early summer following their fall maturity and are present as small plants in first-year fields. These plants live over the winter, grow in height the second summer and bloom the second fall. The flower stalk dies, leaving a basal rosette of leaves that lives over the winter, and produces another flower stalk the following year. The density of aster seedlings under old aster plants in third-year fields is very high, but few seedlings survive and those that live make very little growth.

Some broomsedge seeds germinate during the spring following the fall in which they mature and others germinate during the summer and late fall. There are few broomsedge seedlings in the first- and second-year fields, but the survival of such seedlings is high. The survival of broomsedge plants beyond the seedling stage is almost 100 percent. A broomsedge plant blooms in its second fall and the clump continues to increase in circumference the third year and blooms again.

Ragweed is a summer annual; the seeds germinate in early spring and the plants bloom in late summer. The survival and growth of ragweed plants is greatest in fields where the density of other plants is least.

Horseweed, ragweed and crabgrass are the only plants present in first-year fields that have either density or size enough to become dominants.

## FIELD SURVEYS

METHODS. Fifteen first-year fields near Durham and four first-year fields in Alexander County in the upper Piedmont of North Carolina, were surveyed in fall condition. The past cultivational history of each field was obtained from the owner or tenant. Ten quadrats, one-fourth by one meter in size were spaced at regular intervals in each of the fields and counts were made of asters and broomsedge by age classes. General observations as to the abundance of other species and amount of soil erosion were made.

Eleven second-year fields in fall condition were surveyed near Durham, histories were obtained, conditions of soil observed, and abundance of each species noted. Asters and broomsedge were counted in four of the eleven fields, using the same size and number of quadrats in each as in first-year fields. Several of these second-year fields had been observed during the search for permanent quadrat locations, but had been rejected because the owner was not sure they would not be plowed that season; consequently, in such fields the dominants of two seasons were observed.

RESULTS. *First-year fields.* Horseweed was clearly the dominant plant in ten of the nineteen first-year fields. All of these fields except one had been last cultivated in July or August of the preceding year. The last crop in seven of these horseweed-dominated fields had been corn; garden vegetables were the last crop in two, and sweet potatoes in the other one. This last field had been observed during the year following the October harvesting of potatoes. It appeared bare of all vegetation during the winter, and throughout the following summer possessed a dense cover of horseweed plants that were smaller and less mature than the horseweeds in neighboring fields. These retarded horseweed plants did not bloom until late September and October.

Three of the first-year fields were dominated by a mixture of horseweeds and asters. The last crop in two of these fields had been corn, and the last crop in the other one was garden vegetables. One of the corn fields and the garden had been last cultivated in June and the other corn field in July.

Six of the first-year fields were clearly dominated by ragweed with practically no horseweeds and only a few scattered blooming asters. Four of these had been plowed in the fall of the year before and planted in winter wheat, one had been planted in winter vetch following cotton the preceding fall, and the other was a cornfield that had been last cultivated in June and in which the soil was badly eroded.

Young asters were found in every first-year field studied, ranging in density from 0.1 in a large wheat-ragweed field that was a long distance from any visible seed source, to 28.6 in a garden plot that had a surrounding border of blooming asters. The average density of young asters in all nineteen fields was 5.0 with a frequency of 71.5 per cent. In general, the fields that showed greatest evidence of erosion had the lowest densities of young asters. In fields that had been recently eroded by torrential rains of November, 1948, many nearly dead young asters were observed with a large part of their root systems exposed where the soil had been washed away.

Broomsedge seedlings less than a year old were found in the quadrats of only nine of the nineteen fields, with an average density of 0.8. Only one older broomsedge plant was recorded in the entire 190 quadrats counted in first-year fields.

The other species present were in general the same ones found in the first-year fields studied with permanent quadrats and they occurred with a corresponding abundance.

*Second-year fields.* Of the eleven second-year fields all except two were dominated by asters. One of those was almost completely covered with *Plantago virginica* in the spring and with Diodia in the fall. The other had an almost complete cover of crabgrass in some areas and Diodia in others with the Dioda-dominated areas appearing much more eroded than the crabgrass-dominated parts. A few stunted horseweeds, scattered bunches of blooming broomsedge, and an occasional blooming aster were present.

The first-year histories of all but two of these second-year fields were determined by direct observation or by information obtained from the owners or tenants. Two were dominated by a mixture of horseweed and aster following a last crop of early abandoned corn. One was a mixture of horseweed and aster following a spring planting of lespedeza the preceding year. Three were ragweed-dominated following wheat, and one following sweet potatoes. Blooming asters had an average density of 4.1. Blooming broomsedge had a density of 0.4. Broomsedge seedlings had a density of 0.15 in the quadrats of the four fields counted.

CONCLUSIONS. The time of year at which the last cultivation of a field takes place greatly influences the trend of succession on first-year fields. Fields last cultivated in early summer are usually dominated by a mixture of horseweeds and asters the following summer. Fields last cultivated in late summer after most of the aster seeds of the season have germinated are almost always dominated by horseweed. Fields last cultivated in late fall after most of the horseweed seeds have germinated are usually dominated by ragweed the following summer.

The density of young aster plants is greater in non-eroded fields than in eroded fields. Eroded spots in horseweed-dominated first-year fields are usually dominated by ragweed.

Most second-year fields are dominated by asters even though they are dominated the first year of abandonment by either a mixture of horseweeds and aster, by horseweed alone, or by ragweed. A few fields, usually badly eroded, are not aster-dominated the second year.

### MEASUREMENT OF GROWTH

METHODS. Measurements of numerous individuals of aster and broomsedge were made in December, 1948, to determine sizes at different ages in different habitats. Five small sample plots were distributed at random in four fields that had been cultivated the preceding summer, and diameters of all horseweed plants falling within these areas were measured. Similar plots were located in four of the horseweed-dominated fields used for the first-year survey. The size of horseweed seedlings was compared with that of the seedlings found in zero-year fields.

All aster and broomsedge plants growing within the one-fourth by one meter quadrats in four of the first-year survey fields and four of the second-year survey fields were measured, with height measurements of aster and broomsedge seedlings, and both height and basal circumference of older broomsedge plants being taken. Blooming asters and all broomsedge plants beyond the seedling stage in the quadrats of two of the third-year permanent quadrat fields were measured in the same manner.

RESULTS. *Horseweed.* In the zero-year fields 106 horseweeds rosettes were measured. Only one of these plants was less than a half-inch in diameter; the remaining ones ranged in size from 1/2-4 1/2 inches, averaging one inch in diameter. Of the 698 horseweed seedlings measured in the first-year fields 656 were one-fourth inch or less in diameter and none of the other 62 were more than one inch in diameter.

*Aster.* In first-year fields 55 young asters ranged in size from one to five inches in height and averaged 2.2 inches. The 194 young asters measured in second-year fields ranged in size from 1/2-4 inches and averaged 0.9 inches in height. Blooming asters (70) measured in second-year fields ranged in height from 12 to 57 inches and averaged 34 inches, but those (43) in third-year fields ranged in height from 3 to 67 inches and averaged 27 inches.

*Broomsedge.* Nineteen broomsedge seedlings measured in first-year fields were from 2 to 9 inches in height and averaged 5 inches. Six broomsedge seedlings found in the quadrats of the second-year survey fields were 3 to 7 inches high and averaged 5.3 inches. Nine broomsedge plants in second-year fields that were between one and two years old averaged 40 inches in height and 3 inches in basal circumference. Twenty-five broomsedge plants in third-year fields—one and a half year old plants being difficult to distinguish from older plants—averaged 39 inches in height and 10 inches in basal circumference.

CONCLUSIONS. Horseweed seedlings in second-year fields are only about one fourth as large as they are in first-year fields.

Young aster plants grow to be about two inches tall by fall in first-year fields, but in second-year fields where young asters are growing under mature asters, they are only about half as large.

Broomsedge seedlings grow as well in second-year fields as they do in first-year fields. Broomsedge plants reach their maximum height in second-year fields, but continue to increase in circumference the following year.

### FACTORS INFLUENCING SURVIVAL AND GROWTH
#### WATER AND LIGHT

METHODS. Seedlings of horseweed, aster, and broomsedge were grown in the greenhouse during the summer of 1948 to see how they would respond to variations in water and light. Seeds of the three species were planted separately in pots of sandy loam, the asters being planted five days before horseweed and broomsedge so that the seedlings of this slowly germinating species would be approximately the same age as those of the other two species. The pots were placed in the greenhouse in such a way that one third received full sunlight, one third were shaded with cheesecloth over a rack in such a way as to receive one-half full sunlight, and the other third were shaded to reduce the light to one-fourth full sunlight.

All pots were watered daily until the seedlings were ten to fifteen days old. At that time the plants were thinned to forty to an eight-inch pot, or less in the case of asters where fewer than that number had germinated. Within each variation of light one pot of each species was watered every day, another pot of each species was watered every seven days, another every fourteen days, and a fourth pot of each species was watered at a twenty-one day interval. At the end of three weeks of differential watering, the surviving plants were counted. The differential watering was continued for another four weeks. The surviving plants were then removed from the soil, oven dried, and their average weight determined as a measure of the growth that had been made by the plants that had been subjected to different environmental conditions of light and water.

RESULTS. *Horseweed.* During the first three weeks of differential watering the mortality of horseweed seedlings was as follows:

Full sunlight

    14 day watering ...............12%

    21 day watering ...............75%

One-fourth full sunlight

    21 day watering ...............50%

All the horseweed seedlings in the other variations of light and water were living at the end of the entire experiment. There was a further slight loss of plants during the second period of differential watering under the same treatments in which plants died during the first period as follows:

Full sunlight

    14 day watering ..................03%

    (of plants surviving first watering period)

    21 day watering ................10%

One-fourth full sunlight

    21 day watering ................25%

Judging by the average dry weight of plants, the optimum conditions for horseweed growth were one-fourth full sunlight with a fourteen-day interval between waterings. In general the poorest growth was made in full sunlight. The best watering period for all variations of light was the two-week interval, and the poorest growth was made at the three-week watering interval.

Figure 1 shows the survival and growth of horseweed seedlings for the entire period of the experiment.

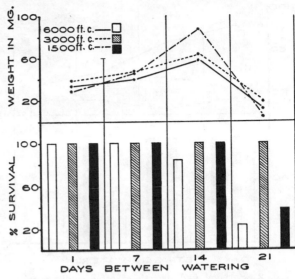

FIG. 1. Survival and growth of horseweed seedlings with variations in water and light. Differential watering started when plants were ten to fifteen days old. Growth expressed in final dry weight of surviving plants. Optimum conditions for growth are one-fourth full sunlight (1500 foot candles) with a fourteen day watering interval.

*Aster.* There were some deaths of asters in six of the twelve treatments as follows:

Full sunlight

    7 day watering .................50%

    14 day watering .................70%

    21 day watering .................70%

One-half full sunlight

    14 day watering .................53%

    21 day watering .................70%

One-fourth full sunlight

    21 day watering .................96%

All of the aster seedlings that survived the first period of differential watering were still living at the end of the second period.

Although the mortality among the asters was greatest in full sunlight, the plants that lived made the greatest growth in full sunlight. In every variation of watering the asters in full sunlight were definitely larger than those in the other two variations of light (Fig. 2).

*Broomsedge.* The deaths of broomsedge seedlings during the first period of differential watering were as follows:

Full sunlight

    7 day watering .................02%

    14 day watering .................50%

    21 day watering ...............67%

One-half full sunlight

    21 day watering .................70%

One-fourth full sunlight

    21 day watering ...............87%

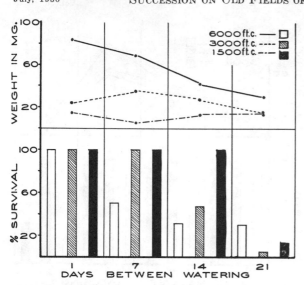

FIG. 2. Survival and growth of aster seedlings with variations in water and light. Differential watering started when plants were ten to fifteen days old. Growth expressed in final dry weight of surviving plants. Optimum conditions for growth of asters are abundant water and light.

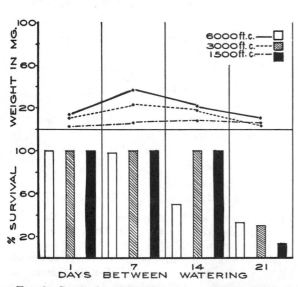

FIG. 3. Survival and growth of broomsedge seedlings with variations in light and water. Differential watering started when seedlings were ten to fifteen days old. Growth expressed in final dry weight of surviving plants. Optimum conditions for growth are full sunlight (6000 foot candles) with watering every seven days.

All broomsedge seedlings that survived the first period of differential watering lived until the end of the experiment (Fig. 3).

Seedlings in both conditions of reduced light soon showed a definite chlorosis, which became more pronounced with additional time, while those plants in full sunlight were dark green in color. Broomsedge seedlings showed their optimum growth in full sunlight with the seven day interval between watering. The seven-day watering interval produced the best

growth in all three variations of light, with gradual decrease in growth as the interval between watering was lengthened. The plants grown in one-fourth full sunlight showed consistently less growth at every watering interval than the plants grown with more light.

CONCLUSIONS. Horseweed seedlings are drought-resistant, capable of enduring two to three weeks of drought without death of a large number of plants. They make their best growth in reduced light when watered every two weeks.

About half of the aster seedlings died in full sunlight when deprived of water for one week. Mortality is somewhat reduced with shading, but growth is also greatly reduced. Asters make their best growth with an abundance of both light and water.

Broomsedge seedlings can endure one to two weeks in full sunlight without severe loss of plants. Mortality is reduced with shading, but growth is also reduced. Broomsedge makes best growth in full sunlight when watered once a week.

### SUBSTANCES PRODUCED BY LIVING PLANTS

METHODS. Experiments were carried out in the greenhouse during the late winter and early summer of 1948 to determine the effect of substances produced by living plants of each of the dominant species of old field succession upon the growth of others of the same species or upon individuals of the other two species. Clay pots were fitted with drain tubes and filled with unsterilized sandy loam soil from a field which had been cultivated the preceding year. Young plants of aster, horseweed, and broomsedge from fields were set one to a pot, except in the pots which were left without plants to be used as controls. When these donor plants were established and growing, receiver pots were set up; seeds of the three species being studied were planted separately in pots containing soil from the same source as that used in the donor pots.

The pots of seedlings of each species were arranged so that three pots of each species were watered with drip water from horseweed, three from aster, three from broomsedge and three from control pots containing soil in which no plants were growing. Each of the three sets of replications were placed at different exposures in a greenhouse room. The donor pots were watered with distilled water every three to five days when the receiver seedlings were young, and every five to seven days after the plants were well established. Receiver plants were given no water except that which percolated through the soil of the donor pots. None of the receiver plants showed any sign of wilting on this watering schedule.

Plants of other species were pulled out as they germinated and the receiver plants were gradually thinned, always leaving the largest plants, until only two plants remained in each pot.

The receiver plants were measured periodically, the diameter being used for the rosette stage of horseweed and height for the later stages of horseweed and all stages of aster and broomsedge. During the first week in August, 1948, when the receiver plants were five months old and some of the horseweed plants were beginning to bloom, they were removed from the soil, dried in an oven, and their weights compared. The data were analyzed to see if there were any significant differences in size at any stage that could be attributed to differences in treatment.

RESULTS. At the end of the experiment when the plants were five months old, most of the individuals which had been grown in the greenhouse much larger than plants of the same age that were growing in the fields under natural conditions. The horseweed plants ranged in size from 5 to 36 inches tall, the asters from 7 to 47 inches and the broomsedge from 6 to 34 inches.

Statistical analyses of the data for size measurements and final dry weights showed that there were more variations within each treatment than there were between treatments; consequently no differences in size at any time could be attributed to substances produced by living plants and passed to other plants in the soil water.

CONCLUSIONS. None of the old field dominants produced substances that are carried in soil water and thus inhibit or stimulate the growth of any one of the others.

## DECOMPOSITION PRODUCTS

METHODS. Greenhouse experiments were carried out in the spring and summer of 1948 to determine the effect of decaying organic matter from each of the dominants of old field succession upon that species and upon the other two. Horseweed, aster, and broomsedge were grown in pots containing chopped roots or tops of one of the dominants mixed with sandy loam from a field that had been cultivated the preceding year. An attempt was made to estimate the amount of such plant parts that might normally be found in a given amount of old field soil at some stage in the succession. These estimates indicated that 115 grams of slightly damp roots or 80 grams of air-dry tops added to four thousand grams of soil in each pot would approximate the normal field conditions. Samples of each kind of plant part were ovendried to determine the amount of moisture in each. Three replications of each species were grown in soil containing one of the following kinds of organic matter: (1) horseweed roots, (2) horseweed tops, (3) aster roots, (4) aster tops, (5) broomsedge roots, (6) broomsedge tops. Three replications of each species to be used as controls were grown in soil containing no plant parts.

(1) Seeds were planted on February 26, 1948, and plants were watered with distilled water throughout the experiment. Other species were removed as they germinated and the desired species were gradually thinned, always leaving the largest plants until two plants remained in each pot. The plants were

measured at intervals in the same way as in the preceding experiment. When the plants were five months old, they were removed from the pots, oven-dried and their weights compared. The remains of the organic matter were sifted from the soil, washed, oven dried, and weighed. Final dry weight was compared with the original to determine the amount of decay that had taken place.

(2) If the plants in the preceding part (1) of the experiment should show a difference in growth in the soils containing different kinds of organic matter, it would not be known whether these differences were caused by some toxic substances, by mineral deficiencies, or by some other cause. In an effort to see the relation of mineral deficiencies to differential growth, should there be any, part of the experiment was repeated using a complete nutrient solution suggested by Hoagland and Arnon (1938) instead of distilled water so that there could be no mineral deficiencies. Horseweed plants were grown in sand, some of the pots containing horseweed roots, some containing horseweed tops and others containing no plant parts. Parts (1) and (2) of the experiment were carried out in the same general way except that in part (2) the plants were watered with nutrient solution instead of with distilled water.

(3) Horseweed plants were grown in unsterilized soil and watered with complete nutrient solutions with the same combinations of living plants and plant parts as used in the sand-nutrient solution experiment (2) to see if the soil organisms present in the soil but not in the sand would make a difference in growth.

RESULTS. *Horseweed.* Noticeable differences in the diameters of horseweed seedlings in the soil-distilled water part of the experiment were evident with two of the treatments as early as two weeks after the seeds germinated. The plants growing in pots containing horseweed roots were noticeably smaller than the controls and other treatments, and the seedlings growing in soil containing aster roots were consistently larger than any of the others.

When the plants were two months old, the six horseweed plants growing with horseweed roots averaged 4.3 cm. in diameter, the ones with aster roots 12.1 cm., and the ones in the controls 8.5 cm. Statistical analysis of the data for this stage showed that there was less than one chance in twenty that these variations in size could be attributed to conditions other than the differences in kind of organic matter in the soil. Figure 4 shows the relative size of plants with different treatments when they were two months old. Horseweeds growing in soil containing aster roots continued to be larger than the others during the entire five months the plants were growing, and statistical analysis showed this difference to be significant at the five percent level. As the plants increased in age there was so much variation within each treatment that the differences between treatments became insignificant. Horseweed

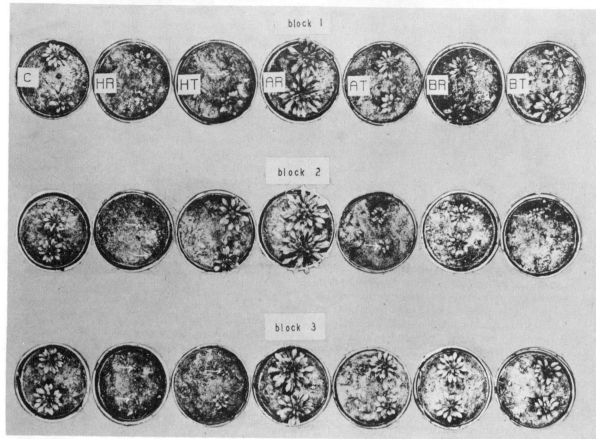

FIG. 4. Two-months-old horseweed plants growing in soil containing the following kinds of organic matter: HR-horseweed roots, HT- horseweed tops, AR- aster roots, AT- aster tops, BR- broomsedge roots, BT- broomsedge tops, C- Control (no organic matter added). Block 1, 2, and 3 are three replications of each treatment. Aster roots (AR) added to soil produced a significant increase in size, and horseweed roots (HR) resulted in reduced size of plants when compared with control. Other treatments produced no significant differences.

plants growing with horseweed roots remained smaller than the controls, but failed to show a significant difference in size after they were two months old.

In the sand-nutrient solution part of the experiment all plants grew luxuriantly, with little difference at any time in size of individuals. The six plants growing with horseweed roots at two months averaged 24.5 cm. in diameter, those with horseweed tops averaged 27.5 cm., and those in the controls 24.5. These differences are statistically insignificant at the 5 percent level.

In the soil-nutrient solution part of the experiment those plants growing in soil containing organic matter were consistently larger at every measurement than those growing in soil without additional organic matter. When the seedlings were six weeks old the diameters of plants growing with horseweed roots was 6 cm., those with horseweed tops 10.1 cm. and those in the controls 4.1 cm. These differences are significant at the 5 percent level. When the plants were two and a half months old, the plants with horseweed roots averaged 23.3 cm., those with horseweed tops 23.3 cm., and in the control 21.6. The differences within the treatments were so small that

the differences between the control and the other two treatments proved significant. The final dry weights showed that those plants grown with horseweed roots averaged (15.65 gms.) twice as much as the controls (7.75 gms.), and the differences proved to be significant. The dry weights of those plants grown in soil containing horseweed tops (8.88 gms.) were not significantly greater than the control.

*Aster.* Asters grown in the soil-distilled water part of the experiment showed a decided difference in size for different treatments when they were two months old. Figure 5 shows the asters at the age of two months when the stunting effect of horseweed roots and tops and broomsedge tops, and the stimulating effect of aster roots was quite apparent. Plants in soil containing aster roots were definitely the largest, averaging 14.1 cm. in height, and those in soil containing horseweed roots were significantly (at the 5 percent level) smaller than the controls, which averaged 11.0 cm. By the time the plants were three months old the variations within each treatment were so great that the differences between treatments were not significant except in the case of those plants growing with aster roots, which were almost twice

FIG. 5. Two-months-old aster plants growing in soil containing the following kinds of organic matter: HR-horseweed roots, HT- horseweed tops, AR- aster roots, AT- aster tops, BR- broomsedge roots, BT- broomsedge tops, C- Control (soil with no organic matter added). Block 1, 2, and 3 are three replications of each treatment. Aster roots (AR) added to the soil produced a significant increase over the control and aster tops (AT), broomsedge tops (BT), horseweed tops (HT), and horseweed roots (HR) resulted in plants significantly smaller than the control.

as tall as any of the others. Although the height measurements in later stages failed to show significant differences, the final dry weights showed significant differences in four of the six treatments that were compared with the controls. At the end of the experiment the asters grown with aster roots were largest (average, 14.3 gms.); those in soil containing horseweed roots (3.58 gms.), horseweed tops (3.75 gms.), and broomsedge tops (3.38 gms.) were significantly smaller than the controls (10.75 gms.).

*Broomsedge.* Height measurement of broomsedge failed to be a fair evaluation of size, as it did not show the amount of tillering and circumference of clumps. There were no significant differences in height at any time among the plants grown with different treatments. Final dry weight, however, showed that those broomsedge plants grown in aster roots (av. wt. 8.80 gms.) were more than twice as heavy as those grown without organic matter (3.62 gms.). Plants grown in soil containing broomsedge roots (3.45 gms.) and broomsedge tops (3.27 gms.) were slightly smaller than the control and those with horseweed roots (5.34 gms.), horseweed tops (5.62 gms.), and aster tops (5.72 gms.) were slightly larger than the controls.

*Decay and plant growth.* The amounts of undecayed plant parts remaining in soil after plants had been growing in it for five months could not be determined accurately because it was difficult to separate small particles of organic matter from the soil. In spite of the possible experimental error, some information was obtained concerning the rate of decay of the different plant parts and its correlation with growth of the plants.

Ninety-eight percent of the aster roots placed in soil had decayed at the end of five months. All three species in soil containing aster roots made much greater growth than plants receiving any other treatment. Broomsedge roots showed the next highest amount of decay (71 percent) and no plants were stunted when grown with broomsedge roots. Broomsedge tops, with 67 percent decay, stunted horseweed in early stages and aster at all stages. Horseweed roots with 64 percent decay stunted horseweed in early stages and aster at all stages. Aster tops (32 percent decay) and horseweed tops (27 percent decay) significantly reduced the growth of asters.

When horseweeds were grown in sand and watered with nutrient solution, horseweed roots (30 percent decay) and horseweed tops (27 percent decay) did not affect the growth, and all plants grew equally well. When horseweed plants were grown in soil watered with nutrient solution, those plants growing with horseweed roots (98 percent decay) made much more growth than those growing with horseweed tops (65 percent decay). Plants growing in soil without added organic matter made less growth than those with the other two treatments.

CONCLUSIONS. The kind of decaying organic matter in the soil does influence growth of the dominant plants of old fields. Growth of plants seems to be related to the amount of decay of organic matter, and the amount of decay is not the same for different plant parts. Aster roots in soil decay more rapidly than other plant parts tested and produced the greatest growth in all three species. Horseweed roots in soil inhibit the growth of horseweed seedlings and of aster at all stages. Broomsedge tops, aster tops, and horseweed tops inhibit the growth of asters.

Plants grown in sand or soil containing organic matter to which nutrient solution has been added are not inhibited in growth.

### COMPETITION BETWEEN ASTER AND BROOMSEDGE

METHODS. Field observations had shown that asters of all ages made little growth where broomsedge was increasing in number and size of clumps, and greenhouse experiments had indicated that living broomsedge produced no substances that inhibit the growth of asters. A controlled field experiment was set up to determine the effect of competition of broomsedge upon aster plants, and to determine if possible the basis of competition. It was hoped that an answer to the problem of why broomsedge replaces aster in old field succession might be partially solved by the results of such an experiment.

Three large broomsedge plants were selected in one of the third-year permanent quadrat fields. With each of these plants at the center, circles with one-meter radii were cleared by pulling up all the plants except the broomsedge and by removing the top inch of soil. On July 17, 1948, after the soil had been thoroughly wetted by a recent rain, young aster plants about an inch high that had been grown in the greenhouse were set at one-eighth meter intervals from the broomsedge on four radii of each circle. The plants that died during the first few days following resetting were replaced and by the end of a week all aster plants were established and living. On September 26, near the end of a five-week drought, the plants were checked for survival, the living plants were removed from the soil, and oven-dried. The average dry weights of all plants equidistant from a broomsedge plant were calculated.

The soil moisture conditions near the end of the five-week drought were determined in each of the experimental plots and also in the three third-year fields with permanent quadrats to see if water might be critical in competition. Soil samples were taken $\frac{1}{8}$, $\frac{3}{8}$, and $\frac{5}{8}$ meters from the broomsedge plants at the center of each plot. The percentages of total water present, and the wilting percentage of each sample were determined, and from these data the water available to plants was calculated. Soil samples were taken beside quadrats one, five, and ten in each of th third-year permanent quadrat fields and available water calculated in like manner.

The distribution of broomsedge roots was determined by digging around the plants in the center of each plot to see how the extent of the root system corresponded with the survival of the asters.

RESULTS. The following table gives the percentage of plants dying and the average dry weight of the surviving plants for each distance from a broomsedge plant, and the available water present after drought at three of the positions.

| Distance from broomsedge in meters | Percent of plants dying | Average dry weight of surviving plants in grams | Percent of available water in soil |
|---|---|---|---|
| $\frac{1}{8}$ | 33.3 | 0.0598 | 1.70 |
| $\frac{2}{8}$ | 33.3 | 0.1140 | |
| $\frac{3}{8}$ | 8.0 | 0.2000 | 3.52 |
| $\frac{4}{8}$ | 0 | 0.3905 | |
| $\frac{5}{8}$ | 8.8 | 0.4570 | 6.40 |
| $\frac{6}{8}$ | 0 | 0.4200 | |
| $\frac{7}{8}$ | 17.0 | 0.2060 | |

Most of the broomsedge roots extended to between two-eighth and three-eighth of a meter from the edge of each clump, with very few roots being found beyond this distance. More aster plants died in the regions where roots of broomsedge and aster were growing in the same soil than in other areas, and the surviving plants made less growth than elsewhere. The available water after drought was very low (1.70 percent) in soil occupied by broomsedge roots, but was greater outside the range of these roots (6.40 percent). Two of the twelve plants growing near the edge of the cleared plots died, and the surviving plants made less growth than ones located near the middle of the radii.

One of the third-year permanent quadrat fields which was clearly dominated by asters in 1947 and by broomsedge in 1948 showed the lowest available water of any of the third-year fields following a period of five weeks with very little rain. Soil samples from beside quadrats one, five, and ten showed the available water to be 1.83 percent, 2.58 percent, and 3.38 percent.

A second third-year field which was dominated by asters in 1947 showed a clear broomsedge dominance in 1948 on most of the field which was on a slight slope, but retained aster dominance in a small low area at the end of the field where the first quadrat was located. Soil samples showed the available water near the aster-dominated first quadrat to be 2.84 percent, but at quadrats five and ten which were up the slope in the broomsedge-dominated areas the values were 2.38 percent and 1.83 percent.

The other third-year field was aster-dominated in 1947 and although the number and size of broomsedge plants had increased slightly, the field was still aster-dominated in 1948. The available moisture was much higher in this field than in the other two, being 5.85 percent, 7.45 percent and 6.66 percent at the three stations tested.

CONCLUSIONS. The survival and growth of asters is poor when they are growing near thriving broomsedge plants. Competition for water may be one of the controlling factors in the replacement of aster dominance by broomsedge in old field succession.

## CORRELATIONS AND GENERAL CONCLUSIONS

### CAUSES OF OLD FIELD SUCCESSION

#### THE GENERAL TREND

The object of this study was to contribute to our knowledge of the causes of secondary succession by solving some of the problems concerning one particular example, namely, early old field succession in the Piedmont of North Carolina. To do this a number of general and specific questions needed to be answered. The foregoing experiments and observations were an attempt to answer as many of the specific questions as possible. The general questions usually could not be answered by one experiment or observations alone, but required evidence from several or all of the experiments and observations.

Although all of these questions have not been answered satisfactorily, several have been partially or nearly clarified, and the conclusions should add substantially to an understanding of succession in general.

WHY HORSEWEED IS USUALLY THE DOMINANT OF FIRST-YEAR FIELDS. The answer to the question of why horseweed rather than some other plant is usually the dominant of first-year fields lies largely in the facts of its life cycle, and to a much less extent in its response to the environmental conditions present in first-year fields. Corn, tobacco, cotton, garden vegetables, and other crops that are last cultivated in July or August occupy much of the farm land in the Piedmont of North Carolina. The fact that horseweed seeds are mature and ready to germinate at the time of year when most farm land in the Piedmont of North Carolina has been cultivated for the last time in a season gives it an advantage over other plants. The other old field species that possess genetic possibilities of being plants as large as horseweed are spring germinating species, and many of them are slow-growing perennials that do not reach their maximum size the first year.

Horseweed is a composite which produces many small wind-borne seeds, so that an adequate supply of seeds is rarely lacking. Although the density of horseweed plants in first-year fields is usually high enough to insure a fair to good stand, the density is also low enough so that there is no severe competition among individuals of the same species. Under favorable conditions horseweed grows to be the largest plant of any species commonly found in first-year fields. Ragweed, also commonly present, sometimes approaches the size of horseweed, but being a spring-germinating species, gets started after horseweed is well established, and thus fails in competition with horseweed. Crabgrass is often present in large numbers, but even under the best environmental conditions rarely grows more than a foot high. Consequently it shares dominance with horseweed and does not replace it.

Horseweeds make their early growth in the fall, winter, and early spring when environmental conditions are favorable for the species. They are relatively drought-resistant plants, and a large number of them survive the fall droughts that normally occur in the Piedmont. They make their best growth in reduced light, and the short days with low light intensities during the fall and winter months are favorable for their growth. The ground cover of crabgrass plants that is often present in old fields at the time when horseweed seedlings are young is not harmful to them, but may be helpful in reducing light.

WHY HORSEWEED FAILS TO HOLD DOMINANCE AFTER THE FIRST YEAR. Greenhouse experiments showed that horseweed seedlings were definitely stunted when they were grown in soil containing decaying horseweed roots, even though competition had been removed. Field observations and measurements showed that horseweed seedlings growing in fields in which the dead horseweed plants of the preceding summer were still standing were much smaller than those in fields that had been cultivated the previous summer. Although the stunting of horseweed seedlings in second-year fields could be caused partially by the inhibiting effect of decaying horseweed roots in the soil, this could not have been the only cause, for horseweed plants growing with horseweed roots in the greenhouse where competition was not a factor, finally overcame the initial stunting effect. There were more than six times as many horseweed individuals per unit area in second-year fields as in first-year fields, and young asters were usually present in sufficient numbers to make competition a factor. The initial stunting effect of horseweed roots combined with the continued competition of numerous horseweed individuals and young asters could be enough to cause the loss of dominance by horseweed the second year. In eroded second-year fields where few young asters were present, the numerous horseweed seedlings were of the same small size as those in similar-aged fields containing many young asters, so it would seem that the inhibiting effect of horseweed roots and the competition among the large numbers of horseweed individuals could cause the small size of horseweeds without the added competition of asters.

The loss of dominance of horseweeds in second-year fields is not caused by the shading effect of asters or other plants. At the time the young horseweed plants are growing in second-year fields there are few other plants to diminish the amount of light reaching the seedlings; the bare stalks of the preceding horseweed stand obstruct little light and young asters are too small to interfere with light reaching the seedlings. Furthermore, horseweed seedlings grow best with the degree of reduction of light that is the normal condition for fall and winter.

Living aster plants produce no substance carried in soil water that inhibits the growth of horseweed plants; so living asters do not influence the decline of horseweed dominance in any way except in competing with them for water and minerals. As asters increase in size in the spring and summer of the second year, the already stunted horseweeds are at a still greater disadvantage, and never grow large enough to share dominance with asters in second-year fields.

WHY ASTER IS DELAYED IN ASSUMING DOMINANCE UNTIL THE SECOND YEAR. Much of the agricultural land in the Piedmont of North Carolina is cultivated for the last time in July or August. Aster seeds mature so late in the fall that the weather is normally too cool by that time for aster seeds to germinate. Consequently the germination is delayed until the following spring. Asters germinate in cultivated fields during the spring and early summer and are destroyed by the subsequent cultivation of such fields. No aster seedlings were found in the plots that were spaded on June 15 and later, and permanent quadrats showed an increase in aster seedlings between June and September in only one of the nine fields. This indicates that most of the aster seeds do germinate before the last of June, but that a few may be delayed in germination past that time. Oosting & Humphreys (1940) reported no buried viable seeds of aster found in soils around Durham that had previously been occupied by old field vegetation, so it is not likely that aster seeds brought to the surface by summer cultivations would germinate. Consequently the last cultivation of farm land in this area usually occurs after most of the asters have germinated and the young seedlings are thus destroyed. An occasional surviving aster was observed in a recently plowed field in the late summer of 1948, indicating that some asters do escape the plow. These few plants that are not destroyed by cultivation, or are derived from late germinating seeds, account for the occasional blooming aster seen in first-year horseweed-dominated fields.

Although aster seedlings show best survival with reduced light, they make best growth in full sunlight. Young asters growing in a horseweed-dominated field are somewhat shaded during the first few months of their life. This partially accounts for the fact that asters grown in the greenhouse with abundant water and no shading made much more growth than asters grown in the fields. Dead horseweed stalks cast but small shadows, so the asters are exposed to essentially full sunlight in the fall, winter, and following spring and summer after the previously dominant horseweeds die.

Decaying horseweed roots were found to have a greater stunting effect upon asters than they did upon horseweeds. Aster seedlings, however, are usually three to six months old before the horseweed plants, under which they grow, die and begin to decay. It cannot be said, however, that decaying horseweed roots do not inhibit the growth of asters to some extent, and that may be another reason why asters in the field grew more slowly than they did in the greenhouse.

Horseweeds, living or dead, do not stimulate the growth of asters. The living horseweeds may aid to some extent in the survival of aster seedlings by providing shade, but that same shade and the inhibiting effects of dead horseweed roots stunt the growth of asters. Therefore asters make some growth their first season in spite of the horseweeds, not because of them. Asters in the greenhouse bloomed their first season. It is possible that if no horseweeds or other plants were present in first-year fields to reduce the light and to compete for available soil moisture, asters might be dominant in a field in the fall of the first year of abandonment.

WHY ASTER FAILS TO HOLD DOMINANCE AFTER THE SECOND YEAR. In the water and light experiments in the greenhouse aster seedlings showed their best survival in reduced light, as long as water was available, but made their best growth in full sunlight with abundant water. Asters were definitely the least drought-resistant of any of the three species studied. With a two-week watering interval the survival of seedlings increased progressively as the light was reduced, but with a three-week watering interval the reverse was true; there was a greater survival in full sunlight and nearly all of the plants died in the reduced light.

In the spring of the third year there were a large number of seedlings present under the shade of the old asters, broomsedge and other vegetation. Most of these seedlings died before fall, and the surviving ones made very little growth.

The old asters that had bloomed the preceding year made considerable growth until about mid-summer, at which time many of them, especially the ones that were growing near large broomsedge plants, made little further growth and showed a rolling and yellowing of the leaves. Most of the old aster plants that had bloomed the preceding year lived and bloomed the second fall, but since they averaged only 27 inches high, they were not conspicuous in the fields where broomsedge plants averaged 39 inches.

In the field experiment where asters were placed in direct competition with large broomsedge plants, those asters whose roots occupied the same soil as that occupied by broomsedge roots showed greater mortality and less growth than those asters growing in soil not occupied by broomsedge roots. It is true that those plants close to the broomsedge were shaded a greater part of the day than those further away, but with all the other vegetation removed from the plots, all asters received full sunlight more than half of each day. The available soil moisture was less in the areas occupied by broomsedge roots than in soil not occupied by them. Young broomsedge plants are more drought-resistant than young asters, and older broomsedge plants in fields have a very high rate of survival. These facts, combined with the wide distribution of species of Andropogon in areas of North America where annual rainfall is low, suggests that broomsedge is relatively drought-resistant. When asters and broomsedge are competing for moisture in the same soil and when the available soil water is low, the broomsedge lives and continues to grow and the asters make little growth and finally die.

The soil moisture measurements in third-year fields confirm the idea that competition for water is one of the determining factors in the replacement of asters by broomsedge in old field succession. Those fields in which the available water is low during droughts are more clearly dominated by broomsedge than are those fields in which the available water is higher, and broomsedge dominance in such fields with higher moisture may be delayed a year until the broomsedge plants increase in size and number.

The reduced light in third-year fields is clearly one of the factors influencing the loss of dominance by asters in old fields. Few aster seedlings survive and grow to maturity in old fields after the vegetative cover of mature asters, broomsedge and other vegetation increases; the old asters fail to make sufficient growth in the reduced light to compete satisfactorily with the increasing broomsedge plants and finally die.

No evidence was found that living broomsedge or living asters produce any substances that inhibit the growth of asters. Both decaying horseweed roots and tops, which inhibit the growth of asters, are present in the soil at the time asters are losing dominance, but the actual amount of organic matter from the small horseweed plants that remain from second-year fields is too small to be an important factor in the elimination of asters.

WHY BROOMSEDGE IS DELAYED IN ASSUMING DOMINANCE UNTIL THE THIRD YEAR. There are few broomsedge seedlings of any age in old fields for the first two years after abandonment. Quadrat counts showed that there were few broomsedge seedlings in the first- and second-year fields at any time, and general observations even following rainy seasons, failed to show seedlings of this plant in numbers in any except third-year or older fields. Those few seedlings seen in the first- and second-year fields were usually found in open sunny portions of the quadrats rather than under the partial covering of crabgrass which was usually present.

No tests were made to see what percentage of broomsedge seeds germinate, but in all the greenhouse experiments involving planting of the three species, there was never any trouble in obtaining a full stand of broomsedge seedlings when layered seeds were used.

The water and light experiments showed that broomsedge seedlings are relatively drought-resistant. A large percentage of them are able to survive one to two weeks in full sunlight without watering with some increase in survival, but not in growth, with decreased lighting at the same watering intervals.

Broomsedge seeds are small and wind-borne, but are not so small as those of horseweed or aster, and may not be so easily transported. No tests were made to determine how far broomsedge seeds are commonly transported from their seed source. Although no old field in the Piedmont is far from a stand of broomsedge, it is possible that the seeds may not be carried far enough to produce a full stand. Oosting and Humphreys (1940) found three viable broomsedge seeds in 200 cubic inches of soil (maximum depth 5⅜ inches) taken from a zero-year field, one from a second-year field, and 37 from a fifth-year field. These data indicate the scarcity of viable seeds in old fields during the first two years of abandonment and the great number present after broomsedge becomes established. Those few plants that do appear in first-year fields do not produce mature seeds until the fall of the second year, and since the seeds require a period of cold dormancy they are not ready to germinate until the following spring. Consequently the spring of the third year is the first time an abundance of seeds is present in old fields.

Neither products of living horseweed or aster, nor products of their decay inhibit the growth of broomsedge. Broomsedge plants did grow somewhat better in soil containing organic matter from horseweed tops, horseweed roots, and aster-tops, and decidedly better in soil containing aster roots than in soil containing little organic matter.

Some environmental conditions in third-year fields are favorable for the growth of broomsedge plants and others are unfavorable. The abundance of organic matter found in soils of third-year fields seems to be beneficial to the growth of broomsedge plants, but the reduced light is unfavorable. Because broomsedge plants are more drought-resistant than asters, they are able to compete successfully with the asters and other vegetation present in third-year fields. The environmental conditions influence the survival and growth of broomsedge plants in fields once they are there, but the initiation of broomsedge dominance in old fields is probably retarded largely by the lack of seeds, and this condition is not remedied until the few first invaders are old enough to produce the seeds necessary for a full stand.

## VARIATIONS FROM THE GENERAL TREND

An understanding of the causes of the general trend of succession in old fields of the Piedmont of North Carolina helps to explain variations from the general trend.

WHY SOME FIRST-YEAR FIELDS ARE RAGWEED-DOMINATED. Ragweed seeds require a period of cold dormancy and do not germinate until the spring following their maturation. In the fields studied the largest and most vigorous plants were found in the first-year fields and especially in those where the density of other plants was low. Although the spring density of ragweed plants was highest in third-year fields, the mortality of seedlings was also highest and the plants never grew to be large. Although no tests were made as to the light and water requirements of ragweed, field observations suggest that it does not compete successfully with other dominants.

Ragweed dominated all first-year fields in which wheat had been planted the preceding fall. Wheat is planted in this region in October and early November. The plowing of soil in preparation for wheat planting destroys the young horseweed seedlings that germinate in the early fall months. The plants from the horseweed seeds that germinate after wheat is planted are not able to compete successfully with the full stand of winter wheat, and remain small or die. Ragweed germinates the following spring and passes through its young seedling stage under the protection of the wheat. When the wheat is harvested in early June, it is removed as a competitor, full sunlight is available for the ragweed, horseweeds and most other plants are absent, and ragweed assumes complete dominance.

Young asters are present in the ragweed fields and succession proceeds normally to asters the following year. Young asters are of approximately the same size in these fields as in horseweed dominated ones, which indicates that any fast growing species which shades asters and competes with them for water retards their growth.

One field from which sweet potatoes were harvested in late fall was dominated by ragweed the following year and another such field was dominated by horseweed. The sweet potato field that was followed by horseweed was adjacent to a large field dominated by horseweed. The number of horseweed seeds available from the adjacent field was high and those seeds germinated in late fall or early spring, to produce a full crop of horseweed plants against which ragweed seedlings failed in competition.

Another ragweed-dominated field had been fall-plowed and planted in winter vetch with much the same results as fields with winter wheat.

Eroded edges and spots in fields otherwise dominated by horseweed are usually occupied by ragweeds. Horseweeds probably germinated in these areas the preceding fall, and although the flat rosettes of horseweed would have a tendency to keep the soil from being washed away from the roots, severe erosion could remove or cover up the entire plant. In areas which are swept clean of horseweed seedlings by winter rains, ragweeds germinate the following spring and grow to be fair sized plants without competition.

One extremely eroded field in which the corn crop of the previous year had been last cultivated in June produced a pure stand of ragweed. Winter erosion had probably removed most of the horseweeds, asters, and other vegetation, and the spring-germinating ragweed grew without competition to be dominant in the field.

WHY ASTERS OCCASIONALLY SHARE DOMINANCE WITH HORSEWEEDS IN SOME FIELDS. Fields that are last cultivated in early summer before all of the asters have germinated usually have a mixture of horseweeds and asters as dominants the following year. The asters germinate in early summer, the horseweeds in the fall, and both species live together over the winter and share dominance the following year. Such fields appear to have horseweed as the only dominant when it blooms in July and August since it is then taller than the numerous asters, but aster appears to be dominant in the late fall when its blooms are conspicuous and the dead horseweed stalks are less noticeable.

WHY ASTER OCCASIONALLY PERSISTS IN DOMINANCE PAST THE SECOND YEAR. Asters usually give way to broomsedge in the third year because the seedlings and older asters fail in their competition for light and water with the broomsedge and other vegetation. The reduced light probably affects the seedlings as much as the competition for water, but with old asters water is a more critical factor than the reduction of light. In fields where there is no shortage of soil water because of type of soil, local drainage, or amount of precipitation, the old asters grow at least as tall as broomsedge and do not die as soon as they do in the fields where available water is low. In such fields, however, aster seedlings of the second or third generations rarely grow to maturity and the number and size of broomsedge plants increases within several years' time so that the old asters finally die, and the field is dominated by broomsedge.

THE EFFECT OF EROSION ON THE GENERAL TREND OF SUCCESSION. Erosion seems to affect aster dominance in second-year fields more than it does any other part of the normal sequence of succession. Young asters live for a full year as small upright plants less than three inches tall. Many nearly dead asters of this size were observed in eroded fields, following heavy rains, with the soil partially washed away from their root systems. Within a year's time few asters would escape one or more rains heavy enough to cause severe erosion in a field with some slope and no protecting terraces or cover crop.

Erosion causes some damage to horseweed, also, but to a smaller degree than to aster. Horseweed is a shorter-lived plant whose rosette form is somewhat soil binding. Horseweed passes through its younger stages at a time of year when precipitation is usually gradual rather than of the sudden storm type so common in the summer when asters are in their young stages.

Ragweed is common in eroded fields of both first and second years, because it seems to grow best where the competition of other plants has been removed in some way. Diodia is a small plant less than a foot high that often occupies eroded second-year fields. There were very few Diodia plants in any of the fields in the March counts, but it was present in fields in June, especially in eroded second-year fields. Some of these plants were present in third-year fields, but they rarely grew to be more than a few inches tall. This plant does not seem to be able to compete with other vegetation, and like ragweed is a short-lived summer annual that grows best when other vegetation is scant. For this reason it is commonly a dominant in eroded fields.

## CAUSES OF SECONDARY SUCCESSION IN GENERAL

These partial answers to some of the questions concerning causes of secondary succession in old fields in the Piedmont of North Carolina should help in the understanding of causes of secondary succession in general. In his discussion of causes of succession Clements (1916) says that a plant or community reacts upon the environment in such a way that it may become less favorable to the organism responsible for the change and more favorable for other species. He says that a time ultimately comes when the reactions are more favorable to the occupants than to the invaders and that then the existing community becomes more or less permanent.

This study indicates that another important factor may enter into a particular sequence of dominant species in secondary succession. The peculiarities of the life cycles of these species, especially the time of year at which the seeds mature and germinate and the relation of the time of seed germination to the time at which secondary succession is initiated, often gives one species a decided advantage over another in becoming the invading dominant (Fig. 6). Weaver & Clements (1938) emphasize the importance of adaptations which faciliate seed dispersal as a major cause in determining which species will first become established. This may be the reason why broomsedge is delayed in assuming dominance, but in the case of horseweed and aster, which seem to be equally abundant in this area and equally capable of migration, the time of seed maturity is the chief factor that determines the sequence of dominance.

One species does not always influence the environment in such a way that it is made more favorable for the next species in the successional sequence. Aster could definitely grow better without the influences exerted by horseweed and would probably assume dominance a year earlier than it does if horseweed or some other large annual were not present.

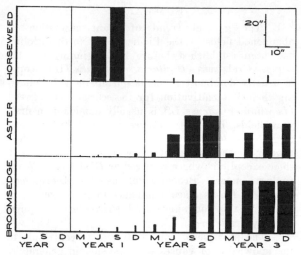

FIG. 6. Average size of horseweed, aster, and broomsedge plants in old fields for the first three years following abandonment. Height of column represents height of plant and base of column shows diameter at the widest point (all measurements in inches). M- March, J- June, S- September, D- December. Measurements for horseweed, an annual, are for different plants each year, but those for the perennials, aster and broomsedge, indicate sizes of the same plants. Young aster and broomsedge plants, though not in the graph, are present in second-and third-year fields. Because of the relative size, horseweed is the dominant of first-year fields; aster, of second-year fields; and broomsedge, of third-year fields.

There is some evidence that environmental conditions are more favorable for broomsedge after other plants have been growing in a field for several years so that the organic content of the soil increases, but this is not the chief reason why broomsedge is delayed in assuming dominance.

However, a species often makes its environment so unfavorable to itself that the species fails to survive. The influence of horseweed upon horseweed is the chief cause of the loss of dominance by the species. Aster influences its environment so that the survival and growth of seedlings of that species is so limited that the species can hold dominance only as long as the first generation of individuals can survive. The fact that broomsedge seedlings fail to make good growth in reduced light suggests that it, too, changes its environment so that conditions are unsuitable for reproduction.

Went (1942) suggests that the occurrence of one plant may influence the presence of certain other plants through some unknown agent, presumably chemical. If this were true it would be possible for chemical products of one species to stimulate or inhibit the growth of that plant or of other species and thus partially determine the sequence of succession of dominants in succession. This may be true in some situations, but no evidence was found to indicate that products of living dominants influence the general trend of succession in old fields of the Piedmont.

## SUMMARY

1. The general trend of plant succession in abandoned fields of the Piedmont of North Carolina had been established before the beginning of this study. Crabgrass (*Digitaria sanguinalis* (L.) Scop.) is usually dominant in fields during the fall following their last cultivation for the season. Horseweed (*Leptilon canadense* L.) is usually dominant in first-year fields, but is sometimes replaced by ragweed (*Ambrosia elatior* L.). Aster (*Aster pilosus* Willd.) usually is the dominant of second-year fields, with some exceptions where ragweed or *Diodia teres* Walt. replaces aster. Broomsedge (usually *Andropogon virginicus* L.) assumes dominance the third year, and maintains this dominance until it is replaced by pines a few years later.

2. The purpose of this study was to contribute to the knowledge of causes of succession in general by investigating the causes of early old field succession in the Piedmont of North Carolina. For this purpose certain problems concerning the major dominants of the first three years of succession—horseweed, aster, and broomsedge—needed to be solved. These problems involved the reasons why each species assumes dominance at a particular time and why each loses dominance at a definite later time. Questions concerning variations from the general trend needed to be answered.

3. Answers to these questions were sought in the life cycles and responses to environmental factors of the three dominant species. Life cycles were studied by means of experimental tests of seed germination, permanent quadrats in fields of different ages, surveys of numerous fields and by measurements of size of plants growing in different habitats. The responses of each species to variations in water and light, to substances produced by living plants, and to decay products of organic matter in the soil were tested in greenhouse experiments.

4. The studies of life histories and environmental factors yielded several pertinent facts for each species as follows:

a. Horseweed seeds mature as early as August, and germinate with no dormant period in the late summer and fall. The plant lives over winter as a rosette, grows to maturity, blooms and dies by late summer of the following year. Horseweed is a drought-resistant species whose seedlings grow best in reduced light. Young horseweeds are stunted by decay products from horseweed roots and cannot compete satisfactorily with individuals of the same species or with other vegetation.

b. Aster seeds mature in the fall too late to germinate because of cool weather. They germinate the following spring and the seedlings grow to be about two to three inches tall the first year, live over winter, and bloom the following fall. The flower stalk dies and a basal rosette lives and produces another flower stalk the following year. Asters make their best growth with abundant water and light.

Asters grown in the greenhouse with abundant water and light bloomed the first season. Aster plants were stunted by decay products of horseweed roots, horseweed tops, and broomsedge tops, when they were grown in the greenhouse in soil containing those plant parts. Aster plants appearing after the first generation rarely survive and bloom in the field under natural conditions.

c. Broomsedge seeds mature in the late fall and will not germinate without a period of cold dormancy. A few seedlings appear in old fields the first year of abandonment and do not produce seeds until the fall of the second year. Broomsedge seedlings are relatively drought-resistant and grow best in full sunlight, showing a definite chlorosis and reduced growth in shade. The survival of broomsedge plants of all ages in old fields is high and the species is able to compete successfully with the less drought-resistant asters. Broomsedge shows slightly better growth in soil containing organic matter, especially aster roots, than it does in soil with little organic matter.

5. The above generalizations can be used to explain to a large extent the causes of early old field succession in the Piedmont of North Carolina.

a. Horseweed usually assumes dominance in first-year fields because its seeds are ready to germinate when much farm land is being cultivated for the last time in a season. The low light intensities of fall and winter, and the lack of competition by other plants in first-year fields are favorable for the best growth of the species. Ragweed, a summer annual, may replace horseweed as the dominant of first-year fields if the normal crop of horseweed is eliminated by late fall plowing or by severe erosion.

Horseweed loses its dominance after the first year because it is stunted in the seedling stage by decay products from horseweed roots and also because it cannot compete successfully with the large number of individuals of the same species and with young asters which are abundant in second-year fields.

b. Asters are delayed in assuming dominance until the second year because the seeds do not germinate until the spring following maturity and although the seedlings do not die, they cannot make much growth in competition for light and water with the already established horseweeds. When the first crop of horseweed dies, competition is removed and asters make sufficient growth in spite of the inhibiting effects of decaying horseweed roots to be the dominant species of second-year fields.

Aster sometimes shares dominance with horseweed in first-year fields where the last cultivation of the season takes place in the early summer before all the aster seeds have germinated.

Aster loses its dominance because the seedlings are intolerant of shade and cannot grow to maturity under the old asters, broomsedge and other vegetation, and because the first generation of asters cannot compete with the more drought-resistant broomsedge. Asters may hold dominance past the second year if, for some reason, the lack of soil water does not become critical, but they cannot hold it indefinitely because of the failure of seedlings to grow to maturity.

    c. Broomsedge is delayed in assuming dominance until the third year because there is not an adequate supply of seeds present to produce a full stand until the first few invaders are old enough to produce seeds. Environmental conditions are almost as favorable in first- and second-year fields as in third-year fields for the growth of broomsedge seedlings.

    6. This study suggests that the particular timing of the events in the life cycles of the first series of invaders and its relation to the season of the year at which secondary succession is initiated may influence the dominant species more than changes in environment. Although the influence of a species on its environment often may produce conditions that keep the species from surviving, those conditions do not always make the environment more favorable for the next invader. The second invader may finally attain dominance in spite of, and not because of, the changes in environment brought about by the first dominant.

    There was no evidence from this investigation that toxic substances produced by one living plant influence other plants in such a way as to change the trend of succession. The rate of decay of different kinds of organic matter and the influence of that rate of decay upon the available minerals in the soil does affect the growth of plants and the trend of succession.

## LITERATURE CITED

Brenchley, W. E. 1919. Some factors in plant competition. Ann. Appl. Biol. **6**: 142-170.

Benedict, H. M. 1941. The inhibitory effect of dead roots on the growth of bromegrass. Amer. Soc. Agron. Jour. **33**: 1108-1109.

Bonner, J. 1946. Further investigations of toxic substances which arise from guayule plants: relation of toxic substances to the growth of guayule in soil. Bot. Gaz. **107**: 343-351.

Bonner, J. & A. W. Galston. 1944. Toxic substances from the culture media of guayule which may inhibit growth. Bot. Gaz. **106**: 85-198.

Clements, F. E. 1916. Plant succession. Carnegie Inst. Wash. Publ. **242**. 512 pp.

Crafton, W. M. & B. W. Wells. 1934. The old field prisere: an ecological study. Elisha Mitchell Sci. Soc. Jour. **49**: 225-246.

Coile, T. S. 1940. Soil changes associated with loblolly pine succession on abandoned agricultural land of the Piedmont Plateau. Duke Univ. School of Forestry Bul. **5**: 1-85.

Davis, E. F. 1928. The toxic principles of Juglans nigra as identified with synthetic juglone and its toxic effects on tomato and alfalfa plants. Amer. Jour. Bot. **15**: 620.

Gray, R., & J. Bonner. 1948. An inhibitor of plant growth from the leaves of Encelia farinosa. Amer. Jour. Bot. **35**: 52-57.

Hoagland, D. R. & D. I. Arnon. 1938. The water-culture method for growing plants without soil. Calif. Agr. Exp. Sta. Cir. **347**.

Oosting, H. J. 1942. An ecological analysis of the plant communities of Piedmont, North Carolina. Amer. Midl. Nat. **28**: 1-126.

Oosting, H. J. & M. E. Humphreys. 1940. Buried viable seeds in a successional series of old field and forest soils. Torrey Bot. Club Bul. **67**: 253-273.

Oosting, H. J. & P. J. Kramer. 1946. Water and light in relation to pine reproduction. Ecology **27**: 47-53.

Pickering, S. U., & The Duke of Bedford. 1914. The effect of one crop upon another. Jour. Agric. Sci. **6**: 136-151.
    1917. The effect of one plant on another. Ann. Bot. **31**: 181-187.
    1919. Action of one crop on another. Roy. Hort. Soc. Jour. **43**: 372-380.

Proebsting, E. L. & A. E. Gilmore. 1940. The relation of peach root toxicity to the establishment of peach orchards. Amer. Soc. Hort. Sci. Proc. **38**: 21-26.

Went, F. W. 1942. The dependence of certain annual plants on shrubs in southern Californian deserts. Torr. Bot. Club Bul. **69**: 100-114.

Weaver, J. E. & F. E. Clements. 1938. Plant Ecology. New York. 1-601.

Reprinted from LIMNOLOGY AND OCEANOGRAPHY
Vol. 13, No. 3, July 1968, pp. 448–464

# A SAND–BOTTOM EPIFAUNAL COMMUNITY OF INVERTEBRATES IN SHALLOW WATER

## Edward W. Fager

Scripps Institution of Oceanography, La Jolla, California 92037

### ABSTRACT

A community of nine species of epifaunal invertebrates living on sand in shallow water was censused for six years. The community consisted of three coelenterates, three gastropods, two echinoderms and one decapod. Seven of the species had aggregated distributions, but individuals of the first and fourth most abundant ones were randomly distributed. The relationship of distribution to settlement and mortality is discussed. The importance of each species population in relation to its demands on the environment, and its effects on it, was assessed in terms of frequency, density, biomass, cover, and motility. The results suggest that it is often misleading to label some species in a community "important" and others "unimportant," especially if this means that the latter are ignored in studies of community structure and dynamics. Populations of the nine species comprising the community remained constant (within sampling variability) over the six years. This community of few species, thus, appears to be a steady-state system. This was unexpected in view of the short species list, the lack of indication of substantial interspecific interactions, and the rigorous conditions in the environment.

### INTRODUCTION

This paper is concerned with the community of invertebrates living on the sand plain between the submarine canyons in La Jolla Bight, under water of 5–10-m depth. It is an attempt to describe the spatial and temporal structure of a relatively simple community in a uniform environment and from this to derive some understanding of community ecology.

The 5- to 10-m depth range was originally chosen because it allowed 50–60 min working time underwater per dive and avoided the complications of surf in shallower water and the problems of decompression introduced by prolonged work at greater depths. It has turned out that this region supports a characteristic invertebrate community, clearly separated from those animals that live in the surf zone and with relatively few overlaps with the fauna found at depths greater than 10 m.

It will be evident from later sections that the topography and sediment are essentially uniform over a large area and that while water movement, temperature and, to a lesser extent, salinity vary temporally, the variations are widespread over the area studied. The sand plain is sufficiently large to reduce edge effects and

within it solid substrates occupy only a small fraction of the total area. The barriers provided by the deep water of the submarine canyons and the limited amounts of shallow water at their heads make this effectively a closed system for the adult invertebrates considered in this study. It is, of course, not closed for any planktonic species nor for the larvae of the resident species if they have extended pelagic stages.

This study owes a great deal to the work of R. J. Ghelardi and A. O. Flechsig who made most of the dives with me. The nitrogen determinations were done by Miss T. Schultze. The anemones were determined by Dr. Cadet Hand, the gastropods by Dr. R. Stohler, and the fish by Mr. A. O. Flechsig. Financial support came from National Science Foundation Grants G-7141 and GB-5800 and from the Marine Life Research Program, the Scripps Institution's component of the California Cooperative Oceanic Fisheries Investigations, sponsored by the Marine Research Committee of the State of California.

### BOTTOM CHARACTERISTICS

La Jolla Bight is a rather shallow indentation in the coastline. It is somewhat protected to the north by the general westerly trend of the California coast and to the south by Point La Jolla and Point Loma but receives long-period swell approaching from the southwest to northwest (70–80° window). It is primarily this swell that gives rise to the wave surge that affects the bottom at depths of 5–10 m. Short-period waves have little effect at these depths.

Two submarine canyons come into La Jolla Bight (Fig. 1). One of them, Scripps Canyon, is about 960 m north of the Scripps Institution of Oceanography (SIO) pier; the other, La Jolla Canyon, is off the La Jolla Beach and Tennis Club, about 1,325 m south. They bring relatively deep water close to shore.

North of Scripps Canyon, the bottom sediment is fine sand, although at the head of the canyon there is a small intertidal rocky reef, and at times rock is exposed subtidally on the southern edge of the canyon and attached algae grow there. Directly south of La Jolla Canyon there is a small area of coarse sand and then an extensive area of rock from the intertidal out to depths over 20 m. Attached algae and surf grass, *Phyllospadix scouleri*, are abundant on the rocks.

The region between the canyons where this work was done is roughly triangular, with the base of the triangle along the shore and its apex at the confluence of the inner edges of the canyons. Except along the edges of the canyons whose walls are very steep, the sand plain has a nearly constant slope of 2–3% seaward from the surf zone out to a depth of about 30 m. The area between the depths of 5 and 10 m below MLLW is about $3.15 \times 10^5$ m$^2$.

The only solid substrates in the plain are the SIO pier extending out to a depth of about 5 m, a few large concrete blocks and oil drums put down for experimental purposes in the past, 20–30 brass stakes and four hose buoys inserted for this study, dense patches of the sand dollar *Dendraster excentricus*, and isolated individuals and beds of two species of tube-building polychaetes. In total these stable sub-

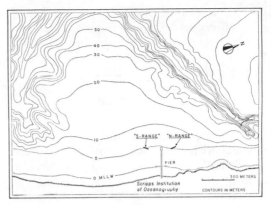

Fig. 1. Map of area of study. "*S-range*" and "*N-range*" mark the locations of the two series of permanent stations.

strates do not represent more than a small fraction of 1% of the area. Various intertidal organisms that attach to solid substrates extend out to sea on the pier pilings and some small attached algae grow on the pilings, on the concrete blocks and oil drums, on the hose buoys, and on the polychaete tubes. There are no macroscopic plants on the sand, but there is a sparse diatom flora on the sand grains (F. Round, personal communication).

The sand is fine and well sorted. The median grain diameter decreases gradually from 0.20 mm on the beach to 0.09 mm at a depth of about 30 m. At the depth of this study it is about 0.12 mm; 90% is in the size range, 0.08 to 0.19 mm. Most of the sand is quartz, mixed with about 5% heavy minerals, 3% micaceous materials, and less than 3% silt. There are only minor seasonal and local variations in the character of the sediment (Inman 1953).

An annual sediment cycle moves sand off the beach during autumn and winter storms and puts it back during spring and summer. This beach cut and fill is reflected in a concurrent fill and cut at depths out to about 10 m. Based on 15 sets of 10 measurements each, made at intervals of 1–9 weeks over a period of 17 months, the median net change in sand level at water depths of 6–8 m was 0.5 cm/week. Only five measurements showed zero change in sand level over a week. The

maximum change measured was a fill of
over 25 cm in less than five days. It was
about two months before the sand returned to its former level and the measuring rods could be located.

## WATER CHARACTERISTICS

The area receives little runoff from the
land except during the uncommon winter
storms. Although these provide a surface
layer of clay-filled low salinity water, the
salinity at 5-m depth is not affected appreciably. Over the years 1956–1962, the
range of daily salinities recorded for bottom water at the end of the SIO pier was
32.07 to 34.04‰, with a seven-year average
of 33.63‰.

The highest monthly mean bottom temperatures are recorded in July–September
(around 18C) and the lowest in December–February (around 15C). The mean
temperatures, however, give a false impression of the temperature regime under
which the animals live, because during the
period from April through October when
the water is thermally stratified, the inshore edge of the thermocline is often
found at depths of 5–10 m. Internal waves
can then produce rapid changes in temperature. With a thermometer laid on the
bottom we have observed changes of over
5C in a matter of minutes and rapid
changes of up to 8C have been recorded
by thermistors placed near the bottom just
off the SIO pier (C. L. Hubbs, personal
communication).

At the depths considered in this study,
the wave surge resulting from the long-
period swell keeps the top few millimeters
of sand almost constantly in suspension
and moves it inshore–offshore so that animals living on the sand surface are usually
in a miniature sandstorm. The water
movement is sometimes so violent that a
diver, even though heavily weighted, can
not stay in position, and the bottom can be
seen through a cloud of sand only at rare
intervals. The movement scours away sand
around solid objects that project above the
surface. This puts a stress on the animals
that is met either by some sort of anchor

imbedded in the sediment or by the ability
to burrow rapidly. All of the species
appear to be able to adjust to rapid
changes in sand level.

In addition to the inshore–offshore
movement, there is a net water movement
shoreward along the bottom and often a
longshore current. The latter most frequently tends toward the north (Shepard
1950). It may be important in the transport of plant detritus and associated animals from the rocky area south of La Jolla
Canyon.

Rip currents occur all along the beach,
most frequently at certain locations. The
seaward heads of these currents are generally at depths of 5–6 m. They may have
an effect on the distribution of some of
the animals—directly during settlement
(Fager 1964) and indirectly by affecting
the availability of detrital material used
as food.

## METHODS

Most of the work was done in the years
1957–1959, with just enough to check for
changes in 1960–1963. The field observations and sampling were all done using
SCUBA. With this tool it has been possible to carry out repeated, detailed
studies of the distribution patterns of the
animals without disrupting the habitat or
depleting the populations. It has also provided some observations on behavior, especially species interactions. More than
500 man hours were spent underwater, and
402 quantitative counts at "random" locations and 270 at "permanent stations" were
obtained. The apparatus and methods
used in obtaining these data have been
described by Fager et al. (1966) and only
briefly will be discussed here.

The larger animals living on the sand
surface or extending through it were sampled by dropping a brass circle (area,
m²/4) in such a way that the diver could
not see the exact location where it would
fall. Two divers then recorded the animals in the two halves of the circle. Repe-
tition of counts by experienced divers indicated little or no variation between divers.
If carried out carefully, the approach of

the diver and the dropping of the ring had no apparent effect on the animals.

Practical considerations made this method of positioning the samples the one of choice, but it did result in a haphazard, though presumably unbiased, pattern of samples rather than a strictly random one. A few sets of samples were placed randomly in the study area by dropping markers from a skiff run at relatively constant speed across it. The timing of dropping the markers was determined by sets of numbers drawn from a random number table. Analysis of the resulting counts did not indicate any significant differences between these random samples and those placed haphazardly.

It was initially thought that the circle counts would be reliable for animals down to a size of 5 mm or a little less if they lived on the sand surface or moved about just beneath it. To check this, a comparison was made between population density estimates obtained from m²/4 circle counts and from sand cores (5 cm deep, 35-cm² area) taken during the same months and in the same areas (394 circles/230 cores). Three species of small gastropods (*Balcis* sp., *Olivella baetica*, *Turbonilla attrita*) and one species of isopod (*Ancinus* sp.) that were easily visible when moving on the sand surface were used in the comparison. In all cases the ratios, mean number per m² (cores)/mean number per m² (circles), were significantly greater than 1.0 (Table 1). Thus, many of the individuals must have been buried in the sand, probably near the surface but quiescent and, in the case of the gastropods, with the siphon retracted. This would mean, for example, that on the average only one individual in 27 (95% limits, 13–42) of the *Olivella baetica* population was active at any one time.

The circle counts seemed to be more satisfactory for the larger animals. However, because locations where any of these animals were evident were avoided when taking cores, the only species that was taken frequently enough in the cores to allow a comparison was *Amphiodia occidentalis*. The ratio, mean number per m²

TABLE 1. *Comparison of core and circle density estimates. Values are mean numbers per m², ratios of these and 95% confidence limits of the means and ratios, based on 230 cores and 394 circle counts*

|  | Cores* | Circles† | Cores/circles |
|---|---|---|---|
| *Balcis* sp. | 18.7 ± 9.0 | 0.28 ± 0.10 | 66.8 ± 41.2 |
| *Olivella baetica* | 29.8 ± 14.5 | 1.10 ± 0.30 | 27.1 ± 14.6 |
| *Turbonilla attrita* | 6.2 ± 3.6 | 0.37 ± 0.10 | 16.8 ± 10.7 |
| *Ancinus* sp. | 6.2 ± 5.0 | 0.43 ± 0.18 | 14.4 ± 13.1 |

* Cores—5 cm deep, 35 cm².
† Circles—m²/4, only animals visible on the surface counted.

(cores)/mean number per m² (circles), for this species was 1.8 ± 1.2.

Two sets of five permanent stations each were established, one north and one south of the pier (Fig. 1). Each station was marked by two 0.6-mm-diameter brass stakes driven into the sand 1.5 m apart to position a template that fitted onto them. We could, thus, return repeatedly to the same place on the bottom and determine the position of an animal. Tests showed that the determination of position was good to ±1–2 cm, the error arising mostly from the diver's difficulty in reaching and maintaining a position directly above the animal. When the template was not in place, there was little or no disturbance of either the bottom sediment or the water movements in the area where counts were made.

The species studied at the permanent stations were mostly coelenterates. As these were not easily marked, it was assumed that if an individual of a species was seen repeatedly within ±2 cm of the location of previous sightings of the species, it was the same individual. Given the relatively low densities of the species, the probability of having the same locations occupied repeatedly would be small if their occupation depended on random movements of different individuals.

All determinations of biomass, size, and motility of a species were made on a series of individuals selected to represent

TABLE 2. *List of epifaunal species recorded during the study*

Anthozoa
  *Harenactis attenuata* Torrey
  *Renilla köllikeri* Pfeffer
  *Stylatula elongata* (Gabb)
  *Zaolutus actius* Hand

Polychaeta
  *Diopatra splendidissima* Kinberg
  *Owenia fusiformis* Delle Chiaje

Malacostraca
  *Ancinus* sp.
  *Blepharipoda occidentalis* Randall
  *Cancer gracilis* Dana
  *Crangon nigromaculatus* (Lockington)
  *Holopagurus pilosus* Holmes
  *Heterocrypta occidentalis* (Dana)
  *Inachoides tuberculatus* Lockington
  *Lepidopa myops* Stimpson
  *Portunus xantusii* (Stimpson)

Gastropoda
  *Acteon punctocaelatus* (Carpenter)
  *Balcis* sp. (= *micans* Carpenter ?)
  *Epitonium tinctum* Carpenter
  *Nassarius fossatus* (Gould)
  *Nassarius perpinguis* (Hinds)
  *Olivella baetica* Carpenter

*Olivella biplicata* (Sowerby)
*Pleurophyllidia californica* Cooper
*Polinices recluzianus* (Deshayes)
*Turbonilla attrita* Dall and Bartsch
*Turbonilla tridentata* Carpenter

Asteroidea
  *Astropecten armatus* Gray
  *Astropecten californicus* Fisher

Ophiuroidea
  *Amphiodia occidentalis* (Lyman)
  *Amphiodia urtica* (Lyman)

Echinoidea
  *Dendraster excentricus* (Eschscholtz)

Holothurioidea
  *Molpadia arenicola* (Stimpson)

Pisces
  *Citharichthys stigmaeus* Jordan and Evermann
  *Hypsopsetta guttulata* (Girard)
  *Paralichthys californicus* (Ayres)
  *Platyrhinoides triseriata* (Jordan and Gilbert)
  *Pleuronichthys ritteri* Starks and Morris
  *Pleuronichthys verticalis* Jordan and Gilbert
  *Rhinobatos productus* (Ayres)
  *Urolophus halleri* Cooper

the size structure of the field population. Measurements of coelenterates and distance between arms of brittle stars were made in the field on animals that were as little disturbed as practicable. Sizes for the other species are a combination of field and laboratory determinations. For the motile species, rates of movement were also estimated in the field for undisturbed animals. Organic nitrogen was determined on oven-dried (100C, 15–18 hr) material by standard micro-Kjeldahl technique. Wet and dry weights were considered unsatisfactory measures of biomass because of large differences between the species in the amounts of structural material, mostly inorganic. As Paine (1964) has pointed out, ashing may also give unsatisfactory results when comparisons are made between species differing widely in inorganic content. Organic nitrogen as a measure of biomass avoids these difficulties and, as most of it can be equated with protein, is a good measure of the living tissue present.

CHARACTERISTICS OF THE EPIFAUNA

At these depths, 39 species were seen resting on, crawling over, or extending through the sand (Table 2). Eight of the species were fish and, as discussed later, seemed to be well separated ecologically from the abundant epifaunal invertebrates. Nineteen of the invertebrates were seen on less than half of the dives and occurred less than five times in the quantitative samples. They are not considered further because of lack of information. The remaining 12 species were present in every month, were recorded on more than half of the dives and in more than five quantitative samples. One of these species, *Dendraster excentricus*, generally occurs in dense beds at depths greater than 10 m. A large proportion of the individuals observed in the depth range here considered had injured tests, often with barnacles growing on them. It appears reasonable to consider the *Dendraster* as displaced from the normal habitat and not part of this community of animals, although, as shown later, they are a source of food. Another species, *Balcis* sp., is an ectoparasite on the *Dendraster* and has the same status as the latter. A third species, *Olivella baetica*, has also been left out of consideration because the sampling techniques used for this study gave gross underestimates of its population density (*see* discussion in methods section). The remaining nine species are considered to constitute the characteristic epifaunal assemblage in this habitat— the species that were always seen and that dominated the habitat, both numerically and in terms of their demand and impact on it. Table 3 presents information on habit, type of distribution, reproduction, food, and predators. Table 4 lists the frequency of occurrence and estimates of numbers, organic nitrogen, area covered per square meter, and motility.

The burrowing anemone *Harenactis attenuata* was the most frequent and abundant invertebrate on the sand at these depths. These anemones live with the column buried in the sand and only the sand-colored disc and tentacles showing at the surface. They are alternately partially covered and uncovered by sand as it is moved by the wave surge. The animals are not attached to any solid substrate but hold their position by means of an anchoring bulb. This easily breaks off so that uninjured animals are difficult to obtain for laboratory studies. Observations at the permanent stations have shown that the anemones move up and down in the sand to adjust for moderate change in sand level (2 cm or less per week) and do so without appreciable lateral movement (Table 5). Even following an unusually large and rapid fill (over 25 cm in less than five days), individuals were found at the same positions after the sand surface had returned to its usual level two months later.

Tentacle spread of what appeared to be mature individuals was 2.5 to 3.0 cm. The animals have turned out to be unexpectedly long-lived in the field. At the permanent stations, 11 of 45 individuals that were first seen in July 1958 were still present over five years later in October 1963 (*see* Table 5 for examples) and the median period of persistence was over two years. During this time there was no noticeable change in size although this must be interpreted with caution because coelenterates are notoriously difficult to characterize by measurements of disc width or tentacle spread, and these were the only measurements available without uprooting the animals. There was little recruitment during the five years; only seven young were recorded as having settled in the 2.5 m² covered by the permanent stations. These aspects of the life history are reflected in the lack of appreciable change in estimates of population density over a six-year period (Fig. 2); the 95% confidence intervals of the estimates of mean numbers per m²/4 show broad overlaps and 22 of the 26 intervals include the overall mean value of 1.62 individuals per m²/4.

The food items most commonly seen in the grasp of the tentacles were small *Dendraster*. Short strands of *Phyllospadix* were also frequently caught, presumably for the animals on the surf grass; in two cases isopods of the genus *Idothea* were found partially digested by the anemone but still clinging to a surf grass fragment. Other observed food items were a badly broken up polychaete and a damaged *Holopagurus*. These observations suggest that the food of this species is composed largely of animals displaced from their normal habitat and rolled slowly along the bottom by the net inshore movement of the water. *Harenactis* was never observed to capture active prey; nothing has been seen to eat *Harenactis*.

This species is very rare at depths less than 5 m and greater than 10 m. Within this depth range the density did not change over the region between the submarine canyons except for a small increase in density just off the end of the SIO pier, possibly due to the presence of a more or less persistent rip current at this position. The pattern of distribution was examined

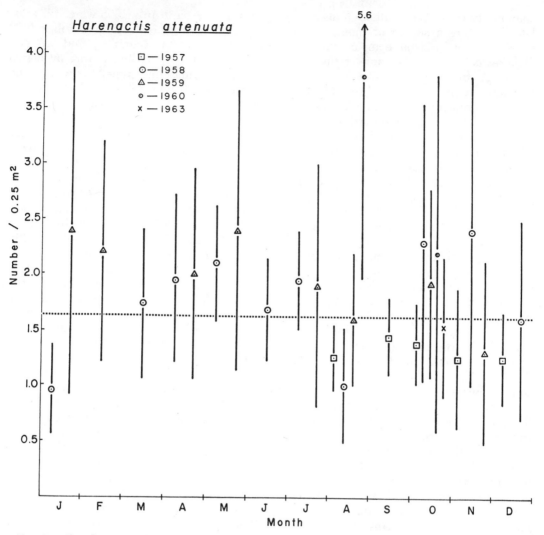

FIG. 2.    Abundance of *Harenactis attenuata*.  Values given are means and 95% confidence intervals for the mean, $\bar{x} \pm t_{0.05} s_{\bar{x}}$, per m²/4 sample.  Dotted line is overall mean.

in four different ways: by fitting the distribution of numbers of individuals per m²/4 sample to a Poisson distribution; by examining the change in the ratio of variance to mean as successively larger (up to 3,600 cm²) samples were formed by combining adjacent samples in a line of 144 contiguous samples of 225 cm² each; by counting runs of like signs along lines, placed parallel, perpendicular, or at 45° angles to the shore, where a plus was recorded when at least one *Harenactis* was present within an interval of 10 cm along the line and a minus when none was present; and by looking at the distribution of distances to nearest neighbor and the percentage of reflexives (Clark and Evans 1954, 1955) in randomly selected plots of 3.24 m² each.  None of these gave significant evidence of nonrandom distribution of individuals.  This is in direct contrast to the distribution patterns of the other abundant organisms, except *Amphiodia*, all of which have provided evidence of patchiness.  The implication is that, for *Harenactis* within this depth range, the

TABLE 3. *Characteristics of the abundant epifaunal invertebrates*

| | Habit* | Distri-bution† | Reproduction‡ | | | Food‖ | Predators‖ |
|---|---|---|---|---|---|---|---|
| | | | Mating | Eggs | Young§ | | |
| *Harenactis attenuata* | S | R | – | – | 8–11 | Dead crustaceans, polychaetes, and *Dendraster* | — |
| *Zaolutus actius* | S | A | – | – | 1–8 | Crustaceans | *Epitonium* |
| *Renilla köllikeri* | S(M) | A | – | – | 8–11 | — | *Astropecten Pleurophyllidia* |
| *Amphiodia occidentalis* | S–M | R | – | 10 | 2–11 | Plant detritus | — |
| *Nassarius perpinguis* | M | A | – | – | 7–12 | Dead fish and crustaceans | — |
| *Holopagurus pilosus* | M | A | 5 | – | 9 | Plant detritus | *Polinices* |
| *Polinices recluzianus* | M | A | 12–3 | 1–10 | 1–10 | Hermit crabs | — |
| *Nassarius fossatus* | M | A? | 4 | 5 | 5–6 | Dead fish, crustaceans, pelecypods, and holothurians | — |
| *Astropecten armatus* | M | A? | – | 3 | 11–1 | *Dendraster* and *Renilla* | — |

* S = sedentary; M = motile.
† R = random ($s^2/\bar{x} \sim 1.0$); A = aggregated ($s^2/\bar{x} > 1.0$, at the 95% level).
‡ Based on field observations; numbers are months in which mating, eggs or gravid females, and young were seen.
§ Individuals were recorded as young if they were less than ¼ the size of the average large individual.
‖ Only relationships actually observed in the field are recorded.

probabilities of settling and of survival after settling are independent of physical or biological differences between locations, including the presence or absence of other members of the same species. The data from the permanent stations indicate that, once settled, individuals stay in place (Table 5) and live a long time.

The anemone, *Zaolutus actius*, was the second species in abundance and third in frequency in the sand (Table 4). Its distribution will here be considered only outside of the *Owenia* bed that was described earlier (Fager 1964). It is smaller than *Harenactis*; individuals that appeared to be mature were 1 to 1.5 cm across the tentacles. The disc and tentacles were generally held 0.5 to 1.0 cm above the sand surface. Also in contrast to *Harenactis*, this species was always attached to some solid substrate, usually to the tubes of polychaetes but sometimes to small pebbles. In the laboratory, individuals moved laterally a few centimeters without emerging from the sand. This would mean that individuals living in dense beds of tube-building polychaetes could change their positions. The median period of persistence at the permanent stations was four months, measured by resightings of individuals; the maximum was 11 months. If this measure of longevity is not invalidated by movement, this species is much shorter lived than *Harenactis*. A single caprellid and a young *Lepidopa myops* were the only food items recorded for this species. The position of the tentacle crown well above the sand surface and a more rapid response to stimuli suggest that *Zaolutus* may customarily feed on zooplankton organisms rather than the displaced animals utilized by *Harenactis*. In the laboratory, it easily captured and ingested adult *Artemia*, but did not live long when these were the only food provided.

As was true of the preceding species, the population density of *Zaolutus* remained

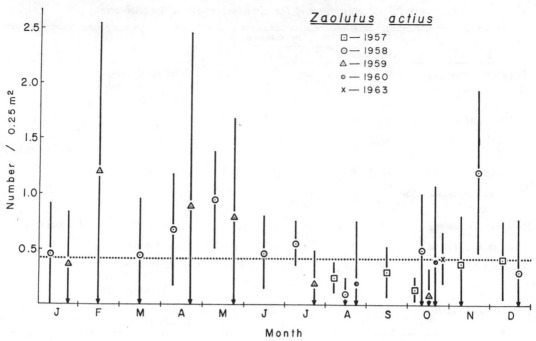

FIG. 3. Abundance of *Zaolutus actius*. Values given are means and 95% confidence intervals for the mean, $\bar{x} \pm t_{0.05} s_{\bar{x}}$, per m²/4. Dotted line is overall mean.

essentially constant over the six years of observation (Fig. 3); 18 of 24 confidence intervals include the overall mean, 0.44 individual per m²/4. Large numbers of recently settled young were observed in March–July 1958, but young have seldom been seen since at the depths considered. The species was generally more abundant at greater depths, probably because the tube-building polychaete *Owenia fusiformis* to which it attaches was usually more abundant there. Where *Zaolutus* was abundant, a small gastropod *Epitonium tinctum* was frequently seen and appeared to be a specific predator. Individual snails were often found with the proboscis inserted far into the gastrovascular cavity of an anemone. The anemone did not retract under this stimulus.

The distribution of *Zaolutus* individuals was definitely patchy [index of dispersion significantly ($p < 0.05$) greater than 1.0]. This may, of course, be a secondary effect, resulting from the patchiness of the solid objects, mostly worm tubes, required for attachment.

Further information on the pattern of distribution was obtained from 100 samples of m²/4 in which the numbers of individuals were recorded separately for each half of the sample. If the density within the patches was appreciably higher than that between and the patches were large relative to sample size (m²/4) or were themselves aggregated, one would expect the counts on the two sides to be generally similar and, therefore, the differences between them to be small. If, on the other hand, the patches were smaller than m²/4 and were randomly distributed, all possible differences would be equally likely. For example: with a set of 4 half-samples with 0 individuals, 5 with 1, and 3 with 2, the theoretical distribution of differences for the latter case would consist of 12 (4 × 3) differences of 2, 35 (4 × 5 + 5 × 3) differences of 1 and 19 (4 × 3/2 + 5 × 4/2 + 3 × 2/2) differences of 0. In the case of *Zaolutus*, there was a slightly larger proportion of small differences in the observed than in the theoretical, but this was not significant even at the 20% level (Kol-

TABLE 4. *Community structure*

| | Frequency* | Density† | Biomass‡ | Area§ | Motility‖ |
|---|---|---|---|---|---|
| *Harenactis attenuata* | 511 | 1,089 (6.48) | 360–410 | 30–50 | — |
| *Zaolutus actius* | 178 | 296 (1.76) | 10–20 | 1–3 | — |
| *Renilla köllikeri* | 248 | 282 (1.68) | 80–105 | 35–50 | — |
| *Amphiodia occidentalis* | 102 | 109 (0.65) | 10–20 | 20–35 | — |
| *Nassarius perpinguis* | 44 | 62 (0.37) | 1–5 | 1 | 75–110 |
| *Holopagurus pilosus* | 28 | 44 (0.26) | 30–40 | 1–3 | 30–60 |
| *Polinices recluzianus* | 10 | 17 (0.10) | 5–10 | 2 | 75–105 |
| *Nassarius fossatus* | 8 | 12 (0.07) | 1–5 | 1 | 200–275 |
| *Astropecten armatus* | 6 | 7 (0.04) | 20–30 | 5–15 | 50–70 |

* Number of m²/4 samples in which species occurred, out of a total of 672.
† Number of individuals observed in 672 m²/4 samples. Values in ( ) are mean numbers of individuals/m².
‡ Estimated milligrams organic nitrogen per m².
§ Estimated area occupied by population, cm²/m².
‖ Estimated times (min) required for the populations of motile species to cover an area equal to that occupied by the *Renilla* population, assuming movement 4% of the time (based on estimates of activity in the population of *O. baetica*, cf. section on methods).

mogorov-Smirnov test; Tate and Clelland 1957). It appears, therefore, that the patches in this species are smaller than m²/4 in area and are randomly distributed in relation to each other.

The colonial pennatulid *Renilla köllikeri* was the third most abundant and second most frequent epifaunal organism (Table 4). It lives with the colony flat on the sand surface and the peduncle inserted downwards into the sand. The peduncle can be somewhat inflated and serves as a remarkably good anchor; colonies have been seen capping small mounds of sand 5 cm or so above the general level and holding the mound against violent wave surge. The larger colonies were 7.5 to 8.0 cm across. The data from the permanent stations indicated that this animal, in contrast to *Harenactis*, moves about a good

deal. Colonies and groups of colonies seen in one location in a particular m²/4 area on one day would, by the next day, be elsewhere in the circle or gone. In the laboratory, colonies moved on the sand surface at an average rate of 2 mm/min by passing successive waves of contraction back along the edges from the apex. In doing this, they trailed the peduncle on the sand surface. Under the usual conditions in the field, any colony that moved in this manner would be quickly tumbled about by the wave surge and finally deposited on the beach; colonies inadvertently kicked out of the sand by a diver suffered this fate. *Renilla* is, however, rarely found cast up on the beach. It must, therefore, have some mechanism of movement in the field that enables a colony to move while holding itself firmly in the sand. The

TABLE 5. *Constancy of position of individuals of* Harenactis attenuata *at permanent stations*

| Animal | 1958 | | 1959 | | | 1960 | 1963 | Location |
| | Jul | Oct | Jan | Apr | Aug | Aug | Oct | |
|---|---|---|---|---|---|---|---|---|
| A | 29/14* | 30/15 | 28/17 | 28/15 | 30/15 | † | 27/16 | South 1 |
| B | 20/8 | 21/7 | 19/8 | 20/6 | 20/6 | † | 20/4 | South 2 |
| C | 40/22 | 40/23 | 38/22 | ‡ | 40/22 | 38/23 | 38/22 | North 2 |
| D | 12/9 | 15/9 | 12/11 | 12/9 | 12/10 | 11/9 | 10/9 | North 3 |
| E | 22/9 | 22/9 | ‡ | 23/7 | 23/6 | 22/9 | 21/8 | North 4 |

* Numbers are coordinates of positions at permanent stations, measured in cm from two reference lines. Of the 45 large individuals seen at the permanent stations, 11 were in the same position (never more than ±2 cm from a mean position) for over five years and an additional 13 held their position for over two but less than five years.
† Stakes on the south range were not found on the August 1960 dive.
‡ Individual not observed on this dive, probably retracted beneath sand surface.

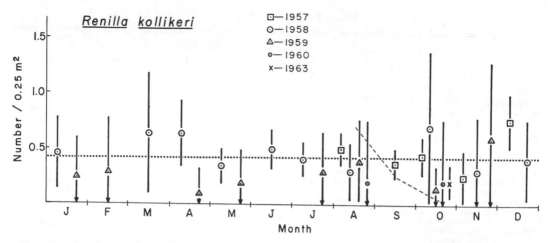

FIG. 4. Abundance of *Renilla köllikeri*. Values given are means and 95% confidence intervals for the mean, $\bar{x} \pm t_{0.05}s_{\bar{x}}$, per m²/4. Dotted line is overall mean. Dashed line is for a special count of newly-settled young that were not included in the regular censuses.

movement has so far precluded the study of longevity of the colonies.

The movement is apparently not random, for the colonies were definitely aggregated [index of dispersion significantly ($p < 0.05$) greater than 1.0]. This aggregation might arise from the response of a colony to changed characteristics of water or sand movement on the bottom caused by the presence of one or more other colonies; the group, perhaps, mutually increasing the individual colony's ability to withstand wave surge.

The observed distribution of differences between numbers of individuals in halves of samples did not depart from the theoretical distribution at the 20% level (cf. discussion under *Zaolutus* for details of method). Most patches of this species are, therefore, apparently smaller than m²/4 in area and randomly distributed in relation to each other.

Colonies have been seen at depths of 30 m or more, but those that occurred out beyond 10-m depth appeared to be unhealthy as judged by the flaccid texture of the colony and the limited numbers of extended polyps. The species was absent at depths less than 5 m.

A heavy annual set of young *Renilla* (2–10 polyps per colony) was usually observed, commencing in August and continuing through part of November. Colonies in the laboratory released planulae in late July (1958). Because of difficulties in making accurate counts of these small colonies, they were not included in the regular population censuses. A set of special counts indicated that their presence often doubled the mean number of colonies per m²/4 but the increases persisted only briefly (Fig. 4, dashed line). As these small colonies could easily be torn out of the bottom by wave surge, most of the loss of young can probably be attributed to physical processes. The loss may be increased by predation because all of the sightings of *Pleurophyllidia californica*, an opisthobranch reputed to be a specific predator on *Renilla* (Ricketts and Calvin 1952), were during the months when the young *Renilla* were present. *Pleurophyllidia* was once seen feeding on a large colony. *Astropecten* is a much more common predator on larger *Renilla*; about 1 in every 10 starfish examined had the peduncle of a colony protruding from the mouth opening. It is not known whether this starfish would eat very small colonies.

If the young are excluded, the population density remained essentially constant over the period of six years (Fig. 4); 22 of 26 confidence intervals include the overall mean, 0.42 individual per m²/4.

In the field, *Renilla* colonies have not been observed feeding. It is suspected that they feed on microzooplankton. In the laboratory, individual polyps caught, but seemed to have some trouble eating, newly hatched *Artemia* nauplii.

The distributions of the preceding three species were examined to see whether the occurrence or numbers of individuals of one species were related to those of another species. None of the three $2 \times 2$ contingency tables (presence–absence in $m^2/4$ quadrats) differed appreciably from expectation and the abundances of the species were not significantly correlated. There is thus no statistical evidence that the presence, absence, or abundance of one of the numerically dominant species affected the presence, absence, or abundance of the others.

The brittle star, *Amphiodia occidentalis*, the fourth most abundant and frequent species, was always found with the disc buried, oral surface down, a few centimeters beneath the sand surface and, usually, with only two or three arms extending through the surface. Distance between arms ranged from 4 to 12 cm. A water current carrying sand grains and detritus particles moved down one of the arms and another moved up another arm. In deeper water, where wave surge has less effect and, therefore, reducing conditions develop in the sand relatively near the surface, the positions of individual brittle stars were marked on calm days by small conical piles of blackened sand brought up from the reduced sand layer in which the disc was situated.

Individuals of *Amphiodia* were resighted at the same location in the permanent station circles for maximum periods of one month. Animals that were dug out had no difficulty in moving across the sand and reburying. There was no evidence of clumping.

What were recorded as young of this species were observed almost throughout the year. The records may, however, be unreliable because a second, less common, smaller species (*Amphiodia urtica*) does occur in the area and sightings were not all checked by collection of the individuals.

*Nassarius perpinguis*, the smaller (avg spire height, 1.5 cm; estimated volume, 0.4 cc) of the two gastropods of this genus found on the sand, was about five times as abundant as its larger congener, *Nassarius fossatus* (avg spire height, 4 cm; estimated volume, 5.4 cc). Both spend much of their time just beneath the sand surface with the siphon exerted. Large numbers of both species were actively attacking every fish carcass seen. When a dead fish was staked down on the bottom as bait, the snails emerged from the sand and crawled actively toward it if there was a current and they were on the downstream side. They fed together without apparent interference; *N. perpinguis* tended to crawl into or under the fish more than *N. fossatus* did. Both species reacted to the flesh of the dead fish but not to its carefully separated skin. *N. perpinguis* was also seen feeding on dead *Blepharipoda occidentalis* and on *Balanus* sp., the latter having been recently removed from one of the hose buoys. *N. fossatus* was seen feeding on both of the preceding, plus dead *Portunus xanthusii* and *Inachoides tuberculatus* and moribund *Molpadia arenicola* and *Donax gouldii*. The two species of *Nassarius* have never been seen feeding on active living material. There is no field evidence suggesting a difference in food habits or behavior or any interspecific interference.

For both species, the index of dispersion was greater than 1.0 ($p < 0.05$, in the case of *N. perpinguis*). The cause of aggregations was clear when the gastropods were feeding on larger dead animals. The continued aggregation when not feeding may reflect earlier attraction to a food source followed by limited dispersal after the food was consumed.

Both of the species reacted strongly to being touched by a tube foot of the common sand star *Astropecten armatus*. The reaction involved extrusion of the snail nearly out of its shell and violent threshing about of the foot. This resulted in the animal being thrown considerable distances, in jumps of 5–15 cm. The reaction continued for some time after contact with the tube foot had been lost. *Astropecten* attempted to hold the snails but medium sized snails easily escaped, even when held on the oral surface of the starfish until a good grip should have been obtained. It, therefore, seems unlikely that this starfish is a successful predator on adults of these gastropods (Feder 1963).

*N. fossatus* has several times been observed laying eggs, always in May. The stalked egg cases were affixed to a worm tube (*Diopatra splendidissima*), to strands of *Phyllospadix* that were embedded in the sand, and once to a polyethylene transect line that had just been put down. *N. perpinguis* was never seen laying eggs. On the other hand, while young of *N. fossatus* have never been common and those seen have always been about a quarter the size of the larger individuals of this species, very small (3–4-mm spire height) individuals of *N. perpinguis* were quite common in sand cores in July 1958 and have been taken frequently in cores in summer months of other years.

The hermit crab *Holopagurus pilosus* seems well-adapted to life in the sand, easily burying itself so that only the eyes, antennae, and a small area in the mouth region are visible, the latter kept clear by motion of the maxillipeds. The crab constantly picks up particles from the sand surface with its chelipeds and passes them to the mouth. When the wave surge was strong, individuals tended to stay buried and pick up food as it came to them; when it was weaker they moved about over the sand. Most of the material they picked up seemed to be of plant origin; they were not attracted to dead fish.

One instance of predation has been observed. A *Polinices recluzianus* had partly drilled through another *Polinices* shell that contained a *Holopagurus*.

The distribution of numbers of individuals per sample of the hermit crab indicated aggregation. Field observations of behavior suggested that individuals were aware of each other's presence at short distances so the aggregation may have arisen through social interaction. On two occasions (Sep 1957 and Jan 1960) quite different, very dense aggregations were observed. In both cases, 100–200 crabs were found packed tightly in several layers, the uppermost one at the sand surface, in an area 10–20 cm on a side. Except for the crabs, there seemed to be no difference from the surrounding sand. Recent observations indicate that such patches may remain in one place for as long as three weeks. There was no evidence of mortality, molting, or breeding; the individuals were active, not soft, small to medium size for the species and none carried eggs. In an unselected sample of 138 individuals, 67 were in *Olivella biplicata* shells, 12 in *Mitrella* sp., three in *Iselica* sp., two in *Amphissa* sp., 41 in *Olivella baetica*, eight in *Nassarius perpinguis*, two in *Acteon punctocaelatus*, and one each in *Epitonium* sp., *Balcis* sp., and *Turbonilla tridentata*. As the first four gastropods in the list do not occur in the immediate area, their shells must have come from some distance yet they comprised 61% of the sample. The larger *Holopagurus* were usually in *Polinices recluzianus* shells but one was found in the rather fragile shell of a land snail, *Helix* sp.

The moon snail *Polinices recluzianus* was frequently seen partly buried in the sand or moving through the surface layer. Its predation on *Holopagurus* has already been mentioned. The snail was attracted to dead fish but it did not stay with the bait as the *Nassarius* did. Perhaps it was unable to feed. The animals on which snails of this genus are known to prey, medium to large pelecypods, were rare in this sand habitat.

Mating pairs of *Polinices* were seen only during winter and early spring months but the characteristic egg collars were present nearly all the year. Very small stages were never recorded, even in the sand cores, but individuals about one quarter the size of adults were present throughout the year.

*Astropecten armatus* was the only starfish living on sand at these depths. A smaller, more slender, species of the same genus, *A. californicus*, occurred seaward of the distribution of *A. armatus*, being abundant at depths of 15 m and more while *A. armatus* was most abundant at 5–10-m depths and was seldom seen as deep as 15 m.

As noted above, *Astropecten* frequently ate *Renilla* but its commonest prey was the sand dollar *Dendraster excentricus*. These were not taken from the dense beds but were usually individuals displaced shoreward from them. *Astropecten* was attracted to dead fish but did not persist on the bait. Its reaction to the two species of *Nassarius* (*see above*) suggests that even though it could not hold the adults it might be a successful predator on the young and other smaller gastropods.

## DISCUSSION

The homogeneity of benthic communities over considerable areas has often been noted (Sanders 1960; Thorson 1957). The community discussed in this paper is a widespread, frequently recurring group of species living along the coasts of southern California and northern Baja California, subtidally on fine sand at depths of 5–10 m and intertidally on sand flats in bays (Ricketts and Calvin 1952). At first glance the two habitats appear dissimilar, but they have certain characteristics in common—considerable water movement but no surf, rapid changes in temperature, sources of appreciable quantities of plant and animal detritus, and a uniform shifting substrate composed of fine, well-sorted sand. The uniformity in the area of this study is reflected in the random distributions of individuals of two of the abundant species, *Harenactis* and *Amphiodia*. Such distributions may be interpreted as indicating that settlement and survival are equally likely at all locations. The other species, being aggregated, impose a biological pattern on the physical uniformity. The pattern is the result of the activities of the species and may be connected with factors influencing their survival. It ap-

pears to have little effect on the habitat as it is impermanent, shifting with the movements of the animals, and at any one time occupies less than 2% of the surface area.

The separation of the invertebrate epifauna from the other major sections of the sand-bottom community, the vertebrate epifauna and the invertebrate infauna, is to some extent arbitrary. There are, however, three sorts of justification for the separation. The least important is the size of the animals, although this does indicate something of their requirements and capabilities. Most individuals of the invertebrate epifauna are in the size range 1 to 10 cm and, while young of the most abundant vertebrate, *Citharichthys stigmaeus*, are less than 10 cm long and a few uncommon polychaetes and nemerteans that live in the sand are over 1 cm long, there are surprisingly few overlaps with species in the other two groups. The second, more fundamental, separation is in terms of food. The most abundant epifaunal invertebrate, *Harenactis*, and four of the less abundant ones eat larger pieces of detrital plant and animal material. Two other species, *Astropecten* and *Polinices*, are predators, probably to a large extent within the community. The other two species, *Renilla* and *Zaolutus*, appear to capture small living zooplankton. The infaunal invertebrates, on the other hand, feed on either comminuted detrital material or the bacterial and algal films on the sand grains or on other members of the infauna, and the vertebrates feed mostly on larger living crustaceans and polychaetes or on the smaller vertebrates. Finally, there seems to be little direct interaction between the three sections. There was no evidence that the infauna species were used as prey by the epifaunal invertebrates unless they had been injured and had become part of the general surface detritus. Predation by the vertebrates on the epifaunal invertebrates considered here was not observed in the field. One species, *Z. actius*, was found in stomachs of an uncommon flatfish collected at these depths (Ford 1965).

Table 4 is an attempt to assess the importance of the species in the community from a variety of viewpoints. The reason for the attempt is that it would be convenient if one could simplify the study of communities by only having to consider a relatively few "important" species. In the simple community considered here, *Harenactis* would be the most important to someone "counting heads." In terms of standing crop it could continue to be the most important to a hypothetical omnivore though the low productivity suggested by the observations might move it below species such as *Renilla* that produce relatively large numbers of young each year. From the point of view of an organism looking for a place to settle and not be eaten, it would be no more important than *Renilla* or *Amphiodia*, and all three species might be less important than some of the much rarer, but actively motile, species. As possible competitors for a potentially limited food resource, scattered haphazardly over the sand bottom and moved about by currents and wave surge, the sedentary species may also be less important than the actively motile ones.

Each of the measures used in Table 4 has some limitations as a way of describing the structure of a community. The most commonly used statistics, individuals per species and the indices of diversity that can be derived from them, are probably the least informative ecologically for they indicate little of the demands of a species in terms of food and space or of its possible effects in modifying the environment. Biomass could be more satisfactory both as a measure of the potential contribution of the standing crop as a food resource and, where it can be used as an index of respiration, as an indicator of the demand of the species population on the food resources available in the habitat. By ignoring the activity of the species, however, it too may give an incomplete representation of the species' place in the community. In cases, such as this one, where the activity of the motile species appears to consist mostly in searching for food and does not

lead to much alteration of the environment, information on area covered per unit time may provide a satisfactory basis for assessing this aspect of a species' importance. If the species extensively altered the habitat by its activities, such a simple measure would be inadequate. In addition to these limitations, there is evidence that in some communities, species that would not be considered important by any of these or related measures may be essential to the persistence and well-being of the species that dominate both numerically and in terms of biomass and activities affecting the environment (Limbaugh 1961).

The species composition of the community and the abundances of the individual species did not change over the six-year period of study, suggesting that this is a steady-state biological system. Five of the species are dependent on detrital material, much of it coming from rather distant rocky areas. After storms, the sand bottom is littered with a mixture of pieces of formerly attached algae, surf grass, and the animals clinging to these. More than half of the time, however, detrital material is scarce on the bottom and only one or two small pieces of vegetable matter may be seen along a 50-m transect. Pelagic zooplankton killed in the surf might, if the rip currents then transported them seaward, do something to smooth out the fluctuations in food supply but the amount available from this is probably small.

The evidence for population control of the most abundant species, *Harenactis attenuata*, is strong but there is no indication of the mechanism. No predators have been seen feeding on it. The random distribution of individuals indicates that they do not react to each other's presence and that all of the habitat is equally suitable. The evidence from the permanent stations shows that individuals stay in one position and are quite long-lived (estimated maximum exponential death rate of adults = 0.00077/day). As a corollary to the latter, few newly settled young have been seen. If food were the usual control, one might expect a general decrease in population density from the seaward to the shoreward edge of the species distribution because of the transport of food along the bottom in this direction by the relatively persistent inshore current. There was no evidence for such a decrease. Competition with the other abundant anemone, *Zaolutus*, is not excluded but field observations on spacing, behavior, and food suggest that they play well-separated roles in the community. Finally, there is the possibility, although it appears unlikely, that the apparent control is illusory because a period of only six years may be too short to obtain conclusive evidence for instability in a population of such long-lived animals.

The second most abundant of the epifaunal invertebrates, *Zaolutus actius*, requires a small pebble or a rigid polychaete tube for attachment and, as these are uncommon, their abundance may limit the population density. Evidence for this is provided by the 300-fold to 600-fold increase in *Zaolutus* density associated with the transitory presence in the area of this study of a dense bed of the tube-building polychaete *Owenia fusiformis* (Fager 1964). The greater density of adults of the predatory gastropod, *Epitonium* sp., in this bed and the frequency with which strings of its egg cases were found there suggest that this biological control could take over in populations of *Zaolutus* freed from restrictions imposed by the scarcity of suitable substrate. *Zaolutus* is also preyed on by an uncommon flatfish *Pleuronichthys ritteri*. It constituted about 30% of the stomach contents of 12 individuals (Ford 1965).

The third most abundant species, *Renilla köllikeri*, occurs in aggregations, suggesting interaction between individual colonies. There is an annual set of young that for short periods can more than double the population density but these young quickly disappear, probably mostly by destruction by sand movement but also by predation by the opisthobranch *Pleurophyllidia californica*, which has been seen in numbers only during the season when the young *Renilla* are present. The adults are frequently eaten by the relatively abundant starfish *Astropecten armatus*. Perhaps the most likely control mechanism is interaction between this species and its predators, particularly *Astropecten* which has several alternate prey to which it might pay more or less attention depending on their relative abundances.

None of the rest of the epifaunal invertebrates was present in large enough numbers to enable one to state with certainty that their population densities remained constant. However, the available figures suggest constancy and the animals certainly neither became extinct nor very abundant during the six-year period. There is some evidence that the hermit crab population might be limited by the scarcity of suitable empty shells, but no evidence has come to hand even to suggest a plausible mechanism of population control for any of the other five species.

Six years of field observations have not revealed extensive or frequent interspecific interactions. This is reinforced by the fact that the pattern of cooccurrence of the three most abundant species in $m^2/4$ samples indicated no effects on each other's presence or abundance. Interspecific interactions seem to be potentially important in only one (*Renilla*) of the three cases where some information is available to suggest a possible mechanism of population control. In the other two, the most likely mechanism involves a limitation of physically suitable places to live in the environment. The community is comprised of relatively few species (nine with abundances $\geqslant 0.04$ per $m^2$). The abundances of the nine species range over two orders of magnitude, but the distribution of individuals among species does not seem to be appreciably more skewed than those found for communities living in other habitats (Hairston 1959; Englemann 1961). There is no current evidence that any of the 30 other, rarer, species seen on the sand surface or the invertebrates living in the sand interact substantially with these nine species. The community inhabits an environment that is variable and rigorous, in terms of movements of water and substrate, extent and rapidity of temperature change, and uncertainty of food supply. In view of the generally accepted concept that stability is to be found in communities consisting of large numbers of interacting species living under relatively constant environmental conditions, the constancy of this community and its component species populations is surprising.

## REFERENCES

CLARK, P. J., AND F. C. EVANS. 1954. Distance to nearest neighbor as a measure of spatial relationships in populations. Ecology, **35**: 445–453.

———, AND ———. 1955. On some aspects of spatial pattern in biological populations. Science, **121**: 397–398.

ENGLEMANN, M. D. 1961. The role of soil arthropods in the energetics of an old field community. Ecol. Monographs, **31**: 221–238.

FAGER, E. W. 1964. Marine sediments: Effects of a tube-building polychaete. Science, **143**: 356–359.

———, A. O. FLECHSIG, R. F. FORD, R. I. CLUTTER, AND R. J. GHELARDI. 1966. Equipment for use in ecological studies using SCUBA. Limnol. Oceanog., **11**: 503–509.

FEDER, H. M. 1963. Gastropod defensive responses and their effectiveness in reducing predation by starfishes. Ecology, **44**: 505–512.

FORD, R. F. 1965. Distribution, population dynamics and behavior of a bothid flatfish, *Citharichthys stigmaeus*. Ph.D. thesis, Univ. California, San Diego. 243 p.

HAIRSTON, N. G. 1959. Species abundance and community organization. Ecology, **40**: 404–416.

INMAN, D. L. 1953. Areal and seasonal variations in beach and nearshore sediments at La Jolla, California. Beach Erosion Board, Tech. Mem. No. 39, U.S. Corps of Engineers, Washington, D.C. 82 p.

LIMBAUGH, C. 1961. Cleaning symbiosis. Sci. Am., **205**: 42–49.

PAINE, R. T. 1964. Ash and calorie determinations of sponge and opisthobranch tissues. Ecology, **45**: 384–387.

RICKETTS, E. F., AND J. CALVIN. 1952. Between Pacific tides, 3rd ed. (Revised by J. W. Hedgpeth). Stanford Univ. Press, Stanford, Calif. 515 p.

SANDERS, H. L. 1960. Benthic studies in Buzzards Bay. III. The structure of the soft-bottom community. Limnol. Oceanog., **5**: 138–153.

SHEPARD, F. P. 1950. Longshore current observations in southern California. Beach Erosion Board, Tech. Mem. No. 13, U.S. Corps of Engineers, Washington, D.C. 54 p.

TATE, M. W., AND R. C. CLELLAND. 1957. Nonparametric and shortcut statistics. Interstate Printers and Publishers, Danville, Ill. 171 p.

THORSON, G. 1957. Bottom communities (sublittoral and shallow shelf), p. 461–534. *In* J. W. Hedgpeth [ed.], Treatise on marine ecology and paleoecology, v. 1. Geol. Soc. Am. Mem. 67.

Reprinted from *J. Anim. Ecol.* **30**, 373-383, November 1961

# THE ECOLOGY OF LOUGH INE

## XI. THE CONTROL OF ALGAE BY *PARACENTROTUS LIVIDUS* (ECHINOIDEA)

### By J. A. KITCHING and F. J. EBLING

*Departments of Zoology, Universities of Bristol and Sheffield*

The sea urchin *Paracentrotus lividus* is widespread on clean rock or shell gravel in the shallow sublittoral of Lough Ine, although almost absent from the adjoining coast (Ebling, Sleigh, Sloane & Kitching 1960) except in a few intertidal rock pools. The most extensive beds of *Paracentrotus* are along the north shore of the lough, and in Curlew Bay, on the north side of Castle Island (Fig. 1). These areas are practically free from

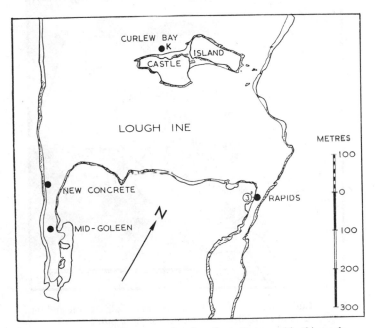

FIG. 1. A map of Lough Ine, showing the stations used in this work.

obvious algal growth, whereas algae are abundant in places where *Paracentrotus* is less plentiful. In this paper we describe observations and experiments on the relation between *Paracentrotus* and these various algae.

## OBSERVATIONS

### *The distribution of* Paracentrotus *in Curlew Bay*

The bottom of Curlew Bay is covered by lamellibranch shells with some rocks, stones and gravel, all resting on mud. Many of the shells are empty; *Anomia ephippium* is by far the commonest species. Further particulars of the sedentary fauna are summarized in Table 1 and in the Appendix. In the shallower water, near the shore, the bottom was practically free of algae throughout July and August of 1959; but it was well populated with

*Paracentrotus,* many of them carrying shells on the dorsal side, like hats. In the slightly deeper water farther out and also to the west there was a very dense covering of algae, mainly *Enteromorpha clathrata,* but including also some *Chylocladia verticillata, Polysiphonia* spp., *Ceramium* spp., *Ectocarpus confervoides* and others. The boundary of the dense weed cover as seen in 1959 is shown approximately in Fig. 2, although it was not possible to take account of all the pockets and irregularities.

The population of *Paracentrotus* in relation to occurrence of algae and nature of bottom was examined along two sections, running out northwards into the bay from shore-marks J and K. For this purpose a heavy wire frame, measuring 1 m × 1 m, was moved by 1 m steps outwards along each section, and observations were made of the percentage area of bottom overgrown by algae, of the number of *Paracentrotus,* and of the percentage of the bottom occupied by boulders, or by shells and stones, or by mud,

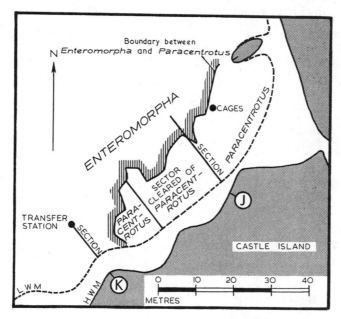

FIG. 2. Curlew Bay, showing the distribution of algal cover and the position of the sector cleared of *Paracentrotus.*

within each metre square. The algae were removed so that the bottom could be examined, and specimens of the algae were kept for identification. Young *Paracentrotus* and *Paracentrotus* completely covered by shells or stones would have escaped detection. The results are summarized in Fig. 3.

### Clearance of Paracentrotus

On 7 July 1959 a part of Curlew Bay was completely cleared of *Paracentrotus.* The cleared area amounted to about 290 m². It extended from low-water mark to the edge of the *Enteromorpha* and was delimited on the east and west by leading marks; it is shown in Fig. 2. Members of the party, provided with gloves and collecting sacks, extended in a line and worked over the area twice; although the water was still shallow, it was convenient to collect the outermost sea urchins with the help of a mask and snorkel. We removed 1957 sea urchins; undoubtedly some escaped us, hidden under shells, but except for small ones these must have been very few. The effects of the removal of *Paracentrotus* and of its transfer to other sites are described in the following sections.

### Changes in Curlew Bay

Those parts of Curlew Bay already covered with *Enteromorpha* remained so throughout July and August 1959. The area cleared of *Paracentrotus* was 10% covered by algae on 23 July 1959, 25% on 10 August, and 50% on 3 September. However, the dry weight of algae per square metre was much less than in that part of the bay normally dominated by *Enteromorpha*. Those parts of the bay still occupied by *Paracentrotus* continued practi-

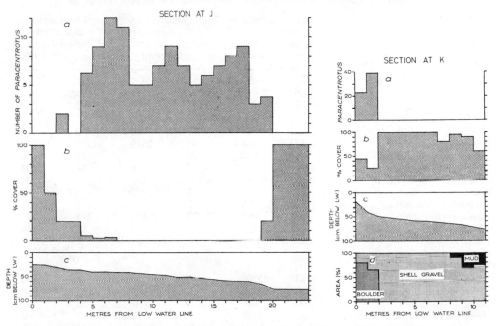

FIG. 3. Diagrams of the section at J and K (Fig. 2) showing (*a*) the number of *Paracentrotus* per square metre, (*b*) the percentage coverage of the bottom with algae, (*c*) the bottom profile, (*d*) the nature of the bottom expressed as the percentage area covered with boulders, gravel, or mud.
Throughout the sections at J the bottom consisted of shell gravel resting on mud.

cally free of weed, with a coverage of less than 1%. The boundaries between the *Paracentrotus*-freed sector and the uncleared areas on either side of it gradually widened to irregular bands 1 to 2 m wide. Apart from this, the *Paracentrotus*-freed sector remained completely clear of visible *Paracentrotus* throughout the summer of 1959.

In early July 1960, we found that the area cleared of *Paracentrotus* in July 1959 was thickly and completely covered with *Enteromorpha* and other algae. The area to the east of the cleared area, previously free of algal cover, carried large dense patches of algae interspersed with clear patches containing numerous *Paracentrotus*. The area to the west of the cleared area remained much as before, free of weed and well populated by *Paracentrotus*, and merged into the area of Section K, now also populated by *Paracentrotus* and free of weed (see below).

Samples of bottom, 1 m × 1 m, were collected from the cleared and adjacent untreated areas in July and in late August or early September of 1959, and from the cleared area in late August 1960. All weed, shells and stones were lifted by hand into buckets until the underlying mud was fully exposed. Most fast-moving organisms would have escaped. Counts of the commonest sedentary species are given in Table 1. Additional records are given in the Appendix. Some small *Paracentrotus* were discovered under shells in the areas covered by *Enteromorpha*, but their capacity for feeding would presumably be unimportant compared with that of adults. Most of the common animals are evenly distributed among the samples and there is little evidence of change. However, the two

Table 1. *Sedentary fauna of metre squares in Curlew Bay*

(Less important constituents are mentioned in the Appendix)

|  | From area covered by *Enteromorpha* throughout July and August | | From area occupied by *Paracentrotus* throughout July and August | | From sector cleared of *Paracentrotus* on 7 July 1959 | |
|---|---|---|---|---|---|---|
|  | B 23 July 1959 | E 2 Sept. 1959 | A 8 July 1959 | C 26 Aug. 1959 | D 29 Aug. 1959 | F 27 Aug. 1960 |
| On bottom: | | | | | | |
| *Anthopleura balli* | 85 | 89 | 1 | 0 | 0 | 12 |
| [2]*Pomatoceros triqueter* | 1350 | 799 | 3095 | 2519 | 1805 | 2238 |
| [1]Polyplacophora (Chitons) | 61 | 90 | 21 | 33 | 31 | 50 |
| [1]*Acmaea virginea* | 10 | 57 | 47 | 101 | 64 | 97 |
| [1]*Gibbula cineraria* | 100 | 147 | 161 | 231 | 213 | 149 |
| [1]*Ocenebra erinacea* | 2 | 1 | 0 | 3 | 2 | 0 |
| [1]*Nassarius incrassatus* | 0 | 0 | 2 | 11 | 8 | 1 |
| [1]*Anomia ephippium* | 307 | 492 | 229 | 310 | 293 | 223 |
| [1]*Chlamys varia* | 17 | 6 | 15 | 12 | 12 | 16 |
| *Paracentrotus lividus* | 1 + 2 small | 0 + 5 small | 10 | 7 + 3 small | 1 | 1 (small) |
| Mainly on algae: | | | | | | |
| *Caprella acanthifera* | *160 | *5200 | 0 | 0 | 0 | *3200 |
| [3]*Rissoa parva* | *1500 | *3700 | 0 | 0 | 566 | *90 000 |
| [4]*Bittium reticulatum* | *1300 | *600 | 4 | 0 | 32 | *1600 |
| *Amphipholis squamata* | *30 | *280 | 4 | 7 | 11 | *200 |
| Dry weight of algae (grams): | *180 | *150 | 0 | 0 | 37 | *240 |

\* Estimated from a portion of the material
[1] Only occupied shells were counted
[2] Tubes counted; some may have been unoccupied
[3] Shells counted; mostly small, probably almost all occupied
[4] Dark, undamaged shells, inhabited at time of collection or not long before; many larger, bleached, damaged, uninhabited shells were found on the bottom but these are not included.

gastropods *Rissoa parva* and *Bittium reticulatum* and the amphipod *Caprella acanthifera*, all found in large numbers on the weed, are absent or almost absent from the samples collected in the *Paracentrotus*-occupied area; and the ophiuroid *Amphipholis squamata* was also much more plentiful among weed. Small *Rissoa parva* and *Bittium reticulatum* had become established in the newly-grown weed in the *Paracentrotus*-freed area by early September, but *Caprella* was still missing and *Amphipholis* was scarce. All four were abundant in the dense algal cover of the *Paracentrotus*-freed area in August 1960. The anemone *Anthopleura balli* was abundant in the untreated areas dominated by weed. Apparently the limpet *Acmaea virginea* was also distributed unevenly.

## TRANSFER EXPERIMENTS

The *Paracentrotus* were kept submerged in sacks both during the collecting and during transport to various sites in the lough and Rapids shown in Fig. 1. Previously there were no *Paracentrotus* in these places. The results of these transfers are summarized below.

### West side of Curlew Bay, on section at K

On 7 July 1959, 1326 *Paracentrotus* were dropped in an elongated heap on the section, where they lay surrounded by dense *Enteromorpha*. On 15 July the *Paracentrotus* occupied an irregular area 6 m × 1-2 m, with the central patch eaten clear; all appeared healthy, and there were no dead shells. On 10 August they occupied an area 6 m × 3½ m; most were at the perimeter in contact with *Enteromorpha* (Fig. 4). A gale blew from the south-east on 13 August, veered to the south-west over 14 August, and moderated on 15 August; the waves drove many shells carrying *Enteromorpha* into the *Paracentrotus* area. By 3 September the area occupied by *Paracentrotus* had been cleared of weed and

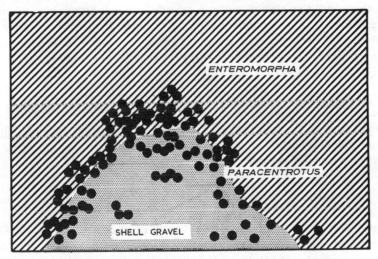

FIG. 4. The distribution of *Paracentrotus* at transfer station K on 10 August 1959. Only one end of the oval patch is represented. The positions of the *Paracentrotus* have been traced from a colour photograph.

extended; the *Paracentrotus* was mainly on the perimeter. On our return at the beginning of July 1960, a wide area around Section K, which had been covered with *Enteromorpha* in 1959, was found to be free of weed and well populated with *Paracentrotus* which we presume to have been those placed there a year before.

### New Concrete

On 7 July 1959, 140 *Paracentrotus* were dropped on a bottom consisting of comminuted slate, stones and rocks densely covered with *Enteromorpha*. On 8 July the *Paracentrotus* were all right way up and many wore shell hats; the patch was surrounded by *Enteromorpha*. On 15 July all appeared healthy and were still in a close group. By 12 August the *Paracentrotus* had spread and occupied a patch 1½ m in diameter. By 5 September all had aggregated on rocks on the shallow side of the patch, and many wore *Anomia* hats brought with them from Curlew Bay; two dead *Paracentrotus* shells were seen. No *Paracentrotus* remained in August 1960.

### Mid Goleen

On 7 July 1959, ninety-five *Paracentrotus* were dropped on the muddy bottom. On 8 July, the *Paracentrotus* were in a close patch, right way up, wearing hats. On 15 August the *Paracentrotus* were scattered but apparently healthy, except for two dead. By 5 September many *Paracentrotus* were distributed in an irregular patch free of weed; no dead shells were seen; there was scattered *Enteromorpha* outside the patch. On 12 August 1960 twelve *Paracentrotus* remained in a weed-free patch about 1½ m in diameter.

### Rapids off Mark 3 on Quay (*Bassindale* et al. *1948, Fig. 1*)

On 8 July 1959, 396 *Paracentrotus*, kept overnight underwater off Glannafeen Quay, were dropped on the boulder-covered bottom while the current was running weakly out. Owing to other work this station was not revisited until 3 September, when no *Paracentrotus* remained. On 3 September 1959, 200 more *Paracentrotus* were deposited shortly before high slack water, while the current was weak. On 7 September only thirty-three remained.

### Gut contents

A number of *Paracentrotus* were collected on 13 July from the north shore of the lough, brought back to the Glannafeen Laboratory, and opened immediately. The gut contents were found to consist almost entirely of algal remains. In one specimen a few exoskeletons of a copepod were found.

### EXPERIMENTS WITH CAGES

Six galvanized wire cages 32 (high) × 64 × 43 cm were placed on 7 July 1959 in Curlew Bay in the *Paracentrotus*-infested area east of the cleared sector (Fig. 2). The bottoms of the cages were covered with rocks and shells collected from this area and free from obvious algal growth. Six adult *Paracentrotus* were placed in one cage, three in a second, one in a third, but none in the others.

The cages were lifted for examination and emptied on 6 September 1959. A lot of drifted seaweed, mainly *Enteromorpha*, was entangled on the tops and sides. In the three cages without *Paracentrotus* the rocks and shells were 100% covered with algae, including *Enteromorpha clathrata*, *Ectocarpus confervoides*, *Ceramium rubrum* var. *pedicellatum* and *Polysiphonia* spp. There was 33-50% coverage in the cage with one *Paracentrotus*, about 30% coverage in the cage with three *Paracentrotus*, and no coverage at all (with macroscopic algae) in the cage with six *Paracentrotus*.

### DISCUSSION

Rees (1935) described a succession of the smaller algae in the sheltered waters of Lough Ine, culminating in *Enteromorpha*. Our observations and experiments have shown that in Curlew Bay *Paracentrotus lividus* destroys the algae as fast as they grow, and prevents the establishment of those elements of the fauna especially associated with algae, namely, the gastropods *Rissoa parva* and *Bittium reticulatum*, and the amphipod *Caprella acanthifera*. It probably also destroys some animals living on the shell bottom but we have no evidence of this. The part played by *Paracentrotus* in the shallow sublittoral resembles that played by limpets in the littoral, demonstrated experimentally in the Isle of Man (Jones 1948).

We do not know why *Paracentrotus* does not dominate the whole of Curlew Bay. The unoccupied areas are mainly deeper, and it is possible that more mud settles in them. When *Paracentrotus* transferred to the west side of Curlew Bay had eaten a clear patch in the *Enteromorpha*, a slight deposit or film of mud was noticeable on the shells and stones which were revealed. It is also possible that the abundance of *Anthopleura balli* is an indication of greater sedimentation. *Paracentrotus* transferred to New Concrete congregated on rocks, abandoning the fine-grained sediment of comminuted slate. Normally in Lough Ine *Paracentrotus* is found only on a clean bottom. We do not know if it fails to settle, or to survive, on mud, or whether it migrates elsewhere. There does not appear to be any obvious means of orientation towards shallow water as the bottom is almost flat. Nevertheless, *Paracentrotus* is fairly active except in the presence of food, and a kinesis activated by unfavourable conditions might be expected to bring a substantial proportion of the population into a favourable habitat.

## ACKNOWLEDGMENTS

Materials for the field work were prepared in the Department of Zoology, University of Bristol, and we are greatly indebted to Mr G. L. E. Wing, Mr N. M. Ablett and Mr J. Sharland for the excellent technical help which they have once again contributed. We are grateful to the Colston Research Society and to the University of Sheffield Research Fund for financial assistance and to the Royal Society (Browne Fund) for equipment.

We wish to thank Dr E. M. Burrows (University of Liverpool), Mr S. P. Dance (British Museum), Dr Peter Dixon (University of Liverpool), Mrs Margaret Duhig (University College, Dublin), Mr N. A. Holme (Marine Biological Association, Plymouth), Dr R. H. Millar (Scottish Marine Biological Association, Millport) and Miss S. M. Stone (British Museum), for systematic contributions enumerated in the flora and fauna lists.

The following took part as students in the field work: In 1959 — Halina Bialkowska, Elizabeth Cross, Ann Ferguson, Eirlys Griffiths, Judith Hobbis, Helga Kolb, A. G. Macdonald, C. J. Mapes, Mabel Martin, Louise Muntz, I. Newton, Margaret Rust, Alison Soddy, R. J. Stephens, Janet Stephenson, Gillian Styles, J. D. Treharne, Mary Walters; in 1960 — R. A. Avery, Elizabeth Cross, M. J. D'Oyly, Eirlys Griffiths, Louise Muntz, Rosemary Parsons, N. B. Potter, Gillian Styles. Catering was carried out by Miss Celia Fildes.

The work at Lough Ine was based on the Glannafeen Laboratory.

## SUMMARY

1. The complete population of *Paracentrotus lividus* (nearly 2000 individuals) was cleared from an area of nearly 300 m² of the shallow sublittoral of Lough Ine in early July 1959.

2. The cleared area gradually became covered with algae, especially *Enteromorpha*.

J.A.E.  M

It was about 50% covered with a short growth by early September, and by July 1960 was completely covered by a growth fully as heavy as that in nearby regions not populated by *Paracentrotus*.

3. The *Enteromorpha* and other algae which grew in the cleared area developed a population of caprellids (*Caprella acanthifera*), small gastropods (especially *Rissoa parva*) and ophiuroids (*Amphipholis squamata*) similar to that found among algae in near-by regions.

4. Over 1300 living *Paracentrotus* were transferred to a near-by region free of *Paracentrotus* but densely overgrown by algae, mainly *Enteromorpha*. The transferred animals gradually moved outwards, leaving a central area completely cleared of algae. Other smaller experiments gave similar results.

5. The gut contents of *Paracentrotus* collected in Lough Ine were found to consist almost entirely of algal remains.

6. Rocks protected from *Paracentrotus* by galvanized wire cages developed a dense covering of algae within 2 months.

## REFERENCES

Aleem, A. A. (1952). *Olpidiopsis Feldmanni* sp. nov., Champignon marin parasite d'Algues de la famille des Bonnemaisoniacées. *C.R. Acad. Sci., Paris,* **235**, 1250-2.

Bassindale, R., Ebling, F. J., Kitching, J. A. & Purchon, R. D. (1948). The ecology of the Lough Ine rapids with special reference to water currents. I. Introduction and hydrography. *J. Ecol.* **36**, 305-22.

Ebling, F. J., Sleigh, M. A., Sloane, J. F. & Kitching, J. A. (1960). The ecology of Lough Ine. VII. Distribution of some common plants and animals of the littoral and shallow sublittoral regions. *J. Ecol.* **48**, 29-53.

Feldmann-Mazoyer, G. (1940). *Recherches sur les Céramiacées de la Méditerranée occidentale.* Alger.

Irvine, D. E. G. (1956). Notes on the British species of the genus *Sphacelaria* Lyngb. *Trans. Bot. Soc. Edinb.* **37**, 24-5.

Jones, N. S. (1948). Observations and experiments on the biology of *Patella vulgata* at Port St. Mary, Isle of Man. *Proc. Lpool. Biol. Soc.* **56**, 60-77.

Marine Biological Association (1957). *Plymouth Marine Fauna.* Plymouth.

Newton, E. (1937). *A Handbook of the British Seaweeds.* London.

Rees, T. K. (1935). The marine algae of Lough Ine. *J. Ecol.* **23**, 69-133.

## APPENDIX

### Flora List

Collections were made from each of the samples (A-F) mentioned in Table 1 (p. 376) from the sections (J and K) described on p. 374, from the area previously cleared of *Paracentrotus* and revisited on 15 August 1960 (Q), from New Concrete (p. 377), and from the cages on lifting (p. 378). This list summarizes a detailed report made for us on these collections by Dr E. M. Burrows of the Hartley Botanical Laboratories, University of Liverpool. Dr Burrows was assisted by Dr Peter Dixon for some of the Rhodophyceae.

CHLOROPHYCEAE

*Chlorochytrium cohnii* Wright F, in the thallus of *Schizonema*.

*Enteromorpha clathrata* (Roth) Grev. Abundant in B, D, E, F, J, K, Q, New Concrete, cages. Some plants in D and E infected with a chytrid fungus.

*Enteromorpha compressa* (L.) Grev. D, E, F, cages.

*Enteromorpha intestinalis* (L.) Link K.

*Percursaria percursa* (C. Ag.) Rosenv. J, K, cages.

*Ulva lactura* L. B, D, E, F, J, K. Plants at J and K with developing propagules of a *Sphacelaria*.

*Bulbocoleon piliferum* Pringsh. F, in the thallus of *Colpomenia peregrina*.

*Pringsheimiella scutata* (Rke.) Marchav. F, on sponge.

*Chaetomorpha linum* (Müll.) Kütz. New Concrete.

*Cladophora* sp. B, E, Q, cages, New Concrete.
*Codium fragile* (Sur.) Hariot subsp. *tomentosoides* (van Goor) Silva D, K.

PHAEOPHYCEAE
*Ectocarpus confervoides* (Roth) Le Jol. s. lat. D, E, F, K, Q, New Concrete, cages. Unilocular and plurilocular sporangia noted in D.
*Myrionema strangulans* Grev. F, on *Enteromorpha compressa*.
*Leathesia difformis* (L.) Aresch. B, D, E.
? *Spermatochnus paradoxus* (Roth) Kütz. A, B, J, K, Q.
? *Stilophora* sp. J.
*Stictyosiphon griffithsianus* (Le Jol.) Holm. et Batt. (= *Phloeospora brachiata* Born.) J.
*Striaria* sp. A.
*Asperococcus bullosus*? Lamour. A.
*Asperococcus fistulosus*? (Huds.) Hook. J, New Concrete.
*Colpomenia peregrina* Sauv. F.
*Scytosiphon lomentaria* (Lyngb.) Endl. D, E.
*Cutleria multifida* (Sm.) Grev. D (female plants), F, cages.
*Sphacelaria pennata* (Huds.) Lyngb. (See Irvine 1956) A, D, E, F (with a chytrid fungus in some of the apical cells), J, K, Q, New Concrete, cages.
*Dictyota dichotoma* (Huds.) Lamour. B, E, F.
*Cystoseira* sp. A (very small quantity).
*Cystoseira tamariscifolia* (Huds.) Papenf. J.

RHODOPHYCEAE
*Porphyra* sp. New Concrete.
*Acrochaetium* sp. F, Q.
*Asterocytis ramosa* (Thwaites) Gobi D.
*Rhodochorton floridulum* (Dillw.) Nägeli E.
*Melobesia minutula* Fosl. F.
*Falkenbergia rufolanosa* (Harv.) Schm. E (infected with a chytrid fungus, *Olpidiopsis feldmanni* Aleem; see Aleem 1952).
*Chylocladia verticillata* (Lightf.) Bliding D, E, K, Q. Female and tetrasporic plants noted in D, E, and Q.
*Callithamnion* sp. F.
*Ceramium ciliatum* (Ellis) Ducluz. B, D, E (tetrasporic plants), F.
*Ceramium diaphanum* (Roth) Harvey/*Ceramium strictum* (Kütz.) Harv. complex, sensu G. Feldmann-Mazoyer (1940) E, Q.
*Ceramium rubrum* (Huds.) Ag. D and J (tetrasporic plants noted in both samples), F.
*Ceramium rubrum* var. *pedicellatum* J. G. Agardh (see Newton 1931) D (female and tetrasporic plants), E (male and female plants, occasionally monoecious; also tetrasporic plants), Q (female plants), cages.
*Crouania attenuata* (Bonnem.) J. Ag. B, E (on *Polysiphonia*; tetrasporic plants), J (on *Polysiphonia fruticulosa*).
*Laurencia obtusa* (Huds.) Lamour. F.
*Ptilothamnion pluma* (Dillw.) Thur. Q.
*Polysiphonia brodiaei* (Dillw.) Grev. D, E, F. Tetrasporic plants noted in D.
*Polysiphonia fruticulosa* (Wulf.) Spreng. B, E, F, J, K.
*Polysiphonia elongata* (Huds.) Harv. D, cages.
*Polysiphonia macrocarpa* Harv. F.
*Polysiphonia nigrescens* (Grev.) Sm. D, tetrasporic plants.
*Polysiphonia urceolata* (Dillw.) Grev. Cages.
*Polysiphonia violacea* (Roth) Grev. D, E, J, Q, cages, New Concrete. Tetrasporic and female plants noted in D, tetrasporic in Q.

CYANOPHYCEAE
*Anabaena* sp. F (in quantity).
*Calothrix* sp.? New Concrete.
*Lyngbya* sp. D, E, F, K, Q, New Concrete.

## Fauna List

This list is incomplete. Fast-moving species would have escaped, and some of the rarer or more difficult species have been ignored because the material collected was inadequate. Further particulars of the samples (A, B, etc.) are given in Table 1 (p. 376). Numbers in brackets are of specimens found. Naming by outside authorities is indicated as follows: 1 — Miss S. M. Stone, of the British Museum (Natural History); 2 — Mrs Margaret Duhig, of the Zoology Department, University College, Dublin; 3 — Mr S. P. Dance, of the British Museum (Natural History); 4 — Mr N. A. Holme, of the Marine Biological Laboratory, Plymouth; 5 — Dr R. H. Millar, of the Marine Station, Millport. Polychaetes were identified by F. J. E. and the remaining specimens by J. A. K.

[1]SPORIFERA
*Leucosolenia botryoides* (Ellis & Solander) B.
*Sycon ciliatum* (Fabricius) B, on *Chlamys opercularis*.
*Polymastia mammillaris* (Müller) B.
*Hymeniacidon perleve* (Montagu) B, E.
*Haliclona?* *macandrewi* (Bowerbank) B, E.
*Halichondria bowerbanki* Burton B.

ANTHOZOA
*Anthopleura balli* (Cocks) Table 1.

NEMERTINI
*Lineus* sp. A (1), B (1), C (1), E (1), F (1).

POLYCHAETA
*Lepidonotus clava* (Montagu) C (1).
*Eulalia viridis* (O. F. Müller) A (1).
*Kefersteinia cirrata* (Keferstein) C (4), D (4), F (14).
*Odontosyllis gibba* Claparède C (3), D (1), E (2).
*Micronereis variegata* Claparède D (1), E (3), F (2).
*Perinereis cultrifera* (Grube) B (1).
*Platynereis dumerili* (Audouin & M. Edwards) A (1), D (6), E (2), F (2).
*Lumbriconereis gracilis* Ehlers E (1).
*Scalibregma inflatum* Rathke F (1).
*Pomatoceros triqueter* (L.) Table 1.

ISOPODA
*Janira maculosa* Leach A, C, D, F.

[2]AMPHIPODA
*Cheirocratus sundevalli* (Rathke) C (2 ♀ ♀).
*Melita obtusata* (Montagu) B (1 ♀)
*Pherusa fucicola* Leach A few at A, B, C, D, and E; both sexes numerous at F.
*Dexamine spinosa* (Montagu) D (2 ♀ ♀), F (1 ovigerous female and juveniles).
*Aora typica* Krøyer B (2 ♂♂ and 2 ♀ ♀).
*Microdeutopus anomalus* (Rathke) A few at A, B, and C; F, ♂♂ and ovigerous ♀ ♀.
*Pleonexes gammaroides* Bate A few at A, D, E, F.
*Erichthonius brasiliensis* (Dana) B (1), E (17).
*Caprella acanthifera* Leach Table 1.

DECAPODA
*Athanas nitescens* (Montagu) E (female carrying eggs).
*Palaemon serratus* (Pennant) F.
*Eupagurus* sp. C (1 small).
*Portunus arcuatus* Leach E, F (10 small).

POLYPLACOPHORA
*Lepidochitona cinerea* (L.) Nearly all the Polyplacophora in Table 1 were of this species.

GASTROPODA
*Patella aspera* Lamarck C (1 small), D (1 small).
*Acmaea virginea* (Müller) Table 1.
*Gibbula cineraria* (L.) Table 1.
[3]*Alvania beani* Thorpe A (2), D (2), E (many, mostly empty shells), F.
[3]*Rissoa parva* (da Costa) Table 1.

[3]*Bittium reticulatum* (da Costa) Table 1. Also many empty shells among gravel.
[3]*Ocenebra erinacea* (L.) Table 1.
*Nassarius incrassatus* (Ström) Table 1.
*Elysia viridis* (Montagu) D (3).

LAMELLIBRANCHIA
*Modiolus* sp. (spat) B.
*Modiolaria* sp. (spat) B.
*Anomia ephippium* (Table 1).
*Chlamys varia* (L.) (Table 1).
*Kellia suborbicularis* (Montagu) A (1), B (3).
*Cardium* sp. (spat) B, F.
*Venus verrucosa* L. Buried in mud under the shell gravel.
[4]*Venerupis rhomboides* (Pennant) (of the type separated as *V. sarniensis* in the Plymouth Marine Fauna) Empty shells.
[4]*Venerupis aurea* (Gmelin) Occasional living specimens; empty shells often drilled.
*Hiatella arctica* (L.) B (1).

ASTEROIDEA
*Asterias rubens* L. A (3).

OPHIUROIDEA
*Amphipholis squamata* (Delle Chiaje) Table 1.

ECHINOIDEA
*Paracentrotus lividus* Lamarck

[5]TUNICATA
*Diplosoma listerianum* (Milne Edwards) A (1 colony).
*Ascidia* sp., probably *A. conchilega* Müller B (1).

Reprinted from ECOLOGY, Vol. 49, No. 5, Late Summer, 1968

# STRUCTURE AND FUNCTION IN CALIFORNIA GRASSLANDS

S. J. McNAUGHTON

*Department of Bacteriology and Botany, Syracuse University, Syracuse, N. Y.*

(Accepted for publication May 29, 1968)

*Abstract.* Functional and floristic properties of annual grasslands on serpentine and sandstone soils at an elevation of 180 m on Stanford University's Jasper Ridge were determined along an intuitive habitat gradient from northeast to southwest exposures. The most frequent species contributed the most to peak standing crop in only half the stands. *Stipa pulchra,* the only native species among the important species, was more important on serpentine than on sandstone sites. *Bromus mollis,* the other consistently important species, increased in importance with decreasing moisture supply on both soils. The sandstone grasslands sustained a greater biomass, were more productive, and were less diverse than serpentine grasslands. Within the grasslands as a whole, productivity was inversely related to diversity and positively related to dominance. Stability, however, was related to neither productivity, diversity, or dominance. Thus productivity may increase in such a system with no sacrifice in stability. Properties of sandstone grasslands were clearly related to the habitat gradient from cool, moist sites to warm, dry sites. There was no such relationship in serpentine grasslands. Dominance-diversity curves generally fit previously described models, except on southwestern serpentine exposures. The annual grassland vegetation is a mosaic of floristic composition and ecological properties, shifting in response to habitat patterns but without abrupt discontinuities.

## INTRODUCTION

California's annual grasslands, occupying extensive areas in the Central Valley and along the Pacific Coast (Munz and Keck 1949, Biswell 1956, Kuchler 1964) (Fig. 1), form a vegetation type that is unique in North America: a distinct and extensive community type consisting largely of introduced species (Biswell 1956). Nearly 400 alien species have been recorded in these grasslands, and in most sites aliens constitute the major vegetative cover. Although most authors believe

that the prehistoric vegetation was perennial (Munz and Keck 1949, Wells 1964), historical evidence is meager and the earliest references are to annual prairies (Biswell 1956). Twenty-nine years of protection from grazing and fire produced grasslands in Monterey County which were still dominated by *Bromus rigidus, B. mollis, Avena fatua,* and *Erodium Botrys* (White 1966). Regardless of their initial cause, it seems likely that the current annual grasslands are more similar than the original prairies to the vegetation which would result from the elimination of disturbance.

This vegetation is essentially reconstructed de novo each growing season (Major and Pyott 1966). Because the soil is a reservoir of a considerable variety of potential occupants, the grassland composition is extremely responsive to fluctuations in habitat conditions. The variations in vegetation character from year to year and under different treatments were recognized early in the systematic investigation of California's grasslands (Talbot, Biswell, and Hormay 1939). Many ecologists have provided evidence of this vegetation's response to fire, grazing, and climatic oscillations (Hendrick 1948, Hervey 1949, Heady 1956, 1958).

The study reported here was designed to determine the effects of soil type and exposure upon composition, diversity, biomass, productivity, and stability of California's annual grasslands. Support was by NIH 5T1–GM–365–04, Division of Systematic Biology, Stanford University. Plant identifications were by J. Thomas. P. Raven, J. Thomas, R. Holm, L. Mason, and E. Leigh of

FIG. 1. Distribution of grasslands in California and location of Jasper Ridge (●) on San Francisco Peninsula.

the population biology group at Stanford University, together with A. Kruckeberg of the University of Washington, provided many helpful comments and discussions.

## THE STUDY AREA

The Jasper Ridge Experimental Area, maintained by the Division of Systematic Biology at Stanford University, had been protected from grazing and burning for over 5 years previous to this study. Since annual communities may be expected to adjust comparatively rapidly to prevailing habitat state (White 1966), these grasslands are probably representative of California grasslands free of disturbance although they may not yet approach steady state. In fact, steady state for these communities may involve year-to-year changes with climatic oscillation.

Jasper Ridge is an inland Coast Range foothill on the San Francisco peninsula approximately 3 km long and 1 km wide with its long axis lying in a northwest-southeast direction. The protected area varies in elevation from 90 m along San Francisquito Creek to 200 m at the crest. Redwoods (*Sequoia sempervirens*) occur along the creek, oak-madrone forest (*Quercus agrifolia* and *Arbutus menziesii*) and chaparral (*Adenostoma fasiculatum, Ceonothus cuneatus,* and *Arctostaphylos crustacea*) occur on the shoulders of the ridge, and the crests are grasslands with an occasional individual of California blue oak (*Quercus douglasii*) interspersed. The parent material of the ridge is largely sedimentary rock, but it is traversed by a serpentine intrusion. Cooper's (1922) pioneering studies on the effects of serpentine-derived soil upon vegetation were done on Jasper Ridge.

The grasslands studied are located on sandstone (Fig. 2) and serpentine (Fig. 3) soils at an elevation of 180 m. The principal nutritional dif-

FIG. 3. General view of the serpentine grasslands looking at the same exposures as in Fig. 2 on the same date. Note the large outcrops of undifferentiated serpentine and numerous large rocks.

ference in California sandstone and serpentine soils is the much lower calcium:magnesium ratio of the latter. McMillan (1956) found that this ratio averaged 2.95 for sandstone and 0.17 for serpentine, with the magnesium content being about six times greater in serpentine soils. The effects of this unique soil property upon vegetation are well known (Cooper 1922, Whittaker 1954a, 1954b, 1960, Walker 1954, Kruckeberg 1954, McMillan 1956).

## METHODS

Beginning on January 1, 1966, and on the first of every month through July 1, 1966, three quadrats 1 m by ½ m placed end to end perpendicular to the slope of the hill were harvested on northeast, northwest, southeast, and southwest slopes on sandstone and serpentine soil areas. Position of quadrats on slopes was random. Aboveground standing crop was dried at 105°C for 8 hr, and the yield of each quadrat was determined separately. During May, which represented the period of peak standing crop, two 5-m transects, one parallel and one perpendicular to the slope, were used to determine frequency and yield of individual species. Fifty random numbers were drawn from Snedecor (1956) to fix sampling points on each transect. At each of these points, frequency was determined by canopy interception and a 4-cm² area was harvested, sorted into species composition, and dried. Each species contribution to peak biomass was determined after drying. The sampling technique, though laborious, allowed a more direct comparison of floristic data (gathered along a transect) with biomass data (gathered by harvesting randomized blocks). Standing crop refers to total plant material present, including litter. Productivity is defined as change in standing crop with time.

FIG. 2. General view of the sandstone grasslands looking north toward southeast (on the right) and southwest (on the left) exposures. Photograph taken on June 10, 1966.

TABLE 1. Relative importance of species on two soil types and four exposures in the Jasper Ridge grasslands— expressed as percentage of peak standing crop and as percentage frequency during the period of peak standing crop

| Species | Sandstone | | | | Serpentine | | | |
|---|---|---|---|---|---|---|---|---|
| | North-east | North-west | South-east | South-west | North-east | North-west | South-east | South-west |
| **A. Standing crop** | | | | | | | | |
| Avena fatua | 44.4 | | 8.6 | | | | | |
| Medicago hispida | 0.7 | | 3.7 | | | | | |
| Avena barbata | | | 1.7 | | | | | |
| Torilis nodosa | | 1.8 | 0.9 | | | | | |
| Centaurea melitensis | | | 2.0 | | | | | |
| Festuca megalura | | | | 0.2 | | | | |
| Lolium multiflorum | 7.0 | 7.4 | | 3.5 | | | | |
| Erodium botrys | 4.4 | 0.8 | 5.9 | 8.3 | | | | |
| Bromus rigidus | 35.4 | 67.8 | 42.6 | 22.6 | | | | |
| Bromus mollis | 7.0 | 21.1 | 21.3 | 38.1 | 7.9 | 19.6 | 27.3 | 53.2 |
| Clarkia purpurea | 1.1 | 1.1 | 4.7 | 1.2 | 3.3 | 1.2 | 2.7 | |
| Hemizonia luzulaefolia | | | 1.2 | 8.3 | 11.8 | | | 5.9 |
| Eriastrum abramsii | | | | 3.0 | | | | 0.8 |
| Lotus subpinnatus | | | 0.2 | 3.7 | 4.0 | 6.5 | 3.6 | 14.4 |
| Stipa pulchra | | | | 16.4 | 40.7 | 41.0 | 26.4 | 10.5 |
| Eschscholzia californica | | | | | 11.8 | 11.6 | 13.4 | 1.3 |
| Festuca grayii | | | | | 1.1 | 1.2 | 10.2 | 1.4 |
| Plantago erecta | | | | | 2.0 | 4.1 | 5.6 | 1.8 |
| Melica californica | | | | | 8.0 | 11.2 | | |
| Linanthus androsaceus | | | | | 1.7 | 0.45 | | |
| Brodiaea laxa | | | | | 0.35 | 3.0 | | |
| Calochortus venustus | | | | | 3.3 | | | 1.0 |
| Agroseris heterophylla | | | | | 0.31 | | | 2.4 |
| Festuca dertonensis | | | | | 0.30 | | 2.1 | |
| Achillea millefolium | | | | | 1.4 | | | |
| Polypogon monospeliensis | | | | | 0.20 | | | |
| Trifolium tridentatum | | | | | | 0.10 | | |
| Brodiaea pulchella | | | | | | | 4.0 | |
| Sitanion jubatum | | | | | | | 3.6 | |
| Lomatium utriculatum | | | | | | | | 6.5 |
| Madia gracilis | | | | | | | 1.0 | 1.6 |
| Poa scabrella | | | | | | | | 0.6 |
| **B. Frequency** | | | | | | | | |
| Avena fatua | 31 | | 4 | | | | | |
| Medicago hispida | 2 | | 3 | | | | | |
| Avena barbata | | | 1 | | | | | |
| Torilis nodosa | | 1 | 1 | | | | | |
| Centaurea melitensis | | | 3 | | | | | |
| Festuca megalura | | | | 1 | | | | |
| Lolium multiflorum | 11 | 8 | | 1 | | | | |
| Erodium botrys | 2 | 1 | 5 | 6 | | | | |
| Bromus rigidus | 32 | 55 | 27 | 18 | | | | |
| Bromus mollis | 20 | 34 | 43 | 63 | 24 | 30 | 40 | 53 |
| Clarkia purpurea | 2 | 1 | 4 | 2 | 4 | 3 | 4 | |
| Hemizonia luzulaefolia | | | 3 | 6 | 18 | | | 7 |
| Eriastrum abramsii | | | | 2 | | | | 1 |
| Lotus subpinnatus | | | 1 | 2 | 6 | 8 | 5 | 14 |
| Stipa pulchra | | | | 4 | 14 | 20 | 14 | 3 |
| Eschscholzia californica | | | | | 4 | 12 | 3 | 1 |
| Festuca grayii | | | | | 3 | 4 | 21 | 4 |
| Plantago erecta | | | | | 10 | 10 | 4 | 4 |
| Melica californica | | | | | 2 | 8 | | |
| Linanthus androsaceus | | | | | 5 | 2 | | |
| Brodiaea laxa | | | | | 3 | 2 | | |
| Calochortus venustus | | | | | 2 | | | 1 |
| Agroseris heterophylla | | | | | 1 | | | 4 |
| Festuca dertonensis | | | | | 1 | | 5 | |
| Achillea millefolium | | | | | 1 | | | |
| Polypogon monosepliensis | | | | | 1 | | | |

Table 1.—Continued

| Species | Sandstone | | | | Serpentine | | | |
|---|---|---|---|---|---|---|---|---|
| | North-east | North-west | South-east | South-west | North-east | North-west | South-east | South-west |
| B. Frequency | | | | | | | | |
| Trifolium tridentatum | | | | | | 1 | | |
| Brodiaea pulchella | | | | | | | 2 | |
| Sitanion jubatum | | | | | | | 1 | |
| Madia gracilis | | | | | | | 1 | 6 |
| Lomatium utriculatum | | | | | | | | 3 |
| Poa scabrella | | | | | | | | 1 |

## Specific Properties of the Grasslands

The principal species in the grasslands of Jasper Ridge are generally grasses, although the composition varies considerably from site to site (Table 1). The only non-graminaceous species to occur with regularity among the dominant species is California poppy (*Eschscholzia californica*), which is important on all serpentine sites but the driest. It is, however, excluded from the sandstone grasslands. *Stipa pulchra* is an important dominant on all of the serpentine sites, but it penetrates the sandstone grasslands only at the dry end of the moisture gradient. If all the serpentine stands are summed, *S. pulchra* is the most important species on serpentine sites contributing an average of 30% of the total standing crop, although it shares dominance with *Bromus mollis* which contributes 27% of the total. The next most important species on the serpentine is *Eschscholzia californica* contributing 9% of the total standing crop. On the sandstone, the three most important species contribute much more to the total standing crop (77%) than the three most important serpentine species (66%). On the sandstone, *Bromus rigidus* contributes 42% of the total overall standing crop, followed by *B. mollis* (22%) and *Avena fatua* (13%).

Considering grasslands on both sandstone and serpentine soils, *B. mollis* was most important, contributing 24.4% of the total standing crop, followed by *B. rigidus* (21.2%), *S. pulchra* (16%), and *A. fatua* (6.7%). Together, these four grasses contributed 69% of the total peak biomass on the Jasper Ridge grasslands. Only one of these species, *S. pulchra,* is native to the California grasslands.

The biomass of populations is emphasized in this treatment because it seems a more realistic term for community evaluation than the commonly used floristic assessment, frequency. Although percentage standing crop and percentage frequency are significantly correlated ($r = 0.794$; $.001 > P$), frequency emphasizes those species which are most conspicuous as a result of their numbers rather than those which contribute most to community structure. Even considering only the two top species per stand (according to biomass), the correlation between percentage frequency and percentage standing crop is high for both serpentine ($r = 0.849$; $.01 > P > .001$) and sandstone ($r = 0.677$; $.1 > P > .05$) sites. However, in spite of the high correlation between the two characters, serious errors may result from using one as an indicator of the other (Table 1). For instance, *B. mollis* is the most frequent species on every serpentine site, and yet on one of these sites it ranks fifth in terms of contribution to standing crop. And on southeast sandstone exposures, *B. mollis* is twice as frequent as *B. rigidus,* but contributes half as much to community biomass. Although the high correlation between the two characters demonstrates a high degree of correspondence, the areas where there is a lack of correspondence could lead to substantial distortions in community assessment. Although frequency data are much easier to collect, they are probably less reliable indicators of community structure and function than such parameters as biomass.

The distribution of *B. mollis* is directly related to the exposure gradient on both substrate types, although the magnitude of the response is more pronounced on serpentine (Fig. 4) than on sandstone (Fig. 5) soils. Waring and Major (1964) found that this grass was confined to the driest and most exposed sites in the vegetation of the Coast Ranges of northern California, and a similar response is evident in these central California coastal grasslands. On serpentine soils, the distribution of *B. mollis,* an introduced annual, and *S. pulchra,* a native perennial, are reciprocally related. *S. pulchra* is the most important species on the cool, moist northern slopes, but its impor-

345

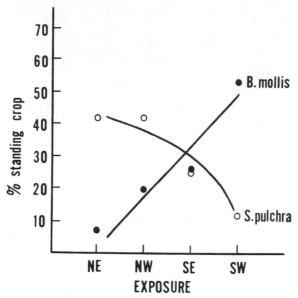

FIG. 4. Distribution of importance of *Bromus mollis* and *S. pulchra* in relation to the exposure gradient on serpentine soils.

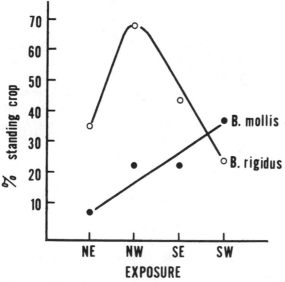

FIG. 5. Distribution of importance of *B. mollis* and *B. rigidus* in relation to the exposure gradient on sandstone soils.

tance declines conspicuously toward the drier end of the habitat gradient. A somewhat different response than either of these is indicated in the pattern of *B. rigidus* distribution along the sandstone habitat gradient (Fig. 5). This species reaches its maximum importance at the intermediate exposures. On the wet end of the gradient, it is displaced by *Avena fatua,* which is important only on the wettest end of the spectrum, while on the dry sites it is displaced by *S. pulchra,* which penetrates the sandstone communities only

on the driest end of the gradient. The distribution of *S. pulchra* is particularly anomalous since it occurs on sandstone only on the driest sites but reaches its greatest development on serpentine soils on the moistest sites. It seems likely that the greater development of the introduced annuals on the sandstone soil effectively excludes *S. pulchra,* a native perennial, except where vigor of the introduced species is restricted by low moisture supply.

The distribution of biomass on the two substrates shows that *S. pulchra* penetrates the sandstone community only where this community's standing crop is reduced to near the serpentine level (Fig. 6). The substantial difference in

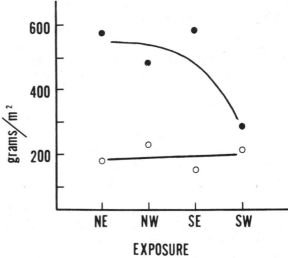

FIG. 6. Biomass of Jasper Ridge grasslands in relation to exposure and substrate. (Solid circles = sandstone; open circles = serpentine).

standing crop (here represented by peak biomass) between the two substrates is one of the most profound differences between grasslands on Jasper Ridge. Community biomass is twice as large on sandstone sites except at the driest exposure where it declines precipitously to near the serpentine level. Community biomass on serpentine, in contrast, is unaffected by exposure and maintains a similar level throughout the habitat gradient.

Productivity on sandstone was even more radically affected than biomass by the exposure gradient with a pronounced decrease in productivity from cool, moist sites to warm, dry sites (Fig. 7). While the biomass fell by about 54% along the habitat gradient, productivity declined by over 80%. By contrast, productivity on serpentine was unaffected by the moisture gradient, but this community was much less productive than the sandstone community except on the driest sites. It seems clear that the principal community limita-

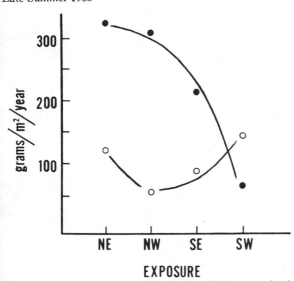

FIG. 7. Productivity of the Jasper Ridge grasslands in relation to exposure and substrate. (Solid circles = sandstone; open circles = serpentine).

TABLE 3. Mean Jaccard's coefficients for different exposures (exposure × 3 additional exposures for a given substrate)

| Exposure | X coefficient | |
| --- | --- | --- |
|  | Sandstone | Serpentine |
| Northeast.................... | 67.6 | 66.5 |
| Northwest.................... | 66.2 | 62.8 |
| Southeast.................... | 60.0 | 61.2 |
| Southwest.................... | 58.8 | 57.1 |

tion on sandstone soils is the rapid drainage of these soils and the resulting low level of moisture on exposed slopes. The limitation to grassland development on serpentine seems to be something other than moisture, presumably the unfavorable nutritional properties of these soils (Cooper 1922, Whittaker 1954a, 1954b, McMillan 1956).

The communities are also distinct floristically, and there are substantial differences between different exposures on the same substrate. A comparison of Jaccard's coefficients (Jaccard 1912) for the different substrates indicates that the grasslands are floristically distinct on the two substrates and that the floristic similarity changes regularly with exposure (Table 2). Floristic similarity

TABLE 2. Jaccard's coefficients for different substrates (sandstone × serpentine comparison)

| Exposure | Coefficient |
| --- | --- |
| Northeast............................ | 17.4 |
| Northwest........................... | 23.5 |
| Southeast............................ | 27.4 |
| Southwest........................... | 34.8 |
| Total flora.......................... | 26.4 |

between grasslands on different substrates increased consistently along the moisture gradient with the similarity on the driest exposure being twice that on the wettest site. The pattern agrees well with the patterns of biomass and productivity along the exposure gradient with increasing community similarity, both floristically and functionally, with increasingly dry exposures. The

within-soil type comparison presents quite a different pattern (Table 3). Within a given soil type, the community becomes floristically more distinct along the exposure gradient from cool, moist to warm, dry exposures on both soil types. There is consistently a greater floristic homogeneity within the sandstone community than on serpentine soils, although the difference is not conspicuous. The decreasing floristic affinities on both substrates along the habitat gradient, compared with the between-substrate comparison, indicate that as sites become increasingly drier, substrate becomes a less important determinant of floristic composition. With increasing dryness along the habitat gradient, the community becomes less similar to sites on the same substrate and more similar to sites on different substrates, although exposure is never the most important determinant of floristic properties.

The most conspicuous aspect of the species-diversity pattern within the grasslands is the floral poverty of northern exposures on sandstone (Fig.

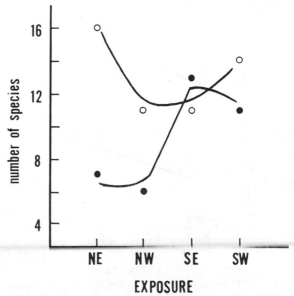

FIG. 8. Floristic diversity of the Jasper Ridge grasslands in relation to exposure and substrate. Solid circles = sandstone; open circles = serpentine).

8).  Floristic richness of the serpentine community is independent of exposure, while the sandstone community is conspicuously affected by position along the habitat gradient.  The serpentine community is more diverse than the sandstone community except on the southeast exposure.  The greater diversity of the serpentine flora compared with the sandstone is probably at least partially a reflection of diverse microtopography on the serpentine. The serpentine is characterized by a considerable complement of undifferentiated material including numerous stone outcrops and large rocks (Fig. 3) compared with the uniform substrate in the sandstone area.  The abundance of exposed rocks and boulders creates numerous microhabitats characterized by drainage off rock surfaces and differential soil depths.  The pronounced difference in the sandstone grasslands along the exposure gradient, however, indicates that this difference between the substrates should not be overemphasized.  An alternative explanation is that those highly productive species, such as *Avena fatua* and *Bromus rigidus,* which are extremely important on the moist end of the sandstone gradient may so monopolize the site resources under these conditions that subsidiary species are excluded.  Their disappearance with drier conditions may allow less effective competitors to penetrate the community.

The concentration of biomass in a limited number of species, as an evaluation of dominance, is quite different between the two substrates and along the moisture gradient on both substrates (Fig. 9).  The dominance pattern on sandstone

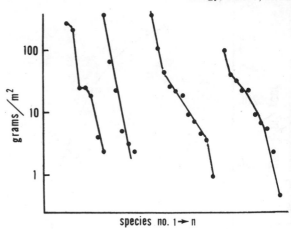

Fig. 10.  Dominance-diversity curves for stands on different exposures on the sandstone soil.  Curves arranged in the order of previous figures: NE, NW, SE, and SW exposures.

is essentially the inverse of the diversity curve with the conspicuous differences being between north and south slopes.  There is more pronounced dominance on sandstone than on serpentine substrates, and dominance on the sandstone is more pronounced on northern exposures and declines abruptly with decreasing moisture.  On the serpentine soil, however, there is a slight tendency for dominance to increase from cool, moist to warm, dry sites.

Dominance-diversity curves (Preston 1948, Whittaker 1965) for the sandstone sites generally fit the steep geometric series of floristically poor sites, although there is some deviation (Fig. 10). Diversity increases along the moisture gradient, as indicated previously, with an accompanying decrease in dominance.  There is pronounced single species dominance on all sites except the northeast exposure where dominance is shared. In addition, the proportion of the total community resources represented by the top species-niche decreases from moist to dry sites.  The greater diversity of the serpentine community is evident in the dominance-diversity curves (Fig. 11).  All sites except the southwest fit the logarithmic series of Preston (1948) characteristic of most well-developed plant communities (Whittaker 1965).  The southwest slope, however, fits none of the conventional models of community structure and represents a community with essentially three niche groups: a top niche occupied by a single dominant and two subsidiary niches partitioned among relatively coequal species.  These biomass-based dominance-diversity curves indicate that the structure of these grasslands changes conspicuously along the habitat gradient and between the two soil types.  Both lumping the total data for a

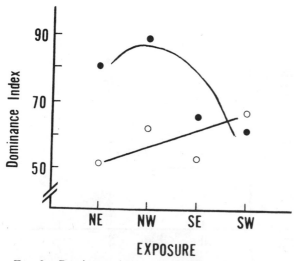

Fig. 9.  Dominance index (percentage of peak standing crop contributed by the two most important species) of the Jasper Ridge grasslands in relation to exposure and substrate.  (Solid circles = sandstone; open circles = serpentine).

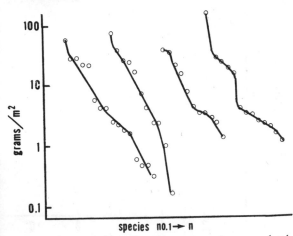

FIG. 11. Dominance-diversity curves for grasslands on different exposures on the serpentine soil. Curves arranged as in Fig. 10.

given substrate and combining all sites give the familiar lognormal distribution when plotted according to Preston's octave plot (Preston 1948). This distribution, however, is what one would expect for a universe, and such a loss of information based on arbitrary or intuitive stand grouping seems neither desirable nor justified. It is clear, based on the dominance-diversity curves and on functional and floristic properties, that the grasslands vary conspicuously on different substrates and on different exposures and that arbitrarily grouping them would sacrifice considerable information about the total grassland dynamics.

These California grasslands represent a floristic and functional continuum of intergrading biomass, productivity, diversity, and species composition. On a floristic basis, there is good reason to separate the grasslands by soil type according to their conspicuously low Jaccard coefficients. However, the biomass of the southwestern sandstone site is much nearer to serpentine communities than to its adjacent sandstone sites. In terms of diversity, the south-facing sandstone exposures are much more similar to serpentine grasslands than to north-facing sandstone slopes. There can be little doubt that substrate has a profound effect upon community properties. But the grassland is a responsive community, and substrate-induced differences in community properties are modified along exposure gradients.

## GENERAL PROPERTIES OF THE GRASSLANDS

Turning to the general properties of the Jasper Ridge grasslands, what is the relevance of models of community structure to an interpretation of the ecology of these grasslands? One of the most widely discussed models of community structure is the one Margalef (1958, 1963, 1965) proposed

based on his studies of marine plankton ecosystems. In this community model, diversity is inversely related to dominance and productivity and directly related to stability. A similar conclusion was derived in Leigh's examination of quasi-Hamiltonian systems of equations, although he restricted his development to predator-prey interactions (Leigh 1965). According to this model, which is in general accord with Margalef's, stability of a species increases with an increase in that species' predators. A proliferation of alternative avenues of energy flow is the generally advanced explanation for this increased stability (Solomon 1953, Burnett 1960). Watt (1965), however, concludes from his studies of biological control of insects that, at carnivore or herbivore trophic levels, stability decreases with the number of predators. Patten's (1963) studies of planktonic communities in the York River, Virginia, indicated that high productive capacity in this community was associated with high diversity.

Dominance and diversity are inversely related in the Jasper Ridge grasslands (Fig. 12). The

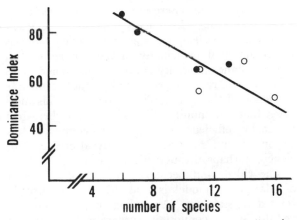

FIG. 12. Relationship between dominance and diversity of grasslands on sandstone (solid circles) and serpentine (open circles) soils on Jasper Ridge.

inverse correlation between these two properties ($r = -0.842$) is highly significant ($.01 > P > .001$). The serpentine grasslands are more diverse, on the whole, than the sandstone grasslands, and this diversity is accompanied by decreased dominance. Even within a substrate type there is a pronounced decrease in dominance with increasing diversity. The tendency for community biomass to be concentrated in the top species on the dominance-diversity curve decreases as the community becomes more diverse.

There was a significant ($.01 > P > .001$) positive correlation ($r = 0.852$) between dominance and productivity in the grasslands (Fig. 13). Conversely, there was a highly significant ($.01 >$

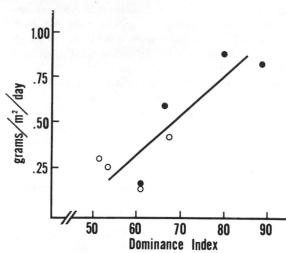

Fig. 13. Relationship between dominance and productivity of grasslands on sandstone (solid circles) and serpentine (open circles) soils on Jasper Ridge.

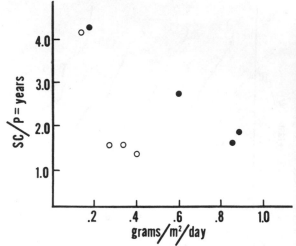

Fig. 14. Relationship between community stability (as indicated by turnover time) and productivity of the grasslands on sandstone (solid circles) and serpentine (open circles) soils on Jasper Ridge.

P > .001) inverse correlation ($r = -0.901$) between number of species in the stand and stand productivity. The efficiency of the grasslands as a photosynthetic energy accumulator decreases with increasing diversity. The most efficient stands are species-poor stands in which biomass is accumulated principally in the top species on the dominance-diversity curve. As more and more species penetrate the community, the productive efficiency of the community decreases. This indicates that community diversification, rather than increasing efficiency through more complete utilization of site resources, actually decreases efficiency, perhaps through niche overlap.

The third, and perhaps most important, tenet of Margalef's model is that diversity is directly related to stability. According to the model, diversity in the community generates stability but is accompanied by a decrease in system productivity. Community stability in the grasslands was assessed as turnover time, the ratio between biomass and productivity. The turnover times all exceeded 1 year, which is the presumed turnover time in grasslands of this type. However, there is a considerable accumulation of litter from year to year and in spite of the comparatively low complement of perennials in these grasslands, the accumulated standing crop is one to four times the annual productivity. It may be argued that in such a system the turnover time is not an accurate assessment of community stability. However, in the absence of grazing and repeated burning, this accumulated standing crop represents a reservoir of energy and stored minerals of the same type as that which contributes most of the standing crop in woody communities (Heady

1956). According to the model, then, productivity and turnover time should be inversely related. Although the relationship (Fig. 14) holds on the sandstone soil ($r = -0.970$; $.05 > P$), it does not hold for either the serpentine sites ($r = -0.870$; $P > .1$) or the grasslands as a whole ($r = -0.531$, $P > .1$). Neither do the regressions of dominance ($r = 0.216$; $P \gg .1$) or diversity ($r = -0.003$; $P \gg .1$) on turnover time fit the predictions of the model. In these grasslands, stability is independent of productivity, diversity, and dominance.

### DISCUSSION AND CONCLUSIONS

The principal defect of these studies of the California grasslands is the lack of information on underground portions of the community which may contribute significantly to community biomass and productivity (Bray 1963). Attempts to sample the underground portions of the community during the first sampling period proved unsatisfactory. Because of the nature of the serpentine soil, with large amounts of undifferentiated material, it was impossible to obtain a reasonable sample of underground biomass. This information, essential to a complete understanding of community ecology, will require a large investigative team or more sophisticated sampling methods than were available for this study.

The information currently available does, however, provide considerable insight into the structure and function of the California grasslands. The serpentine grasslands are more diverse than those on sandstone, and the latter are particularly poor in species. For instance, treating the serpentine and sandstone grasslands as a unit and calculating diversity as the slope of the regression

$$\log Y = a + bX$$

where $Y$ is the number of individuals and $X$ is the number of species (Monk and McGinnis 1966) gives $b = 0.333$ for the sandstone and $b = 0.060$ for the serpentine. The serpentine grasslands are moderately diverse, falling between wet and dry southern mixed hardwood forests, while the sandstone community is less diverse than any community reported by Monk and McGinnis.

The species composition of the Jasper Ridge grasslands is similar to that reported previously for annual grasslands in various regions of California (Talbot, Biswell, and Hormay 1939, Biswell 1956, Heady 1956, 1958, Major and Pyott 1966, White 1966, Naveh 1967). The Jasper Ridge studies indicate that the importance of certain species, notably *Bromus mollis,* may be overemphasized in the reliance upon floristic data. The mean frequency of this species in the grasslands was 38.4%, while its mean contribution to peak standing crop was 24.4%. Frequency overestimates the importance of this species by over 57% in these grasslands. This evaluation is one of degree, however. Whether ranked by frequency or standing crop, *B. mollis* is still the most important species in the grasslands as a whole although its importance changes conspicuously with the moisture gradient. The next most important species in terms of mean standing crop were *B. rigidus* (21.1%), *S. pulchra* (15.9%), and *A. fatua* (6.7%). The importance of *B. rigidus* is particularly striking since it was restricted to the sandstone. Even more surprising was the contribution of *A. fatua* which occurred only on the east slopes of the sandstone. The most important species on serpentine and their contribution to biomass were *S. pulchra* (29.7%), *B. mollis* (27.0%), *Eschscholzia californica* (9.3%), and *Lotus subpinnatus* (7.1%). The most important sandstone species were *B. rigidus* (42.1%), *B. mollis* (21.8%), and *A. fatua* (13.4%). No other sandstone species contributed more than 5% of the total peak biomass. The upper species on the dominance-diversity curve were comparatively more important on the sandstone, while the converse was true for the lower species on the curve.

The concept of the individualistic plant association (Gleason 1939) and the idea of the vegetation continuum (Curtis and McIntosh 1951) are both supported primarily by floristic data, and few data from functional studies have been applied to the problem of the nature of plant communities. In these studies of California grasslands there seems to be even less reason to draw sharp lines based on the data on community biomass or productivity than on the basis of floristics. Although the sandstone and serpentine grasslands are relatively distinct floristically, there is a tendency toward convergence as the site becomes increasingly dry and there is complete overlap of biomass and productivity. Certain species (*B. mollis,* for instance) respond identically to the habitat gradient on the two soil types. Others (*S. pulchra*) are radically different in their response to the habitat gradient on the two soil types. As in their biomass, productivity, and species composition, so there is a tendency toward convergence in dominance-diversity relationships. The dominance-diversity curves could be arranged as a series from cool, moist sites on sandstone to warm, dry sites on serpentine with a complete intergradation of form in the curves. The Jasper Ridge grasslands are a system of inter-acting populations and "the balance among populations shifts with change in environment so that (the) vegetation is a pattern of populations corresponding to the pattern of environmental gradients" (Whittaker 1953).

There is, however, considerable order in these grasslands and this order is manifested in the relationships among productivity, standing crop, dominance, and diversity. Previous comparisons of terrestrial plant communities have emphasized the floristic composition of the communities, but equally important are the functional properties of the vegetation. Reliance upon floristic techniques reduces one to saying that communities are different if they share no species in common. However, the regular relationships among functional properties of these grasslands, which fit the model Margalef (1958) has proposed for planktonic communities, suggest that communities with different species composition, even different growth forms and totally different habitat spectra, have much in common. Although the widespread acceptance of Margalef's model among ecologists is emphasized by the casual manner in which it is often incorporated into discussions (Woodwell 1967), there is a paucity of data on terrestrial plant communities which can be clearly related to this model. The data on the California grasslands suggest that the model has general application. In the grasslands, dominance and diversity are inversely related and increased productivity is generated by increased dominance. The populations represent a responsive mechanism adjusting the community to habitat conditions along the exposure-substrate gradient. The interplay among species populations results in modifications of community productivity, biomass, dominance, and diversity, in response to the habitat gradient. In one important respect, however, the grasslands do not fit Margalef's model. According to the model, diversity is a mechanism which generates community stability, and a price in stability is paid for increasing productivity. The model is logically satisfying because it indicates that something cannot be gotten for nothing: increasing productivity generates a stability cost; increasing stability generates a productivity cost. The grasslands, however, show no relationship between stability and productivity, dominance, or diversity. Although the data are not exhaustive, it suggests the possibility that productivity may be optimized without jeopardizing community stability. However, the Margalef model emphasizes successional states and the grasslands are a spatial rather than a temporal field. When they become available, data on successional sequences similar to those recorded here for the California grasslands will be particularly important in testing the applicability of the model to terrestrial systems.

## LITERATURE CITED

Biswell, H. H. 1956. Ecology of California grasslands. J. Range Manage. 9: 19–24.

Bray, J. R. 1963. Root production and the estimation of net productivity. Can. J. Bot. 41: 65–72.

Burnett, T. 1960. Control of insect pests. Fed. Proc. 19: 557–561.

Cooper, W. S. 1922. The broad sclerophyll vegetation of California. Carnegie Inst. Wash. Publ. 319. 124 p.

Curtis, J. T., and R. P. McIntosh. 1951. An upland forest continuum in the prairie-forest border region of Wisconsin. Ecology 32: 476–496.

Gleason, H. A. 1939. The individualistic concept of the plant association. Amer. Midland Natur. 21: 92–110.

Heady, H. F. 1956. Changes in a California annual plant community induced by manipulation of natural mulch. Ecology 37: 798–812.

———. 1958. Vegetational changes in the California annual type. Ecology 39: 402–416.

Hendrick, D. W. 1948. The mulch layer of California annual ranges. J. Range Manage. 1: 22–25.

Hervey, D. F. 1949. Reaction of a California annual-plant community to fire. J. Range Manage. 2: 116–121.

Jaccard, P. 1912. The distribution of the flora in the alpine zone. New Phytol. 11: 37–50.

Kruckeberg, A. R. 1954. The ecology of serpentine soils. III. Plant species in relation to serpentine soils. Ecology 35: 267–274.

Kuchler, A. W. 1964. Map: potential natural vegetation of the conterminous United States. Amer. Geogr. Soc., New York.

Leigh, E. G. 1965. On the relation between the productivity, biomass, diversity, and stability of a community. Proc. Nat. Acad. Sci. (U. S.)53: 777–783.

Major, J., and W. T. Pyott. 1966. Buried, viable seeds in two California bunchgrass sites and their bearing on the definition of a flora. Vegetatio 13: 253–282.

Margalef, D. R. 1958. Information theory in ecology. Gen. Systems 3: 36–71.

———. 1963. On certain unifying principles in ecology. Amer. Natur. 97: 357–374.

———. 1965. Ecological correlations and the relationship between primary productivity and community structure, p. 355–364. In C. R. Goldman [ed.] Primary productivity in aquatic environments. Mdm. Inst. Ital. Idrobiol., 18 Suppl., Univ. Cal. Press, Berkeley, Calif.

McMillan, C. 1956. The edaphic restriction of Curpressus and Pinus in the Coast Ranges of central California. Ecol. Monogr. 26: 177–212.

Monk, C. D., and J. T. McGinnis. 1966. Tree species diversity in six forest types in north central Florida. J. Ecol. 54: 341–344.

Munz, P. A., and D. D. Keck. 1949. California plant communities. El Aliso 2: 87–105.

Naveh, Z. 1967. Mediterranean ecosystems and vegetation types in California and Israel. Ecology 48: 445–458.

Patten, B. C. 1963. Plankton: optimum diversity structure of a summer community. Science 140: 894–898.

Preston, F. W. 1948. The commonness, and rarity, of species. Ecology 29: 254–283.

Snedecor, G. W. 1956. Statistical methods applied to experiments in agriculture and biology. 5th ed. Iowa St. Coll. Press, Ames, Iowa. 534 p.

Solomon, M. E. 1953. Insect population balance and chemical control of pests. Chem. Ind. Rev. 1953: 1143–1147.

Talbot, M. W., H. H. Biswell, and A. L. Hormay. 1939. Fluctuations in the annual vegetation of California. Ecology 20: 394–402.

Walker, R. B. 1954. The ecology of serpentine soils. II. Factors affecting plant growth on serpentine soils. Ecology 35: 259–266.

Waring, R. H., and J. Major. 1964. Some vegetation of the California coastal redwood region in relation to gradients of moisture, nutrients, light, and temperature. Ecol. Monogr. 34: 167–215.

Watt, K. E. F. 1965. Community stability and the strategy of biological control. Can. Entomol. 97: 887–895.

Wells, P. V. 1964. Antibiosis as a factor in vegetation patterns. Science 144: 889.

White, K. L. 1966. Old-field succession on Hastings Reservation, California. Ecology 47: 865–868.

Whittaker, R. H. 1953. A consideration of climax theory: the climax as a population and pattern. Ecol. Monogr. 23: 41–78.

———. 1954a. The ecology of serpentine soils. I. Introduction. Ecology 35: 258–259.

———. 1954b. The ecology of serpentine soils. IV. The vegetational response to serpentine soils. Ecology 35: 275–288.

———. 1960. Vegetation of the Siskiyou Mountains, Oregon and California. Ecol. Monogr. 30: 279–338.

———. 1965. Dominance and diversity in land plant communities. Science 147: 250–260.

Woodwell, G. M. 1967. Radiation and the patterns of nature. Science 156: 461–470.

Reprinted from *Ecology*, Vol. 42, No. 3, July, 1961

# ON BIRD SPECIES DIVERSITY

ROBERT H. MACARTHUR AND JOHN W. MACARTHUR

*Department of Zoology, University of Pennsylvania and Marlboro College, Marlboro, Vermont*

It is common experience that more species of birds breed in a mixed wood than in a field of comparable size. It is also well known that tropical forests seem to support more species than their temperate counterparts. These facts are often explained in terms of the number of "niches" or "ways of life" which the habitat provides. In this paper, a somewhat more precise analysis is attempted.

The actual number of species is better replaced by a number called the "bird species diversity," calculated as follows: Let $p_i$ be the proportion of all of the bird individuals which belong to the $i^{th}$ species. Then the bird species diversity, is $-\sum_i p_i \log_e p_i$. This is a formula used by communication engineers to calculate the information generated, *e.g.*, by a typist who uses the different keys with frequencies $p_i$. Thus, for instance, a one species community always has zero diversity; 2 species, one with 99 individuals and one with 1 individual, will have diversity of $-.99 \log_e .99 - .01 \log_e .01 = .046 + .010 = .056$ (close to zero), while 2 species each with 50 individuals will have diversity of $.347 + .347 = .694$. This illustrates why diversity is a better measure than actual number of species, for the community with 99 of one and 1 of the other seems closer to the community with one species. Margalef (1957) has frequently used a similar measure in his plankton studies. In terms of this, the question becomes: "What is it about the environment which controls the bird species diversity?"

One more refinement of the general problem is necessary. For, even if all the bird species were equally abundant, a bird census of a small area (say an acre) would have only a few of the species. Since an acre supports 3 or 4 pairs of birds, not more than 3 or 4 species could be expected to have nests in the given acre. And if the area is so homogeneous that adjacent 1 acre (say) territories are occupied by the same 3 or 4 species, then the whole area cannot have more than 3 or 4 species. This is contradicted by the abundant evidence that stands of vegetation with the degree of homogeneity resulting from a uniform history of cutting

and other interference have very many (up to 106 at least in Mexico—Davis (1955)) species of breeding birds. Therefore, of course, the territories of most species are scattered rather sparsely over the area and the territories of very few species form a mosaic. It must be concluded that either the species are scattered randomly over the habitat, or else, more plausibly, that birds use some fairly subtle differences in local habitat as criteria for habitat selection. Returning to the bird species diversity, it clearly can increase as the area increases. Since there is no adequate theory of "species-area" or "diversity-area" curves, all censuses must cover approximately the same area so that variations in the bird species diversity reflect differences in habitat composition rather than variations in size of census area. Although many of the censuses reported here were taken over larger areas, the breeding bird populations of a randomly chosen 5 acres of each will be compared.

The procedure of the research described here was to census a wide variety of habitats, differing in (1) plant species composition, (2) foliage height profiles, and (3) latitude, and to determine how much each of these factors influenced the bird diversity.

## MEASUREMENTS

Plant species composition was measured by an index of plant species diversity computed with the formula used for bird species diversity. $p_i$ now refers to the total area of the leaves of the $i^{th}$ plant species, expressed as a proportion of the total leaf area of all of the species on the census plot. It would be a formidable job to measure areas of individual leaves, but fortunately a much easier and more accurate method bypasses this: Imagine all the leaves lying on the ground as in the autumn. If there are, on the average 4 layers of leaves on the ground, then there are 4 acres of leaf per acre of this habitat, and if we were to push a sticky needle through the fallen leaves at random points, then an average of 4 leaves would adhere to it. And the areas of the leaves are automatically taken into consideration so that if ¼ of the leaves picked up were of some large leafed species, it would indicate precisely the same total leaf area of that species as of a small leafed species whose leaves were picked up with the same frequency. Rather than wait for the leaves to fall, it is easier to erect a stiff wire and count the leaves it touches (since leaves on trees do not lie horizontally, some error is introduced in this way, but it gives a convenient approximation). For the canopy, rather than using a wire, a sighting was made vertically through a 10 foot aluminum pipe of 1¼ inch diameter and the number of leaves which a wire would intersect was estimated.

For coniferous trees, and sometimes for deciduous, it seems preferable to use fraction $X$ of sky not obscured by foliage and estimate the number n of leaves which a wire would intersect by the formula $e^{-n} = X$ which is the first term of the Poisson distribution.

Thus, if 90% of the sky is obscured by foliage a fraction equal to $\frac{1}{10}$ is unobscured and since $e^{-2.3} = \frac{1}{10}$, this is equivalent to an average of 2.3 randomly placed leaves (of any size!) above the point from which observation was made. In future measurements vertical photographs analyzed by a recording microdensitometer will be substituted for the more subjective estimates of percentage. Since leaves may not not be randomly placed this is obviously only an approximation, but in practice it seems quite accurate.

From the foliage height profiles a number called the foliage height diversity was calculated using the same formula ( $-\sum_1 p_i \log_e p_i$ ) as before. In this case $p_i$ is the proportion of the total foliage which lies in the $i^{th}$ of the chosen horizontal layers. The profiles were constructed as follows: At a sequence of heights above

the ground a white board, marked in squares, was moved horizontally away from an observer at the same height until ½ of its surface was obscured by leaves from the observer's view. In forests, the board atop a high pole was erected at trial distances from the observer until an acceptable one was found. The distance D between the observer and the board was then measured and the foliage density k at that height was estimated from $e^{-kD} = \frac{1}{2}$ or $k = \log_e 2 / D$.

This formula too is only approximate, but seemed satisfactory. Roughly it is derived as follows. The area of leaf silhouetted against the board will be nA, say, where A is the area of the board and n is the leaf silhouette per unit of board area. The volume of space in which these leaves lie is DA, so the leaf silhouette area per unit of volume of space is

$$\frac{nA}{DA} = \frac{n}{D} = k.$$

As before, n can be estimated by the first term of a Poisson distribution so that $e^{-n} = \frac{1}{2}$ or $n = \log_e 2$. The method assumes that the proportion of leaf area which is similar in all 3 layers. The size of the board is thus unimportant (since the A's cancel out) except that a large board gives an average over more vegetation ($10'' \times 18''$ was used inm ost of this work). In each plot, at least 16 such measurements were averaged at each of the following heights above the ground: 6", 2', 5', 10', 20', 30', 45', 60'. A profile of foliage density was drawn by eye passing through each of these calculated points. The profiles of the primarily deciduous areas censused are shown in Figure 1. (The Florida

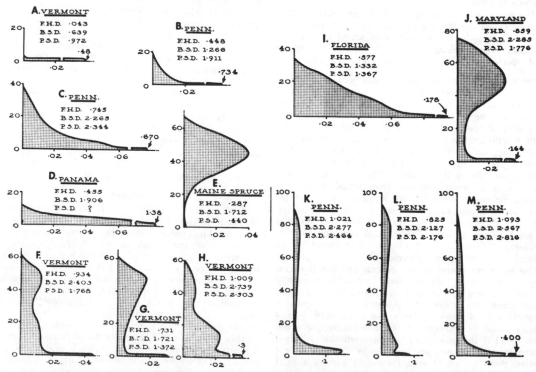

Fig. 1. The densities of foliage (measured in square feet of leaf silhouette per cubic foot of space) are plotted along the abscissae. The height in feet above the ground is the ordinate. F.H.D. is foliage height diversity, B.S.D. is bird species diversity, and P.S.D. is plant species diversity.

bird census was taken by Wolfenden *et al.* 1959, who kindly allowed measurements to be made in this area). The area of the profiles is divided into 3 horizontal layers and the proportions of the whole that each constitutes is the $p_l$ used in the formula.

### RESULTS

The actual censuses are in Table I, in which the number of territories, or fraction of territories, is entered.

The layers 0'-2', 2'-25' and over 25' are marked on the profiles in Fig. 1 and the corresponding foliage height

TABLE I. Numbers of breeding bird territories per 5 acres for the regions shown in Fig. 1

| | A | B | C | E | F | G | H | I | J | K | L | M |
|---|---|---|---|---|---|---|---|---|---|---|---|---|
| mourning dove | | | | | | | | | | | | 1 |
| yellow billed cuckoo | | | | | | | | .5 | | | | |
| r. t. hummingbird | | | | .5 | | | | | | | | .5 |
| flicker | | | 1 | | | | 1 | | | | | .5 |
| red-bellied wood pecker | | | | | | | | .5 | | | | |
| yellow-bellied sapsucker | | | | | | 1 | | | | | | |
| hairy woodpecker | | | | | 1 | .5 | | | | | | |
| downy woodpecker | | | | | | | 1 | | | | | |
| crested flycatcher | | | | | | | | 1 | 1 | | 1 | |
| acadian flycatcher | | | | | | | | 1.5 | | | | |
| wood pewee | | | | | | | | | 2 | 2 | | 1 |
| olivesided flycatcher | | | | | | 1.5 | | | | | | |
| blue jay | | | | | | | | | 1 | 1 | | 5 |
| black-capped chickadee | | | | 1 | | .5 | | | | | | |
| tufted titmouse | | | | | | | | 1.5 | 1.5 | 1 | | 1 |
| white-breasted nuthatch | | | | 1 | | | | | | 1 | | |
| brown creeper | | | | 1 | | | | | | | | |
| winter wren | | | | | | 1 | | | | | | |
| catbird | | | 1 | | | | | | 1 | | | 1 |
| robin | | | | | .5 | | .5 | | | | | |
| wood thrush | | | | | | | | | 1 | | 1.25 | |
| olive-backed thrush | | | | | 2 | | | | | | | |
| veery thrush | | | | | | 1 | | | | | | |
| gnatcatcher | | | | | | | 1 | | | | | |
| golden-crowned kinglet | | | | 1 | | | | | | | | |
| white-eyed vireo | | | | | | | 1 | | | | | |
| yellow-throated vireo | | | | | | | 1 | | | | | |
| red-eyed vireo | | | | | 1 | 3 | 1 | | 2.5 | 2 | 4 | 1 |
| black and white warbler | | | | | | .5 | | | | | | |
| prothonotary warbler | | | | | | | | | 2 | | | |
| blue-winged warbler | | | .5 | | | | | | | | | |
| Nashville warbler | | | | | | | 1 | | | | | |
| parula warbler | | | | | | | | | 1 | | | |
| magnolia warbler | | | | .5 | 1.5 | 1.5 | | | | | | |
| black-throated blue warbler | | | | | | 1 | | | | | | |
| myrtle warbler | | | | 2 | | 5 | | | | | | |
| black-throated green warbler | | | | 5 | 1 | | | | | | | |
| blackburnian warbler | | | | 1 | 2 | 1 | | | | | | |
| bay-breasted warbler | | | | 3 | | | | | | | | |
| prairie warbler | | | 2 | | | | | | | | | |
| ovenbird | | | | | 1.5 | | | | | 3 | 3 | .5 |
| Kentucky warbler | | | | | | | .75 | | | | | |
| mourning warbler | | | | | | | | | | | | |
| yellowthroat | | 1 | 2.5 | | | | 3 | | | | | 2 |
| yellow-breasted chat | | | 2 | | | | | | | | | |
| Canada warbler | | | | | | | 2 | | | | | |
| redstart | | | 1 | | 1.5 | | | | 2 | | | 1.5 |
| grackle | | | | | | .5 | | | | | | |
| scarlet tanager | | | | | | | | | | 2 | | |
| summer tanager | | | 1 | | | | | | | 1 | | 1 |
| cardinal | | | 1.5 | | | | | | | | | 1.5 |
| indigo bunting | 1 | .5 | | | | | | | | | | |
| goldfinch | | | .25 | 1.5 | | | | | | | 1 | 1 |
| towhee | | | | | .5 | | 1 | | | | | |
| slate-colored junco | 2 | 1 | 3 | | | | | | | | | |
| field sparrow | | | | | | | 1 | | | | | |
| white throated sparrow | | | .5 | | | | | | | | | 1 |
| song sparrow | | | | | | | | | | | | |

diversity and bird species diversities are shown as well as plant species diversity and latitude. These are plotted as a graph in Figure 2, showing a close fit to the line:

bird species diversity = 2.01 foliage height
diversity + .46,

calculated by least squares. Various other subdivisions of the profile into horizontal layers were tried, and the layers 0-2', 2'-25' and > 25' were chosen as those layers which made the collection of points on the graph most orderly. It is of interest that this subdivision was chosen after the Vermont censuses were taken in 1959 and that it continued to be appropriate for the censuses in 1960, elsewhere. Such subdivisions as 0-3', 3-30' and > 30' were nearly as good, but more nearly equal subdivision (*e.g.* 0-15', 15'-30', > 30') made a very scattered

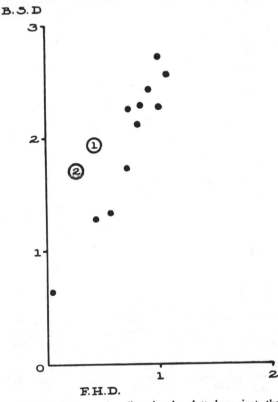

FIG. 2. Bird species diversity is plotted against the foliage height diversity of deciduous forest plots. Point 1. is census D of tropical savannah and point 2 is census E of pure spruce forest.

graph. The linearity of the cluster of points indicates that the addition of a new layer of a given amount of foliage results in the same increase in bird species diversity, (not however the same increase in number of bird species) no matter which layer (0-2', 2-25' or > 25') is added, and no matter which other layers are present to begin with. Thus, we can say that the layers 0-2', 2'-25' and > 25' are roughly equally important to the birds. (The reasons for this will be discussed later.) Looked at from this point of view, we can see the trouble with the other subdivisions. For definiteness, consider 0-15', 15'-30', > 30'. Adding a 0-15' layer to a habitat without it causes a much greater increase in bird species diversity than the addition of the layer $> 30'$. There is nothing biological about the number of layers chosen. Four or 5 layers in a roughly similar subdivision would be more cumbersome to analyse but would presumably be even more accurate. In particular, the layers $0\text{-}\frac{1}{2}'$, $\frac{1}{2}'\text{-}6'$, $6'\text{-}15'$ and $> 15'$ suggested by Elton and Miller (1954) allow a rather good prediction of the bird species diversity.

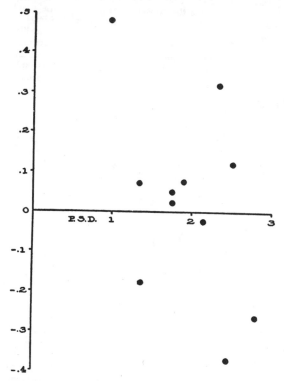

FIG. 3. The ordinate is the residual scatter, after partial regression of bird species diversity on foliage height diversity. This is plotted against plant species diversity, showing that knowledge of plant species diversity does not provide additional knowledge of bird species diversity. The least squares equation was B.S.D. = 2.546 F.H.D. — .152 P.S.D. — .250, and the residual scatter was computed from the formula B.S.D. — 2.546 F.H.D. — .048.

The next question is: How much of the remaining scatter, i.e. how much of the variability in bird species diversity not accounted for by the variation in foliage height diversity, can be accounted for in variations of plant species diversity and latitude? Remarkably enough, the answer is "None." This is seen most easily by glancing at Figure 3 which shows that the residual scatter after partial regression is more or less independent of plant species diversity. Thus, although plant species diversity alone is a good predictor of bird species diversity it is because plant species diversity is high when foliage height diversity is high, and, when this is taken account of, plant species diversity can contribute nothing further. In other words, habitats of the same profile have the same bird species diversity whether composed of few or many plant species. As a striking example of this, the almost pure stand of white spruce

on Mount Desert Island in Maine which the authors studied earlier (MacArthur 1957) had as great a bird species diversity as the forests of very mixed composition in Pennsylvania and Maryland.

The lack of effect of latitude is puzzling but is only tentative since a rather poor sample of latitudes have been examined. Furthermore, a brief trip to Panama yielded a tentative bird species diversity in a savannah area of 1.906 and foliage height diversity of .455 (see Fig. 2). Thus, the tropical bird species diversity is much greater than the temperate one for habitats of comparable profile. The excess of tropical savannah over temperate fields is about equal to the excess of the bird species diversity in the tropical forest over temperate forests. These facts will be discussed further in a separate paper.

## DISCUSSION

These results are rather statistical in nature. What is their meaning in terms of individual birds or species? The simplest explanation which seems to account for the observations, describes the "shape" of a bird's niche. Let us return to the picture of many territories distributed over an area and consider the following evolutionary argument. A large number of species can be accommodated in an environment in a variety of ways of which there are 2 extremes. Each species may have different habitat preference and feed throughout this habitat on all kinds of food, or, all species may share the entire habitat, each species feeding on a different variety of food or in a different situation within the habitat. The first extreme violates what might be called the "jack of all trades—master of none" principle that natural selection favors the increased efficiency resulting from a certain amount of specialization. In the other extreme, specialization has proceeded so far that time and energy are wasted in travelling between spots for which the specializations are adapted. It is hard to say just where the balance of these opposing requirements would be reached, but it is clear that greater specialization resulting in increased efficiency would always be favored as long as no time or energy are wasted. And no time or energy will be wasted if niches are "convex" in the sense that between any 2 fairly distant feeding places there will be a fairly natural route also consisting of feeding places. A specialization to a single tree species in a mixed forest would clearly violate this since, in passing from one suitable tree to another, the bird would go through many unsuitable ones. Thus, natural selection would tend to eliminate a situation in which bird species diversity depended upon tree species diversity, unless, as in some fruit eating species, a very remarkable improvement in efficiency is achieved along with the restriction in feeding position. Thus, one principal result of these censuses can be predicted on assuming that niches are convex.

Next, we may ask "why are the layers 0-2', 2-25', $> 25'$ equally important? Is it because birds respond to different heights, or is it because they respond to different configurations of vegetation in different layers?" In the latter case, herbs, bushes and trees presumably correspond to the layers 0-2', 2-25' and $> 25'$ respectively, although small trees count as bushes etc. There is good evidence for this latter explanation. For, although deciduous forests vary principally with height above the ground and hence have a bird diversity predictable from the height profile, conifers (especially spruce) have a marked "inside" and "outside" for which species are specialized (MacArthur 1957). Hence bird species diversity would be high in a mature spruce forest even if few layers were present. This is precisely what happens in the Maine white spruce wood mentioned earlier, with bird species diversity of 1.712 and foliage height diversity of .287 which is seriously off the graph of deciduous forests (Fig. 1).

A different way of looking at the data gives additional insight. Watt (1947) has pointed out that plants are distributed in patches. Hutchinson and MacArthur (1959) attempted to explain the sizes of coexisting organisms in terms of an environment composed of a mosaic of kinds of patches. Different combinations of patches formed the habitats selected by different species. The present research can be easily interpreted in terms of this picture of the environment. In fact, our results suggest that the patches forming the birds' environmental mosaic are sections of canopy C (over 25'), patches of bushes B from 2-25', and the herbaceous and other cover H less than 2' from the ground. And the sequence of patches encountered in moving through the habitat (or in taking ever larger samples) is then represented by a sequence of letters e.g. C, B, H, H, B, C, , , , with certain random properties but also subject to the condition that the long term frequency of C's, B's, and H's should conform to their respective densities ($p_i$) in the particular habitat. If the sequence is ergodic, which defines what we call a homogeneous habitat, then it is well known that the uncertainty of the next letters in the sequence is appropriately measured by the formula $- \sum_i p_i \log_e p_i$ which we used. If, instead of considering the uncertainty of future single letters in the sequence, we ask for the uncertainty of future pairs of letters, the formula becomes $- 2 \sum_i p_i \log_e p_i$ which is $2 \times$ foliage height diversity, which is essentially the predicted value of the bird species diversity. Thus we can say that bird species diversity is determined as if the birds recognized suitable habitats by pairs of foliage types ($> 25'$, 2-25', 0-2'). The species area curve could then be predicted from this.

### ACKNOWLEDGMENTS

This work was supported (in different stages) by grants from the University of Pennsylvania, The American Academy of Arts and Sciences, and The National Science Foundation (No. G11575). Drs. G. E. Hutchinson, Peter Klopfer and Monte Lloyd have discussed aspects of this research at length and it has benefited from their ideas. James Preer helped make the measurements.

### SUMMARY

1. Bird censuses on a wide variety of areas are compared in order to see what aspects of environmental variation control bird species diversity.

2. Indeciduous forests, bird species diversity can be predicted in terms of the height profile of foliage density. Plant species diversity, except by influencing this profile, has nothing to do with bird species diversity. The layers 0-2', 2'-25', $> 25'$ seem equally important in determining bird species diversity; these layers presumably correspond to different configurations of foliage. This should not be interpreted as evidence that a forest is made up of discrete layers. These 3 layers are constructed by the observer.

3. An evolutionary argument is given which predicts the observations and at the same time suggests that niches should be "convex." Supporting evidence is provided.

4. These results provide no evidence about the real causes of tropical diversity (i.e. whether the temperate regions, given enough time, can support as great a diversity as the tropics now have) or about the diversity which could be expected in a composite census of 2 habitats. These are essentially different problems and are under investigation now.

### REFERENCES

Davis, L. I. 1955. Census 27. Audubon Field Notes 9: 425-426.

Elton, C. and R. Miller. 1954. The ecological survey of animal communities. J. Ecol. 42: 460-496.

Hutchinson, G. E. and R. H. MacArthur. 1959. A theoretical ecological model of size distributions among species of animals. Amer. Nat. 93: 117-125.

MacArthur, R. H. 1957. Population ecology of some warblers of northeastern coniferous forests. Ecology 39: 599-619.

Margalef, R. 1957. La teoria de la informacion en ecologia. Barcelona. Memorias de la real academia de ciencias y artes.

Watt, A. S. (1947). Pattern and process in the plant community. J. Ecol. 35: 1-22.

Woolfenden, G. 1959. Census 14. Audubon Field Notes 13: 466.

Reprinted from *J. Anim. Ecol.* **30**, 1-8, May 1961

# THE NUMBER OF SPECIES OF INSECT ASSOCIATED WITH VARIOUS TREES

### By T. R. E. SOUTHWOOD

*Department of Zoology, Imperial College, London*

It is common knowledge amongst ecologists and collectors that some trees have many species of insect denizen and others, usually recently introduced, comparatively few. But the number of species of insect associated with a certain tree would seem to reflect not only the actual time it has been present in Britain but also, and of rather more importance, its general abundance or scarcity throughout this period. If this hypothesis is correct, then in other parts of the world where the pattern of tree dominance is different from that in Britain, we should expect the comparative numbers of insect species to vary accordingly.

The coniferous forest belt is far more extensive in Russia than in Britain and thus pine, spruce, larch and fir (the last three introduced species in Britain) will be comparatively

Table 1. *Comparative series of the numbers of insect species on various deciduous (unmarked) and coniferous\* forest trees in Britain and European Russia*

| Tree | Britain | Russia |
|------|---------|--------|
| Oak (*Quercus*) | 284 | 150 |
| Willow (*Salix*) | 266 | 147 |
| Birch (*Betula*) | 229 | 101 |
| Hawthorn (*Crataegus*) | 149 | 59 |
| Poplars (*Populus*) | 97 | 122 |
| Apple (*Malus*) | 93 | 77 |
| \*Pine (*Pinus*) | 91 | 190 |
| Alder (*Alnus*) | 90 | 63 |
| Elm (*Ulmus*) | 82 | 81 |
| Hazel (*Corylus*) | 73 | 26 |
| Beech (*Fagus*) | 64 | 79 |
| Ash (*Fraxinus*) | 41 | 41 |
| \*Spruce (*Picea*) | 37 | 117 |
| Lime (*Tilia*) | 31 | 37 |
| Hornbeam (*Carpinus*) | 28 | 53 |
| \*Larch (*Larix*) | 17 | 44 |
| \*Fir (*Abies*) | 16 | 42 |
| Holly (*Ilex*) | 7 | 8 |

more abundant. The numbers of insect species on certain deciduous and coniferous trees in Britain and in Russia are given in Table 1. The figures for Britain are taken from Table 4 and are for certain major groups, those for Russia from Gusev & Rimsky-Korsakov's (1940) list of pests and so, although it is of no importance in the present discussion, the actual values are only directly comparable within series. It will be seen that there is a considerable measure of agreement between the two sets of figures, but that the coniferous trees all have comparatively more associated insect species in Russia than in England. This is supported by the correlation coefficients; for all the trees the coefficient is $+0.62$, but when the conifers are excluded it rises to $+0.84$. In other words the numbers of insect species on the conifers in the two countries are much less closely associated than the numbers on the trees of the deciduous forest belt. Thus this comparison between Britain and Russia supports the hypothesis; the trees that are more abundant in Russia have comparatively more insect species.

The second area with which comparison will be made is Cyprus. Some idea of the relative abundance of various trees in that island can be obtained from Holmboe (1914). The more important trees are *Juniperus foetidissima* (forests, especially on the higher mountains and in mountain meadows), *J. phoenicea* (maquis scrub-woods of lowlands), *Pinus nigra*, sub-species *pallasiana* (upland forest), *P. halepensis* (lowland forests), *Quercus alnifolia* (evergreen oak of forests), *Q. infectoria* (deciduous oak of lowland regions), *Alnus orientalis* and *Platanus orientalis* (dominant trees of marshes and river valleys) and *Crataegus azarolus* ('all over the island'). The endemic *Cedrus libani* sub-species *brevifolia* is mentioned as an important forest tree in Cyprus by Pliny and Theophrastus, but it had become rare by 1900, probably owing to extensive felling since the

Table 2. *Comparison of the number of Heteroptera and Homoptera Auchenorrhyncha on various trees in Britain and Cyprus*

| Tree type | Britain | | Cyprus | |
|---|---|---|---|---|
| | Species | Number | Species | Number |
| Deciduous oaks (*Quercus*) | *robur* L. <br> *petraea* (Matt.) Liebl. } | 47 | *infectoria* Oliv. | 6 |
| Evergreen oaks (*Quercus*) | *\*ilex* L. | 0 | *alnifolia* Poech. | 2 |
| Alder (*Alnus*) | *glutinosa* (L.) Gaertn. | 18 | *orientalis* Decaisne | 3 |
| Hawthorn (*Crataegus*) | *oxyacanthoides* Thuill. <br> *monogyna* Jacq. } | 18 | *azarolus* L. | 4 |
| Mountain ash (*Sorbus*) | *aucuparia* L. | 1 | *cretica* Fritsch | 1 |
| Maple (*Acer*) | *campestre* L. | 4 | *obtusifolium* Sibth. et Smith | 1 |
| Plane (*Platanus*) | *\*orientalis* L. | 0 | *orientalis* L. | 4 |
| Apple (*Malus*) | spp. | 19 | *\*spp.* | 1 |
| (*Prunus*) | *spinosa* L. | 5 | *\*spp.* | 1 |
| Juniper (*Juniperus*) | *communis* L. | 6 | *foetidissima* Willd. | 10 |
| | | | *phoenicea* L. | 5 |
| Pine (*Pinus*) | *sylvestris* L. | 17 | *nigra pallasiana* Loub. | 6 |
| | | | *halepensis* Mill. | 3 |
| Cedar (*Cedrus*) | *\*libani* L. | 0 | *libani brevifolia* J. D. Hooker | 1 |

*Introduced species

**Middle Ages.** Neither the apple (*Malus* sp.) nor the cherry, plum or sloe (*Prunus* spp.) figure in either Holmboe's list of 'spontaneous vascular plants in Cyprus' or that of the 'more important wild plants of gardens and plantations', although he quotes an author writing in 1563 who said that 'apples are rare at Famagusta and of bad quality' and says that cherries (*P. cerasus*) thrive in some village gardens.

Lindberg (1948) gives an account of the Heteroptera and Homoptera Auchenorrhyncha collected in Cyprus. The number of species on the various trees are given in Table 2, together with those on the same or closely allied trees in Britain (data from Table 4). Whereas in Britain the dediucous oaks (*Quercus*) are the dominant tree species, in Cyprus, *Juniperus* and *Pinus* share this position and all these trees have comparatively large numbers of associated Hemiptera. Another noteworthy feature of Table 2 is a comparison of the introduced species in both countries. *Platanus*, *Cedrus* and *Quercus alnifolia* all have associated Hemiptera in Cyprus where they are native, in Britain there are none on the same species of the two former or on *Q. ilex*, closely allied to *Q. alnifolia*.

The reverse appears to hold for *Malus* and *Prunus*, species of which are native in Britain, whilst in Cyprus they seem to be comparatively rare introductions.

The British fauna may also be compared with that of Sweden. The number of species of Lepidoptera and the main groups of phytophagous Coleoptera (Phytophaga and Rhynchophora) associated with the various Swedish trees has been obtained from Aurivillus (1917, 1920, 1924) Benander (1929, 1950, 1953), Nordström & Wahlgren (1935-41) Spessivtsaff (1925) and Wahlgren (1915).

The data for Britain are based on Stokoe & Stovin (1944, 1948), Ford (1949) and Walsh (1954) and are given in detail in Table 4. An exact comparison based on the number of species is precluded because these different authorities, standards of 'major host plants' may not be the same. However, it is legitimate to compare the ranks of the trees in the two countries (Table 3).

Table 3. *Comparative series of the number of species of Lepidoptera and Coleoptera associated with various trees in Sweden and Britain*

|  | Sweden | | Britain | |
|  | No. spp. | Rank | No. spp. | Rank |
|---|---|---|---|---|
| Willows (*Salix* spp.) | 198 | 1 | 224 | 2 |
| Birch (*Betula* spp.) | 177 | 2 | 213 | 3 |
| Oak (*Quercus* spp.) | 146 | 3 | 237 | 1 |
| Poplars (*Populus* spp.) | 114 | 4 | 78 | 6 |
| Spruce (*Picea abies*) | 93 | 5 | 27 | 14 |
| Pine (*Pinus sylvestris*) | 90 | 6 | 73 | 7 |
| Sloe (*Prunus spinosa*) | 90 | 6 | 103 | 5 |
| Alder (*Alnus glutinosa*) | 63 | 8 | 68 | 10 |
| Apple (*Malus* spp.) | 63 | 9 | 72 | 8 |
| Hawthorn (*Crataegus* spp.) | 54 | 10 | 131 | 4 |
| Elm (*Ulmus* spp.) | 46 | 11 | 69 | 9 |
| Beech (*Fagus sylvatica*) | 46 | 12 | 57 | 11 |
| Hazel (*Corylus avellana*) | 34 | 13 | 55 | 12 |
| Mountain Ash (*Sorbus aucuparia*) | 32 | 14 | 27 | 14 |
| Lime (*Tilia* spp.) | 31 | 15 | 22 | 17 |
| Ash (*Fraxinus excelsior*) | 17 | 16 | 29 | 13 |
| Hornbeam (*Carpinus betulus*) | 11 | 17 | 27 | 14 |

If the present hypothesis is correct, then the following trees which have higher ranks in Sweden than Britain, should be relatively more abundant in Sweden than Britain: willow, birches, poplars, spruce, pine, alder and lime. Likewise oak, sloe, hawthorn, elm, hazel, ash and hornbeam should be rarer in Sweden, and apple, beach and mountain ash of similar relative abundance in the two countries. Dr A. Melderis, of the Botany Department, British Museum (N.H.), who is conversant with the floras of both countries, has been kind enough to comment on these comparisons and considers that, in general, they are correct. There are certain discrepancies, lime and sloe are probably equally common in both countries and mountain ash more abundant in Sweden than in Britain. It is felt that the measure of agreement (fourteen out of seventeen comparisons) is so large as to support the present hypothesis.

It may be suggested that it is unreasonable to compare islands, such as Britain or Cyprus, with continental areas, as the fauna of islands may be impoverished during successive climatic changes and be unable to replenish completely from the main land mass. However, the great majority of insects, even wingless Collembola, are carried on air currents to some extent, as evidenced by Elton's (1925) observations on Spitzbergen and the work of others on the insects in the upper air (Hardy & Milne 1938, Freeman 1945, 1952, Glick 1939), that small sea barriers such as the English Channel are unlikely to be of any significance. If the abundance of a tree alters greatly in an area, one might expect corresponding changes in the fauna, and these might show the effect of insular isolation, if such exist. As juniper has become rarer in southern England one Heteropteran attached to it appears to have become extinct, whilst in contrast four new species have recently become established on pine since the extensive conifer afforestation (Southwood 1957). Two of these may have spread from Scotland, but the other two were formerly unknown in Britain and their introduction from the Continent, together with three new species of Micro-Lepidoptera with the same host plant, may be modern evidence of the relative un-importance of the English Channel as a barrier. (Plant quarantine regulations have prevented the importation of nursery stocks during this period.)

Another approach to this problem would be to compare two continental areas such as Russia and Sweden. Unfortunately, the necessary data on the exact relative abundance of different trees in Russia are not available, nor is such a comparison easily made for an area so large and diverse. However, some brief comparison may be made between the Russian (Table 1) and the Swedish data (Table 3) already given. One of the largest changes in rank is the case of hornbeam, which has more insect species in Russia where indeed it is more abundant. Pine, spruce (both also in the southern Russian forests) and beech are somewhat more strongly represented in the Russian flora than in the Swedish, and this is what would be expected from a study of their associated insect species. In con-trast, there is relatively less arctic tundra scrub with dwarf birch, willow and alder in Russia than in Sweden, and these trees have higher ranks in Sweden than in Russia.

Only general comparisons are possible with Russia, Sweden and Cyprus; a more detailed study has been made in the case of Hawaii and this shows the same relation of abundance and number of insect species (Southwood 1960a). However, lack of a quanti-tative measure of the relative abundance of the different trees throughout recent geologi-cal history precludes a detailed numerical test of the hypothesis for these countries. But for Britain Godwin (1956) has compiled all the Quaternary records of plant remains. The number of records for each tree is a combined measure of the length of time it has been in Britain and its abundance throughout this time. Godwin stresses that, as some plants are more likely to be preserved or identified than others, and as sampling has been more extensive in some areas and strata than others, the data should not be regarded as strictly quantitative. None the less, it is felt that the number of different records for a tree in Godwin (1956) does give a numerical assessment, albeit approximate, of its history that is of value for the present comparison.

Godwin's (1956) records for each tree together with the number of species of the major groups of plant feeding insects associated with it are given in Table 4. The figures for the Heteroptera are based on Appendix 3 of Southwood & Leston (1959), those for the Homoptera Auchenorrhyncha and Psylloidea mainly on Edwards (1896), for the Macro-Lepidoptera on the 'main host plants' given for each species by Stokoe & Stovin (1944, 1948) the Micro-Lepidoptera on Ford (1949) and the Coleoptera on Walsh (1954). The latter unfortunately is not completely satisfactory for the present purpose, often referring to genera rather than species.

The correlation coefficient of the relationship between the history of the tree (Godwin's records) and the total number of insect species (given in Table 1) is highly significant (0·85, P< 0·001). It is noteworthy too that even when the introduced species belong to the same genus as a native tree, *e.g.* sycamore (*Acer pseudoplatanus*) and common maple

(*A. campestre*), not all the insects of the indigenous tree are able to transfer to the alien, even though they may have another unrelated tree as an alternate host; Hering (1951) made similar observations on leaf-miners in the Berlin botanic gardens. Of the introduced trees, spruce (*Picea abies*) has the largest number of associated insect species, whilst the firs (*Abies* spp.) also have a comparatively high number; it is interesting that Godwin

Table 4. *The commoner British trees, their history and associated insects*

| | History in Britain since Pleistocene Period | Number of records in Godwin (1956) | Associated insect species | | | | | |
|---|---|---|---|---|---|---|---|---|
| | | | Heteroptera | Homoptera (part) | Macro-Lepidoptera | Micro-Lepidoptera | Coleoptera | Total |
| Oak (*Quercus robur* L. and *Q. petraea* (Matt.) Liebl. | Native | 197 | 37 | 10 | 106 | 81 | 50 | 284 |
| Birch (*Betula* spp.) | ,, | 182 | 12 | 4 | 94 | 84 | 35 | 229 |
| Hazel (*Corylus avellana* L.) | ,, | 136 | 16 | 2 | 18 | 28 | 9 | 73 |
| Willow (*Salix* spp.) | ' ,, | 134 | 22 | 20 | 100 | 73 | 51 | 266 |
| Alder (*Alnus glutinosa* (L.) Gaertn.) | ,, | 87 | 14 | 8 | 28 | 27 | 13 | 90 |
| Hawthorn (*Crataegus* spp.) | ,, | 67 | 17 | 1 | 64 | 53 | 14 | 149 |
| Ash (*Fraxinus excelsior* L.) | ,, | 59 | 10 | 2 | 16 | 9 | 4 | 41 |
| Pine (*Pinus sylvestris* L.) | ,, | 54 | 15 | 3 | 10 | 28 | 35 | 91 |
| Holly (*Ilex aquifolium* L.) | ,, | 44 | 0 | 0 | 2 | 2 | 3 | 7 |
| Yew (*Taxus baccata* L.) | ,, | 42 | 0 | 0 | 1 | 0 | 0 | 1 |
| Sloe (*Prunus spinosa* L.) | ,, | 30 | 4 | 2 | 48 | 43 | 12 | 109 |
| Poplars (*Populus* spp.) | ,, | 30 | 8 | 11 | 33 | 26 | 19 | 97 |
| Elm (*Ulmus*) spp.) | ,, | 30 | 11 | 4 | 33 | 26 | 10 | 82 |
| Beech (*Fagus sylvatica* L.) | ,, | 27 | 4 | 3 | 24 | 16 | 17 | 64 |
| Common maple (*Acer campestre* L.) | ,, | 18 | 2 | 2 | 8 | 12 | 2 | 26 |
| Hornbeam (*Carpinus betulus* L.) | ,, | 17 | 1 | 0 | 7 | 16 | 4 | 28 |
| Juniper (*Juniperus communis* L.) | ,, | 17 | 6 | 0 | 4 | 8 | 2 | 20 |
| Spruce (*Picea abies* (L.) Karst.) | Native in interglacial reintroduced *c.* 1500 | 15 | 9 | 1 | 6 | 13 | 8 | 37 |
| Lime (*Tilia* spp.) | Native and introduced | 14 | 7 | 2 | 15 | 5 | 2 | 31 |
| Mountain ash (*Sorbus aucuparia* L.) | Native | 13 | 0 | 1 | 2 | 17 | 8 | 28 |
| Fir (*Abies* spp.) | Native in interglacial reintroduced *c.* 1600 | 10 | 5 | 0 | 2 | 1 | 8 | 16 |
| Sweet chestnut (*Castanea sativa* Mill.) | Introduced A.D. 100 | 10 | 0 | 0 | 0 | 5 | 0 | 5 |
| Apple (*Malus* spp.) | Native and introduced | 7 | 18 | 3 | 21 | 42 | 9 | 93 |
| Walnut (*Juglans regia* L.) | Introduced *c.* 1400 | 3 | 0 | 0 | 0 | 1 | 2 | 3 |
| Holm oak (*Quercus ilex* L.) | Introduced 1580 | 2 | 0 | 0 | 0 | 2 | 0 | 2 |
| Larch (*Larix decidua* Mill.) | Introduced 1629 | 1 | 3 | 0 | 6 | 6 | 2 | 17 |
| Sycamore (*Acer pseudoplatanus* L.) | Introduced *c.* 1250 | 1 | 1 | 0 | 5 | 8 | 0 | 15 |
| Horse-chestnut (*Aesculus hippocastanum* L.) | Introduced *c.* 1600 | 0(?11) | 0 | 2 | 1 | 1 | 0 | 4 |
| Acacia (*Robinia pseudacacia* L.) | Introduced 1601 | 0 | 0 | 0 | 0 | 1 | 0 | 1 |
| Plane (*Platanus orientalis* L.) | Introduced *c.* 1520 | 0 | 0 | 0 | 0 | 0 | 0 | 0 |

(1956) considers that these trees were native in Britain before the last glacial phase, apparently becoming extinct by the post-glacial.

The regression equation of the number of insect species on the history and abundance of the tree (Godwin's records) has been calculated and is drawn in Fig. 1. Because of the inherent weaknesses in the data too much stress should not be laid on the precise position of the line, but it is apparent that certain trees have either far more or far fewer insects than can be accounted for in terms of their history. In other words when the effect of their history is removed some trees stand out as being 'good' host plants for insects and others especially 'bad'.

Those trees which have a large number of insects attached to them (when the effect of history is eliminated) fall into two families. Three are Rosaceae — hawthorns (*Crataegus*), sloe (*Prunus spinosa*) and apple (*Malus*) — although the point for the fourth common tree member of the family, the mountain ash (*Sorbus aucuparia*), lies on the regression line. The others are the two Salicaceae — the willows (*Salix*) and poplars (*Populus*); the records for each genus have to be lumped as many of the plant records cannot be determined to species (Godwin 1956). It is probable that as each of these genera contain a large

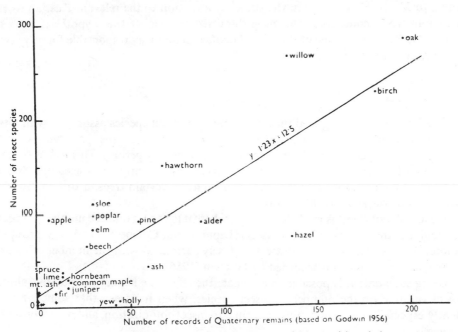

Fig. 1. Graph showing the relationship between a tree's history (*x*) and the number of associated insect species (*y*). (+, introduced trees).

number of species compared with the other tree genera, (*e.g.* birch 3, oak 2, beech 1) they provide a larger number of niches than the other trees. Alternatively, the Salicaceae may be especially favourable host plants for insects; this appears to be the case with Rosaceae and it is interesting, as Hering (1951) has remarked, that a number of insects feed only on these two comparatively unrelated plant families. In some cases the assumption of the second host seems to have been comparatively recent; *e.g.* the *Salix* feeding bug *Orthotylus marginalis* Reuter, seldom found an apple at the beginning of this century, is now common in many orchards. Apple has, of course, become increasingly abundant in Britain in the last centuries.

There are four trees which have remarkably few associated insects: hazel (*Corylus avellana*), ash (*Fraxinus excelsior*), holly (*Ilex aquifolium*) and yew (*Taxus baccata*). The presence of hazel in this group is surprising since it is in the Fagales group of tree families and not an isolated taxonomic position as is the ash (family Oleaceae), the only British tree in the second main series of the Dicotyledones, the Metachlamydeae. The paucity of insects on the holly and yew, which is true throughout their range, is especially marked and must be associated with their structural or biochemical features.

The probable mechanism underlying this relationship between tree abundance and the number of insect species is outlined by Southwood (1960b).

## ACKNOWLEDGMENTS

I am most grateful to Professor A. R. Clapham, F.R.S., and Professor O. W. Richards, F.R.S., who have kindly criticized drafts of this paper; to Dr A. Melderis who took a great deal of trouble over the comparison of the abundance of various trees in Britain and Sweden, to Mr G. H. Thompson who drew my attention to the relevant Russian works, and to numerous colleagues who have discussed aspects of this hypothesis with me over the last few years. None of them is, of course, in any way responsible for any errors of fact or interpretation.

## SUMMARY

1. The hypothesis is suggested that the number of insect species associated with a tree is a reflection of the cumulative abundance of that tree in the particular country throughout recent geological history (*e.g.* in the Quaternary period). This means that the dominant native trees will have most insect species, and recently introduced ones fewest.

2. General comparisons between the insect fauna of certain trees in Britain, Sweden, Russia and Cyprus support the hypothesis.

3. A more detailed test is made for Britain, where it is shown that the number of species of the major plant feeding orders of insects (Lepidoptera, Coleoptera and most groups of Hemiptera) associated with British trees is closely correlated with the number of records of their Quaternary remains recorded by Godwin (1956).

4. Using such data it is possible to eliminate the effect the history (cumulative abundance) of the tree on the number of insect species, when it is seen that some trees are evidently especially resistant or unsusceptible to insect colonization, and others probably the reverse.

## REFERENCES

Aurivillius, C. (1917). Coleoptera. Phytophaga. *Svensk Insektfauna*, 9, Rekv. nr. 19

Aurivillius, C. (1920). Coleoptera. Rhynchophora. 1. *Svensk Insektfauna*, 9, Rekv. nr. 23

Aurivillius, C. (1924). Coleoptera. Rhynchophora. 2. *Svensk Insektfauna*, 9, Rekv. nr. 26

Benander, P. (1929, 1950, 1953). Lepidoptera. II. Microlepidoptera Tineina, Tortricina, Micropterygina och Tineides Aculeatae. *Svensk Insektfauna*, 10, Rekv. nrs. 31, 39, 43.

Edwards, J. (1896). *The Hemiptera-Homoptera (Cicadina and Psyllina) of the British Islands*. London.

Elton, C. S. (1925). The dispersal of insects to Spitsbergen. *Trans. R. Ent. Soc. Lond.* 1925, 289-99.

Ford, L. T. (1949). *A Guide to the Smaller British Lepidoptera*. London.

Freeman, J. A. (1945). Studies in the distribution of insects by aerial currents. The insect population of the air from ground level to 300 feet. *J. Anim. Ecol.* 14, 128-54.

Freeman, J. A. (1952). Occurrence of Collembola in the air. *Proc. E. Ent. Soc. Lond.* (A) 27, 28.

Glick, P. A. (1939). The distribution of insects, spiders, and mites in the air. *Tech. Bull. U.S. Dep. Agric.* 673, 1-150.

Godwin, H. (1956). *The History of the British Flora*. Cambridge.

Gusev, V. I. & Rimsky-Korsakov, M. N. (1940). *Key to the Identification of Injuries to Forest and Park Trees as well as to Shrubs in the European part of U.S.S.R*. Leningrad.

Hardy, A. C. & Milne, P. S. (1938). Studies in the distribution of insects by aerial currents. Experiments in aerial tow-netting from kites. *J. Anim. Ecol.* 7, 199-229.

**Hering, E. M. (1951).** *Biology of the Leaf Miners.* The Hague.

**Holmboe, J. (1914).** Studies on the vegetation of Cyprus based upon researches during the spring and summer 1905. *Bergens Mus. Skrift.* **1** (2), 1-344.

**Lindberg, H. (1948).** On the insect fauna of Cyprus. Results of the expedition of 1939 by Harold, Hakan and P. H. Lindberg. II. Heteroptera and Homoptera Cicadina der insel Zypern. *Comment. Biol. Helsingf.* **10** (7), 25-175.

**Nordström, F. & Wahlgren, E. (1935-41).** *Svenska Fjärilar.* Stockholm.

**Southwood, T. R. E. (1957).** The zoogeography of the British Hemiptera Heteroptera. *Proc. S. Lond. Ent. Nat. Hist. Soc.* 1956, 111-35.

**Southwood, T. R. E. (1960a).** The abundance of the Hawaiian trees and the number of their associated insect species. *Proc. Hawaii. Ent. Soc.* 1959, 299-303.

**Southwood, T. R. E. (1960b).** The evolution of the insect/host tree relationship — a new approach. *XI Int. Cong. Ent.*, Vienna ( 1: 651 - 655 ).

**Southwood, T. R. E. & Leston, D. (1959).** *The Land and Water Bugs of the British Islands.* London.

**Spessivtseff, P. (1925).** Coleoptera. Rhynchophora 6 Fam. Bark-borrar. Scolytidae. *Svensk Insektfauna,* **28** (3), Rekv. nr. 28.

**Stokoe, W. J. & Stovin, G. H. T. (1944).** *The Caterpillars of British Butterflies.* London.

**Stokoe, W. J. & Stovin, G. H. T. (1948).** *The Caterpillars of British Moths.* 2 vols. London.

**Wahlgren, E. (1915).** Lepidoptera. II. Microlepidoptera Pyralidina. *Svensk Insektfauna,* **10,** Rekv. nr. 18.

**Walsh, G. B. (1954).** Plants and the beetles associated with them. *Amat. Ent.* **11,** 89-98.

Reprinted from *Science*, May 23, 1969, vol. 164, pp. 947–949. Copyright © 1969 by the American Association for the Advancement of Science.

# Generation and Maintenance of Gradients in Taxonomic Diversity

Abstract. *Latitudinal gradients in diversity of organisms represent an equilibrium distribution for at least the last $270 \times 10^6$ years. Faunas endemic to tropical regions evolved significantly faster than extra-tropical faunas. The latitude-dependent difference in rates of evolution also represents an equilibrium condition for at least the last $270 \times 10^6$ years and has consequences for paleontological correlation of rocks because the attainable resolution depends on rate of evolution and will thus be greater in tropic regions than in extra-tropical ones.*

Latitudinal gradients in taxonomic diversity of organisms have recently been accorded attention by geologists because of their implications about past environments and possible continental movements. For such geological studies it is sufficient to know that an empirical relationship exists between diversity of organisms and latitude. The associated problem of identifying mechanisms by which diversity gradients are generated and maintained is biological rather than geological. It appears, however, that the perspective of geological time, permitting consideration of the evolutionary history of organisms, may constrain the number of possible mechanisms.

Strong diversity gradients sloping poleward from the equator are characteristic for widely distributed, large groups of living organisms having a good distribution potential. Such gradients characterize diversity among genera and families, as well as among species (*1*). The fact that gradients are strongly expressed among higher taxa suggests but does not prove that they have existed for a long time. In considering the equilibrium condition of this biological pattern the realm of geology is entered, for the problem is dependent on the scale of geological time.

The equilibrium condition of this pattern can be tested by examining the diversity of well preserved, adequately collected, and extensively studied fossil groups. We have chosen for this purpose two widely distributed invertebrate groups, Permian brachiopods and Cretaceous planktonic foraminifera.

In the region for which we have data (Northern Hemisphere) for the Maestrichtian interval of the Cretaceous (about 70 to $80 \times 10^6$ years B.P.) a typical diversity gradient existed among species of Cretaceous planktonic foraminifera (Fig. 1). This gradient existed despite the fact that climatic belts in the Cretaceous apparently were ill-defined, and world climate was milder than at present with a concomitant reduction in slope of the

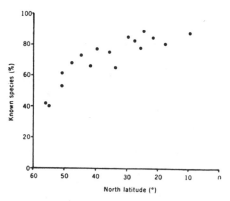

Fig. 1. Diversity among species of Maestrichtian planktonic foraminifera in the Northern Hemisphere as percent of total number of species known plotted against latitude. The gradient in diversity is similar to that typically found in living organisms.

thermal gradient between the equator and the poles. A second test can be made with Permian brachiopods, using a measure of diversity among families normalized for sampling efficiency (*2*) (Fig. 2). Permian brachiopods show a typical gradient in the latitudes for which we have data despite the peculiar Permian climate characterized by intense Southern Hemisphere glaciation which apparently left the Northern Hemisphere untouched (*3*).

Typical diversity gradients existed

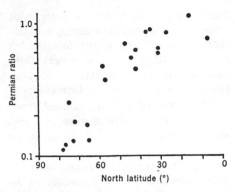

Fig. 2. Diversity among families of Permian brachiopods in the Northern Hemisphere as shown by the Permian ratio. This ratio is Tethyan Endemics : Cosmopolitan Dominants and tends to normalize for the sampling inequities common in the geologic record. The gradient in diversity is similar to that typical of living organisms and Cretaceous planktonic foraminifera.

during intervals of time climatically somewhat like the present in the occurrence of glacial conditions (Permian) and strongly contrasting with the present in the existence of broadly distributed equable conditions (Cretaceous). Thus, a gradient in diversity sloping poleward from the equator has existed for at least the last 270 × 10⁶ years; this gradient represents an equilibrium condition for large groups of organisms with wide distribution.

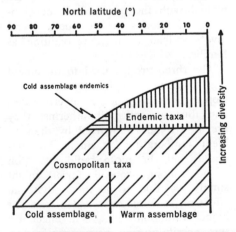

Fig. 3. Composition of "warm" and "cold" assemblages of families in terms of cosmopolitan and endemic elements. The "cold" assemblage is seen to consist almost entirely of cosmopolitan elements, while the "warm" assemblage contains the cosmopolitan elements and many endemic forms as well.

More than a simple change in diversity along the gradient is involved—populations at the high and low ends of the diversity curve differ widely in a taxonomic sense and are generally divisible into "warm" and "cold" assemblages, respectively. A cluster analysis (4) has been used on data for the distribution of families of living clams which objectively separates stations characterized by the warm-water and cold-water assemblages (2, 5). The cold-water assemblage virtually lacks endemic families and consists of families cosmopolitan in their distribution (Fig. 3). Stations comprising the warm-water assemblage have cosmopolitan families, but they have many endemic families as well (2).

We may examine separately the cosmopolitan and endemic warm-water subsets in the distribution of bivalve mollusks. Of particular significance is any difference in evolutionary history of the subsets which might be related to generation or maintenance of an equilibrium condition characterized by a diversity gradient sloping from the equator poleward.

One possibility is to consider the relative antiquity of the families comprising the two subsets by plotting percent of clam families against the time of their origin (Fig. 4). While the data lack precision (6), they are adequate to show that cosmopolitan elements (which comprise virtually all of the cold-water assemblage) are relatively old and in particular include few families evolved in the last 50 million years. The curves shown in Fig. 4 are modified survivorship curves (7) which, as Simpson has noted, should be reciprocals of evolutionary rates. Thus, among living clams the families found in cold water are evolving slowly relative to families endemic to warm water.

It is suggested by the data that typical diversity gradients owe their form to higher evolutionary rates in warm than in cold regions. It is conceivable that rates have generally been equivalent the world over, but that the rigors of Pleistocene and Recent climates have created a temporary bias by systematically excluding more recently evolved families from the colder regions.

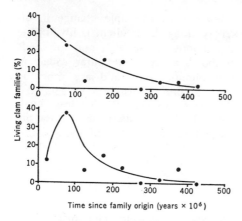

Fig. 4. Modified survivorship curves for families of living clams belonging to the warm-water endemic (top) and cold-water (cosmopolitan) groups (bottom). While the data lack precision, it appears clear that evolution has been considerably faster in the warm assemblage than in the cold assemblage.

To determine whether or not relative differences in evolutionary rates between warm- and cold-water areas represent an equilibrium situation, recourse again can be made to the fossil record. Cretaceous planktonic foraminiferal genera which occur at sample stations north of 50°N are ancient relative to those at stations between the equator and 50°N (Fig. 5). Clearly, high rates of evolution were concentrated in the tropical realm of Cretaceous time and were notably lacking at high latitudes.

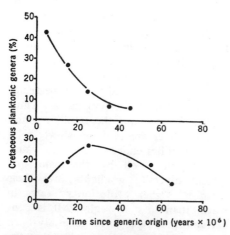

Fig. 5. Modified survivorship curves for Cretaceous planktonic foraminiferal genera taken between 0° and 50°N (top) and those from north of 50°N (bottom). Again evolution has clearly been faster in the warm-water region close to the equator than elsewhere.

Stehli performed a similar analysis of longevity in Permian brachiopod families (2) and found a pattern in which endemic Tethyan (warm water) families appear to have evolved at high rates while cosmopolitan forms appear to have evolved at much slower rates.

These three examples show that rapid evolution in tropical areas is an equilibrium situation as is slow evolution in extra-tropical regions. Both the generation and the maintenance of diversity gradients are due to this relative difference in evolutionary rates (Fig. 2). It may also be seen that, at least among the taxa here employed, adaptations which permit the occupation of major new niches and thus lead eventually to the development of higher taxa take place in the tropics and some of the more successful groups later contribute representatives to the cosmopolitan fauna (and thus to cold-water regions). Although species and perhaps some genera do evolve in the cold regions, they do not seem to have the potential for crossing major adaptive thresholds, or else major thresholds are not available in this region, and new lower taxa thus do not lead to the establishment of new families. The potential for threshold-crossing adaptations of major significance is evidently high in the tropics, and such adaptations frequently develop there and are exploited with the concomitant development of groups whose success and diversity lead to their recognition as families.

The three groups used to document the existence of rapid evolution in the tropics are all marine invertebrates, and thus are all poikilotherms; they are all strongly influenced by the ambient temperature. It might be supposed that the more rapid evolution found among tropical forms might simply be due to a thermodynamic effect on reaction rates and a resultant higher mutation rate. As a check on this possibility we have examined a homoiothermic group—the mammals—which should be independent of such an effect. It is evident that the effect is as strongly expressed among mammals (Fig. 6) as among the poikilotherms (8). We conclude therefore that

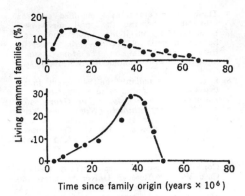

Fig. 6. Modified survivorship curves for living mammal families of warm (central-west Africa) (top) and cold (northern Eurasia) regions (bottom). This homoiothermic group shows the same latitude-dependent variation in evolutionary rates seen among the other groups examined.

the more rapid evolution in the tropics is not simply a matter of reaction rates. We believe that the cause of rapid evolution in the tropics is to be found ultimately in the greater capture of solar energy in this region and secondarily in the response of organisms to this higher and more constant energy level, but we are not yet able to furnish proof.

The existence of evolutionary equilibria in which there are demonstrably higher rates in warm than in cold regions has significant geological implications. Foremost among these are the consequences for the correlation of rocks by means of the fossils they enclose. Paleontological correlation is, of course, most effective in establishing the synchrony of rock units when it can make use of distinctive fossils belonging to rapidly evolving groups. Conversely, paleontological correlations based on relatively staid and slowly evolving forms provide minimum precision. The high rates of evolution characteristic of the tropics favor stratigraphic correlations of sediments deposited in this environment. The low evolutionary rates of colder regions militate against precision in dating and correlating sediments deposited there.

One may further generalize that east-west correlations (within the tropical climatic belt) will be more facile and precise than north-south correlations which must of necessity deal with the slowly evolving elements (cosmopolitan forms) that are common to both assemblages. East-west correlations in extra-tropical regions must also deal with the unfavorable cosmopolitan elements and may be expected to yield minimum precision. It has been noted (2) that this effect is probably the cause of some of the notorious confusion regarding correlation between the Tethyan (warm) and Boreal (cold) faunal realms during the Permian period.

For the geologist interested in evolution, the rapid evolution of the tropics suggests that it is in this climatic zone that "missing links" should be sought, for, as noted above, it is here that threshold-crossing adaptations of major significance occur.

Our model suggests a mechanism by which the gross form of the typical diversity gradient is generated and maintained. This model does not account for variation in slope of the diversity gradient of a given group as a function of time, but this is clearly shown in the fossil record. For instance, the diversity of genera and species of planktonic foraminifera increases in the mid-Cretaceous, wanes in the early Senonian, increases toward the end of the Cretaceous, and then suddenly undergoes a drastic reduction at the end of the Cretaceous. A similar situation has been noted among Cenozoic members of this group of protozoans (9).

Variations such as these must be biological as well as physical in origin, but causes cannot as yet be confidently identified. Considerable evidence does seem to exist, however, that climatic change is the most important single cause of time-dependent variation in the slope of diversity gradients.

FRANCIS G. STEHLI
ROBERT G. DOUGLAS
*Department of Geology,*
*Case Western Reserve University,*
*Cleveland, Ohio 44120*

NORMAN D. NEWELL
*American Museum of Natural History,*
*New York 10024*

## References and Notes

1. A. G. Fischer, *Evolution* 14, 64 (1960); F. G. Stehli, A. L. McAlester, C. E. Helsley, *Bull. Geol. Soc. Amer.* 78, 455 (1967); F. G. Stehli, in *Evolution and Environment*, E. Drake, Ed. (Yale Univ. Press, New Haven, Conn., 1968), pp. 163–227.
2. F. G. Stehli, *Smithson. Misc. Collect.*, in press.
3. The present-day geographic latitude has been assumed for the sample stations used in plotting, a procedure which seems justified as far back in time as the Permian.
4. G. F. Bonham-Carter, *Kansas Geol. Survey, Comp. Contr.* 17 (1967), p. 1.
5. F. G. Stehli, in *The History of the Earth's Crust*, R. Phinney, Ed. (Princeton Univ. Press, Princeton, N.J., 1968), pp. 195–207.
6. The "noise" level is high because true ranges are rarely accurately known and because there is considerable uncertainty involved in assigning absolute time limits to the relative time scale.
7. These curves are termed modified survivorship curves because the total survivorship is unknown for the living families and cannot be known until all become extinct. See, for instance, G. G. Simpson, *The Major Features of Evolution* (Columbia Univ. Press, New York, 1953).
8. Lists of mammalian families present in the two faunas compared were taken from P. J. Darlington [*Zoogeography: The Geographical Distribution of Animals* (Wiley, New York, (1957)], and the geologic antiquity of each family was drawn from G. G. Simpson, *Bull. Amer. Mus. Nat. Hist.* 85, 1 (1945).
9. W. A. Berggren, *Abstr. of Papers*, Geol. Soc. Amer. Ann. Mtg. (1968).
10. Contribution No. 55, Department of Geology, Case Western Reserve University, Cleveland, Ohio 44120. Supported by NSF grant GA-1466, Petroleum Research Fund grant 3485-A2, and AEC grant AT(11-1)-1796. We thank E. Mayr for reading the manuscript.

13 January 1969

Reprinted from LIMNOLOGY AND OCEANOGRAPHY
Vol. 6, No. 4, October, 1961, pp. 400–415

# PHOSPHORUS BUDGET OF A MUSSEL POPULATION[1]

## Edward J. Kuenzler

University of Georgia Marine Institute, Sapelo Island, Georgia[2]

### ABSTRACT

The phosphorus budget of a *Modiolus demissus* population in a Georgia intertidal salt marsh was studied. Percentage phosphorus in mussel bodies decreased from 1% of the dry weight in small individuals to 0.6% in adults. There was also a seasonal variation in phosphorus content of adults; the maximum occurred during spawning early in September, the minimum in November. The standing crop of phosphorus in the population was 37.2 mg $P/m^2$, the body fraction comprising 67%, the shell 30%, and the liquor 3%. Prorated losses and elimination rates ($\mu g\ P/m^2$ day) of the population were: mortality 21; gametes 11; dissolved organic 23; phosphate 260; and feces 460. Quantities of phosphorus present in natural marsh water (mg $P/m^2$) were: particulate 14; phosphate 19; and dissolved organic 6. The mussel population removed 5.4 mg $P/m^2$ of particulate phosphorus and 0.07 mg $P/m^2$ of phosphate daily, of which 0.78 mg $P/m^2$ was required as food and 4.7 mg $P/m^2$ was deposited as pseudofeces. The turnover time of phosphorus in the population was 115 days. The major effect of the population on the ecosystem was the removal of particulate matter from sea water; the turnover time of the particulate phosphorus in the water was 2.6 days under the supposition that the mussel population was the only agent involved. Mussels are more important as biogeochemical agents than as energy consumers.

Determination of the participatory turnover time of a substance via any route in a system sets the maximum turnover time of that system. Determination of the turnover time of a substance for an entire system fixes the maximum flux rate via any one route in the system.

## INTRODUCTION

Phosphorus is indispensable in the biosphere because it is involved in fundamental metabolic processes of energy transfer, both respiration and photosynthesis (McElroy and Glass 1951, 1952). There is available to the organisms which make up the biosphere only a limited amount of the phosphorus which they need for their life processes. Phosphorus passes from the environment to the biotic community during plant growth, from organism to organism by grazing, predation, and parasitism, and eventually back to the environment by excretion or death and decomposition. There are also many strictly chemical transformations and physical or geological movements of phosphorus and its compounds. Hutchinson (1952) has reviewed the biogeochemistry of phosphorus, its occurrence, abundance, and pathways in the lithosphere, atmosphere, and hydrosphere. The

present study was undertaken to determine the rate at which phosphorus flows through a population of the mussel, *Modiolus demissus* Dillwyn, in an estuarine, intertidal salt marsh near Sapelo Island, Georgia, and to evaluate the effect on the ecosystem of this particular pathway.

Kuenzler (1961) discussed the population density and distribution, the recruitment, growth, and mortality rates, and the energy flow of these mussels. *Modiolus* is a typical filter-feeding lamellibranch, ingesting some of the particulate matter from sea water, but rejecting a large part as pseudofeces. Recent workers disagree concerning the ability of animals to obtain nutritionally important quantities of dissolved organic matter from sea water (Jørgensen 1955; Collier 1959; Stevens 1960). Possible large differences in the extraction capability of different species and the differing concentrations of dissolved organic matter in different localities make generalization hazardous. The ability of lamellibranchs to obtain phosphate, however, directly from sea water was demonstrated by Ronkin (1950) and Pomeroy and Haskin (1954).

[1] Contribution No. 32 from the University of Georgia Marine Institute. This work was supported by a research grant to Dr. L. R. Pomeroy from the National Science Foundation.

[2] Present address: Woods Hole Oceanographic Institution, Woods Hole, Massachusetts.

Hutchinson (1957) gave a detailed survey of work on the phosphorus cycle in fresh-water lakes. An understanding of cycles in fresh-water communities is beginning to be reached, largely through employment of radio-phosphorus as a tracer (Hutchinson and Bowen 1947, 1950; Coffin, *et al.* 1949; Hayes, *et al.* 1952; Hayes and Phillips 1958). The phosphorus cycle in the sea has not been investigated nearly as thoroughly. Barnes (1957) reviewed current knowledge of the cycles and regional distribution of phosphorus in the sea, and Emery and Stevenson (1957) reviewed studies of phosphorus in estuaries and lagoons. Bruce and Hood (1959) used $P^{32}$ and a plastic bag to study *in situ* phosphorus exchanges between water, particulate matter, and mud of a Texas bay. Pomeroy (1960) reported the concentrations, turnover rates, and residence times of phosphate in estuarine, coastal, and offshore marine waters of the Georgia coast. The general distribution of the element and the outlines of its circulation in the sea are now known, but apparently no one has investigated intensively the phosphorus budget of any marine population.

I wish to thank Dr. E. P. Odum and Dr. L. R. Pomeroy for their many helpful criticisms during the progress of this work. I am grateful to Dr. R. J. Conover for also reading and criticizing the manuscript.

### METHODS

#### Phosphorus available to Modiolus

The total quantity of phosphorus available to the mussel population in its food is primarily a function of the size-range of food particles filterable and ingestible, the concentration of these particles in the sea water flooding the marsh, and the volume of sea water per unit area of marsh.

The size range of ingestible particulate matter was determined by allowing mussels acclimated to the laboratory to feed upon suspensions of graded particles of dried *Spartina alterniflora* leaves for 20 to 30 min. The mussels were then opened and the stomach contents were drawn out for microscopic examination. The effectiveness

of filtration for each range of particle size was thus estimated.

The amount of particulate food available to the mussel population in marsh water was estimated by a filtration method similar to that described by Goldberg, *et al.* (1952). Known volumes of natural water from the marsh and tidal creeks were collected during flood tide. These samples were passed through a 164 $\mu$ screen (to eliminate particles previously shown to be too large for food) and then through a tared cellulosic membrane filter (Millipore) of 0.45 $\mu$ pore size. Then the membrane filter was washed with distilled water, dried, and reweighed, giving the total weight of particulate matter in the 0.45 $\mu$ to 164 $\mu$ size range. The concentration in the water multiplied by the volume of water covering the marsh at high tides equals the maximum amount of particulate matter available to the mussels.

The phosphorus present in natural marsh water was determined as three different fractions: 1) the particulate; 2) the dissolved organic; and 3) the dissolved inorganic, or phosphate. The two dissolved fractions were determined on membrane-filtered water samples. All samples were prepared in duplicate and analyzed by the methods of Hansen and Robinson (1953).

The volume of sea water from which mussels obtain their food depends upon the depth of the water, and this depends upon the elevation of the marsh. Kuenzler (1961) showed the relationship between marsh elevation and water depth, and the area covered by different marsh types.

#### Diatom cultures

The diatoms needed for feeding experiments were grown in mass culture. A unialgal culture of a *Nitzschia*-like diatom (size $4 \times 40$ $\mu$; hereafter designated "Nitzschia") was used for most of the feeding experiments, but a mixture of two diatom species (sizes $5 \times 10\mu$ and $10 \times 27\mu$) was also used. Bacteria were sometimes present in the culture, but their mass was probably less than 5% of that of the diatoms. Centrifugation of the algae from the culture medium prior to feeding the mussels probably further reduced the number of bacteria since they would not be thrown out of suspension as effectively as the diatoms. Labeled diatoms were prepared by adding $P^{32}$ to the cultures several days before they were fed to the mussels. Some bacteria are rich in phosphorus (Buchanan and Fulmer 1928), and some are also able to take up phosphate from sea water (Renn 1937). Bacteria in the diatom cultures were almost certainly labeled with $P^{32}$, but their effect on the experimental feeding of *Modiolus* was probably small.

### Phosphorus in mussels

Phosphorus in mussel tissue was determined by the method outlined by Lindner (1944). This consisted of oxidation of the material in sulfuric acid and hydrogen peroxide, followed by a colorimetric determination of phosphorus based on the formation of the blue phospho-molybdate ion. Light absorbency was measured by a Beckman DU spectrophotometer at 650 m$\mu$, 10 min after addition of the last reagent, and compared to a standard curve. Samples of shell required the addition of hydrochloric acid after oxidation in order to dissolve the calcium salts. This HCl was neutralized before bringing the solution to its final volume.

### Feeding rates

The rate at which *Modiolus* feeds was estimated from the rate of decrease in radioactivity as the mussel filtered a suspension of $P^{32}$-labeled diatoms. The general method was described by Chipman and Hopkins (1954). The mussel was placed in 3 L of sea water in a battery jar for several hours so that it might become acclimated and filter this water free of suspended matter. The water temperature was maintained at 10°C in February and at 25°–30°C in August experiments. The labeled diatoms were centrifuged from the culture medium, washed with a small amount of sea water to eliminate the dissolved $P^{32}$, then resuspended in sea water. The accumulated feces and pseudofeces were carefully siphoned from around the mussel, and the suspension of diatoms was

added. The aerator oxygenating the water for the mussel also ensured homogeneity of the suspension and helped prevent settling of the diatoms. Battery jars without mussels were used to determine the diatom settling correction. One-milliliter samples were taken immediately after addition of the diatoms and at 10-min intervals thereafter. The samples were dried on planchets and their radioactivity measured by means of an end-window G-M tube connected to a scaler. Since the $P^{32}$ was almost completely confined to the diatoms and bacteria, decrease in activity corresponded to decrease in number of cells in suspension.

The quantity of water effectively cleared was calculated by a formula similar to that used by Chipman and Hopkins (1954):

$$r = \frac{(\ln C_0 - \ln C_t)(V)}{t}$$

where $r$ is the rate (L/hr) at which the suspension is swept clear of particles; $V$ is the volume of suspension in liters; and $\ln C_0$ and $\ln C_t$ are the natural logarithms of the radioactivities of the samples (cpm/ml) at the beginning and after 5 hr, respectively. Since the decrease in activity closely approached linearity on a logarithmic scale during the first 30 min, the filtration rate was determined by using $C_0$ and $C_t$ calculated from the least squares regression of the natural logarithms of radioactivity against time.

Feces, passed while the animal was in the labeled suspension, were periodically siphoned from the bottom, briefly washed in distilled water, and placed on planchets to determine radioactivity. At the conclusion of the 2- to 4-hr feeding period, the mussel was transferred to ordinary sea water for 10 to 12 hr and then killed for body analysis or discarded. The radioactivities of feces and of dissolved excreta passed during the postfeeding period were measured. The bodies of some mussels were dried, weighed, and wet-ashed in hot $H_2SO_4$ and 30% $H_2O_2$. This solution was neutralized and aliquots of it were dried on planchets to determine the quantity of $P^{32}$ assimilated by the mussel. Pieces of the shell of some mussels were arranged on planchets so that 80% to 90% of the bottom of the planchet was covered, and these activities were measured. Correction was made for loss due to self-absorption in the shell and for coincidence and decay losses when necessary.

To determine the rate at which food passed through the gut, the percentage of the maximum rate of elimination of fecal $P^{32}$ was computed for each 30-min period after feeding. Averages of these percentages for all 10 experiments were plotted against time. The integral of the curve of rate of elimination gave the average length of time that material from one feeding remained in the gut.

The rate of uptake of phosphate by *Modiolus* was determined in the same manner as the filtration rate, except, instead of labeled diatoms, about 28 $\mu$c of $P^{32}O_4$ was measured into the sea water after the mussel had filtered out the suspended matter. The first experiment lasted 2 hr, the second lasted 2 days.

### Phosphorus elimination rate

In addition to the data gained from the $P^{32}$ experimental feedings, the rate of phosphorus elimination was measured using analytical chemical techniques. The method was patterned after that of Pomeroy and Haskin (1954). Experiments were run at three temperatures, 6°, 15°, and 24°C, during the periods January 9 to 13, March 28 to April 4, and May 7 to 11, 1959. The experimental temperatures approximated environmental temperatures in the marsh on those dates. The mussels were collected from the marsh a few hours before beginning the experiment and were thoroughly scrubbed and rinsed. Measurements were made of the three previously described phosphorus fractions in the supernatant of sea water which had been held without stirring for about a month. Two to five mussels of approximately the same size were placed in each battery jar with 0.5 to 2.0 L of this sea water supernatant. The jars were placed in a temperature-controlled water bath and the sea water in the jars

was aerated. The mussels almost always opened and began pumping shortly after being placed in the jars; those experiments begun with mussels which later failed to open were discarded. After 24 hr the inside of each battery jar was vigorously scrubbed with a rubber policeman and the sea water and particulate matter were thoroughly mixed. Finally, the three phosphorus fractions were again measured in samples of this water. The amount of phosphorus eliminated per unit time was determined by difference.

### RESULTS

### *Phosphorus content of mussels*

Samples of shell from 7 mussels which had whole shell weights ranging from 0.67 to 55 g had a mean phosphorus content of 0.015% ($s = 0.005$). Samples from 2 smaller mussels which had shells weighing 0.17 and 0.32 g gave values of 0.046% and 0.042%, respectively. The phosphorus in the shell is probably mostly in the conchiolin but some may be in the form of calcium phosphate which will rapidly change to the carbonate during shell formation (Bevelander 1952; Asano and Ito 1956).

The percentage of phosphorus in the body fraction of large mussels changes during the year, being lowest in winter and highest during spawning in September (Fig. 1). The wide range in phosphorus content in the smallest size-class is probably due to differences in size distribution of the mussels within these samples. Bodies which contain more than 1.0% phosphorus are almost always less than 10 mg dry wt. Mussels this small were not present in the September-through-January samples. Analysis of variance indicated that, except in September, the lower percentage of phosphorus in larger mussels is probably a real characteristic (variance ratio less than 10%). Early in September, however, this same characteristic is hidden under the variability caused, presumably, by the release of phosphorus-rich gametes from some individuals. Analysis of variance also indicated (variance ratio less than 1%) that there was a real seasonal change in phosphorus con-

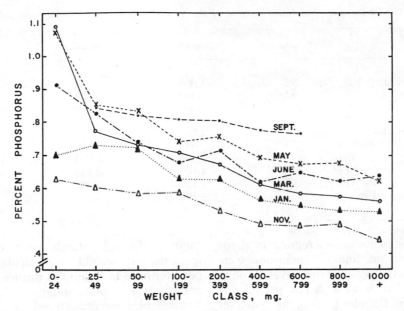

Fig. 1.  Mean percentage of phosphorus in the body fraction of *Modiolus*.

tent of mussels of body weight greater than 100 mg.

Since the liquor fraction contained both body fluids and sea water, the dry weight of the liquor varied with variations in sea water salinity. The phosphorus content of the liquor, therefore, was expressed as a percentage of body weight. The mean value of 23 samples was 0.029% ($s = 0.006$). The mean phosphorus content of 8 samples of byssus from mussels growing in beakers in the marsh was 0.05% ($s = 0.006$).

From the data on population density (Kuenzler 1961), the amount of phosphorus incorporated in the mussel population was estimated. Using 4.1 g/m² as the mean density and 0.02% as the weighted mean phosphorus content of all classes throughout the year, one obtains 25 mg P/m² present in the body fraction. The approximate mean shell weight of 70 g/m² times the weighted mean phosphorus content of 0.015% gives about 11 mg P/m² in the shells. The liquor fraction, containing phosphorus equal to 0.029% of the body weight, adds another 1.2 mg P/m².

The rates of change of the phosphorus in four fractions of the *Modiolus* population (Table 1) were calculated from the recruitment, growth, and mortality rates and the population densities given by Kuenzler (1961) combined with knowledge of the phosphorus content of the various size classes (Fig. 1). The large loss of phosphorus from the body during July and August which is evident in the growth column reflects the loss of weight by the spawning mussels since the phosphorus concentration in the animals was maximal in early September (Fig. 1). From the large positive values, indicating phosphorus accumulation, in May–June and September–October, it would appear that a similar large accumulation took place in July–August, only to be converted to gametes by the end of the spawning period. The total amount of phosphorus released in the gametes or by the gonads, then, might actually be twice as great as the net loss of 4,300 μg/m². Since most gametes and larvae perish, this is a real loss by the population. The population lost more phosphorus during the study period than it gained (Table 1).

*Phosphorus available to* Modiolus

Two experimental feedings showed the maximum particle size ingested by *Modiolus* to be about 160 μ (Table 2). Some of the

TABLE 1.  *Changes in phosphorus content of the* Modiolus *population. Values are* $\mu g\ P/m^2$

|  |  | Recruitment | Growth | Mortality | Net |
|---|---|---|---|---|---|
| **BODY** |  |  |  |  |  |
| January–February |  | 5.2 | –1,600 | –3 | –1,600 |
| March–April |  | 9.8 | –380 | –350 | –720 |
| May–June |  | 16 | 5,900 | –870 | 5,000 |
| July–August |  | 6.2 | –4,300 | –3,300 | –7,600 |
| September–October |  | 13 | 2,600 | –2,700 | –80 |
| November–December |  | 2.7 | 540 | –240 | 300 |
|  | Per Year | 53 | 2,800 | –7,500 | –4,700 |
| **SHELL** | Per Year | 30 | 1,100 | –3,100 | –1,900 |
| **LIQUOR** | Per Year | 1.7 | 130 | –350 | –220 |
| **BYSSUS** | Per Year |  | –160 |  | –160 |
| Total |  |  |  |  | –7,000 |

*Spartina* fragments were irregular in shape so that their maximum dimensions were greater than the pores of the sieves through which they had passed. A few particles in the stomach, therefore, were as much as 1.5 times larger (maximum dimension) than would have been expected (column 2, Table 2). Many particles, large and small, are rejected when mussels are offered a dense suspension of particulate matter, but only small particles are ingested. The minimum size of particles found in the stomach of *Modiolus* was about 3 $\mu$.

The concentration of phosphorus available to mussels in the marsh was estimated from the preliminary data in Table 3. Samples were collected in small creeks, creek heads, or high marsh during flood tide. With the exception of the particulate phosphorus in January through March 1959, measurements of the phosphorus in the three fractions were made by the Hansen and Robinson (1953) method. The estimates for the particulate phosphorus in January through March were calculated from the dry weight of particulate matter per liter on 3 to 6 samples during high tide and the mean percentage of phosphorus. Ten samples were analyzed to obtain the phosphorus content, 0.20% ($s = 0.05$), of this particulate fraction. The data are regarded as only preliminary because a more detailed study of the waters in the vicinity of Sapelo Island is currently being conducted by Dr. L. R. Pomeroy.

The data concerning the phosphate and dissolved organic fractions are insufficient to permit generalizations beyond their approximate concentrations. In the particulate fraction, however, a downward gradient in concentration is noticeable from the creeks to the high marsh, away from the original water source. Some of this decrease in concentration is attributable to filtration by the mussel population and some to settling of the particles or filtration by other marsh animals. Kuenzler (1961) showed the center of mussel density to be about 220 cm above MLW, *i.e.*, at the same level as the creek heads. Therefore the mean value of 44 $\mu$g/L in the creek heads (Table 3) is representative of the amount of particulate phosphorus available to a large fraction of the mussel population. Since samples were taken on both the ebb and flood tides, this value of 44 $\mu$g/L was regarded as the mean concentration throughout the tidal cycle over the marsh.

The approximate amount of phosphorus present in the water and ultimately avail-

TABLE 2.  *Particles ingested by* Modiolus demissus

| Mussel pair | Sizes of particles fed ($\mu$) | Sizes of particles in stomach ($\mu$) | Quantity in stomach | Quantity of pseudofeces |
|---|---|---|---|---|
| A | <79 | 3 to 130, mostly <79 | abundant | abundant |
| B | 79 to 164 | 15 to 240, mostly <150 | abundant | abundant |
| C | 164 to 198 | 10 to 60, mostly centric diatoms | almost empty | abundant; *Spartina* fragments >160 $\mu$ |

TABLE 3. *Phosphorus in marsh water. Values are* μg P/L

| | Creeks | Creek heads | Short *Spartina* high marsh |
|---|---|---|---|
| **Particulate phosphorus** | | | |
| June 28, 1956[1] | 43 | | |
| November 28, 1958 | 47 | 56 | |
| December 15, 1958 | 56 | 26 | |
| January 29, 1959 | 42 | 29 | 27 |
| February 7, 1959 | 78 | 58 | 52 |
| March 26, 1959 | 84 | 53 | 39 |
| Mean | 58 | 44 | 39 |
| **Phosphate phosphorus** | | | |
| June 28, 1956[1] | 25 | | |
| December 15, 1958 | 51 | 60 | |
| January 29, 1959 | 46 | | |
| Mean | 41 | 60 | |
| **Dissolved organic phosphorus** | | | |
| June 28, 1956[1] | 22 | | |
| December 15, 1958 | 14 | 19 | |
| January 29, 1959 | 11 | | |
| Mean | 16 | 19 | |

[1] Dr. L. R. Pomeroy, unpublished data.

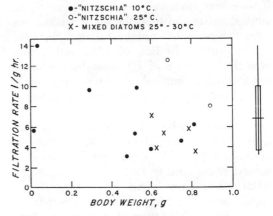

FIG. 2. Filtration rate of *Modiolus*. Shown at the right are the mean, the range, and one standard deviation.

able to the mussels was calculated by multiplying the mean volume of water inundating the marsh times the concentrations of phosphorus in the water. At 220-cm elevation the mean water depth per covering tide was 21.4 cm; therefore there was about 214 L/m² tide covering the mussel beds. The concentrations of phosphorus present in marsh water at the creek heads (Table 3) were assumed to be the concentrations available to the majority of mussels. At a mean volume of 214 L/m² these concentrations gave values of 9,420, 12,800, and 4,060 μg P/m² present in the three fractions, particulate phosphorus, phosphate, and dissolved organic phosphorus, on the average flood tide. Since there are 1.93 tides per day, 77% of which cover 220-cm elevation, the above values are equivalent to 14,000, 19,000, and 6,040 μg P/m² day, respectively.

*Feeding rate*

The data from the 16 feeding rate experiments (Fig. 2) show a tendency for a higher feeding rate at higher temperatures. Furthermore, at the same temperature and utilizing the same food, there was some tendency for the smaller mussels to filter at a higher rate per unit weight than the larger ones. However, since the differences due to mussel size, food size, or water temperature were not great, the average filtering rate was determined by lumping all of the data. This mean value is 6.8 ($s = 3.2$) L/g hr; the distribution curve has a positive skew (Fig. 2). The centrifugate of the water in which the mussels were feeding showed that only 3.6% ($s = 2.4$) of the total radioactivity was in soluble form. The centrifugate of the control battery jars, used for determining the diatom settling correction, showed no distinct gain of P³² due to loss from the diatoms during the experiment.

Jørgensen (1949) showed a higher feeding rate per gram in small *Mytilus edulis* than in larger individuals. Rice and Smith (1958) showed a decrease in filtering rate with small food particle size or large body size in the clam, *Venus* (= *Mercenaria*) *mercenaria*. They also showed that the filtering rate decreased in very dense (170 cells/mm³) or very thin (0.4 cells/mm³) suspensions of diatoms. With *Modiolus*, in the present study, the density was always above 7 cells/mm³, but 6 experiments were run at densities of 170 to 210 cells/mm³.

There was no obvious decrease at these high densities; in fact, the highest filtration rate occurred at the highest diatom density. An important finding of Rice and Smith was that the rate of filtration by the clam of a labeled natural plankton suspension was about the same as the rate for unialgal suspensions.

Uptake of dissolved $P^{32}$ by *Modiolus* was quite slow compared to uptake of diatom-contained $P^{32}$. The clearance rates of dissolved phosphate in two experiments were 0.021 (2-hr experiment) and 0.065 2-day experiment) L/g hr, averaging about 0.6% of the rate of filtration of particulate matter. The clearance rate for phosphate in this paper was considered to be 1% that for particulate matter.

Pomeroy and Haskin (1954) reported an uptake rate of phosphate from sea water by oysters of about 4 $\mu$g P/oyster day. The phosphate excretion rates of their unfed oysters decreased from about 560 $\mu$g P/oyster day for the first 2 days to 20 $\mu$g P/oyster day after 33 days. The latter rate was designated the basal excretion rate of phosphate by the oyster, but the former rate is probably more nearly the natural rate. They reported that the oysters might have voided previously accumulated wastes during the first 2 days of the experiment, but it is unlikely that the natural rate was much less than half their reported value. Assuming a natural rate of phosphate excretion by the oyster of 280 $\mu$g P/day (half the initial rate) and assuming the oyster eliminates as phosphate about half its total intake of phosphorus (as shown for *Modiolus* below), the total intake would be 560 $\mu$g P/oyster day. The uptake rate of phosphate-phosphorus from sea water by the oyster, then, may also be nearly 1% of the total intake of phosphorus. Since not all of the particulate phosphorus which a pelecypod removes from natural water is digested and absorbed, the utilization rate of inorganic phosphorus may be more than 1% of the utilization rate of ingested, natural particulate phosphorus. The efficiency of uptake of phosphorus by mussels feed-

TABLE 4. *Uptake and elimination of $P^{32}$ by Modiolus when fed radioactive diatoms. Values are mean percentages of the loss in radioactivity of the suspension of diatoms*

| | Loss in radio-activity (%) | Standard deviation |
|---|---|---|
| Body and liquor | 34 | 5 |
| Feces | 13 | 2 |
| Soluble excreta | 6.4 | 1.8 |
| Shell | 0.37 | 0.14 |
| Total | 54 | |

ing on cultured diatoms is considered in the following section.

### Phosphorus elimination rate

The uptake and elimination of $P^{32}$ by 4 mussels when fed radioactive "Nitzschia" in February are shown in Table 4. A little more than half of the original radioactivity in the suspension was recovered; the remainder was probably lost when the pseudofeces were discarded during washing of the fecal strips. The greatest amount of $P^{32}$, 34%, was taken up by the combined body and liquor. Feces accounted for 13% of the total uptake from the radioactive suspension in these four experiments, or 11% ($s = 3$) in all 9 experiments where fecal elimination was measured. The high uptake efficiency shown by the ratio of $P^{32}$ in the body to that in the feces is indicative of the digestibility of the diatoms which were fed. Microscopic examination of "Nitzschia" showed that it had very thin frustules, and analyses proved that only 26% of the dry weight was ash. Vinogradov (1953) gives values of from 40% to 80%, usually about 50%, ash in marine diatoms. Hence phosphorus in thick-frustuled natural diatoms may be less easily obtained. Most of the activity found in the shell fraction was on the periostracum surface. This indicated that a large part of the 0.37% uptake by the shell consisted of diatoms which had stuck to the outside and were not completely removed prior to counting or resulted from sorption.

Spawning condition affects retention of phosphorus. Two sexually mature individ-

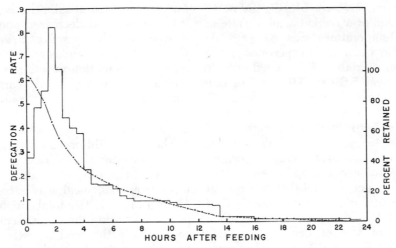

FIG. 3. Time course of defecation. The histogram is the mean fraction of the maximum rate of elimination of labeled feces (scale at left). The dashed curve is the percentage of ingested food remaining in the gut for periods up to 23 hr after feeding (scale at right).

uals, a male and a female, retained amounts of $P^{32}$ in the combined body and liquor equal to 27% and 31% of the loss by the suspension for 21 days after feeding on labeled diatoms. Another mussel which was in the spent condition after being kept in ordinary sea water like the above male and female, through the same dates following a labeled meal, retained only 8% of the loss by the suspension. This is in agreement with other evidence of an accumulation of phosphorus in gametes and loss upon spawning.

The histogram in Figure 3 shows the mean rate of elimination of radioactive feces during each 30-min period after feeding. Since almost all of the diatom suspension was removed during the first half hour, the feeding was considered a very short one, coinciding with only the beginning of the fecal elimination histogram. The maxmium rate occurred about 2 hr after feeding. The dashed curve is an integral of the rates of elimination and depicts the amount of food remaining in the gut at any time after feeding. Assuming that virtually all the ingested food has been eliminated within 24 hr, only 8% remained in the gut as long as 12 hr.

The radioactivity of the body and liquor, the feces, and the shell was measured in the mussel which had taken up dissolved $P^{32}$ for two days. In the feces was found 4.8% of the radioactivity lost by the solution. This $P^{32}$ might have been taken up when the mussel fed on bacteria which had previously removed it from the water, or it might have been taken up by sorption or by bacteria after the faces were eliminated. The body and liquor combined accounted for 31% of the loss from the original solution. The mussel had been in ordinary sea water for 13 hr before it was killed for analysis so any labeled material in the gut should have been largely eliminated (Fig. 3). The shell accounted for 4% of the loss from the original solution, and there seemed to be no difference between the activity of the outside and the inside of the shell. Whether this activity was simply a sorption of $P^{32}$ to the shell or a physiological deposition is not known.

Elimination rates measured by the change in particulate, phosphate, and dissolved organic phosphorus in water containing freshly collected mussels were informative from several standpoints. Analysis of variance showed that elimination rates usually did not vary significantly with temperature. The mean rate of elimination of phosphorus in feces was 56 ($s = 22$) $\mu$g/g day (body dry wt), based on a total of 39 experiments at the three temperatures, 6°, 15°, and 24°C. The mean rate of excretion of phosphate at the three temperatures was 64 ($s = 50$) $\mu$g P/g day in a total of 44 experiments. The mean rate of excretion of dissolved organic phosphorus was 5.6 ($s = 5.9$) $\mu$g P/g day in a total of 29 experiments at 15° and 24°C. The mean rate of elimination of dissolved organic phosphorus in 9 experiments at 6°C was 33 ($s = 48$) $\mu$g/g day. This was not included in the above averages because both analysis of variance and the standard error of difference showed that this rate at 6° does not fit with the values obtained at 15° and 24°C. The reason for a much higher rate of loss of dissolved organic phosphorus at 6° is not known. Temperatures at Sapelo Island are this low for only brief periods during the year, so the error involved in omitting this value is probably not very great.

The large standard deviations are indicative of the variability in rate of phosphorus elimination from experiment to experiment. One cause of differences in excretion rate of phosphate was variation in sea water salinity. Of the 20 phosphate excretion experiments at 24°C, half were performed using water of 12‰ salinity and the other half, 30‰. All of the water was obtained from Doboy Sound, the low salinity water having been collected after a period of heavy rains. The mean excretion rate in the normally saline water was 87 ($s = 54$) $\mu$g P/g day, but the rate in the diluted sea water was 13 ($s = 32$) $\mu$g P/g day. In spite of the large standard deviations, these rates are significantly different ($P < 0.01$). These data on phosphate excretion at low salinity have been included in the mean for the three temperatures given above because salinities this low or lower were found in 8 out of 79 marsh water samples taken near Sapelo Island by Dr. L. R. Pomeroy (personal communication). Additional work is necessary to determine if salinity has a specific effect upon phosphate excretion or if, perhaps, this is only one consequence of a general osmotic-balance mechanism of salt retention. Kanwisher (1959) showed a pronounced decline in respiratory rate in

*Littorina littorea* at salinities below 25‰, so it is possible that decreased phosphorus excretion may simply reflect a lowered metabolic rate in *Modiolus* at low salinities. If phosphate retention during periods of lowered salinity is a general characteristic of euryhaline organisms, it could markedly affect the dynamics of the phosphorus cycle in estuaries.

The salinity differences did not appear to affect the elimination rate of fecal phosphorus. Moreover, since about 92% of the feces from one meal was excreted within 12 hr (Fig. 3), the total amount of feces produced during the experiment really represents only the food ingested during the preceding tide. Since there are two tides per day in nature, the amount of fecal phosphorus eliminated in the marsh is almost certainly twice what was passed in the laboratory. The time course of phosphate excretion indicated a somewhat lower excretion rate after the first day, but the results were not conclusive enough to permit calculation of a correction factor. The amount of phosphate or dissolved organic phosphorus released from the feces by bacterial action after defecation was not measured, but it should be small compared to that released by the mussel.

It is improbable that significant amounts of phosphorus are eliminated in the mucus which binds the pseudofeces together. Any phosphorus so secreted would be a secondary product since mucin does not characteristically contain phosphorus. No analyses were performed, but judging from the ease with which pseudofeces were fragmented, the quantity of mucus in pseudofeces seemed small. Therefore it was assumed that this route of phosphorus loss was negligible.

### DISCUSSION

The quantities of phosphorus in the average mussel population (at 220-cm elevation) and in the water over the population, and the routes and rates of flow between these parts of the marsh ecosystem may now be compared (Fig. 4). The body represents only 5% of the total weight of the mussel, but it contains two-thirds of the

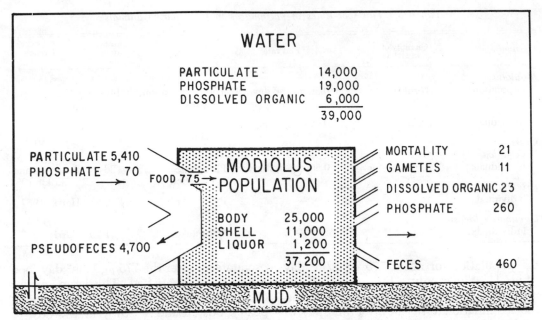

Fig. 4. Diagram of phosphorus flow through the mussel population. Values for the water and the mussel population are µg P/m²; rates are µg P/m² day. The flux rates of phosphorus in food and pseudofeces are calculated values necessary to balance the other, measured flux rates.

phosphorus. The liquor phosphorus amounts to about 3% of the total; the shell contains the rest.

The population phosphorus changes given in Table 1 show that the combined gains by body, shell, and liquor due to recruitment and growth were 4,100 µg P/m² yr, whereas the losses due to mortality and byssus production were 11,100 µg P/m² yr. It is possible that the population losses were really almost 3 times the growth and recruitment gains during the study period, but it is more probable that the field experiment overestimated the losses and underestimated the gains (Kuenzler 1961). The true values for the population are probably intermediate between the growth and mortality values and should be equal if the population density remains constant. This assumed, intermediate value of 7,600 µg P/m² yr, or 21 µg P/m² day is shown in Fig. 4 as mortality loss.

The mean elimination rates for fecal, phosphate, and dissolved organic phosphorus were multiplied by the biomass per square meter to obtain the elimination rates per square meter. The rate of loss of phosphorus in feces, doubled to correct for the laboratory underestimation caused by rapid rate of fecal elimination, was 460 µg/m² day. The mean rate of phosphate elimination was 260 µg/m² day, that of dissolved organic phosphorus was 23 µg/m² day. The experimental mussels were not examined thoroughly for disease or parasites, but none appeared to be in poor condition. The commonly occurring thigmotrich protozoans and other small parasites and commensals were undoubtedly present in many mussels; the excretion rates, then, as well as the growth and mortality rates, are those of the mussels with their parasites and commensals.

The amount of phosphorus which leaves the population in gametes during the spawning season was inferred from the decrease in phosphorus content of the population during that season. A minimal estimate, based on the net loss of phosphorus by the population and prorated over the year, was 11 µg P/m² day. The true rate may be twice as high for the reasons already given.

The rate of phosphorus ingestion must equal the sum of the rates of its loss from

TABLE 5.  *Turnover times of phosphorus in four marine animals*

| System | Quantity of P in system | Flux rate | Route | Turnover time, days | Reference |
|---|---|---|---|---|---|
| Modiolus population | 37 mg/m² | 0.32 mg/m² day | Total population losses | 115 | |
| Modiolus individuals | 6.2 mg/g | 0.064 mg/g day | Phosphate excretion | 97 | |
| Crassostrea virginica individuals | 20 mg/oyster | 0.56 mg/oyster day | Phosphate excretion | 36 | Pomeroy and Haskin 1954 |
| Artemia sp. individuals | — | — | P³² uptake | 0.58 | Harris 1957 |
| Gammarus locusta individuals | — | — | P³² uptake | 1.79 | Harris 1957 |

the population, or about 775 μg P/m² day (Fig. 4). Since only a little over half the ingested phosphorus is released in feces, the assimilation efficiency for phosphorus is almost 50% in nature. The efficiency of assimilation of phosphorus from "Nitzschia" was higher (Table 4) but this diet cannot be considered representative of the natural one.

The final segment of the cycle in Figure 4, removal of phosphorus from the water, may now be estimated. The rate at which the particulate fraction is removed is the product of the concentration in the water, the rate of filtration, the population density, and the time available for filtration. These four values, 44 μg P/L, 6.8 L/g hr, 4.1 g/m², and 4.4 hr/day, respectively, gave a removal rate of particulate matter equal to 5,410 μg P/m² day. No correction for the decrease in concentration with time was necessary in the calculation since the mean concentration of particulate matter in the water was based upon samples taken on both flood and ebb tides and was, therefore, already corrected for filtration by the mussels. Assuming the removal rate of phosphate to be 1% that of particulate phosphorus, the rate of removal of phosphate by the mussels would be about 70 μg P/m² day. The utilization of dissolved organic phosphorus by mussels has not been proved and is not shown in Figure 4.

From the above calculations, about 4,700 μg P/m² day remains to be deposited as pseudofeces after the 775 μg P/m² day food requirement is satisfied. This large amount of rejected matter is not unusual among pelecypods. Lund (1957), in a study of the feeding of the oyster, found the volume ratio of pseudofeces to feces to be 4.4:1 in natural sea water. The ratio decreased to 2:1 in suspensions which were less dense than natural. Since waters are normally turbid over Georgia salt marshes, filter-feeders could be quite selective in their feeding and reject large quantities of particulate matter.

The turnover time for mussels is longer than those of three other species of marine invertebrates (Table 5). The turnover time for the mussel population, 115 days, is an average for the year. This turnover time may vary seasonally due to changes in feeding, excretion, growth, mortality, and gamete-production rates. The flux rate, 320 μg P/m² day, is the sum of the rates via all pathways out of the population except the feces. Material which has simply passed through the gut has never really entered the body of an animal. Assuming that the fecal phosphorus represents undigested food materials and not true excretion products, it should not affect the turnover time of the population. It probably affects significantly the turnover times of some phases of the water or mud systems, however.

The turnover time for individual mussels might have been estimated with less precision, but with much less effort, by measuring only the phosphorus content of the tissues and the most important flux rate, phosphate excretion (Fig. 4). This gives close agreement with the 115 day estimate, yet it eliminates the laborious field work necessary to determine the flux rates attributable to mortality and gamete production. It may be possible to estimate turnover times for other species and populations by the abbreviated method if the animals and the environments are not too different from those of the present study. It should not be assumed, however, that phosphate excretion is the major pathway of phosphorus out of every population. A population of fast-growing, short-lived organisms might lose proportionately more phosphorus by way of mortality than does *Modiolus*. Larger amounts of phosphorus may be lost in reproductive processes by other populations. Significant losses in other species might be due to secretions or periodic molting. Furthermore, the rate of phosphate excretion might be influenced not only by the metabolism of the animal but also by the availability of phosphorus in the diet; phosphorus may be conserved by animals in a phosphorus-deficient environment. Use of the rate of phosphate excretion alone to estimate phosphorus turnover time may provide a satisfactory estimate for many animals, but a more detailed study will be necessary for many others.

Very few studies of phosphorus turnover in marine animals are found in the literature. Pomeroy and Haskin (1954) did not report turnover time, as such, but gave the data for *Crassostrea virginica* necessary for the calculations (Table 5). Since they reported that the oyster probably voided some previously accumulated wastes at the beginning of the experiment and since allowance cannot be made for phosphorus in tissues other than the body, nor for routes other than phosphate excretion, nor for the effects of storage prior to the experiment, the actual turnover time for oysters may differ somewhat from 36 days. Harris (1957) determined the turnover times for *Artemia* sp. and *Gammarus locusta* to be 14 and 43 hr, respectively, based on the rate of uptake of $P^{32}$ by these crustaceans. His results may be criticized because 1) his formula requires a system with constant precursor activity (Russell 1958), whereas the water in his experimental vessels had decreasing amounts of $P^{32}$ and, presumably, increasing amounts of $P^{31}$ which would cause a lowering of the precursor specific activity; and 2) he showed bacteria to be necessary as intermediaries in the transfer of $P^{32}$ to the crustaceans, and a large part of the measured uptake might have been by bacteria which were on the outside of the animals or undigested in the gut. The phosphorus turnover times of these animals in nature are probably longer than the estimates given by Harris, but they are probably much shorter than those of larger or more slowly metabolizing animals. Good measurements of turnover time for ecologically important crustaceans is desirable since the concentrations of nutrients in aquatic systems may frequently be limited by the rate at which animals can regenerate them.

The mussel population in the salt marsh is only one route of phosphorus into or out of the water. A good measurement of the flux rate by way of this population, however, fixes the maximum turnover time for the water. If the rate of flow of the nutrient into the water by way of another population is determined, this additional value can only serve to decrease the original estimate of turnover time of the system. This will also be true at the population level; discovery of new pathways for a nutrient to, or from, a population can only decrease any former estimate of the turnover time based on the flux to, or from, the population. Conversely, determination of the turnover time for a whole system from knowledge of the rates of appearance or disappearance of a nutrient, for example, sets the maximum flux rate via any one route of the system. Thus, if it were known from the rate of disappearance of $P^{32}$ added to a lake that the turnover time of phosphate in the lake water was four days, then there could be no one population or other component exchanging phosphorus in the lake with a flux rate sufficient to turn over all the

TABLE 6. *Participatory turnover times of phosphorus in sea water due to the* Modiolus *population in the salt marsh*

| Phosphorus fraction | Route | Maximum turnover time, days |
|---|---|---|
| Particulate | Filtration | 2.6 |
| Phosphate | Elimination | 73 |
| Dissolved organic | Elimination | 260 |

phosphate in the lake in four days by itself.

These concepts may be succinctly expressed by the following equations:

$$T_t = \frac{Q}{\Sigma F} \qquad \text{or:} \quad \frac{1}{T_t} = \sum \frac{1}{T_p}$$

where $T_t$ is the turnover time of a substance in a system; $Q$ is the total quantity of the substance in the system; $\Sigma F$ is the sum of the flux rates via all routes of the system; and $T_p$ is a participatory turnover time, that is, the turnover time of the substance in the system calculated from any one route. The first equation shows that the estimated turnover time of a whole system will decrease as more and more routes are measured; the second equation shows that the turnover time of the whole system must be less than the turnover time calculated from any participating route.

It is evident that the mussel population has a marked effect on the salt water over the marsh (Table 6). These turnover times for phosphorus in marsh water are participatory turnover times, maximum values calculated under the hypothetical assumption that the mussel population constitutes the only route for particulate phosphorus to leave the water, or for phosphate and dissolved organic phosphorus to enter the water. The biggest effect is the rapid removal of particulate matter from the sea and the deposition of most of it as pseudofeces. The decrease in particulate matter in the sea water with distance from the creeks has already been shown (Table 3) and now the effect of the mussels upon the clearing of the water appears evident. Certainly this is not a permanent loss of phosphorus from the water, but it may account for a significant part of the accumulation of phosphorus and other nutrients in salt marshes. Part of the phosphorus in the pseudofeces and feces is brought back into suspension by water currents, and most of the remainder may eventually return to the water phase as phosphate or dissolved organic matter through the action of important marsh-mud populations such as crabs, snails, polychaetes, nematodes, and bacteria (arrows at lower left of Fig. 4). These marsh populations are all working in parallel and the true turnover times for phosphate and dissolved organic phosphorus in the water phase must be less than 73 and 260 days, respectively (Table 6).

Very little research has been done on marine systems by other workers. Hayes, *et al.* (1952) calculated phosphorus turnover times for two small marine ecosystems from data in the literature. Each system was a rather small salt-water lake which ultimately connected with the sea. The turnover times of dissolved phosphate in the water were 3.2 and 2.4 days based upon the rate of loss of phosphate from the water to lake solids (phytoplankton, mud, etc.) following addition of commercial fertilizer. Bruce and Hood (1959) studied shallow bays and demonstrated that the dissolved phosphate concentration increased at night and decreased in daylight, and that the phosphate was rapidly taken up by the mud. They also reported the turnover rate (*sic*) to be 10 to 20 days, but it is not clear to which compartment or phosphorus fraction this turnover time applies. Pomeroy (1960) used $P^{32}$ to study the phosphate flux between natural suspended matter and water at offshore, estuarine, and marsh stations of the Georgia coast. He found residence times of phosphate to be from 1.7 to 7 days (mean = 3.6) in three samples of salt marsh water near Sapelo Island. Since the particulate phosphorus reservoir is less than half that of the mussel population (Fig. 4), the ability of the plankton population to turn over phosphate in so short a period indicates a flux rate 10 to 100 times as rapid as that of the mussels. It is evident that the suspended matter has by far the greatest effect on the dissolved phosphate budget; the mussels, in turn, have the major effect on the particulate matter in the water.

In conclusion, the mussels have a relatively long turnover time for phosphorus in spite of an abundance of the element in the surrounding waters. The major fractions of phosphorus present in sea water are ineffectively used (Fig. 4), the phosphate being only slightly utilized and the particulate phosphorus being largely wasted, even after the mussels have filtered it out of suspension. Food requirements other than phosphorus must be satisfied by the filtration process; phosphorus, at least, does not appear to be a limiting nutrient. The mussels, however, have a definite effect upon the water over the marsh, daily removing one-third of the particulate phosphorus from suspension. They regenerate a small part of this into phosphate and reject the remainder in pseudofeces and feces which drop to the mud surface. It appears, therefore, that the mussel population may be very important in the phosphate cycle as a depositional agent, furnishing raw materials to deposit-feeders which regenerate the phosphate. The continual sedimentation effected by the mussels may also play a large part in salt marsh development.

The importance of a population is frequently assessed in terms of its contribution to the entire energy flow of its ecosystem. The total annual energy flow of the mussel population, 56 kcal/m² yr, was reported to be about the same as those of the snail, crab, nematode, insect, bird, or mammal populations, but one or two orders of magnitude less than that of the bacteria of the salt marsh (Kuenzler 1961). The rates of water filtration and sediment deposition by the mussels, however, are probably not approached by any other population in the marsh. The mussels, therefore, seem to be more important as biogeochemical agents than as energy consumers in the salt marsh ecosystem.

## REFERENCES

ASANO, M., AND M. ITO. 1956. Comparative biochemical studies on aquatic animals. II. Phosphorus turnover in freshwater fish and shellfish. Tohoku J. Agric. Res., 7: 291–302.

BARNES, H. 1957. Nutrient elements. In: Treatise on Marine Ecology and Paleoecology. Vol. 1. Ecology. J. W. Hedgpeth [Ed.]. Mem. Geol. Soc. Amer., 67: 297–343.

BEVELANDER, G. 1952. Calcification in molluscs. III. Intake and deposition of Ca⁴⁵ and P³² in relation to shell formation. Biol. Bull., 102: 9–15.

BRUCE, H. E., AND D. W. HOOD. 1959. Diurnal inorganic phosphate variations in Texas bays. Publ. Inst. Mar. Sci. Univ. Texas, 6: 133–145.

BUCHANAN, R. E., AND E. I. FULMER. 1928. Physiology and Biochemistry of Bacteria. Vol. I. Growth phases; composition and biophysical chemistry of bacteria and their environment; and energetics. Williams and Wilkins, Baltimore.

CHIPMAN, W. A., AND J. G. HOPKINS. 1954. Water filtration by the bay scallop, Pecten irradians, as observed with the use of radioactive plankton. Biol. Bull., 107: 80–91.

COFFIN, C. C., F. R. HAYES, L. H. JODREY, AND S. G. WHITEWAY. 1949. Exchange of materials in a lake as studied by the addition of radioactive phosphorus. Canad. J. Res. D., 27: 207–222.

COLLIER, A. 1959. Some observations on the respiration of the American oyster Crassostrea virginica (Gmelin). Publ. Inst. Mar. Sci. Univ. Texas, 6: 92–108.

EMERY, K. O., AND R. E. STEVENSON. 1957. Estuaries and lagoons. I. Physical and chemical characteristics. In: Treatise on Marine Ecology and Paleoecology. Vol. 1. Ecology. J. W. Hedgpeth [Ed.]. Mem. Geol. Soc. Amer., 67: 673–693.

GOLDBERG, E. D., M. BAKER, AND D. L. FOX. 1952. Microfiltration in oceanographic research. I. Marine sampling with the molecular filter. J. Mar. Res., 11: 194–204.

HANSEN, A. L., AND R. J. ROBINSON. 1953. The determination of organic phosphorus in sea water with perchloric acid oxidation. J. Mar. Res., 12: 31–42.

HARRIS, E. 1957. Radiophosphorus metabolism in zooplankton and microorganisms. Canad. J. Zool., 35: 769–782.

HAYES, F. R., J. A. McCARTER, M. L. CAMERON, AND D. A. LIVINGSTONE. 1952. On the kinetics of phosphorus exchange in lakes. J. Ecol., 40: 202–216.

———, AND J. E. PHILLIPS. 1958. Lake water and sediment. IV. Radiophosphorus equilibrium with mud, plants, and bacteria under oxidized and reduced conditions. Limnol. Oceanogr., 3: 459–475.

HUTCHINSON, G. E. 1952. The biogeochemistry of phosphorus. In: The Biology of Phosphorus. L. F. Wolterink [Ed.]. Mich. State College Press, East Lansing, pp. 1–35.

———. 1957. A Treatise on Limnology. Vol. I. Geography, Physics, and Chemistry. Wiley, New York.

———, AND V. T. BOWEN. 1947. A direct demonstration of the phosphorus cycle in a small lake. Proc. Nat. Acad. Sci., Wash., **33**: 148–153.

———, AND ———. 1950. Limnological studies in Connecticut. IX. A quantitative radiochemical study of the phosphorus cycle in Linsley Pond. Ecology, **31**: 194–203.

JØRGENSEN, C. B. 1949. The rate of feeding by *Mytilus* in different kinds of suspension. J. Mar. Biol. Ass. U. K., **28**: 333–344.

———. 1955. Quantitative aspects of filter feeding in invertebrates. Biol. Rev., **30**: 391 –454

KANWISHER, J. 1959. Histology and metabolism of frozen intertidal animals. Biol. Bull., **116**: 258–264.

KUENZLER, E. J. 1961. Structure and energy flow of a mussel population in a Georgia salt marsh. Limnol. Oceanogr., **6**: 191–204.

LINDNER, R. C. 1944. Rapid analytical methods for some of the more common inorganic constituents of plant tissues. Plant Physiol., **19**: 76–89.

LUND, E. J. 1957. A quantitative study of clearance of a turbid medium and feeding by the oyster. Publ. Inst. Mar. Sci. Univ. Texas, **4**: 296–312.

McELROY, W. D. 1960. Residence time of dissolved phosphate in natural waters. Science, **131**: 1,731–1,732.

———, AND B. GLASS. 1951, 1952. Phosphorus Metabolism; a symposium on the role of phosphorus in the metabolism of plants and animals. 2 vols. Johns Hopkins Press, Baltimore.

POMEROY, L. R., AND H. H. HASKIN. 1954. The uptake and utilization of phosphate ions from sea water by the American oyster, *Crassostrea virginica* (Gmel.). Biol. Bull., **107**: 123– 129.

RENN, C. E. 1937. Bacteria and the phosphorus cycle in the sea. Biol. Bull., **72**: 190–195.

RICE, T. R., AND R. J. SMITH. 1958. Filtering rates of the hard clam (*Venus mercenaria*) determined with radioactive phytoplankton. U. S. Fish Wildl. Serv., Fish. Bull., **58**:(129): 73–82.

RONKIN, R. R. 1950. The uptake of radioactive phosphate by the excised gill of the mussel, *Mytilus edulis*. J. Cell. Comp. Physiol., **35**: 241–260.

STEVENS, G. C. 1960. Uptake of glucose from solution by the solitary coral, *Fungia*. Science, **131**: 1,532.

VINOGRADOV, A. P. 1953. The Elementary Chemical Composition of Marine Organisms. Mem. Sears Found. Mar. Res., **2**.

# ENERGY FLOW IN THE SALT MARSH ECOSYSTEM OF GEORGIA[1]

## JOHN M. TEAL

*Woods Hole Oceanographic Institution, Woods Hole, Massachusetts*

### INTRODUCTION

Along the coast of the United States from northern Florida to North Carolina runs a band of salt marsh bordered on the east by a series of sea islands and on the west by the mainland. The Marine Institute of the University of Georgia was established on one of these islands, Sapelo, and has tended to focus attention on the marsh. Several studies have provided data from which it is now possible to construct a picture of the energy flow through the organisms of this marsh.

Reasonably detailed studies of the energy flow, or trophic level production have been limited to a few natural ecosystems. These include Cedar Bog Lake, reported in the pioneer work of Lindeman (1942), and 2 fresh-water springs (Odum 1957, Teal 1958). There have been a number of studies of the energetics of laboratory populations (Richman 1958, Slobodkin 1959), and some theoretical comments upon energetics of populations and ecosystems (e.g. Patten 1959, Slobodkin 1960), but work on even the broad details of energy flow in natural ecosystems has lagged.

The present paper draws heavily upon the work of others. The authors are cited in the appropriate places but I wish here to express my appreciation for their cooperation.

[1] Contribution No. 38 from the University of Georgia Marine Institute, Sapelo Island, Georgia. This research was supported by funds from the Sapelo Island Research Foundation and by N.S.F. grant G-6156.

The physical and chemical features of the marsh have been described (Teal 1958, Teal & Kanwisher 1961) but I will briefly define 5 regions into which the marsh was divided in many of these studies (Figure 1).

Creek bank: muddy and/or sandy banks of tidal creeks between low water and the beginning of *Spartina* growth.

Streamside marsh: an area 1-3 m wide of closely spaced, tall *Spartina* located just above the bare creekbank.

Levee marsh: *Spartina* of intermediate height spacing atop the natural levees bordering the creeks.

Short-*Spartina* marsh: flat areas behind the levees with short, widely spaced *Spartina*.

Salicornia marsh: sandy areas near land where plants other than *Spartina* occur, among which *Salicornia* is conspicuous.

The relative areas of these various marsh types were measured on aerial photographs (Table V) to enable calculation of averages for the marsh as a whole.

### The marsh fauna

Animals living in the marsh must be able to survive or avoid the great changes in salinity, temperature and exposure. Salinity of water flooding the marshes varies from 20 to 30 o/oo with values as low as 12 o/oo recorded in heads of creeks just after heavy rains. Salinity of water in the mud may be 5 o/oo in isolated areas where fresh water drains from the islands and 70 o/oo in isolated low areas during rainless summer periods. An average aquatic or soil animal must be able to withstand variations from 20 to 30 o/oo but probably escapes greater extremes by burrowing in the mud and/or migrating short distances.

The limited number of animals which have adapted to these extremes are relatively free from competing species and enemies. For example, mussels living in the marsh are bothered by neither snails nor echinoderms, which take great toll of the estuarine bivalves living only a few meters away. Ants and grasshoppers are each represented by only one common species, *Cremato-gaster clara* and *Orchelimum fidicinium* respectively, which is quite abundant in marsh areas optimal for it. Once adapted to the marsh, the lack of competition from similar animals has perhaps allowed them to occupy a broader niche and

TABLE I. Known macro-fauna of a Georgia salt marsh listed by groups according to distribution and origin

(1a) Terrestrial species living in marsh
    *Orchelimum fidicinium* Rehn & Hebard
    *Ischnodesmus* sp.
    *Prokelisia marginata* (Van Duzee)
    *Liburnia detecta* Van Duzee
    *Tabanus* spp.
    *Culicoides canithorax* Hoffman
    *Dimicoenia spinosa* (Loew)
    *Plagiopsis aneo-nigra* (Loew)
    *Parydra vanduzeei* (Creeson)
    *Chaetopsis aenea* (Wiedermann)
    *Chaetopsis apicalis* Johnson
    *Haplodictya setosa* (Coquillett)
    *Mordellid* sp.
    *Crematogaster clara* Mayr
    *Camponotus pylartes fraxinicola* M. R. Smith
    *Hyctia pikei* Peckham
    *Seriolus* sp.
    *Lycosa modesta* (Keyserling)
    *Philodromus* sp.
    *Grammonata* sp.
    *Hyctia brina* (Hentz)
    *Eustala* sp.
    *Singa keyserlingi* McCook
    *Tetragnatha vermiformis* Emerton
    *Dictyna* sp.
    *Rallus longirostris* Boddaert
    *Termatodytes palustris* (Wilson)
    *Ammospiza caudacuta* (Gmelin)
    *A. maritima* (Wilson)
    *Oryzomys palustris* (Harlan)
    *Procyon lotor* (Linne)
    *Mustela vison* Schreber
(1b) Terrestrial or fresh-water species only on landward edge of marsh
    *Pachydiplax longipennis* Burmeister
    *Pantala flavescens* Fabrisius
    *Erythrodiplax verenice* Drury
    *Anax junius* Drury
    *Erythemis simplicicollis* Say
    *Orphylella* sp.
    *Platunus cincticollis* (Say)
    *Kinesternum s. subrubrum* (Lacepede)
    *Lutra canadensis* (Schreber)

(2a) Estuarine species limited in marsh to low water level
    *Bouganvillia carolinensis* (McCrady)
    *Campanularid* sp.
    *Oerstedia dorsalis* burger
    *Nolella stipata* Gosse
    *Eteone alba* Webster
    *Autolytus prolifer* (O. F. M.)
    *Polydora ligni* Webster
    *Heteromastis filiformis* (Claparede)
    *Crassostrea virginica* (Gmelin)
    *Mercenaria mercenaria* (Linne)
    *Tagelus plebeius* Solander
    *T. divisus* Spengler
    *Mulinia lateralis* Say
    *Epitomium rupicolum* (Kurtz)
    *Balanus improvisus* Darwin
    *Microprotopus maculatoides* Shoemaker
    *Paracaprella* sp.
    *Crangon heterochelis* (Say)
    *Clibanarium vittatus* (Bosc)
    *Molgula manhattensis* (DeKay)
(2b) Estuarine species in streamside marsh
    *Nassarius obsoletus* Say
    *Chthamalus fragilis* Darwin
    *Neomysis americana* (S. I. Smith)
    *Leptochelia rapax* Harger
    *Cassidisca lumifrons* (Richardson)
    *Gammarus chesapeakensis* Bousfield
    *Melita nitida* Smith
    *Callinectes sapidus* Rathbun
    *Panopeus herbstii* Milne-Edwards
    *Eurypanopeus depressus* (Smith)
    *Malaclemys terrapin centrata* (Latreille)
(2c) Estuarine species occurring well into marsh
    *Neanthes succinea* (Frey & Leuckart)
    *Laeonereis culveri* (Webster)
    *Streblospio benedicti* Webster
    *Capitella capitata* (Fab.)
    *Orchestia grillus* (Bosc.)
    *O. Platensis* Kroyer
(3a) Aquatic marsh species with planktonic larvae
    *Manayunkia aestuarina* (Bourne)
    *Modiolus demissus* Dillwyn
    *Polymesoda caroliniana* Bosc
    *Littorina irrorata* (Say)
    *Littoridina tenuipes* (Couper)
    *Eurytium limosum* (Say)
    *Sesarma reticulatum* (Say)
    *S. cinereum* (Bosc)
    *Uca pugilator* (Bosc)
    *U. minax* (LeConte)
    *U. pugnax* (S. I. Smith)
(3b) Aquatic marsh species living entirely within marsh
    *Oligochaetes*-3 spp.
    *Melampus bidentatus* Say
    *Cyathura carinata* (Kroyer)
    *Orchestia uhleri* Shoemaker

be more abundant than would otherwise be possible.

Table I lists the marsh fauna divided into several groups: (1) typically terrestrial insects and arachnids subdivided into those occurring throughout the marsh and those confined to the landward edge, (2) the aquatic species with their center of abundance in the estuaries and 2a confined to regions near low water, 2b occurring in the streamside marsh, or 2c occurring throughout the marsh, (3) marsh species derived from aquatic ancestors with their centers of distribution within the marsh which are subdivided into those with planktonic larvae and those that spend their entire life cycle in the marsh.

The list shows that of the aquatic species, 33 or 60% are in groups 2a and 2b, estuarine forms that have managed to colonize the lowest portion of the salt marsh. They can survive only where periods of exposure at low tides are short. The individuals in the marsh are living at one edge of their species' distribution and their numbers are maintained by migrations from the surrounding waters. Those living above the mud are especially subject to damage by extremes of weather, and species that have penetrated farthest into the marsh are burrowers. The remaining aquatic species are either tolerant enough to inhabit the entire marsh although they are most common in the estuaries, group 2c, or are most common in the marshes themselves. But even among the latter, only 6 do not spend part of their life cycle in the estuaries. These are isopods, amphipods, oligochaetes and the pulmonate snail, *Melampus*, the last 2 of which are derived from fresh water or terrestrial rather than marine ancestors.

That part of the fauna derived from the land is at present the least well known, but the species so far encountered comprise nearly half of the marsh animals. They are, however, far less important in the energetics of the community than their aquatic counterparts, as will be seen below.

Most of the terrestrial species have made only slight adaptation to the marshes. They breath air and resist salinity changes and desiccation by means of their impervious exoskeleton. Most of the larger forms climb the marsh grass to escape

rising tides, but can climb under water to seek refuge from birds. Some insects, such as the ant, *Crematogaster*, are easily drowned, but live within *Spartina* stems and can effectively plug the entrance to their nests.

The distribution of marsh species can be seen in Figure 1. The data are from the samples reported in this paper taken at the sites indicated as well as other samples and general collecting. Most of the insect and spider samples are from Smalley (unpublished). Estuarine species occur mostly near low water and in drainage channels and are reduced on the levees which may dry out between spring tides. The aquatic marsh species are distributed relatively evenly throughout the marsh. Terrestrial species are common throughout the grassy areas, with more species present on the higher ground and in the taller marsh-grass.

### The food web

The herbivorous faunas of many ecosystems can be divided into 2 groups, those which feed directly on living plants and those which feed on plants only after the plants have died and fallen to the ground (Odum and Smalley 1959). The marsh fauna may be grouped in a similar manner (Figure 2).

A group of insects lives and feeds directly upon the living *Spartina: Orchelium*, eating the tissues, and *Prokelisia*, sucking the plant juices. These and their less important associates support the spiders, wrens, and nesting sparrows. A different group lives at the level of the mud surface and feeds on the detritus formed by bacterial decomposition of *Spartina* and on algae. These mud dwelling groups function mostly as primary consumers, although the detritus also contains animal remains and numbers of the bacteria that help break the *Spartina* into small pieces. The carnivores preying on the algal and detritus group are principally mud crabs, raccoons, and rails.

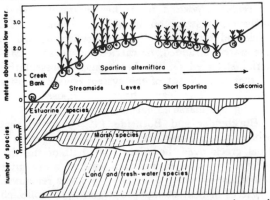

FIG. 1. Representative section of a Georgia salt marsh with horizontal scale distorted non-uniformly. Sample sites indicated by circled numbers. Site 2 represents the beginning of a drainage channel, not an isolated low spot. Symbols for grass are drawn to correct height for average maximum growth at those sites. The number of species of animals of 3 groups listed in Table I are plotted against sample sites. Names of marsh types used herein are also indicated.

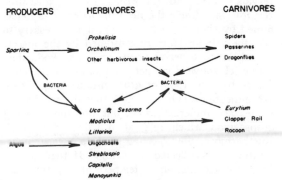

FIG. 2. Food web of a Georgia salt marsh with groups listed in their approximate order of importance.

The species of the detritus-algae feeding group that are important in the economy of the marsh are the fiddler crabs, oligochaetes, *Littorina,* and the nematodes among the deposit feeders, and *Modiolus* and *Manayunkia* among the suspension feeders. Thus, the community consists of 2 parts, one deriving its energy directly from the living *Spartina* and the other deriving its energy from detritus and algae.

## ENERGY FLOW BY TROPHIC GROUPS

### Methods

Some populations were sampled completely enough that production could be measured directly, e.g. *Spartina* and grasshoppers. In other cases production could not be determined from the sampling but was estimated either from turnover time, in which case production equals one maximum population per turnover period, or by assuming that the ratio between respiration and production for the group in question is 0.25 to 0.30 as has been found for other groups (Teal 1958, Slobodkin 1960). Respiration in air was the measure of energy degradation. Some of the mud dwelling forms live in completely anaerobic conditions (Teal & Kanwisher 1961), e.g. nematodes, and the energy degradation under anaerobic conditions is assumed to be equal to that in air. This is supported only by the observation of Wieser and Kanwisher (1961) that nematodes from anaerobic muds are as active under anaerobic conditions as under aerobic.

### Primary production

The only higher plant of importance on the salt marsh is *Spartina alterniflora.* It grows over the entire marsh, is eaten by insects, then dies, decomposes and as detritus furnishes the food for much of the remaining fauna of the marsh. Smalley (1959) measured production of *Spartina* by harvesting and weighing plants at monthly intervals. Teal and Kanwisher (1961) measured respiration. Since the net production was determined by short-term harvesting, it is necessary to add the 305 kcal/m² yr consumed by the insects (see below) to arrive at the true net production. Table II shows that net production of *Spartina* comes to only 19% of gross production. There are indications (Odum 1961) that the production values are underestimated, but not the standing crops upon which respiration values are based. Furthermore, the *Spartina* used to measure respiration was collected in spring. If there is appreciable acclimation to temperature by this species, then summer values will be lower and winter values higher than indicated, but as summer con-

TABLE II. Data for *Spartina* in Georgia salt marhes. Production figures from Smalley (1959), respiration rates from Teal and Kanwisher (1961)

| Season | | Short Spartina 42% of total area | Levee-Streamside 58% of total area |
|---|---|---|---|
| Winter 2 mo at 10° | Standing crop Respiration | 300 fresh g/m² 235 kcal/m² | 750 fresh g/m² 580 kcal/m² |
| Spring 3 mo at 17.5° | Standing crop Respiration | 600 g/m² 1250 kcal/m² | 1350 g/m² 2800 kcal/m² |
| Summer 4 mo at 26° | Standing crop Respiration | 705 g/m² 6450 kcal/m² | 3225 g/m² 29600 kcal/m² |
| Autumn 3 mo at 20° | Standing crop Respiration | 900 g/m² 3240 kcal/m² | 1800 g/m² 6480 kcal/m² |
| Production | | 2570 kcal/m² yr | 8970 kcal/m² yr |

Marsh average: net production = 6580 kcal/m² yr ~ 1650 gm/m² yr
respiration = 28000 kcal/m² yr

gross production = 34580

tributes twice as much (4 vs. 2 months), an adjustment would lower the total figure for respiration. But assuming perfect summer acclimation would bring net production to only 24% of gross production.

In addition to *Spartina,* the algae living on the surface of the marsh mud contribute 1800 kcal/m² yr gross production and not less than 1620 kcal/m² yr net production (Pomeroy 1959).

### Decomposition of *Spartina*

Before the *Spartina* is available to most of the marsh consumers it must be broken down by bacteria. Part of the *Spartina* crop decomposes in place on the marsh, especially that portion in the Short Spartina areas not subject to strong tidal currents. *Spartina* from the streamside marsh, however, is swept off by the water and carried back and forth until it is either decomposed in the water, stranded, or carried out to sea. Material stranded on the beach and representative of that carried out of the system consists mostly of stalks. The leaves have decomposed before leaving the marsh-estuarine system.

Burkholder and Bornside (1957) found that when marsh grass was confined in cages in a tidal creek over the winter, one-half of the dry weight was broken up and washed away after 6 months, by which time only the stems remained.

Pieces of dead standing *Spartina* were collected in mid-winter when decomposition was starting. Algae were not present, hence oxygen consumption was a measure of bacterial activity. From the initial rate of decomposition measured at 15° C, it was estimated that leaves submerged at every tide would be completely consumed in 2 months, stems in 3½ months. Leaves and stems that dry

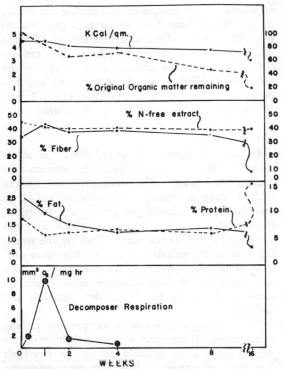

FIG. 3. Decomposition of marsh grass in sea water showing changes in oxygen consumption and composition of grass-bacteria mixture. Line between 8-week point and break shows correct slope.

out in periods between spring tides would last about twice as long.

To find out what changes in composition occur during the breakup of *Spartina*, 10 g of finely-dropped air-dried marsh grass were placed in 500 ml flasks with 200 ml sea water, inoculated with 1 ml of marsh mud and placed on a shaker in the dark at 20° C. The oxygen content of the flasks was not measured but in no case did the material go completely anaerobic. After periods of 0, 2, 7, 14, 28, 56 and 112 days samples were removed. Oxygen consumption of 2 samples was measured and the material from 4 flasks was lumped for analyses of moisture, fat, protein, crude fiber, nitrogen-free extract, ash and caloric content made by Law and Company, Atlanta, Georgia. The results are shown in Figure 3.

Respiration in the flasks rapidly reached a maximum as bacteria grew on the material liberated from crushed cells by the chopping. In 2 weeks this phase passed and bacterial action remained low for the remainder of the experiment. The initial phase is reflected in the decrease in fat and protein percentages but, while fat continued to decline slowly, protein concentration increased gradually until at 16 weeks it was twice as high

as at the beginning. At the same time carbohydrates (N-free extracts) remained constant but fiber, principally cellulose, declined to less than ¼ of its initial value. The caloric content declined by 33%. During the period 82% of the organic matter was consumed.

If this is representative of what happens to the *Spartina* as it is changed from standing marsh grass to detritus then, although the total amount of material is decreased, the animal food value of what remains is increased. Bacteria attack the grass substances and convert a portion into bacterial protoplasm and in this process cellulose in the bacterial-detritus mixture decreases most swiftly and protein least swiftly.

The magnitude of the bacterial metabolism was calculated with figures for respiration of plankton in the estuarine waters and bacteria in the marsh sediments and on the standing *Spartina*. Ragotzkie (1958) found that plankton respiration averaged 1600 kcal/m² yr in estuarine waters. Since the turbidity of the water is high, there is very little phytoplankton and I assumed that all of this respiration represents bacterial action upon *Spartina* detritus. Since a planimetric survey of charts and aerial photos of the region showed that there is twice as much marsh as estuarine area in the system, this represents 800 kcal/m² yr of marsh. From Teal and Kanwisher (1961) we find that the bacteria in the marsh sediments degrade 2090 kcal/m² yr. The average respiration of bacteria on standing, dead *Spartina* is about 60 mm³/gm hr, which, multiplied by the biomass of that *Spartina* (Smalley 1959) comes to 1000 kcal/m² yr. Thus the activities of bacteria account for 3890 kcal/m² yr averaged over the marsh area. This amounts to 59% of the available *Spartina*.

Besides bacteria, colorless blue-green algae are also active in the degradation of *Spartina*. Bits of partly decomposed *Spartina* were often found within the mud which was usually black just around them. Within these bits were often numerous filaments of what were apparently *Thioploca* and *Beggiatoa* or *Oscillatoria*. The algae were alive and active, living in a lightless, highly reduced environment as has been discussed by Pringsheim (1949).

### Herbivorous insects

The salt marsh grasshopper and the plant hopper are the only important animals in this category. The grasshoppers respire 18.6 kcal and produce 10.8 kcal of tissue per m² per year which adds to an assimilation of 29.4 kcal/m² yr (Smalley 1960). The corresponding plant hopper figures are: respiration 205 kcal/m² yr, produc-

TABLE III. Summary of energy-flow for detritus-algae feeders in Georgia salt marsh

| | Respiration | Production | Assimilation | Production Assimilation |
|---|---|---|---|---|
| Crabs........ | 171 | 35 | 206 | 17% |
| Annelids..... | 26 | 9 | 35 | 25%* |
| Nematodes... | 64 | 21 | 85 | 25%* |
| Mussels...... | 39 | 17 | 56 | 30% |
| Snails........ | 72 | 8 | 80 | 10% |
| Totals.... | 372 | 90 | 462 | 19.5% |

* Assumed as means of calc. P.

tion 70 kcal/m² yr and assimilation 275 kcal/m² yr (Smalley 1959). Production of plant hoppers was not measured but calculated on the assumption that the ratio of production to assimilation equals 25%. The grasshoppers assimilate only about 30% of what they ingest which means they produce nearly 70 kcal/m² yr of fecal matter which can probably serve as food for some of the other marsh inhabitants.

## Detritus-algae feeders

Table III gives a summary of the results for the various groups of animals that feed at the surface of the mud-eating Spartina-detritus, algae and to a lesser but unknown extent each other. The groups are considered in turn below.

## Crabs

*Uca pugilator, U. pugnax,* and *Sesarma reticulatum* are the most conspicuous consumers in the marsh. One or more of these species is present in all parts of the marsh. They feed on the surface of the mud for the most part, picking up clawfuls of mud, sorting it with their mouthparts, spitting the rejected material into a claw and depositing it back on the mud and swallowing the remainder. If the spit is compared with the undisturbed mud surface, it is apparent that most of the sorting consists of rejecting larger particles. Spit from *U. pugilator* which live on sand consists of sand from which the smaller particles, the algae and detritus, are gone. In spit from *U. pugnax* feeding on mud rich in diatoms and nematodes most of the larger diatoms and nematodes were no longer distinguishable but the average particle size of the spit was larger than that of the mud and contained many bits of diatom shells. Apparently the large diatoms and nematodes were crushed and then the finer particles were swallowed and the larger ones rejected.

By comparing the amount of feces produced in a few hours by freshly collected animals with the normal rates of respiration and growth, the portion of the ingested food actually assimilated was estimated. Four measurements during the winter on groups of from 5 to 16 animals gave values from 23 to 31%. One measurement on 57 crabs in August gave a value of 75%. Algae and detritus are scarcer in summer than winter on the areas where these crabs were collected and apparently they assimilate a larger part of the digestable material when it is scarce. A parallel situation is found in copepods (Marshall and Orr 1955).

In areas of dense crab populations the entire surface of the marsh is worked over between successive high tides. The feces produced by the crabs feeding on muddy substrates contain about one-third more calories per gram than the mud; feces produced by crabs on sand about 10 times as many calories as the sand. Both by the working over of the marsh surface and the concentration of organic matter in their feces the crabs will have considerable influence upon other organisms, especially the nematodes, annelids and bacteria.

The crab populations were sampled by placing metal rings, 30 cm high, on the marsh while the tide was in and the animals were in or near their burrows, returning at low tide and removing

TABLE IV. Crab populations in g/m² in Georgia salt marshes followed by standard errors. Sizes: s=0-150 mg; m=150-500 mg; 1=>500 mg

| Marsh type | Size | Winter | Spring | Summer | Autumn | Species |
|---|---|---|---|---|---|---|
| Creek bank | s | 0 | ? | 4.89±1.04 | 0 | *Uca pugilator* |
| | m | 0 | 0 | 3.67±0.75 | 0 | |
| | l | 0 | 0 | 33.1±5.6 | 0 | |
| Stream-side | s | 0 | 0 | 4.8±2.8 | 0 | *Sesarma reticulatum* |
| | m | 0.7±0.4 | 3.65±1.15 | 7.35±1.15 | * | |
| | l | 10.2±1.5 | * | * | * | |
| Stream-side | s | 0 | 0 | 2.6±1.6 | 0 | *Eurytium limosum* |
| | m | 0 | 0 | 2.85±0.45 | * | |
| | l | 8.7±1.44 | * | * | * | |
| Levee | s | 0.5±0.3 | ? | 0.8±0.8 | 0.41±0.14 | *Sesarma reticulatum* |
| | m | 0.5±0.5 | 0.2±0.2 | 2.34±0.45 | 1.4? | |
| | l | 12.4±4.35 | 12.4±4.33 | 22.1±0.8 | 17.0? | |
| Levee | s | 0.81±0.36 | 2.27±0.68 | 5.74±0.93 | 2.47±0.67 | *Uca pugnax* |
| | m | 3.0±1.5 | 9.8±2.1 | 7.14±0.65 | 5.0? | |
| | l | 16.7±3.4 | 32.5±9.0 | 54.3±9.5 | 35.5? | |
| Levee | l | 15.6±2.9 | * | * | * | *Eurytium limosum* |
| Short Spartina | s | 1.0±0.45 | 0 | 3.16±0.71 | 1.0±0.45 | *Uca pugnax* |
| | m | 2.30±0.60 | 1.95±0.65 | 5.00±0.85 | 3.65? | |
| | l | 16.25±3.90 | 9.5±2.0 | 12.2±1.70 | 14.25? | |
| Salicornia-Distichlis | s | ? | ? | 1.91±0.43 | 8.13±1.17 | *Uca pugilator* |
| | m | 3.6±0.5 | * | * | * | |
| | l | 114.9±20.4 | * | * | * | |

? indicates no samples were taken, numbers if entered are interpolations. When data for several seasons were pooled, the mean appears, followed by asterisks for other seasons involved in the average.

TABLE V. Respiration of Georgia salt marsh crabs by marsh type. Values are kcal/m²/season

| Marsh type | Species | Winter | Spring | Summer | Autumn | Total | % by adults |
|---|---|---|---|---|---|---|---|
| Creek bank. | U. pl. | 0 | 0 | 69.5 | 0 | 69.5 | 66% |
| Streamside.. | S. r. | 2.9 | 10.5 | 66.6 | 17.4 | 97.3 | 37% |
| Levee...... | S. r. | 3.8 | 8.6 | 49.4 | 17.0 | 78.7 | 81% |
|  | U. px. | 5.9 | 50.0 | 139.6 | 51.2 | 246.6 | 67% |
| Short spartina. | U. px. | 5.5 | 11.6 | 48.0 | 23.3 | 88.4 | 56% |
| Salicornia... | U. pl. | 37.3 | 80.6 | 170 | 100 | 388 | 90% |

everything within the ring, separating, counting and weighing the crabs. Rings of ⅕ m² were used for adults which were picked out by hand but rings of only 0.018 m² were used for the young, which had to be separated by sieving. Crabs of more than 150 mg were ignored in the small samples and vice versa.

The sampling results are shown in Table IV. In general the biomass of crabs follows the same distribution as the numbers of species of marsh animals (Fig. 1). The *U. pugilator* on the creek bank are apparently completely killed during the autumn and replaced the following spring. It seems unlikely that they migrate as they are confined to sandy substrates (Teal 1958) and the Streamside, Levee and Short Spartina marshes are uniformly muddy (Teal and Kanwisher 1961). The values for the Salicornia marsh must be divided by 4 since only about ¼ of the area is occupied by plants and crab burrows, the rest being open sand flats not included in the samples where the crabs feed but do not live.

Table V lists values for respiration of the crabs by marsh types. Respiratory rates are from Teal (1959). The last column gives an idea of the relative importance of the large and small individuals to the population's energy degradation.

By assuming that the crab populations replace themselves annually the energy flow figures in Table VI were calculated

TABLE VI. Energy flow of detritus-eating crabs in a Georgia salt marsh. Data in kcal/m²/yr

| Marsh type | Relative area | Respiration | Production |
|---|---|---|---|
| Creek-bank...... | 10% | 70 | 28 |
| Streamside....... | 10% | 97 | 19 |
| Levee.......... | 35% | 325 | 65 |
| Short Spartina.... | 40% | 88 | 14 |
| Salicornia........ | 5% | 97 | 20 |

| | |
|---|---|
| Average respiration | 171 |
| Average production | 35 |
| Average assimilation | 206 |
| Production efficiency | 17% |

TABLE VII. Summary of annelid sampling in Georgia salt marsh

| Marsh type | Nov-Dec Sample | | Jul-Aug Sample | |
|---|---|---|---|---|
| | N | g/m² | N | g/m² |
| Creek bank......... | 8 | 2.0 ±2.0 | 7 | 0.95 ±0.25 |
| Streamside......... | 15 | 2.9 ±0.6 | 10 | 1.0 ±0.53 |
| Levee.............. | 35 | 1.8 ±0.28 | 38 | 2.2 ±0.32 |
| Short Spartina....... | 39 | 2.2 ±0.95 | 8 | 0.5 ±0.12 |
| Salicornia.......... | 5 | 0.2 ±0.2 | 2 | 0.0 |
| Marsh average....... | | 2.01 ±0.46 | | 1.16 ±0.14 |

## Annelids

The annelids in the marsh are mostly deposit feeders, feeding either from fixed burrows or working their way through the sediments like the oligochaetes, although *Manayunkia* is a filter-feeder. Although *Neanthes*, because of its jaws, might be thought to be predaceous, guts examined at different seasons revealed only diatoms, detritus, and mud and sand.

The annelids were sampled once in November-December and once in July-August. Five samples were taken with a plastic coring tube at spots chosen by taking a pair of random numbers, one indicating the distance north and the other, the distance east of a stake marking the southwest corner of a square meter plot selected at random from the marsh as a whole. The sites are indicated in Fig. 1 and may be seen on an aerial photograph of the marsh in Teal and Kanwisher (1961). Each core was divided into 3 parts at 2 cm intervals and the portion below 6 cm discarded. The annelids were removed by gentle washing in sea water in a sieve with 16 meshes/cm. All samples were examined within 24 hours of collection. Biomass was calculated by multiplying the average weight of each species by the number found in the sample. Average weights were determined for the more common species by weighing on a quartz helix as well as by measuring length and width and calculating the weight based on a specific density equal to sea water. The methods agreed within 15%. Insect larvae collected with the annelids are included in the figures (Table VII).

Table VIII shows the numbers of the most common annelids and insect larvae from selected representative sites. *Capitella*, the oligochaetes, *Streblospio* and *Manayunkia* made up most of the biomass, usually in that order. Two of these, *Capitella* and *Streblospio*, are characteristic not of the marshes but of the estuaries, indicating that the annelids have had to make relatively little adaptation to marsh life. In general they are most

TABLE VIII. Numbers of selected annelids and insect larvae/0.01 m² in representative marsh types in a Georgia salt marsh

| Site | 21 | 6 | 19 | 10 | 8 | 4 | 1 | 7 | 3 |
|---|---|---|---|---|---|---|---|---|---|
| **Winter Series** | | | | | | | | | |
| Capitella capitata........ | 0 | 10 | 30 | 70 | 50 | 30 | 0 | 10 | 0 |
| Steblospio benedicti...... | 50 | 150 | 80 | 40 | 50 | 0 | 20 | 30 | 0 |
| Neanthes succinea........ | 0 | 10 | 0 | 0 | 0 | 0 | 0 | 0 | 10 |
| Manayunkia aestuarina.. | 0 | 0 | 40 | 90 | 0 | 290 | 0 | 0 | 0 |
| oligochaete............. | 10 | 10 | 170 | 80 | 30 | 80 | 40 | 40 | 0 |
| dipteran larvae......... | 0 | 0 | 10 | 0 | 10 | 10 | 0 | 0 | 0 |
| **Summer Series** | | | | | | | | | |
| Capitella capitata........ | 30 | 26 | 14 | 56 | 136 | 38 | 12 | 30 | 0 |
| Streblospio benedicti...... | 14 | 38 | 40 | 6 | 4 | 0 | 4 | 0 | 0 |
| Neanthes succinea....... | 0 | 0 | 0 | 0 | 2 | 0 | 0 | 0 | 0 |
| Manayunkia aestuarina.. | 8 | 10 | 12 | 52 | 0 | 60 | 0 | 0 | 0 |
| oligochaete............. | 78 | 10 | 60 | 88 | 88 | 66 | 30 | 32 | 20 |
| dipteran larvae......... | 2 | 0 | 0 | 0 | 0 | 2 | 0 | 0 | 0 |

numerous in the most productive parts of the marsh as are other animals, except that they are somewhat scarcer on the highest and thus the driest parts of the levees.

Energy flow for the annelids was calculated on the basis of an average respiration rate of 400 mm³/gm hr (Zeuthen 1953) and a production equal to 25% of assimilation. The latter results in a turnover time of 1.6 months which is reasonable since the animals are between 20μ gm and 200μ gm in weight.

### Nematodes

Using the relative areas of various marsh types from Table V, and the weights of nematodes from Teal and Wieser (1961) I calculate that there are about 2.76 g fresh weight/m². The samples were all taken in spring so it must be assumed that the nematode biomass does not change appreciably throughout the year. Wieser and Kanwisher (1961) found that there was only slightly more than a 2-fold variation in a marsh at Woods Hole, Mass. where the climate is considerably colder and more variable. Using the average respiratory rate of 540 mm³/fresh gm/hr (Teal and Wieser 1961) the nematodes would respire an average of 64 kcal/m² yr. Assuming their production to equal 25% of assimilation, production would be 21 kcal/m² yr which would amount to a turnover of the population every 1.6 months. This may be compared with turnovers of 1 year and 1 month quoted by Wieser and Kanwisher (1961) and Nielsen (1949) respectively.

### Snails and Mussels

The mussels (Kuenzler 1961) respire on the average 39 kcal/m² yr and produce 17 kcal/m² yr. The small snails of the current year class had a production equal to 14% of their assimila-

tion but Smalley's population data did not provide a production value for the adults which grew very slowly. Since there is some growth of adult snails as well as the formation of gametes, which amounts to ⅛ of the total production of the mussels (Kuenzler 1961), the snail production must be something less than 14%, and 10% is used here.

### Secondary consumers

The population data for the mud crab, *Eurytium limosum*, were presented in Table III. An average respiration value of 21.9 kcal/m² yr was derived from data of Teal (1959) and a production of 5.3 kcal/m² yr was calculated in the same manner as for the other crabs. For the Clapper Rails, a production of 0.1 kcal/m² yr was calculated from the data of Oney (1954) for population and mortality, and an average respiration of 1.6 kcal/m² yr was calculated on the basis of the weight-metabolism curve of warm blooded animals in Hemmingsen (1950). So figured the total assimilation of the carnivores comes to 30.6 kcal/m² yr divided into 25.1 kcal/m² yr respiration and 5.5 kcal/m² yr production. The raccoons in the marsh have not been studied but on the basis of general observation during 4 years when I was in the marsh nearly every week, they are considered to have an assimilation equal to that of the rails.

As yet there is no study of the carnivorous birds and spiders that feed on the marsh insects. For purposes of this calculation they are assumed to take the same portion of their prey as do the predators feeding on the detritus-algae eaters.

### COMMUNITY ENERGY FLOW

Figure 4 shows the energy flow for the marsh system calculated in the preceding sections. The value for light input is from Kimball (1929). The amount of light that is actually intercepted by the plants is unknown but it is obvious from colored aerial photographs that a considerable portion of the mud is exposed especially in the parts of the marsh not close to a creek. Nevertheless, gross production is 6.1% of the incident light energy. This may be compared with values of from 0.1 to 3.0% reported for various fresh-water and marine areas (Odum and Odum 1959, 1955). The salt marsh occupies a highly advantageous position where nutrients are plentiful and circulation is supplied by the tides.

However, as noted above, a large part of the gross production is metabolised by the plants themselves and net production over light is a little less than 1.4%. This is still high compared to other

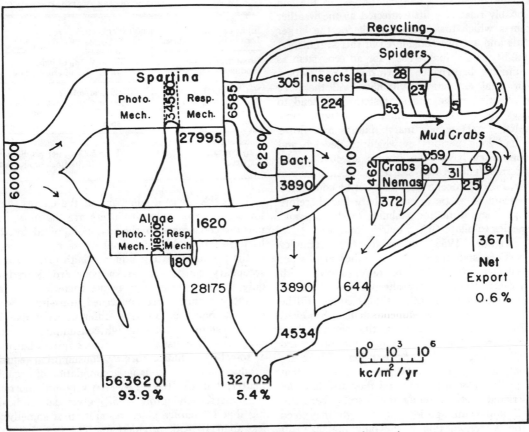

FIG. 4. Energy-flow diagram for a Georgia salt marsh.

systems although values as high as 6.0% have been reported for pine plantations (Ovington 1959).

The herbivorous insects assimilate 4.6% of their potential food, the net production of *Spartina*. They eat the plants directly and there is no significant time lag between production and consumption, since Georgia is far enough south that the *Spartina* grows to some extent throughout the year. The grasshoppers feed on it during the summer whereas the leaf hoppers are most abundant during the cooler seasons.

The relation between production and consumption for the algae-detritus feeders is more complex. Mud algae production is rather constant throughout the year (Pomeroy 1959) and algal turnover is much more rapid than *Spartina* turnover. When the algae-detritus feeders utilize algae there is little or no time lag between production and primary consumption, but when they feed on *Spartina* detritus and the associated bacteria, there is a definite time lag. Detritus is produced throughout the year as the older leaves die and are broken up, but most of the *Spartina* dies in autumn and winter after seed formation. Low winter temperatures

retard formation of detritus and spread the supply out into the spring. At the beginning of summer, a new supply forms as the leaves of the spring growth die and decay. Whatever the actual time relationships may be, it is certain that there is considerable delay before detritus feeders can use the *Spartina* and the longer the delay, the less food remains.

These animals compensate for the variations in detrital supply by eating algae. The most conspicuous and abundant consumers of the marsh, the fiddler crabs, have perhaps the most omnivorous food habits. They can survive on detritus, algae, bacteria or animal remains (Teal 1958), i.e. they have a very unrestricted diet.

Odum and Odum (1959) and MacArthur (1955) have suggested that the fluctuations characteristic of certain communities may be correlated with the presence of few species as in arctic or desert areas. In the salt marsh we have a system with few species but one which seems to exhibit considerable stability. In the 5 years during which these studies were carried on there were no noticeable changes in population size in any of the important animals. (The microfauna of the soil is probably relatively little affected by the weather extremes which make life difficult for the larger animals and are not considered in this argument.)

Stability is a valuable asset for an ecosystem as it minimizes disturbance which might lead to partial or total extinction. Stability will therefore have selective value and ecosystems will tend to develop more stable configurations with time (Dunbar 1960). Salt marsh faunas and floras have had long periods in which to develop and although they have been greatly affected by the considerable changes in sea level which occurred during the Pleistocene they may not be considered as youthful as arctic areas. There has therefore been sufficient time for stability to develop and for species to adapt to the marsh conditions.

MacArthur (1955) shows that a community may achieve stability by having either many species with restricted diets or fewer species with broad diets. The former alternative will permit greater efficiency and, other things equal, will be the one selected. The salt marsh has, however, the 2nd alternative. Among the detritus-algae feeders there are only a few important species and they all have a very unrestricted diet. There are also only a few species among the carnivores that prey on the detrital feeders and they also have an unrestricted diet. Among the insects there are only 2 important species and though they feed only on *Spartina,* this is the only higher plant growing on most of the marsh and so the only food available. These 2 insects are not especially restricted in other ways; they feed on various parts of the plants and in various degrees of exposure. The situation among the spiders and carnivorous insects has not been adequately investigated but there seem to be more species in these groups and perhaps more specialization in their niches.

There are 2 principal reasons why the salt marsh should have the less efficient alternative of the 2 paths to community stability. There is only one higher plant on the marsh and consequently a lack of variety of possible niches such as could be found in a forest at the same latitude. Possibly even more important is the restriction of biomass by the removal of much of the marsh production by the tidal currents. As Hutchinson (1959) has pointed out, if the total biomass is restricted, "then the rarer species in a community may be so rare that they do not exist." With these 2 limitations of the possible numbers of species that can survive in the marsh community, the only road to stability is the development of broad, unrestricted food habits such as is found in the marsh.

TABLE IX. Summary of salt marsh energetics

| | |
|---|---|
| Input as light | 600,000 kcal/m²/yr |
| Loss in photosynthesis | 563,620 or 93.9% |
| Gross production | 36,380 or 6.1% of light |
| Producer Respiration | 28,175 or 77% of gross production |
| Net Production | 8,205 kcal/m²/yr |
| Bacterial respiration | 3,890 or 47% of net production |
| 1° consumer respiration | 596 or 7% of net production |
| 2° consumer respiration | 48 or 0.6% of net production |
| Total energy dissipation by consumers | 4,534 or 55% of net production |
| Export | 3,671 or 45% of net production |

Table IX gives a summary of the energy flow for the system. The producers are the most important consumers in the marsh followed by the bacteria which degrade about $\frac{1}{7}$ as much energy as the producers. The animals, both primary and secondary consumers, are a poor 3rd degrading only $\frac{1}{7}$ as much energy as the bacteria. As far as the consumers are concerned, the situation in the salt marsh is not very different from that in other systems. But the high consumption by the producers is unusual. In a stable system such as a so-called "climax forest" consumption equals production and there is no accumulation of organic matter, but the trees are relatively unimportant consumers. Ovington (1957) gives data indicating that in mature pines respiration is something less than 10% of production. The fact that salt marsh *Spartina* respires over 70% of its production may be associated with existence in an osmotically difficult situation.

In spite of the high rate of producer respiration, net production in the salt marsh is 1.4% of incident light which is higher than in most systems studied (Teal 1957). Table IX shows that 45% of this production is lost to the estuarine waters. The fauna of the estuaries has not been quantitatively studied but the numbers of shrimp and crabs taken by the local fishery give evidence of their abundance. Since the waters of these estuaries are so turbid and well mixed that the phytoplankton spend most of their time in the dark and their net production is zero (Ragotzkie 1958), the estuarine animals must be living on the exported marsh production. There is about $\frac{1}{2}$ as much estuarine as marsh area behind the sea islands and since 45% of the marsh production is exported to the estuaries, there can be 1.6 times as much consumer activity in the latter region as in the former.

The tides are of supreme importance in controlling the environment of the salt marshes. They limit the number of species that can occupy the system and so make it simple enough to be studied

in the detail reported here. They are responsible
for the high production of *Spartina,* as witnessed
by the luxuriant growth along the tidal creeks
as compared with that on the Short Spartina areas.
At the same time the tides remove 45% of the
production before the marsh consumers have a
chance to use it and in so doing permit the estuaries to support an abundance of animals.

## REFERENCES

Burkholder, P. R., and G. H. Bornside. 1957. Decomposition of marsh grass by aerobic marine bacteria.
Bull. Torrey Bot. Club 84: 366-383.

Dunbar, M. J. 1960. The evolution of stability in
marine environments. Natural selection at the level
of the ecosystem. Amer. Nat. 94: 129-136.

Hemmingsen, A. M. 1950. The relation of standard
(basal) energy metabolism to total fresh weight
of living organisms. Rep. Steno. Mem. Hosp. 4: 1-58.

Hutchinson, G. E. 1959. Homage to Santa Rosalia or
Why are there so many kinds of animals? Amer.
Nat. 93: 145-160.

Kimball, H. H. 1929. Amount of solar radiation that
reaches the surface of the earth on land and on the
sea, and methods by which it is measured. Mon.
Weather Rev. 56: 393-398.

Kuenzler, E. J. 1961. Structure and energy flow of a
mussel population in a Georgia salt marsh. Limnol.
and Oceanogr. 6: 191-204.

Lindeman, R. L. 1942. The trophic-dynamic aspect of
ecology. Ecology 23: 399-418.

MacArthur, R. 1955. Fluctuations of animal populations and a measure of community stability. Ecology 36: 533-536.

Marshall, S. M., and A. P. Orr. 1955. Experimental
feeding of the copepod *Calanus finmarchicus* (Gun-
ner) on phytoplankton cultures labelled with radioactive carbon. Pap. Mar. Biol. Oceanogr., Deep Sea
Res. Suppl. 3: 110-114.

Nielsen, C. O. 1949. Studies on the soil microfauna.
II. The soil inhabiting nematodes. Natura Jutlandica
2: 1-131.

Odum, E. P. 1961. Personal communication.

——, and H. T. Odum. 1959. Fundamentals of Ecology. Philadelphia: Saunders.

——, and A. E. Smalley. 1959. Comparison of population energy flow of a herbiverous and a deposit-feed-
ing invertebrate in a salt marsh ecosystem. Proc.
Nat. Acad. Sci.

Odum, H. T. 1957. Trophic structure and productivity
of Silver Springs, Florida. Ecol. Monogr. 27: 55-112.

——, and E. P. Odum. 1955. Trophic structure and
productivity of a windward coral reef community
on Eniwetok Atoll. Ecol. Monogr. 25: 291-320.

Oney, J. 1954. Final report, Clapper rail survey and
investigation study. Georgia Game Fish. Comm.

Ovington, J. D. 1957. Dry-matter production by *Pinus
sylvestris* L. Ann. Bot. N. S. 21: 287-314.

Patten, B. C. 1959. An introduction to the cyber-
netics of the ecosystem: the trophic-dynamic aspect.
Ecology 40: 221-231.

Pomeroy, L. R. 1959. Algal productivity in the salt
marshes of Georgia. Limnol. and Oceanogr. 4: 367-
386.

Pringsheim, E. H. 1949. The relationship between
bacteria and myxophyceae. Bact. Rev. 13: 47-98.

Ragotzkie, R. A. 1959. Plankton productivity in estuarine waters of Georgia. Inst. Marine Sci. 6: 146-
158.

Richman, S. 1958. The transformation of energy by
*Daphnia pulex.* Ecol. Monogr. 28: 273-291.

Slobodkin, L. B. 1959. Energetics in *Daphnia pulex*
populations. Ecology 40: 232-243.

——. 1960. Ecological energy relationships at the
population level. Amer. Nat. 94: 213-236.

Smalley, A. E. 1959. The growth cycle of Spartina and
its relation to the insect populations in the marsh.
Proc. Salt Marsh Conf. Sapelo Island, Georgia.

——. 1960. Energy flow of a salt marsh grasshopper
population. Ecology 41: 672-677.

Teal, J. M. 1957. Community metabolism in a temperate cold spring. Ecol. Monogr. 27: 283-302.

——. 1958. Distribution of fiddler crabs in Georgia
salt marshes. Ecology 39: 185-193.

——. 1959. Respiration of crabs in Georgia salt
marshes and its relation to their ecology. Physiol.
Zool. 32: 1-14.

——, and J. Kanwisher. 1961. Gas exchange in a
Georgia salt marsh. Limnol. and Oceanogr. 6: 388-
399.

——, and W. Wieser. 1961. Studies of the ecology
and physiology of the nematodes in a Georgia salt
marsh. Ms.

Wieser, W., and J. Kanwisher. 1961. Ecological and
physiological studies on marine nematodes from a
small salt marsh near Woods Hole, Massachusetts.
Limnol. and Oceanogr. 6: 262-270.

Zeuthen, E. 1953. Oxygen uptake as related to body
size in organisms. Quart. Rev. Biol. 28: 1-12.

17 71 188

70 71 72 73  7 6 5 4 3 2 1